Readings in
Biological Science

Edited by

Irving William Knobloch
Michigan State University

Readings in
Biological Science

Second Edition

 Appleton-Century-Crofts
Educational Division

New York **Meredith Corporation**

PREFACE

According to the late Dr. A. C. Kinsey (*Methods in Biology*, 1937), biology courses should be more than a succession of pickled worms and dead cats, of microscopic preparations and dried fungi, or a parade of technical names for nerves and muscles of unfamiliar creatures. Two of the most important functions of biology, he continued, should be to interest the student in the world in which he lives and to equip him with the scientific method for interpreting that world. Another way of stating these ideas is to say that, in the introductory course, facts may not be as important as the interest developed. To aid in the creation of interest, many new devices have appeared upon the market such as overhead projectors, single concept films, better charts and models, and a vast number of books.

The second edition of this book, like the first edition, attempts to place within the students' reach articles of great value which would not ordinarily be encountered. Many of the fine articles of the first edition have been replaced with those detailing the accomplishments of the second half of the twentieth century, including new data on photosynthesis, respiration, protein synthesis, space biology, and heredity. The new material does not supplant the old but only expands its perimeters; it is both supplementary and explanatory.

As in the first edition, we have had the cooperation of numerous editors and scientists and to these kind people, we extend our warmest thanks.

I. W. K.

CONTENTS

PREFACE   V

I   BIOLOGICAL BEGINNINGS   1

1. Excerpts from *Nature of Man, Humours, Aphorisms and Regimen—Hippocrates*   3
2. Excerpts from *De Generatione Animalium* (On the Generation of Animals)—*Aristotle*   7
3. Excerpts from *Enquiry into Plants—Theophrastus*   11
4. Excerpts from *The First Observations on "Little Animals" Protozoa and Bacteria in Waters—Antony van Leeuwenhoek*   14
5. The Evidence of the Descent of Man from Some Lower Form—*Charles Darwin*   20

II   THE STRUCTURE AND FUNCTION OF ANIMALS   31

6. The Unsolved Problem of Development—*John Tyler Bonner*   33
7. The Eve of Meiosis (with Apologies to Clement C. Moore) —*Craig L. Himes*   47
8. Luminescence   50
9. Life's Mysterious Clocks—*Frank A. Brown, Jr.*   53
10. Avian Adaptations   63
11. Blood   67

III   THE STRUCTURE AND FUNCTION OF HIGHER PLANTS   83

12. Photosynthesis—*Johannes van Overbeek, Harry K. Wong*   85
13. Respiration—*William A. Jensen*   94
14. Photoperiod—*Arthur W. Galston*   101
15. Growth Hormones—*Arthur W. Galston*   105
16. The Agricultural Sciences—*R. E. Geyer*   109
17. Tree Ferns—*Henricks Hodge*   119
18. Of Molds and Men—*Richard N. Shoemaker*   122

IV   NUTRITION, HEALTH, AND DISEASE   129

19.   Food, Facts and Fads—*Gladys Cook, May Foley*   131
20.   Horizons in Dentistry—*George C. Paffenbargar*   136
21.   Rats, Bats and Human Diseases   139
22.   Cancer   143
23.   Your Heart   155
24.   Walter Reed and the Conquest of Yellow Fever—
       Grace T. Hallock, Clair E. Turner, John J. Lenz, assistant   163
25.   Plant Pathology and Human Welfare—*A. J. Riker*   175
26.   Medical Utopias—*René Dubos*   186

V   ECOLOGY   191

27.   The Ecology of Man, the Animal—*S. Charles Kendeigh*   193
28.   Biology, Society, and Culture in Human Ecology—
       Frederick Sargent II, Demitri B. Shimkin   199
29.   The Ecology of Disease—*Marston Bates*   208
30.   Wastebasket of the Earth—*William A. Albrecht*   212
31.   Space Tracks—*Dwain W. Warner*   221
32.   Bird Migration   229
33.   The Flower and the Bee—*Mary S. Percival*   233
34.   The Rain Forest—*Marston Bates*   241

VI   CONSERVATION AND ECONOMIC BIOLOGY   253

35.   The Vandals—*Angelo Patri*   255
36.   The Useful and Beautiful Forest—*Erhard Rostlund*   256
37.   Turning Insects Against Themselves   260
38.   Science Attacks the Screwworm—*Norris Randolph*   263
39.   Bristlecone Pine, Oldest Living Thing—*Edmund Schulman*   266

VII   EXOBIOLOGY   269

40.   Significance and Status of Exobiology—*Gilbert V. Levin*   271
41.   The Biology of Space   276
42.   Travelers in Space—*Samuel Moffat, Elie A. Shneour* 281
43.   What Do We Seek in Space?—*Joshua Lederberg*   284

VIII   HEREDITY   287

44.   Gregor Mendel and His Work—*Hugo Iltis*   289
45.   The Language of the Genes—*George W. Beadle*   295

Contents

46. DNA and the Chemistry of Inheritance—*Barry Commoner* 311
47. Heredity and Hiroshima—*David M. Bonner,*
    Stanley E. Mills 314

IX ORIGIN OF LIFE 319

48. Chemical Origin of Life—*Cyril Ponnamperuma* 321
49. Chemical Evolution—*Melvin Calvin* 330
50. Life Begins—*Samuel Moffat, Elie A. Shneour* 331
51. On the Origin and Evolution of Living Machines—
    Harold F. Blum 336
52. Spontaneous Generation—*Irving W. Knobloch* 343

X EVOLUTION 359

53. Man and Natural Selection—*Theodosius Dobzhansky* 361
54. The Two-Million-Year-Old Man 376
55. Continuity and Change—*Samuel Moffat, Elie A. Shneour* 381
56. The Role of Paleontology in the Formulation of
    Evolutionary Thought—*Everett C. Olson* 386
57. Flowers, Insects, and Evolution—*Herman F. Becker* 392
58. Crop Plant Evolution—*Sir Joseph Hutchinson* 399

XI POPULATION AND BIRTH CONTROL 409

59. How Many People Have Ever Lived on Earth?—
    Annabelle Desmond 411
60. The World's No. 1 Problem—*Earl L. Butz* 412
61. The Population Explosion—*Leroy Augenstein* 413
62. How Good is the Rhythm Method?—*Garrett Hardin* 418
63. Interstellar Migration and the Population Problem—
    Garrett Hardin 420

XII PHILOSOPHY AND SCIENCE

64. A Biologist's Reflections on History—*Max Hamburgh* 427
65. Front Seats for Biologists—*Wallace O. Fenn* 437
66. The Road Traversed and the Road Ahead—
    Theodosius Dobzhansky 441
67. Earthlings in the Space Age—*Ritchie Calder* 467
68. The Logical Basis of Biological Investigation—
    Herbert H. Ross 473
69. Science and People—*Warren Weaver* 479

Readings in
  Biological Science

I
Biological Beginnings

1

Excerpts from *Nature of Man, Humours, Aphorisms, and Regimen*

Hippocrates

NATURE OF MAN

He who is accustomed to hear speakers discuss the nature of man beyond its relations to medicine will not find the present account of any interest. For I do not say at all that a man is air, or fire, or water, or earth, or anything else that is not an obvious constituent of a man; such accounts I leave to those who care to give them. Those, however, who give them have not in my opinion correct knowledge. . . .

Now about these men I have said enough, and I will turn to physicians. Some of them say that a man is blood, others that he is bile, a few that he is phlegm. . . . The body of man has in itself blood, phlegm, yellow bile and black bile; these make up the nature of his body, and through these he feels pain or enjoys health. Now he enjoys the most perfect health when these elements are duly proportioned to one another in respect of compounding, power, bulk, and when they are perfectly mingled. Pain is felt when one of these elements is in defect or excess, or is isolated in the body without being compounded with all the others. For when an element is isolated and stands by itself, not only must the place where it left become diseased, but the place where it stands in a flood must, because of the excess, cause pain and distress. In fact when more of an element flows out of the body than is necessary to get rid of superfluity, the emptying causes pain.

Now I promised to show that what are according to me the constituents of man remain always the same, according to both convention and

Reprinted by permission of the publishers and THE LOEB CLASSICAL LIBRARY, HIPPOCRATES, Vol. IV, W. H. S. Jones, trans., Cambridge, Mass.: Harvard University Press, 1931. London: William Heinemann.

nature. These constituents are, I hold, phlegm, blood, black bile, and yellow bile. First I assert that the names of these according to convention are separated, and that none of them has the same name as the others; furthermore, that according to nature their essential forms are separated, phlegm being quite unlike blood, blood being quite unlike bile, bile being quite unlike phlegm. How could they be like one another, when their colours appear not alike to the sight nor does their touch seem alike to the hand? From the following evidence you may know that these elements are not all one, but that each of them has its own power and its own nature. If you were to give a man a medicine which withdraws phlegm, he will vomit you phlegm; if you give him one which withdraws bile, he will vomit you bile. Similarly too black bile is purged away if you give a medicine which withdraws black bile. And if you wound a man's body so as to cause a wound, blood will flow from him. So long as a man lives he manifestly has all these elements always in him.

Phlegm increases in a man in winter; for phlegm, being the coldest constituent of the body, is closest akin to winter. It is in winter that the sputum and nasal discharge of men is fullest of phlegm; at this season mostly swellings become white, and diseases generally phlegmatic. And in spring too phlegm still remains strong in the body while the blood increases. And in summer blood is still strong, and bile rises in the body and extends until autumn. In the summer phlegm is at its weakest. But in autumn, blood becomes least in man, for autumn is dry and begins from this point to chill him. It is black bile which in autumn is greatest and strongest. All these elements are then always comprised in the body of a man, but as the year goes round they become now greater and now less, each in turn and according to its nature.

Now, as these things are so, such diseases as increase in the winter ought to cease in the summer, and such as increase in the summer ought to cease in the winter, with the exception of those which do not depart in a period of days. When diseases arise in the spring, expect their departure in autumn. Such diseases as arise in autumn must have their departure in spring. Whenever a disease passes these limits, you may know that it will last a year.

HUMOURS

The fashions of diseases. Some are congenital and may be learned by inquiry, as also may those that are due to the district, for most people are permanent residents there, so that those who know are numerous. Some are the result of the physical constitution, others of regimen, of the constitution of the disease, of the seasons. Countries badly situated with respect to the seasons engender diseases analogous to the seasons.

If the seasons proceed normally and regularly, they produce diseases that come easily to a crisis. If the summer proves bilious, and if the increased bile be left behind, there will also be diseases of the spleen. So when spring too has had a bilious constitution, there occur cases of jaundice in spring also. When summer turns out like to spring, sweats occur in fevers. When the spring turns out wintry, with after-winter storms, the diseases too are wintry, with coughs, pneumonia or angina. For seasons, too, suffer from relapses, and so cause diseases.

South winds cause deafness, dimness of vision, headaches, heaviness, and are relaxing. A north wind causes coughs, sore throats, constipation, difficult micturition accompanied by shivering, pains in the side and chest. Droughts accompany both south winds and north winds.

It is changes that are chiefly responsible for diseases, especially the greatest changes, the violent alterations both in the seasons and in other things. But seasons which come on gradually are the safest, as are gradual changes of regimen and temperature and gradual changes from one period of life to another.

Sufferers from hemorrhoids are attacked neither by pleurisy, nor by pneumonia, nor by spreading ulcer, nor by boils, nor by swellings, nor perhaps by skin-eruptions and skin-diseases. Blood-spitting may be caused by the season, by pleurisy, or by bile. When swellings by the ear do not suppurate at a crisis, a relapse occurs when the swelling softens; when the relapse follows the normal course of relapses, the swelling rises again and remains, following the same periods as occur when fevers relapse.

APHORISMS

Old men endure fasting most easily, then men of middle age, youths very badly, and worst of all children, especially those of a liveliness greater than the ordinary.

In summer and in autumn food is most difficult to assimilate, easiest in winter, next easiest in spring.

Do not disturb a patient either during or just after a crisis, and try no experiments, neither with purges nor with other irritants, but leave him alone.

In acute disease use purgatives sparingly and at the onset, and then only after a thorough examination.

When sleep puts an end to delirium, it is a good sign.

Spontaneous weariness indicates disease.

It is easier to replenish with drink than with food.

When on a starvation diet, a patient should not be fatigued.

In the case of acute diseases to predict either death or recovery is not quite safe.

Strong drink dispels hunger.

At the beginning of diseases, if strong medicines seem called for, use them; when they are at their height it is better to let the patient rest.

In every disease it is a good sign when the patient's intellect is sound and he enjoys his food; the opposite is a bad sign.

Those who are constitutionally very fat are more apt to die quickly than those who are thin.

Size of body in youth is noble and not unpleasing; in old age it is inconvenient and less desirable than a smaller stature.

Autumn is bad for consumptives.

Cold sweats, occurring with high fever, indicate death; with a milder fever they indicate a protracted disease.

And on whatever part of the body there is sweat, it means that the disease has settled there.

Those who are attacked by tetanus either die in four days or, if they survive these, recover.

Consumption occurs chiefly between the ages of eighteen and thirty-five.

When unnaturally fat women cannot conceive, it is because the fat presses the mouth of the womb, and conception is impossible until they grow thinner.

Kidney troubles, and affections of the bladder, are cured with difficulty when the patient is aged.

If one of the small intestines be severed it does not unite.

It is better to give no treatment in cases of hidden cancer; treatment causes speedy death, but to omit treatment is to prolong life.

Both sleep and sleeplessness, when beyond due measure, constitute disease.

Those diseases that medicines do not cure are cured by the knife. Those that the knife does not cure are cured by fire. Those that fire does not cure must be considered incurable.

REGIMEN

I maintain that he who aspires to treat correctly of human regimen must first acquire knowledge and discernment of the nature of man in general—knowledge of its primary constituents and discernment of the components by which it is controlled.

Now all animals, including man, are composed of two things, different in power but working together in their use, namely, fire and water. Both together these are sufficient for one another and for everything else, but each by itself suffices neither for itself nor for anything else. Now the power that each of them possesses is this. Fire can move all things always, while water can nourish all things always; but in turn each masters or is mastered to the greatest maximum or the least minimum possible. Neither of them can gain the complete mastery for the following reason. The fire, as it advances to the limit of the water, lacks nourishment, and so turns to where it is likely to be nourished; the water, as it advances to the limit of the fire, finds its motions fail, and so stops at this point. When it stops its force ceases, and hereafter is consumed to nourish the fire which assails it.

Males and females would be formed, so far as possible, in the following manner. Females, inclined more to water, grow from foods, drinks, and pursuits that are cold, moist, and gentle. Males, inclined to fire, grow from foods and regimen that are dry and warm. So if a man would beget a girl, he must use a regimen inclined to water. If he wants a boy, he must live according to a regimen inclined to fire. And not only must the man do this, but also the woman. For growth belongs, not only to the man's secretions, but also to that of the woman, for the following reason. Either part alone has not motion enough, owing to the bulk of its moisture and the weakness of its fire, to consume and to solidify the oncoming water. But when it happens that both are emitted together to one place, they conjoin, the fire to the fire and the water likewise. Now if all the fire fall in a dry place, it is set in motion, if it also master the water emitted with it, and therefrom it grows, so that it is not quenched by the onrushing flood, but receives the advancing water and solidifies it on to what is there already. But if it fall into a moist place, immediately from the first it is quenched and dissolves into the lesser rank. On one day in each month it can solidify, and master the advancing parts, and that only if it happen that parts are emitted from both parents together in one place.

2

Excerpts from *De Generatione Animalium* (On the Generation of Animals)

Aristotle

Now some animals come into being from the union of male and female, i.e., all those kinds of animals which possess the two sexes. This is not

From *Oxford Aristotle,* "De Generatione Animalium," trans. A. Platt, by permission of the Clarendon Press, Oxford.

the case with all of them; though in the sanguinea* with few exceptions
the creature, when its growth is complete, is either male or female, and
though some bloodless animals have sexes so that they generate offspring
of the same kind, yet other bloodless animals generate indeed, but not offspring of the same kind; such are all that come into being not from a union
of the sexes, but from decaying earth and excrements. To speak generally,
if we take all animals which change their locality, some by swimming, others by flying, others by walking, we find in these the two sexes, not only in
the sanguinea but also in some of the bloodless animals; and this applies
in the case of the latter sometimes to the whole class, as in the cephalopoda
and crustacea, but in the case of insects only to the majority. Of these,
all which are produced by union of animals of the same kind generate also
after their own kind, but all of which are not produced by animals, but
from decaying matter, generate indeed, but produce another kind, and
the offspring is neither male nor female; such are some of the insects.

But all those creatures which do not move, as the testacea and animals
that live by clinging to something else, inasmuch as their nature resembles
that of plants, have no sex any more than plants have, but as applied to
them the word is only used in virtue of a similarity and analogy. For there
is a slight distinction of this sort, since even in plants we find in the same
kind some trees which bear fruit and others which, while bearing none
themselves, yet contribute to the ripening of the fruits of those which do,
as in the case of the fig-tree and the caprifig.

The same holds good also in plants, some coming into being from seed
and others, as it were, by the spontaneous action of Nature, arising
either from decomposition of the earth or of some parts in other plants,
for some are not formed by themselves separately but are produced upon
other trees, as the mistletoe.

Some animals manifestly emit semen, as all the sanguinea, but whether the insects and cephalopoda do so is uncertain. Therefore this is a question to be considered, whether all males do so, or not all; and if not all,
why some do and some not; and whether the female also contributes any
semen or not; and, if not semen, whether she does not contribute anything
else either, or whether she contributes something else which is not semen.

Now it is thought that all animals are generated out of semen, and that
the semen comes from the parents. In this investigation and those which
follow from it, the first thing to do is to understand what semen is, for
then it will be easier to inquire into its operation and the phenomena connected with it. Now the object of semen is to be of such a nature that from
it as their origin come into being those things which are naturally formed,
not because there is any agent which makes them from it . . . but simply
because this is the semen.

Now the offspring comes from the semen and it is plainly in one of the

*Animals with blood. (Ed.)

two following senses that it does so—either the semen is the material from which it is made, or it is the first efficient cause. Now that which comes from the generating parents is called the seminal fluid, being that which first has in it a principle of generation, in the case of all animals whose nature is to unite; semen is that which has in it the principles from both united parents, as the first mixture which arises from the union of male and female, be it a foetus or an ovum, for these already have in them that which comes from both.

Semen, then, is part of a useful secretion. So we must say the opposite of what the ancients said. For whereas they said that semen is that which comes from all the body, we shall say it is that whose nature is to go to all of it, and what they thought a waste product seems rather to be a secretion.

A further proof that it is not a waste product, but rather a secretion is the fact that the large animals have few young, the small many. For the large must have more waste and less secretion, since the great size of the body causes most of the nutriment to be used up, so that the residue or secretion is small.

Again, no place has been set apart by Nature for waste-products but they flow wherever they can find an easy passage in the body, but a place has been set apart for all the natural secretions; thus the lower intestine serves for the excretion of the solid nutriment, the bladder for that of the liquid; for the useful part of the nutriment we have the upper intestine, for the spermatic secretions the uterus and pudenda and breasts, for it is collected and flows together into them. The male stands for the effective and active and the female, considered as female, for the passive and it follows that what the female would contribute to the semen of the male would not be semen but material for the semen to work upon.

So much for the discussion of this question. How is it that the male contributes to generation and how is it that the semen from the male is the cause of the offspring? Does it exist in the body of the embryo as a part of it from the first, mingling with the material which comes from the female? Or does the semen communicate nothing to the material body of the embryo but only the power and movement in it? Now the latter alternative appears to be the right one both *a priori* and in view of the facts. For, if we consider the question on general grounds, we find that, whenever one thing is made from two of which one is active and the other passive, the active agent does not exist in that which is made, and, still more generally, the same applies when one thing moves and another is moved. It is plain then that it is not necessary that anything at all should come away from the male, and if anything does come away it does not follow that this gives rise to the embryo as being in the embryo, but only as that which imparts the motion and as the form; so the medical art cures the patient.

What occurs in birds and oviparous fishes is the greatest proof that

neither does the semen come from all parts of the male nor does he emit
anything of such a nature as to exist within that which is generated, as
part of the material embryo, but that he only makes a living creature by
the power which resides in the semen. For if a hen-bird is in process of
producing wind-eggs and is trodden by the cock before the egg has begun
to whiten and while it is all still yellow, then they become fertile instead
of being wind-eggs. And if while it is still yellow she be trodden by another cock, the whole brood of chicks turn out like the second cock.

The same conclusion is to be drawn from the generation of oviparous
fishes. When the female has laid her eggs, the male sprinkles the milt over
them, and those eggs are fertilized which it reaches, but not the others;
this shows that the male does not contribute anything to the quantity but
only to the quality of the embryo.

In all animals that can move about, the sexes are separate, one individual being male and one female, though both are the same in species, as
with man and horse. But in plants these powers are mingled, female not
being separated from male. Wherefore they generate out of themselves,
and do not emit semen, but produce an embryo, what is called the seed.
For as the egg is an embryo, a certain part of it giving rise to the animal
and the rest being nutriment, so also from a part of the seed springs the
growing plant, and the rest is nutriment for the shoot and the first root.

It is the nature of those creatures which do not emit semen to remain
united a long time until the male element has formed the embryo, as with
those insects which copulate. The others remain so only until the male has
discharged from the parts of himself, introduced something which will
form the embryo in a longer time, as among the sanguinea. For the former
remain paired some part of a day, while the semen forms the embryo in
several days. And after emitting this they cease their union.

In all this Nature acts like an intelligent workman. For to the essence
of plants belongs no other function or business than the production of
seed; since, then, this is brought about by the union of male and female,
Nature has mixed these and set them together in plants, so that the sexes
are not divided in them. But the function of the animal is not only to
generate (which is common to all living things) but they all of them participate also in a kind of knowledge, some more and some less, and some
very little indeed. For they have sense-perception, and this is a kind of
knowledge. Now it is by sense-perception that an animal differs from
those organisms which have only life. But since, if it is a living animal, it
must also live; therefore, when it is necessary for it to accomplish the
function of that which has life, it unites and copulates, becoming like a
plant, as we have said before.

3

Excerpts from *Enquiry into Plants*

Theophrastus

DEFINITIONS OF THE VARIOUS CLASSES INTO WHICH PLANTS MAY BE DIVIDED

Now since our study becomes more illuminating if we distinguish different kinds, it is well to follow this plan where it is possible. The first and most important classes, those which comprise all or nearly all plants, are tree, shrub, under-shrub, herb.

A tree is a thing which springs from the root with a single stem, having knots and several branches, and it cannot easily be uprooted; for instance, olive fig vine. A shrub is a thing which arises from the root with many branches; for instance, bramble Christ's thorn. An under-shrub is a thing which arises from the root with many stems as well as many branches; for instance, savory rue. A herb is a thing which comes up from the root with its leaves and has no main stem, and the seed is borne on the stem; for instance, corn and pot-herbs.

These definitions however must be taken and accepted as applying generally and on the whole. For in the case of some plants it might seem that our definitions overlap; and some under cultivation appear to become different and depart from their essential nature, for instance, mallow when it grows tall and becomes tree-like. For this comes to pass in no long time, not more than six or seven months, so that in length and thickness the plant becomes as great as a spear, and men accordingly use it as a walking-stick, and after a longer period the result of cultivation is proportionately greater. So too is it with the beets; they also increase in stature under cultivation, and still more do chaste-tree Christ's thorn ivy, so that, as is

Reprinted by permission of the publishers and THE LOEB CLASSICAL LIBRARY, Theophrastus, *Enquiry into Plants*, Arthur Hort, trans. Cambridge, Mass.: Harvard University Press, 1916. London: William Heinemann.

generally admitted, these become trees, and yet they belong to the class of shrubs. On the other hand the myrtle, unless it is pruned, turns into a shrub, and so does filbert: indeed this latter appears to bear better and more abundant fruit if one leaves a good many of its branches untouched, since it is by nature like a shrub. Again neither the apple nor the pomegranate nor the pear would seem to be a tree of a single stem, nor indeed any of the trees which have side stems from the roots, but they acquire the character of a tree when the other stems are removed. However, some trees men even leave with their numerous stems because of their slenderness, for instance, the pomegranate and the apple, and they leave the stems of the olive and the fig cut short.

OF "MALE" AND "FEMALE" IN TREES

Taking all trees according to their kinds, we find a number of differences. Common to them all is that by which men distinguish the "male" and the "female," the latter being fruit-bearing, the former barren in some kinds. In those kinds in which both forms are fruit-bearing, the "female" has fairer and more abundant fruit; however some call these the male trees—for there are those who actually invert the names. This difference is of the same character which distinguishes the cultivated from the wild tree, while other differences distinguish different forms of the same kind.

OF THE MEDICINAL USES OF DIVERS PARTS OF PLANTS

As was said, of some plants the root, fruit and juice are all serviceable, as of all-heal among others; of some the root and the juice, as of scammony cyclamen thapsia and others, such as mandrake; for the leaf of this, they say, used with meal, is useful for wounds, and the root for erysipelas, when scrapped and steeped in vinegar, and also for gout, for sleeplessness, and for love potions. It is administered in wine or vinegar; they cut little balls of it, as of radishes, and making a string of them hang them up in the smoke over must.

Of hellebore both root and fruit are useful for the same purposes,—if it is true, as is said, that the people of Anticyra use the fruit as a purge: this fruit contains the well-known drug called sesamodes.

Various parts of all-heal are also useful, and not all for the same purposes; the fruit is used in cases of miscarriage and for disorders of the bladder, while the juice is used in cases of miscarriage and also for sprains and such-like troubles; also for the ears, and to strengthen the voice. The root is used in childbirth, for diseases of women, and for flatulence in beasts of burden.

Of cyclamen the root is used for suppurating boils; also as a pessary for women and, mixed with honey, for dressing wounds; the juice for purgings of the head. They say also that the root is a good charm for inducing rapid delivery and as a love potion.

Of "wild cucumber" (squirting cucumber) the root is used for white leprosy and for mange in sheep.

Of germander the leaves pounded up in olive-oil are used for fractures and wounds and for spreading sores; the fruit purges bile, and is good also for the eyes; for ulcers in the eye they pound up the leaf in olive-oil before applying it.

OF ROOTS POSSESSING REMARKABLE TASTE OR SMELL

The differences between roots are shown in their tastes and in their smells: some are pungent, some bitter, some sweet: some again have a pleasant, others a disagreeable smell. The plant called yellow water-lily is sweet: it grows in lakes and marshy places. It has a large leaf which lies on the water: and it is said that it acts as a styptic if it is pounded up and put on the wound: it is also serviceable in the form of a draught for dysentery.

Liquorice is also sweet; some indeed simply call it "sweet root." It is useful against asthma or a dry cough and in general for troubles in the chest: also, administered in honey, for wounds: also it has the property of quenching thirst, if one holds it in the mouth.

These then are sweet: other roots are bitter, and some unpleasant to the taste.

Madder has a leaf like ivy, but it is rounder: it grows along the ground like dog's-tooth grass and loves shady spots. It has diuretic properties, wherefore it is used for pains in the loins or hip disease.

The root of polypody is rough and has suckers like the tentacles of the polyp. It purges downward: and, if one wears it as an amulet, they say that one does not get a polypus.

OF PLANTS POSSESSING PROPERTIES WHICH AFFECT THE MENTAL POWERS

As to those that affect the mind, strykhnos is said to upset the mental powers and make one mad; while the root of onotheras (oleander) administered in wine makes the temper gentler and more cheerful. This plant has a leaf like the almond, but smaller, and the flower is red like a rose. The plant itself forms a large bush; the root is red and large and, if this is dried, it gives off a fragrance like wine.

4

Excerpts from *The First Observations on "Little Animals" Protozoa and Bacteria in Waters*

Antony van Leeuwenhoek

1ST OBSERVATION ON RAIN-WATER

In the year 1675, about half-way through September (being busy with studying air, when I had much compressed it by means of water), I discovered living creatures in rain, which had stood but a few days in a new tub, that was painted blue within. This observation provoked me to investigate this water more narrowly; and especially because these little animals were, to my eye, more than ten thousand times smaller than the animacule which Swammerdam has portrayed, and called by the name of Water-flea, or Water-louse, which you can see alive and moving in water with the bare eye.

Of the first sort, that I discovered in the said water, I saw, after divers observations, that the bodies consisted of 5, 6, 7 or 8 very clear globules, but without being able to discern any membrane or skin that held these globules together, or in which they were enclosed. When these animacules bestirred 'emselves, they sometimes stuck out two little horns, which were continually moved, after the fashion of a horse's ears. The part between these little horns was flat, their body else being roundish, save only that it ran somewhat to a point at the hind end; at which pointed end it had a

From *ANTONY VAN LEEUWENHOEK AND HIS "LITTLE ANIMALS"* by Clifford Dobell. Reprinted by permission of Harcourt, Brace & World, Inc.

tail, near four times as long as the whole body, and looking as thick, when viewed through my microscope, as a spider's web. At the end of this tail there was a pellet, of the bigness of one of the globules of the body; and this tail I could not perceive to be used by them for their movements in very clear water. These little animals were the most wretched creatures that I have ever seen; for when, with the pellet, they did but hit on any particles or little filaments (of which there were many in water, especially if it hath but stood some days), they stuck entangled in them; and then pulled their body out into an oval, and did struggle, by strongly stretching themselves, to get their tail loose; whereby their whole body then sprang back towards the pellet of the tail, and their tails then coiled up serpent-wise, after the fashion of a copper or iron wire that, having been wound close about a round stick, and then taken off, kept all its windings. This motion, of stretching out and pulling together the tail, continued; and I have seen several hundred animacules, caught fast by one another in a few filaments, lying within the compass of a coarse grain of sand.

I also discovered a second sort of animacules, whose figure was oval; and I imagined that their head was placed at the pointed end. These were a little bit bigger than the animacules first mentioned. Their belly is flat, provided with divers incredibly thin little feet, or little legs, which were moved very nimbly, and which I was able to discover only after sundry great efforts, and wherewith they brought off incredibly quick motions. The upper part of their body was round, and furnished inside with 8, 10 or 12 globules: otherwise these animacules were very clear. These little animals would change their body into a perfect round, but mostly when they came to lie high and dry. Their body was also very yielding: for if they so much as brushed against a tiny filament, their body bent in, which bend also presently sprang out again; just as if you stuck your finger into a bladder full of water, and then, on removing the finger, the inpitting went away. Yet the greatest marvel was when I brought any of these animacules on a dry place, for I then saw them change themselves at last into a round, and then the upper part of the body rose up pyramid-like, with a point jutting out in the middle; and after having thus lain moving with their feet for a little while, they burst asunder, and the globules and a watery humour flowed away on all sides, without my being able to discern even the least sign of any skin wherein these globules and the liquid had, to all appearance, been inclosed; and at such time I could discern more globules than when they were alive. This bursting asunder I figure to myself to happen thus: imagine, for example, that you have a sheep's bladder filled with shot, peas, and water; then, if you were to dash it apieces on the ground, the shot, peas, and water would scatter themselves all over the place.

Furthermore, I discovered a third sort of little animals, that were about twice as long as broad, and to my eye quite eight times smaller than the animacules first mentioned: and I imagined, although they were so small, that I could yet make out their little legs, or little fins. Their motion was very quick, both roundabout and in a straight line.

The fourth sort of animacules, which I also saw amoving, were so small, that for my part I can't assign any figure to 'em. These little animals were more than a thousand times less than the eye of a full-grown louse (for I judge the diameter of the louse's eye to be more than ten times as long as that of the said creature), and they surpassed in quickness the animacules already spoken of. I have divers times seen them standing still, as 'twere, in one spot, and twirling themselves round with a swiftness such as you see in a whip-top a-spinning before your eye; and then again they had a circular motion, the circumference whereof was no bigger than that of a small sand-grain; and anon they would go straight ahead, or their course would be crooked.

Furthermore I also discovered sundry other sorts of little animals; but these were very big, some as large as the little mites on the rind of cheese, others bigger and very monstrous. But I intend not to specify them; and will only say, that they were for the most part made up of such soft parts, that they burst asunder whenever the water happened to run off them.

THE 2ND OBSERVATION. RAIN-WATER

The 26th of May it rained very hard. The rain abating somewhat, I took a clean glass and got rain-water, that came off a slate roof, fetched me in it, after the glass had first been swilled out two or three times with the rain-water. I then examined it, and therein discovered some few very little animals; and seeing them, I bethought me whether they might not have been bred in the leaden gutters, in any water that might erstwhile have been standing in them.

THE 3RD OBSERVATION. RAIN-WATER

On the same date, the rain continuing nearly the whole day, I took a big porcelain dish, and put it in my court-yard, in the open air, upon a wooden tub about a foot and a half high: considering that thus no earthy particles would be splashed into the said dish by the falling of the rain at that spot. With the water first caught, I swilled out the dish, and the glass in which I meant to preserve the water, and then flung this water away: then, collecting water anew in the same dish, I kept it; but upon examining it, I could discover therein no living creatures, but merely a lot of irregular earthy particles.

The 30th of May, after I had, since the 26th, observed this water every day, twice or thrice daily, I now first discovered some (though very few) exceeding little animacules, which were very clear.

On the 31st *ditto,* I discovered more little animals in the water, as well as a few that were a bit bigger; and I imagine that ten hundred thousand of these little animacules are not so big as an ordinary sand-grain. Comparing these animacules with the little mites in cheese (which you can see amoving with the bare eye), I would put the proportion thus: As the size of a small animacule in the water is to that of a mite, so is the size of a honey bee to that of a horse; for the circumference of one of these same little animacules is not so great as the thickness of a hair on a mite.

THE 4TH OBSERVATION. RAIN-WATER

On June 9th, collected rain-water betimes in a dish, as aforesaid, and put it at about 8 o'clock in the morning in a clean wine glass, and exposed it to the air at about the height of the third storey of my house, wondering whether the little animals would appear sooner in water thus standing in the air.

The 10th *ditto,* observing this water, I fancied that I discovered living creatures; but they were so few, and not so plainly discernible, I could not accept this for the truth.

On the 11th *ditto,* seeing this water, with the naked eye, stirred in the glass by a stiff gale of wind (which had now blown from the same quarter for 36 hours; the weather being very cold withal, that it did not irk me to wear my winter clothes), I had no thought of finding any living creatures in it; but upon examining it, I saw with wonder quite 1000 living creatures in one drop of water. These animacules were of the smallest sort that I had yet seen.

The 12th of June, in the morning (the wind being west, with both sunshine and an overcast sky), observing again, I saw the aforesaid animacules in such great numbers in the water which I took from the surface, that now they did not amount to merely one or two thousand in one drop.

The 13th *ditto,* in the morning, examining the water again, I discovered, beside the aforesaid animacules, a sort of little animals that were fully eight times as big as the first; and whereas the small animacules swam gently among one another, and moved after the fashion of gnats in the air, these larger animacules had a much swifter motion; and as they turned and tumbled all around and about, they would make a quick dart. These animacules were almost round.

On the 14th of June I did perceive the very little animacules in no less number.

On the 16th *ditto,* the animacules seen as before; and the water (which had been, in all, about ⅛ of a pint) being now more than half dried out, I flung it away.

5TH OBSERVATION. RAIN-WATER

The 9th of June, I put some of the last-collected water, likewise in a clean wine-glass, in my closet; and on examining it, I described no animacules.

The 10th of June, observing this foresaid rain-water, which had now stood about 24 hours in my closet, I perceived some few very little living creatures, to which, because of their littleness, no figure can be ascribed; and among others, I discovered a little animal that was a bit bigger, and that I could perceive to be oval.

The 11th *ditto,* observing this water again, I saw the foresaid small animacules, though very few in number.

The 12th *ditto,* I saw the very small animacules, as yesterday; and besides these, a small animal that had nearly the figure of a mussel-shell, lying with its hollow side downwards. 'Twas of the length anigh of a louse's eye.

The 13th *ditto,* I also saw one bigger animacule, like that just spoken of. Moreover I discovered animacules which were somewhat longer than an oval. These were about 6 times as long as the foresaid very small animacules, and their head, which was somewhat long drawn out, they ofttimes pulled in, and then looked to be almost round. There were also animacules which appeared perfectly round, their diameter being twice as long as that of smallest animacules of all. These two large sorts were very yielding, so that their body did bend before the least little filament which they chanced to brush against in the water.

The 16th *ditto,* I perceived the oval animacules in yet greater numbers; and they were flat beneath, and round above: and besides these, there were very small animacules that were three times as long as broad, together with divers other sorts which it would take all too long to specify. In the evening of the same day, I discovered little paws on the foresaid oval animacules, which were many in number, in proportion to the animacule. And at this point, I stopped my observations upon this water.

OBSERVATIONS ON WELL-WATER

I have in my yard, standing in the open air, a well, which is about 15-foot deep before you come to the water. It standeth at the south, but so encompassed with high walls, that even when the sun is on the sign of Cancer, the coping of the wall is not shown upon. This water cometh out of the ground, which is well-sand, with such force, that whenever I have tried to empty the well there was always about a foot of water still left in. On a summer's day this water is so cold that 'tis not feasible to keep your hand in it for long. Having no thought that there would be living creatures in it (for 'tis very palatable and clear), I examined it in September of last year, and discovered therein a great number of very small animacules, which were very clear, and a bit bigger than the very smallest animacules, that I've ever seen. And I imagine (having aforetime weighed a grain of water), that there were commonly more than 500 living creatures in one grain of this water. These animacules were very sedate, moving without any jerks.

In the winter I perceived no little animals, nor did I see any of them this year before the month of July, and then not in such great plenty; but in the month of August, their number was much increased.

OBSERVATIONS ON SEA-WATER

The 27th of July, 1676, I betook myself to the seaside, hard by the village of Schevelinge. Finding myself upon the shore, and observing the sea-water as well as I could, I discovered in it divers little animacules. I gave to a certain person who went into the sea, to bathe himself, a new glass vial and besought him that, when he was in the sea, he would rinse it out twice or thrice and then fill it up with water. This having been carried out according to my orders, I tied the vial up tight with a clean bit of bladder: and on reaching home and examining the water, I perceived therein a little animal that was blackish, having a shape as if 'twere made up of two globules. This little animal had a peculiar motion, after the manner of a very little flea, when seen, by the naked eye, jumping on a white paper; yet 'twas only displaced, at every jump, within the compass of a coarse sand-grain, or thereabouts. It might right well be called a water flea; but 'twas not so big, by a long way, as the eye of that little animal which Swammer-dam calls the water-flea.

The 31st *ditto*, having examined this water every day since the 27th, and perceived no little animals in it; upon this date I did now see a good hundred of 'em where at first I had seen but one; but they were now of another figure, and not only smaller, but also very clear. They were like an oblong oval, only with this difference, that they tapered somewhat more sharply to a point at what I imagined to be the head end. And although these were at least a thousand times smaller than a very small sand-grain, I saw, notwithstanding, that whenever they lay high and dry out of the water they burst asunder, and flowed apart or scattered into three or four very small globules and some watery matter, without my being able to discern any other parts.

The 8th of August, I again discovered a very few of the foresaid animacules; and I now saw a few so exceeding small that, even through my microscope, they well-nigh escaped the sight. And here I stopped my observations.

5

The Evidence of the Descent of Man from Some Lower Form

Charles Darwin

He who wishes to decide whether man is the modified descendant of some pre-existing form, would probably first enquire whether man varies, however slightly, in bodily structure and in mental faculties; and if so, whether the variations are transmitted to his offspring in accordance with the laws which prevail with the lower animals. Again, are the variations the result, as far as our ignorance permits us to judge, of the same general causes, and are they governed by the same general laws, as in the case of other organisms; for instance, by correlation, the inherited effects of use and disuse, etc? Is man subject to similar malconformations, the result of arrested development, of reduplication of parts, &c., and does he display in any of his anomalies reversion to some former and ancient type of structure? It might also naturally be enquired whether man, like so many other animals, has given rise to varieties and sub-races, differing but slightly from each other, or to races differing so much that they must be classed as doubtful species? How are such races distributed over the world; and how, when crossed, do they react on each other in the first and succeeding generations? And so with many other points.

The enquirer would next come to the important point whether man tends to increase at so rapid a rate, as to lead to occasional severe struggles for existence; and consequently to beneficial variations, whether in

From Charles Darwin, *The Descent of Man and Selection in Relation to Sex* (New York: D. Appleton & Co., Inc., 1886). Reprinted by permission.

body or mind, being preserved, and injurious ones eliminated. Do the races or species of men, whichever term may be applied, encroach on and replace one another, so that some finally become extinct? We shall see that all these questions, as indeed is obvious in respect to most of them, must be answered in the affirmative, in the same manner as with the lower animals. But the several considerations just referred to may be conveniently deferred for a time: and we will first see how far the bodily structure of man shows traces, more or less plain, of his descent from some lower form.

THE BODILY STRUCTURE OF MAN

It is notorious that man is constructed on the same general type or model as other mammals. All the bones in his skeleton can be compared with corresponding bones in a monkey, bat, or seal. So it is with his muscles, nerves, blood-vessels and internal viscera. The brain, the most important of all the organs, follows the same law, as shewn by Huxley and other anatomists. Bischoff, who is a hostile witness, admits that every chief fissure and fold in the brain of man has its analogy in that of the orang; but he adds that at no period of development do their brains perfectly agree; nor could perfect agreement be expected, for otherwise their mental powers would have been the same.

It may, however, be worth while to specify a few points, not directly or obviously connected with structure, by which this correspondence or relationship is well shewn.

Man is liable to receive from the lower animals, and to communicate to them, certain diseases, as hydrophobia, variola, the glanders, syphilis, cholera, herpes, &c.; and this fact proves the close similarity of their tissues and blood, both in minute structure and composition, far more plainly than does their comparison under the best microscope, or by the aid of the best chemical analysis. Monkeys are liable to many of the same non-contagious diseases as we are; thus Rengger, who carefully observed for a long time the *Cebus Azarae* in its native land, found it liable to catarrh, with the usual symptoms, and which, when often recurrent, led to consumption. These monkeys suffered also from apoplexy, inflammation of the bowels, and cataract in the eye. The younger ones when shedding their milk-teeth often died from fever. Medicines produced the same effect on them as on us. Many kinds of monkeys have a strong taste for tea, coffee, and spirituous liquors: they will also, as I have myself seen, smoke tobacco with pleasure. Brehm asserts that the natives of north-eastern Africa catch the wild baboons by exposing vessels with strong beer, by which they are made drunk. He has seen some of these animals, which he kept in confinement, in this state; and he gives a laughable account of their behaviour and strange grimaces. On the following morning they were very cross and dismal; they held their aching heads with both hands, and wore a most pitiable expression: when beer or wine was offered them, they turned away with disgust, but relished the juice of lemons. An American monkey, an Ateles, after getting drunk on brandy, would never touch it again, and thus was wiser than many men. These trifling facts prove how similar the nerves of taste must be in monkeys and man, and how similarly their whole nervous system is affected.

Man is infested with internal parasites, sometimes causing fatal effects; and is plagued by external parasites, all of which belong to the same genera or families as those infesting other mammals, and in the case of scabies to the same species. Man is subject, like other mammals, birds, and even insects, to that mysterious law, which causes certain normal processes, such as gestation, as well as the maturation and duration of various diseases, to follow lunar periods. His wounds are repaired by the same process of healing; and the stumps left after the amputation of his limbs, especially during an early embryonic period, occasionally possess some power of regeneration, as in the lowest animals.

The whole process of that most important function, the reproduction of the species, is strikingly the same in all mammals, from the first act of courtship by the male, to the birth and nurturing of the young. Monkeys are born in almost as helpless a condition as our own infants; and in certain genera the young differ fully as much in appearance from the adults, as do our children from their full-grown parents. It has been urged by some writers, as an important distinction, that with man the young arrive at maturity at a much later age than with any other animal: but if we look to the races of mankind which inhabit tropical countries the difference is not great, for the orang is believed not to be adult till the age of from ten to fifteen years. Man differs from woman in size, bodily strength, hairiness, &c., as well as in mind, in the same manner as do the two sexes of many mammals. So that the correspondence in general structure, in the minute structure of the tissues, in chemical composition and in constitution, between man and the higher animals, especially the anthropomorphous apes, is extremely close.

EMBRYONIC DEVELOPMENT

Man is developed from an ovule, about the 125th of an inch in diameter, which differs in no respect from the ovules of other animals. The embryo itself at a very early period can hardly be distinguished from that of other members of the vertebrate kingdom. At this period the arteries run in arch-like branches, as if to carry the blood to branchiae which are not present in the higher vertebrata, though the slits on the sides of the neck still remain, marking their former position. At a somewhat later period, when the extremities are developed, "the feet of lizards and mammals," as the illustrious Von Baer remarks, "the wings and feet of birds, no less than the hands and feet of man, all arise from the same fundamental form." It is, says Prof. Huxley, "quite in the later stages of development that the young human being presents marked differences from the young ape, while the latter departs as much from the dog in its developments, as the man does. Startling as this last assertion may appear to be, it is demonstrably true."

After the foregoing statements made by such high authorities, it would be superfluous on my part to give a number of borrowed details, shewing that the embryo of man closely resembles that of other mammals. It may, however, be added, that the human embryo likewise resembles certain low forms when adult in various points of structure. For instance, the heart at first exists as a simple pulsating vessel; the excreta are voided through a cloacal passage; and the os coccyx projects like a true tail, "extending considerably beyond the rudimentary legs." In the embryos of all air-breathing vertebrates, certain glands, called the corpora Wolffiana, correspond with and act like the kidneys of mature fishes. Even at a later embryonic period, some striking resemblances between man and the lower animals may be observed. Bischoff says that the convolutions of the brain in a human foetus at the end of the seventh month reach about the same stage of development as in a baboon when adult. The great toe, as Prof. Owen remarks, "which forms the fulcrum when standing or walking, is "perhaps the most characteristic peculiarity in the human structure;" but in an embryo, about an inch in length, Prof. Wyman found "that the great toe was shorter than the others; and, instead of being parallel to them, projected at an angle from the side of the foot, thus corresponding with the permanent condition of this part in the quadrumana." I will conclude with a quotation from Huxley, who after asking, does man originate in a different way from a dog, bird, frog or fish? says, "the reply is not doubtful for a moment; without question, the mode of origin, and the early stages of the development of man, are identical with those of the animals immediately below him in the scale: without a doubt in these respects, he is far nearer to apes than the apes are to the dog."

RUDIMENTS

This subject, though not intrinsically more important than the two last, will for several reasons be treated here more fully. Not one of the higher animals can be named which does not bear some part in a rudimentary condition; and man forms no exception to the rule. Rudimentary organs must be distinguished from those that are nascent; though in some cases the distinction is not easy. The former are either absolutely useless, such as the mammae of male quadrupeds, or the incisor teeth of ruminants which never cut through the gums; or they are of such slight service to their present possessors, that we can hardly suppose that they were developed under the conditions which now exist. Organs in this latter state are not strictly rudimentary, but they are tending in this direction. Nascent organs, on the other hand, though not fully developed, are of high service to their possessors, and are capable of further development. Rudimentary organs are eminently variable; and this is partly intelligible, as they are useless, or nearly useless, and consequently are no longer subjected to natural selection. They often become wholly suppressed. When this occurs, they are nevertheless liable to occasional reappearance through reversion—a circumstance well worthy of attention.

The chief agents in causing organs to become rudimentary seem to have been disuse at that period of life when the organ is chiefly used (and this is generally during maturity), and also inheritance at a corresponding period of life. The term "disuse" does not relate merely to the lessened action of muscles, but includes a diminished flow of blood to a part or organ, from being subjected to fewer alternations of pressure, or from becoming in any way less habitually active. Rudiments, however, may occur in one sex of those parts which are normally present in the other sex; and such rudiments, as we shall hereafter see, have often originated in a way distinct from those here referred to. In some cases, organs have been reduced by means of natural selection, from having become injurious to the species under changed habits of life. The process of reduction is probably often aided through the two principles of compensation and economy of growth; but the later stages of reduction, after disuse has done all that can fairly be attributed to it, and when the saving to be effected by the economy of growth would be very small, are difficult to understand. The final and complete suppression of a part, already useless and much reduced in size, in which case neither compensation nor economy can come into play, is perhaps intelligible by the aid of the hypothesis of pangenesis. But as the whole subject of rudimentary organs has been discussed and illustrated in my former works, I need here say no more on this head.

Rudiments of various muscles have been observed in many parts of the human body; and not a few muscles, which are regularly present in some of the lower animals can occasionally be detected in man in a greatly reduced condition. Every one must have noticed the power which many animals, especially horses, possess of moving or twitching their skin; and this is effected by the *panniculus carnosus*. Remnants of this muscle in an efficient state are found in various parts of our bodies; for instance, the muscle on the forehead, by which the eyebrows are raised.

The extrinsic muscles which serve to move the external ear, and the intrinsic muscles which move the different parts, are in a rudimentary condition in man, and they all belong to the system of the *panniculus;* they are also variable in development, or at least in function. I have seen one man who could draw the whole ear forwards; other men can draw it upwards; another who could draw it backwards; and from what one of these persons told me, it is probable that most of us, by often touching our ears, and thus directing our attention towards them, could recover some power of movement by repeated trials. The power of erecting and directing the shell of the ears to the various points of the compass, is no doubt of the highest service to many animals, as they thus perceive the direction of danger; but I have never heard on sufficient evidence, of a man who possessed this power, the one which might be of use to him. Some authors, however, suppose that the cartilage of the shell serves to transmit vibrations to the acoustic nerve; but Mr. Toynbee, after collecting all the known evidence on this head, concludes that the external shell is of no distinct use. The ears of the chimpanzee and orang are curiously like those of man, and the proper muscles are likewise but very slightly developed. I am also assured by the keepers in the Zoological Gardens that these animals never move or erect their ears; so that they are in an equally rudimentary condition with those of man, as far as function is concerned. Why these animals, as well as the progenitors of man, should have lost the power of erecting their ears, we cannot say. It may be, though I am not satisfied with this view, that owing to their arboreal habits and great strength they were but little exposed to danger, and so during a lengthened period moved their ears but little, and thus gradually lost the power of moving them. This would be a parallel case with that of those large and heavy birds, which from inhabiting oceanic islands, have not been exposed to the attacks of beasts of prey, and have consequently lost the power of using their wings for flight. The inability to move the ears in man and several apes is, however, partly compensated by the freedom with which they can move the head in a horizontal plane, so as to catch sounds from all directions.

The nictitating membrane, or third eyelid, with its accessory muscles and other structures, is especially well developed in birds, and is of much functional importance to them, as it can be rapidly drawn across the whole eye-ball. It is found in some reptiles and amphibians, and in certain fishes, as in sharks. It is fairly well developed in the two lower divisions of the mammalian series, namely, in the monotremata and marsupials, and in some few of the higher mammals, as in the walrus. But in man, the quadrumana, and most other mammals, it exists, as is admitted by all anatomists, as a mere rudiment, called the semilunar fold.

The sense of smell is of the highest importance to the greater number of mammals—to some, as the ruminants, in warning them of danger; to others, as the carnivora, in finding their prey; to others, again, as the wild boar, for both purposes combined. But the sense of smell is of extremely slight service, if any, even to the dark coloured races of men, in whom it is much more highly developed than in the white and civilized races. Nevertheless it does not warn them of danger, nor guide them to their food; nor does it prevent the Esquimaux from sleeping in the most fetid atmosphere, nor many savages from eating half-putrid meat. In Europeans the power differs greatly in different individuals, as I am assured by an eminent naturalist who possesses this sense highly developed, and who has attended to the subject. Those who believe in the principle of gradual evolution, will not readily admit that the sense of smell in its present state was originally acquired by man, as he now exists. He inherits the power in an enfeebled and so far rudimentary condition, from some early progenitor, to whom it was highly serviceable, and by whom it was continually used. In those animals which have this sense highly developed, such as dogs and horses, the recollection of persons and of places is strongly associated with their odour; and we can thus perhaps understand how it is, as Dr. Maudsley has truly remarked, that the sense of smell in man "is singularly effective in recalling vividly the ideas and images of forgotten scenes and places."

Man differs conspicuously from all the other Primates in being almost naked. But a few short straggling hairs are found over the greater part of the body in the man, and fine down on that of the woman. The different races differ much in hairiness; and in the individuals of the same race the hairs are highly variable, not only in abundance, but likewise in position; thus in some Europeans the shoulders are quite naked, whilst in others they bear thick tufts of hair. There can be little doubt that the hairs thus scattered over the body are the rudiments of the uniform hairy coat of the lower animals. This view is rendered all the more probable, as it is known that fine, short, and pale-coloured hairs on the limbs and other parts of the body, occasionally become developed into "thickset, long and rather coarse dark hairs," when abnormally nourished near old-standing inflamed surfaces.

The fine wool-like hair, or so-called lanugo, with which the human foetus during the sixth month, is thickly covered, offers a more curious case. It is first developed, during the fifth month, on the eyebrows and face, and especially round the mouth, where it is much longer than that on the head. A moustache of this kind was observed by Eschricht on a female foetus; but this is not so surprising a circumstance as it may at first appear, for the two sexes generally resemble each other in all external characters during an early period of growth. The direction and arrangement of the hairs on all parts of the foetal body are the same as in the adult, but are subject to much variability. The whole surface, including even the forehead and ears, is thus thickly clothed; but it is a significant fact that the palms of the hands and the soles of the feet are quite naked, like the inferior surfaces of all four extremities in most of the lower animals.

As this can hardly be an accidental coincidence, the woolly covering of the foetus probably represents the first permanent coat of hair in those mammals which are born hairy. Three or four cases have been recorded of persons born with their whole bodies and faces thickly covered with fine long hairs; and this strange condition is strongly inherited, and is correlated with an abnormal condition of the teeth. Prof. Alex. Brandt informs me that he has compared the hair from the face of a man thus characterised, aged thirty-five, with the lanugo of a foetus, and finds it quite similar in texture; therefore, as he remarks, the case may be attributed to an arrest of development in the hair, together with its continued growth.

It appears as if the posterior molar or wisdom-teeth were tending to become rudimentary in the more civilised races of man. These teeth are rather smaller than the other molars, as is likewise the case with the corresponding teeth in the chimpanzee and orang; and they have only two separate fangs. They do not cut through the gums till about the seventeenth year, and I have been assured that they are much more liable to decay, and are earlier lost than the other teeth; but this is denied by some eminent dentists. They are also much more liable to vary, both in structure and in the period of their development, than the other teeth. In the Melanian races, on the other hand, the wisdom-teeth are usually furnished with three separate fangs, and are generally sound; they also differ from the other molars in size, less than in the Caucasian races. Prof. Schaaffhausen accounts for this difference between the races by "the posterior dental portion of the jaw being always shortened" in those that are civilised, and this shortening may, I presume, be attributed to civilised men habitually feeding on soft, cooked food, and thus using their jaws less.

With respect to the alimentary canal, I have met with an account of only a single rudiment, namely the vermiform appendage of the caecum. The caecum is a branch or diverticulum of the intestine, ending in a cul-de-sac, and is extremely long in many of the lower vegetable-feeding mammals. In the marsupial koala it is actually more than thrice as long as the whole body. It is sometimes produced into a long gradually-tapering point, and is sometimes constricted in parts. It appears as if, in consequence of changed diet or habits, the caecum had become much shortened in various animals, the vermiform appendage being left as a rudiment of the shortened part. That this appendage is a rudiment, we may infer from its small size, and from the evidence which Prof. Canestrini has collected of its variability in man. It is occasionally quite absent, or again is largely developed. The passage is sometimes completely closed for half or two-thirds of its length, with the terminal part consisting of a flattened solid expansion. In the orang this appendage is long and convoluted: in man it arises from the end of the short caecum, and is commonly from four to five inches in length, being only about the third of an inch in diameter. Not only is it useless, but it is sometimes the cause of death, of which fact I have lately heard two instances: this is due to small hard bodies, such as seeds, entering the passage, and causing inflammation.

In man, the os coccyx, together with certain other vertebrae hereafter to be described, though functionless as a tail, plainly represent this part in other vertebrate animals. At an early embryonic period it is free, and projects beyond the lower extremities of a human embryo. Even after birth it has been known, in certain rare and anomalous cases, to form a small external rudiment of a tail. The os coccyx is short, usually including only four vertebrae, all anchylosed together: and these are in a rudimentary condition, for they consist, with the exception of the basal one, of the centrum alone. They are furnished with some small muscles; one of which, as I am informed by Prof. Turner, has been expressly described by Theile as a rudimentary repetition of the extensor of the tail, a muscle which is so largely developed in many mammals.

The spinal cord in man extends only as far downwards as the last dorsal or first lumbar vertebra; but a thread-like structure (the *filum terminale*) runs down the axis of the sacral part of the spinal canal, and even along the back of the coccygeal bones. The upper part of this filament, as Prof. Turner informs me, is undoubtedly homologous with the spinal cord, but the lower part apparently consists merely of the *pia mater*, or vascular investing membrane. Even in this case the os coccyx may be said to possess a vestige of so important a structure as the spinal cord, though no longer enclosed within a bony canal.

The reproductive system offers various rudimentary structures; but these differ in one important respect from the foregoing cases. Here we are not concerned with the vestige of a part which does not belong to the species in an efficient state, but with a part efficient in the one sex, and represented in the other by a mere rudiment. Nevertheless, the occurrence of such rudiments is as difficult to explain, on the belief of the separate creation of each species, as in the foregoing cases. Hereafter I shall have to recur to these rudiments, and shall shew that their presence generally depends merely on inheritance, that is, on parts acquired by one sex having been partially transmitted to the other. I will in this place only give some instances of such rudiments. It is well known that in the males of all mammals, including man, rudimentary mammae exist. These in several instances have become well developed, and have yielded a copious supply of milk. Their essential identity in the two sexes is likewise shewn by their occasional sympathetic enlargement in both during an attack of the measles. The *vesicula prostatica*, which has been observed in many male mammals, is now universally acknowledged to be the homologue of the female uterus, together with the connected passage. It is impossible to read Leuckart's able description of this organ, and his reasoning, without admitting the justness of his conclusion. This is especially clear in the case of those mammals in which the true female uterus bifurcates, for in the males of these the vesicula likewise bifurcates.

The bearing of the three great classes of facts now given is unmistakable. But it would be superfluous fully to recapitulate the line of argument given in detail in my *Origin of Species*. The homological construction of the whole frame in the members of the same class is intelligible, if we admit their descent from a common progenitor, together with their subsequent adaptation to diversified conditions. On any other view, the similarity of pattern between the hand of a man or monkey, the foot of a horse, the flipper of a seal, the wing of a bat, &c., is utterly inexplicable. It is no scientific explanation to assert that they have all been formed on the same ideal plan. With respect to development, we can clearly understand, on the principle of variations supervening at a rather late embryonic period, and being inherited at a corresponding period, how it is that the embryos of wonderfully different forms should still retain, more or less perfectly, the structure of their common progenitor. No other explanation has ever been given of the marvellous fact that the embryos of a man, dog, seal, bat, reptile, etc., can at first hardly be distinguished from each other. In order to understand the existence of rudimentary organs, we have only to suppose that a former progenitor possessed the parts in question in a perfect state, and that under changed habits of life they became greatly reduced, either from simple disuse, or through the natural selection of those individuals which were least encumbered with a superfluous part, aided by the other means previously indicated.

Thus we can understand how it has come to pass that man and all other vertebrate animals have been constructed on the same general model, why they pass through the same early stages of development, and why they retain certain rudiments in common. Consequently we ought frankly to admit their community of descent; to take any other view, is to admit that our own structure, and that of all the animals around us, is a mere snare laid to entrap our judgment. This conclusion is greatly strengthened, if we look to the members of the whole animal series, and consider the evidence derived from their affinities or classification, their geographical distribution and geological succession. It is only our natural prejudice, and that arrogance which made our forefathers declare that they were descended from demi-gods, which leads us to demur to the conclusion. But the time will before long come, when it will be thought wonderful that naturalists, who were well acquainted with the comparative structure and development of man, and other mammals, should have believed that each was the work of a separate act of creation.

II
The Structure and Function
of Animals

6

The Unsolved Problem of Development

John Tyler Bonner

The study of development has for some years suffered from an inferiority complex. As an area of interest it has held its rightful place alongside genetics and evolution and, in fact, this is the very cause of the complex. Ever since Darwin there has been a general satisfied feeling among biologists that the basic outlines of the mechanism of evolution are clear and understood. Beginning with Mendel, and certainly ever since the work of Morgan and his group in the second decade of this century, there also has been a feeling that the basic principles of genetics are known. But development is considered the helpless third child that never is capable of growing and maturing properly; in fact it seems to remain in a perpetual state of disorderly puberty. How many times have I heard the rather wistful refrain that nothing really important in the study of embryology has turned up since the time of Spemann, or Roux, or Aristotle.

The despair has placed development in the position of at least one of the great unsolved problems of biology. Matters are not improved by the close identification of development with cancer. The nature of cancer is not known nor can it be cured in any very rational or specific way, and the hope expressed in many dollars is that, like anthrax, it will suddenly let all its secrets out in a dramatic way and will be cured in the fashion antibiotics cut down bacterial diseases. It is nothing but human nature to wait for the great flash of illuminating lightning that will not only solve the cancer problem, but the problem of development along with it.

Yet I think those who are actively working on the problem of cancer or those who are studying normal development have little hope for such

This article originally appeared in *American Scientist,* Vol. 48 (1960), pp. 514-527. Reprinted by permission.

a flash. Rather, they see the problem as exceedingly complex, with many facets and therefore possibly many answers. One could argue that this pessimistic feeling comes only because they are so close to the details of their experiments that they cannot see the possibility of anything larger, any theory of development of the satisfying and general character of the theories of evolution and genetics. However, if one stands back a few paces, as we shall attempt to do here, the conclusion remains the same: there does not seem to be any place for a new, grand, and unifying scheme.

This does not mean that there is no interest or profit to come from studying development. But, it does mean that if development is put in its proper perspective, especially with relation to genetics and evolution, then we might cease to suffer any complex of inferiority, cease to expect any single, monumental solution, and have a clear picture of where to find healthy progress.

The first problem is that the trilogy of which we have spoken, evolution, genetics, and development, may in itself be misleading because, when these three subjects are placed together, the natural implication is that they can be equated, like an apple, a pear, and an orange because they are all fruits. A moment's reflection will show that this is far from the case, and, again by analogy, it would be more like describing the essentials of the functioning of an automobile by listing fuel, mechanical parts, and combustion. These three are not in any one class; the only thing that brings them together is that together they give at least a partial description of an automobile in operation. By the same token, evolution, genetics, and development combined, give a partial description of the living world and now let us examine how these fit together. This will necessitate the saying of some very simple and obvious things but perhaps this can be justified by our object of putting the area of development in its proper setting.

EVOLUTION

By evolution we mean here its mechanism which is, of course, natural selection. If selection is to operate, two things are required, variation and reproduction; variation to give some basis of choice and reproduction to provide new individuals to harbor the variation. So we immediately see, in our first glance, a relation between the three major areas, for variation is the subject of genetics and reproduction in the sense used here is the subject of development.

It is useful to think of the variation in terms of adaption for this implies variation which has been satisfactory in a particular environment. In examining any one organism, be it a plant or an animal, the point that needs emphasis is that all phases of its life history are adaptive; there is no activity or structure that can escape the fine-toothed comb of natural selection.

This statement does not seem very remarkable until one considers the details of what it means. It means in the first place that the adult, in all its structure and in all its activities, is adapted to its surroundings. Perhaps so much emphasis has been placed on this obvious fact that other equally important ones have been unintentionally neglected. For instance the life span of an organism is adaptive as Weismann was the first to emphasize. Senescence, therefore, is a controlled variation. On the other end of the life history, the whole of development is adaptive. Development is so often thought of as simply a means to an end, the adult, that its own adaptive significance is neglected. But each stage, each step is adapted to its immediate environment as well as being full of the proper potentialities for future adult adaptations. After all, there is no more reason why the preparation for maturity cannot be as subject to variation and selection as the period of decay and senescence. This is directly implied in the old idea of Minot who considered senescence to start at the beginning of development and that the whole life span is one of decreasing rate of senescence. The emphasis is the correct one: an individual organism is not merely an adult but it is the whole life history.

This also means that gametogenesis and all aspects of the sexual system are adaptive as well. Again, this is an old idea but important here because it emphasizes the closeness of the relation between evolution and genetics. In Darlington's phrase there has been an evolution of genetic systems or, in other words, the very methods of producing variation are themselves capable of variation and adaptation. It is like a toolmaker who improves the particular tools he uses in his trade.

GENETICS

Sexuality, which is the most common and successful method of handling variation, is peculiar, however, in that the amount of change that has occurred during the course of evolution is negligible when compared to the changes in other aspects of the life history. For instance, chromosome structure and the basic mechanism of meiosis and fertilization are fairly uniform from the most primitive to the most complex animals and plants. The reason no doubt is that it is such an extremely successful system that any basic change would be inadaptive. It has been preserved and changed only in minor ways because of its great selective advantage.

There are also some well-established alternatives to sexuality as a means of handling variation. Among bacteria we have transduction and there is also the fact that, by direct mutation alone, microorganisms, which have short rapid generations, can have a reasonably effective variation system. Another alternative that should be mentioned is heterocaryosis, found especially among fungi, for here there is no recombination on the chromosome level but there can be recombination of nuclei in that the spores can have different combinations of dissimilar nuclei to start new variants. In fungi, also, there is a special kind of mitotic chromosome recombination which Pontecorvo has described and termed parasexuality. In some peculiar organisms such as the cellular slime molds where there is an aggregate of cells which may be of a diverse genetic constitution we may have a parallel to heterocaryosis and, for this reason, it has been termed heterocytosis. Finally, there are many known instances where the inheritance is handled in the cytoplasm rather than in the nucleus and here, as with the single gene mutation mentioned above, we must expect no recombination, but single direct passage of possibly mutable entities from mother to daughter cell.

All these methods of handling variation, from the sexual ones to the various simpler types, have one thing in common. They require that the key events occur in single cells. This is especially striking in the case of true sexuality for meiosis and fertilization involve the formation of two haploid nuclei fusing to form one diploid zygote nucleus. But, it is equally true of other systems to varying degrees.

This point takes on significance when one recognizes the fact that many organisms, indeed all those which are considered to have a true development, are multicellular (or multi-energid). The reason for this is no doubt that there simply has been, for these forms, an adaptive advantage to an increase in size. Such being the case, we are faced with a paradox: variation must be transmitted and handled by single cells while the adult is multicellular. The inevitable result is clearly a development and therefore one can say that development is the result of reproduction and size.

DEVELOPMENT

If we were to summarize the argument thus far concerning the relation of evolution, genetics, and development one could say that evolution through natural selection is the over-all controlling factor in all change. This change is dependent upon self-perpetuation with variation and, therefore, one of the first steps in evolution has been to set up an effective genetic system, an effective system of handling and transmitting variation. It so happens that all the genetic systems, perhaps partly because they evolved at an early stage in evolution, involve single cells and single nuclei. Therefore, the variation transmission stage is one having small units. Because there has also been a selection pressure for large organisms, the inevitable result is that the gap between the small reproductive cells and the large adult must be filled in by development. But, each step in this development is in itself adaptive to its particular environment. So the evolutionary mechanism lays down the ground rules where each alteration is closely scrutinized by selection; the genetic mechanism, which itself is molded by selection, produces the currency, the method of producing variation so vital to selective processes; and, finally, development is merely a stage in the life history as the variations of evolution become more complex. To put it another way, one cannot produce a large complex organism from a single zygote cell in one magic explosion. The very fact that it is so large and intricate means that it must be built slowly with care and system. It is no different from the problem of building a chicken coop compared with that of building a skyscraper. Evolution, genetics, and development do closely tie in one with another, but they each are of a fundamentally different nature; they are complementary rather than supplementary.

EPIGENESIS

To come now specifically to the problem of the elaboration of the egg to a large adult, we must first keep in mind one of the oldest lessons of embryology. It is simply the idea that one step, one set of conditions leads to another, and that developmental progress is a causal sequence of events. This is the epigenesis of Aristotle and William Harvey; this is the causal embryology of Wilhelm Roux in his *Entwicklungsmechanik*. In modern times, the only significant addition that has been made to this basic scheme of sequential events is that they are controlled and guided by the activities of the genes. Development is now thought of as a period of particularly active gene action. The conclusion is indeed obvious if one remembers that the genes are all in the zygote, along with any cytoplasmic factors that may be of hereditary importance and they are the determinants of the ultimate mature structure. They guide all the steps from fertilization to decrepitude.

Perhaps the reason we think of development as unsolved is that it was in fact solved in basic outline so long ago and the solution is so simple that it has escaped us. When one thinks of its relation to genetics and evolution, and when one thinks of its unfolding from egg to adult as we have just done, then can we not say that the fundamental theoretical framework of development is known and understood; it is an epigenetic system. There is no doubt that this is a correct statement but there may be some question in the minds of biologists as to whether this really represents a solution. Of course, the word "solution" in itself is bound to be unprecise and confusing because we are not dealing with an algebra problem or a theorem of Euclid. What we mean by "solution" here is some vague notion of mental satisfaction to the enquiring scientist. As far as development is concerned there are still things he wants very much to know. It is the hope of any experimental biologist that his discoveries will lead to far-reaching conclusions. The contention here is that we might predict that the conclusions will never be of the magnitude of Mendel's laws or Darwin's theory of natural selection; the generalization of that importance lies in the epigenetic theory of development. But there is ample room for lesser generalizations within this framework. It will now be our task to attempt some understanding of what type of generalizations these might be.

STIMULUS-RESPONSE SYSTEMS

With this in mind, it will be helpful to think of organisms as reaction systems, that is, systems capable of responding to stimuli. To see this clearly one can think of many non-living systems which are able to respond. Besides complicated machines which can be activated, for example, by photocells, one need only turn to the simplest chemical solution containing substances that can combine. In this case, the stimulus, or the activation energy of the physical chemist, might be light or heat or even physical movement, and the chemical components will react or respond. In some responses the stimulus may be highly specific while, in others, a slight energy change of any sort may produce the reaction. It is not usual in chemical reactions or many types of biological reactions to use the terms stimulus and response: more often the biologist guards these terms specifically for nerve or muscle physiology. But they are so generally useful that here they will mean any system that is capable of reaction to either a specific or a general source of activation energy.

It is helpful to gain perspective of biological processes by attempting to imagine how they might have arisen in the origin of life. In the case of stimulus-response systems, one of the first major steps must have been to develop a system that keeps going, a system that is an energy machine, a machine that keeps converting energy in a steady state. This is a very different proposition from a chemical solution that reacts once and then no more. A living system has a continual set of stimuli and a continual set of responses so that, in essence, the motor keeps running. To achieve this kind of stability it is necessary, even in the case of the simple maintenance energetics of an organism, to have a complex set of interlocking stimuli and responses. It is really only through complexity that any kind of a steady state can be achieved.

Along with the complexity, another factor enters into the making of a primitive organism in the origin of life. It is that the complex stimulus-response system must be packaged and be physically defined—it cannot spread out indefinitely into the environment any more than can a clock or an automobile. The cell is of course considered to be this metabolic or energy unit.

The next step is for a system of variation and reproduction. Both of these require further and more elaborate stimulus-response systems. In reproduction we must have the machinery to synthesize and duplicate parts, and in variation we must have machinery to allow orderly and controlled change.

Before proceeding to a discussion of development in these terms let us pause to examine the implications of what has been said. In the first place, we have pointed out that metabolism, reproduction, and variation can be thought of in terms of a sequential series of chemical reactions. The important thing is that they are controlled and this is achieved by a number of factors. First of all there is the packaging, the unifying and isolating of the components of the machine. Second, by making many of the stimuli and responses specific, they can only proceed in one way. This specificity can be achieved by specific chemicals (i.e., enzymes) and by localization of the materials in specific sites within the cell package. Third, the most important feature of control or stability is having many parts, many steps, many sequential stimuli and responses. This is an insurance against catastrophe and error. It is particularly easy to find examples of this principle in the world of mechanical and electronic machines; the more control devices and feedback systems, the greater the chances of smooth and uneventful operation. Therefore, with the notion of sequential stimulus-response systems, we are proposing to look at life as a communication system.

DEVELOPMENT AS A SEQUENTIAL STIMULUS-RESPONSE SYSTEM

Development, which comes from having small gametes and zygotes and a large adult, is necessarily a period where there must be violent changes, changes which can all be conveniently thought of in terms of our stepwise stimulus-response systems. In this we are saying nothing new, but merely using different words to say that development is an epigenetic process where one condition leads to another, and does so in a channelled and controlled fashion. By a different route we have again arrived at our ancient but large generalization about development.

Does this mean that to understand development completely we must methodically unearth the details of each step so that they finally can be put together like a string of beads upon a necklace? We have said that development is a series of interlocking stimulus-response events; what else is there to do but to reconstruct each event? Is this not the reason why those working in the field have the strong notion that there is not one but many answers? Before answering these questions let us glance at this approach and see what progress has already been made along these lines.

CHEMICAL EMBRYOLOGY

The first bravely to recognize and use this approach are the "chemical embryologists." After all, the steps are primarily chemical events and their elucidation must therefore be by chemical means. The progress in this field, along with biochemistry in general, has been one of the great advances in the last few years, but the unfortunate thing is that, with all our new knowledge, our understanding of development has remained distressingly static. Part of the difficulty is simply that it is a new field and the techniques alone make such rapid strides forward that, in some cases, the work of a few years back is wholly out of date and must be repeated. Another problem is that often it is possible to discover beautiful changes in specific chemical constituents from one stage of development to another, but it is not possible to correlate these changes with morphological events in any causal fashion. A classic example of this is the case of fertilizin and antifertilizin discovered by F. R. Lillie in the early part of this century. Despite the large amount of work done on these substances by many workers since then, we still do not know with any certainty what role they play, what step they mediate in normal fertilization. A further difficulty is that often the biochemistry itself is not wholly understood and, therefore, its application to development must necessarily wait. Perhaps the most alarming of all thoughts on this matter is when one considers how many chemical steps there must be between the beginning and the end of development. Of course it might be possible to generalize to some extent and it would indeed be helpful to discover that certain types of reactions are associated with certain types of developmental events. In any case, it is hoped that the chemical embryologist will not be discouraged, for, ultimately, it is imperative that we have the kind of information he seeks to supply.

BIOCHEMICAL GENETICS

Another related approach of increasing importance is that of the biochemical geneticist. His interest, which is really identical, is of gene action during development and he has the advantage of attacking the problem from two sides simultaneously: he has the genetic information as well as the chemical information of the developing organism. The fact that these studies have largely been carried out in molds and bacteria rather than vertebrates is of no disadvantage as far as the general problem of development is concerned.

In simplest terms, the biochemical geneticist seeks to determine the steps involved in the synthesis of a particular substance. He discovers various mutants that will block the synthesis and then by adding different precursors to the medium he can ultimately find a whole chain of events leading to the formation of the substance. In some cases, the genes involved are found on various chromosomes, but there are some striking cases where the genes are in a sequence on a chromosome—the same sequence as the synthetic reactions.

It is perhaps somewhat confusing to equate the synthesis of one substance with development, but basically this is reasonable for, after all, development must be a series of syntheses one following the next. Also, it should be said that recently the attention of biochemical geneticists has turned to the correlation of gene-controlled chemical changes with morphological changes. Therefore, the interest is the same as that of the chemical embryologist but the scope of the studies is extended to examine not only the chemical changes during development, but their genetic control as well.

NUCLEO-CYTOPLASMIC RELATIONS

Still another approach to the problem, and this one is on a less detailed level than the chemical level, is to attempt to determine the respective roles of cytoplasm and nucleus in controlling the course of development. Nowadays, it is not so much whether all the factors lie within the chromosomes or whether the egg cytoplasm also makes an appreciable contribution, although this question still needs further resolution, but rather it is how the nucleus behaves during the course of differentiation. The old concept was that the nucleus remains the same in all tissues of the differentiated adult, largely because it seems to undergo little or no morphological change; the latter is confined entirely to the cytoplasm. But, in recent years, the emphasis has shifted partly because of the work of Beerman and Pavan who showed that the chromosome in developing larvae of certain insects show puffs in different regions correlated with different areas of the embryo, and the implication is that the chromosomes are behaving differently in a regional fashion. The main reason, however, for the shift in emphasis comes from the important work of Briggs and

King who have shown by ingenious transplantation experiments that the nuclei of frog embryos, after a certain stage, become altered and that this alteration is fixed and will pass to the daughter nuclei of one parent nucleus. It is unfortunately not yet clear what are the nature of these alterations, nor is it known what are the real implications of these facts as far as the mechanism of development is concerned. But it does seem to be a bit of information of great potential that might lead to significant new insights into development. It could be the beginning of a more complete understanding of how the signals of the stepwise stimulus and responses pass from the nucleus into the differentiating cytoplasm.

Thus far, all the approaches to the problem of development have to varying degrees attacked detailed steps. As has already been said this is an absolute necessity, but it must nevertheless be admitted that the result to date has been depressingly small as far as elucidating all of development is concerned. To put it baldly, the biochemical geneticist, after some years of work, may piece together five enzymatic steps in the synthesis of one substance. During the development there may be a thousand or many more of such steps. The advance has been more in how the steps occur, for surely their pattern might be a recurring one, but still the whole problem seems gigantic alongside the small chips of progress.

MORE GENERALIZED APPROACHES

There are, however, other approaches to the problem of development than reconstructing each step. They involve trying to see patterns, trying to outline the structure of the stimulus-response sequential communication systems. The work on the respective roles of the nucleus and the cytoplasm is already in this direction, for certainly this is on a more general level than the chemical steps themselves. But this is still not at the stage where it can give us any useful generalizations about development; generalizations that give feelings of greater understanding and that connect many isolated facts together.

One approach on the more general level is that of Waddington who has met the problem of the complexity of development head on and attempted a method of dealing directly with it. This is not an experimental approach but rather the seeking of a reasonable perspective, and therefore it has no possibility of providing any sort of solution to specific problems. As Waddington himself suggests, it is helpful because it "provides a rough and ready picture of the developing embryo," and he adds that it cannot be interpreted rigorously. The picture he has in mind is his "epigenetic landscape," which is a valley running downhill, of varying depth and branching, down which the developmental process proceeds. The valley emphasizes the fact that the process is controlled in its direction, or to use his term, it is "canalized." He also has suggested the word "creode" to emphasize the fact that this valley is a special kind of flowing equilibrium system which restores itself after a disturbance. With this scheme in mind, he proceeds to speculate as to how the whole epigenetic landscape is under the influence of genes and that evolutionary change is related to development by virtue of the complex relation of the genes to the system of epigenetic canals.

If his picture were translated into the terms that have been used in this essay, the valleys are the stepwise stimulus-response sequences. The fact that they are specific and controlled is equivalent to the stability implied by the term creode. The reason for emphasizing the sequential communication system, as has been done here, will now be evident because it allows us to answer the question posed before: as to whether or not it is possible to make any useful generalizations about development below the level of the epigenetic generalization, but above the specific details of each chemical step.

TRANSCENDENT STIMULUS-RESPONSE COMMUNICATION SYSTEMS

Up to this point, we have made the tacit assumption that the steps of development are all minute increments. The implication has been that these gene-controlled changes occur within cells and that they have been operating on a minuscule level. It is easy to show that this is not necessarily the case and, in fact, the broader the sweep of the communication system, the greater is its importance as far as our understanding of development is concerned in the search for a satisfying solution.

Clearly, the smallest communication steps must occur within cells, perhaps even within different parts of the nucleus or between different parts of the cytoplasm, and certainly, as we have already discussed, between the nucleus and the cytoplasm. But, over and above these intracellular stimulus-response systems, there are ones that transcend the cells and constitute an intercellular communication system. Since these are particularly important during development they will presently be discussed in greater detail, but now I should like to point out the fact that one can extend this argument and show that there are also examples of communication systems between parts of organisms, such as between organs. In fact, one may continue even further with this progressive externalization of stimulus-response systems and find examples between organisms in a kind of extension of development. Examples within a species are easily found in the relations between males and females during courtship or between young and parents during the period of parental care. Some of the most striking examples come from social animals such as the various types of social insects. There are also excellent examples of close communication between different species such as the factors which lead to commensalism or any kind of mutualism. It is not within the scope of this essay to consider these matters in any more detail but the point that needs emphasis is that specific, stepwise, gene-controlled stimulus-response systems can operate on many different biological levels.

Now, if one asks what have been the important advances in the study of development in the present century, it is possible to show that they each involve the elucidation of some larger, transcendent communication system. The fact that these communication systems sweep across cell boundaries and integrate the developing embryo automatically provides us with information of a more encompassing sort; it provides us with satisfying factual generalizations about development. In other words the contention here is that if one considers the most striking discoveries in the field of development, they all consist of extracellular communication systems operating between parts of the embryo.

INDUCTION

The most famous example is the discovery of induction by Spemann. It makes no difference that, in the beginning, he first ascribed too many powers to the organizer in the dorsal lip of the blastopore. He showed that one part of the embryo stimulated another part and the importance of this contribution was immediately felt and recognized. The refinements that followed, those of Holtfreter and others, which led to the discovery that the stimulus was chemical, were of great if not equal importance because they also bore upon the elucidation of a major stimulus-response system in the embryo. The only agonizing part of the tale is the search for the identity of the chemical inductor substance, the evocator, but this is agonizing because its identification seems to be something so desirable, so worth knowing and yet so elusive. Even in very recent years, contributions on the nature of induction are in turn ranked as important studies and we could list, among others, the contributions of Holtfreter who has emphasized the role of cytolysis, Barth, Niu, and Twitty who have studied induction in explants, Yamada, Toivonen, and Nieuwkoop who have independently examined the nature of regional induction. There has also been the extremely interesting work of Grobstein on the matter of contact between the induction source and the responding system. This is a shamefully abbreviated list of the many current contributions to the subject of induction but its purpose is to emphasize that this phenomenon has been one of central concern in the study of development, and my contention is that the reason for this is that induction is a major bit of communication between parts of the embryo.

As a corollary in the study of development in plants there is the discovery of the plant growth hormone by Went and others which acts as a stimulus, an inductor. It also is produced in one part of the plant, capable of movement through the plant, and capable of inducing responses in different parts of the plant. This discovery can certainly be favorably compared with induction in animal embryos. Each has produced comparable interest among biologists, and each has been continuously pursued since its inception, and each is an extracellular communication system between parts of the embryo.

GRADIENTS

Gradients are another transcendent communication system in developing organisms. We owe our awareness of gradients to Child who not only demonstrated their existence in many ways but showed how universal they were in developing animals and plants. Because Child attached such special importance to the metabolic aspect of gradients, he perhaps never received his due credit, but, as time progresses, we seem to be gaining a better perspective of his contribution. Rather than emphasize metabolic rates, we would now prefer to emphasize the gradation of particular chemical constituents. Inevitably, such gradations lead to differences in parts and these in turn provide a step towards ultimate morphogenesis and differentiation. The gradients transcend the cells and, by the production of local differences, there are differences in stimuli and therefore responses. Again it is a major communication system that pervades the whole embryo. Its importance is unquestioned and although it has not produced as many studies as the subject of induction, the double gradient system of developing sea urchins has, in the work of Hörstadius and others, provided valuable material for experimental analysis.

COORDINATED CELL MOVEMENTS

As a final example of important modern work concerned with extracellular communication, the studies on the coordination of cell movement during the so-called morphogenetic movement of development are of special interest. First, there were the pioneer discoveries of Harrison and, particularly, Weiss on the sensitivity of the moving cells to the substratum. Later came the notable observations of Holtfreter of the coordination of this movement by a surface coat in the amphibian embryo; all the surface cells are attached to it and it binds, leads, and guides the cells so that they produce the beautifully-controlled movement of gastrulation. In this case, the stimulus is a physical one of a binding to the surface, and the response is by the contact guidance recognized by Harrison and Weiss. The most recent development along these lines is the work of Weiss and Andres, Townes and Holtfreter, and particularly the work of Moscona on the dissociation of cells in the embryo similar to the sponge dissociation experiments of Wilson. The point is that the mixed-up cells wander about in masses of tissue of varying sizes so that ultimately they find their proper place according to their future fate. Here the communication is distinctly between cells and, in some way, they can stimulate and respond to one another as they touch each other so that like cells adhere and unlike cells pass on. The implication of this work as far as normal development is concerned is still uncertain, but the resolution of this problem in cell communication is clearly important and will be eagerly pursued.

These examples of major communication systems in developing organisms are by no means complete. For instance, there is considerable interest in cases of chemotaxis during the course of morphogenetic movements. Also, one might make the prediction that totally new and unsuspected stimulus-response systems that transcend cells will be discovered and carefully pursued.

This is, it would seem to me, the level where the most fruitful generalizations about development are likely to continue to appear. I find it hard to imagine that the study of development will ever spawn a Darwin or a Mendel, but, within the framework of epigenesis, there are many fascinating and intriguing puzzles to be elucidated. These necessarily will involve the untangling of the stepwise stimulus-response communication system. This should not mean that the subject is now cut and dried even though to some extent the course is set. There may be many delightful surprises when we discover the steps themselves. The purpose of this essay is not to discourage, but solely to put development in its proper setting; to see what it consists of, and to see its relation to genetics and evolution.

7

The Eve of Meiosis
(with Apologies to Clement C. Moore)

Craig L. Himes

'Twas prior to meiosis and all through the
    gland,
Action was normal; all was quite grand.
The cells were arranged with infinite care
In hopes that division soon would be there.

The nucleus was nestled all snug in its
    place,
Believing its chances were good in this
    case.
Its gossamer membrane would break down
    on cue,
To see what meiosis was going to do.

When all of a sudden an insidious force
Entered the cell and altered its course;
Into the center it flew like a flash,
Shattering genes with a strong silent splash.

The quiet of interphase now was upset,
Much to the genes' eternal regret.
When what to these wondering units
    appeared
But the shuffling of cistrons they always
    had feared.

Craig L. Himes, "The Eve of Meiosis," *BioScience*, Vol. 15 (12) (1965), p. 796. Reprinted by permission of Craig L. Himes, Assoc. Prof. Bio. Sci., Bloomsburg State College, Bloomsburg, Pa.

With a change in a muton and a switch in
    some more
They no longer knew which came last or
    before.
More rapid than eagles the transitions
    came;
Bases searched for each other by face and
    by name.

"Hey, thymine, where's adenine?"
    "Where's cytosine's mate?"
"Oh, phosphate, where's ribose?" "How
    terrible a fate!"
To the depth of the nucleus, to the core
    of the cell,
Now dash away specter, you've done your
    job well.

As silent as night replacing the day,
So, too, does the mutagen slip out and
    away.
Up to this moment the process was right
But a phantom was here like a thief in the
    night.

And then in a twinkling the particles knew
They had a new message and a trait to
    imbue;
As they drew their new partners and were
    turning around,
Into their midst came more ghosts with a
    bound.

These were brim-full of energy from their
    stem to their stern
And were doing their utmost, each taking
    his turn;
Their bundles of energy they flung off their
    backs
And caught the poor mutons right in their
    tracks.

How smartly they crackled! How quickly
    they danced!
Wreaking havoc galore as they darted and
    pranced;
They severed the sequences of long-
    standing fame,
Doing their worst, and still onward they
    came.

The chromosome stumps they held tight in
    their teeth
And the aura of energy hung like a wreath;
They hit from behind and into the belly
'Till the chromatin shook like a bowl-full
    of jelly.

The plump little molecules—usually jolly
    old elves—
Were uncoiled and re-coiled in spite of
    themselves;
In the wink of an eye these specters sped
Their work of confusion—leaving nothing
    but dread.

They spoke not a word but went straight
    to their work,
Sowing discord and chaos, then turned
    with a jerk
And flinging aside their genetic rape,
They hurriedly made their collective
    escape.

They sprang through the tissue, giving each
    other a whistle,
And away they all flew like the down of a
    thistle;
But the genes heard them call ere they
    fled out of sight,
"You're mutations now—let time make
    you right!"

8

Luminescence

There are certain caves in New Zealand where the ceilings are covered with thousands of glow-worms, each dangling a long luminescent thread. Any sudden noise causes the larvae to turn off their lights, almost as one. After a brief wait, a few of the bolder insects will switch on, followed by a few more, and suddenly the cavern will again be aglow with an eerie light.

The New Zealand glow-worm represents just one of a surprisingly diverse group of plant and animal species which exhibit bioluminescence —the biological emission of light from living organisms. Many animals manufacture their own light—usually in shades of blue but in some cases in red, orange, yellow, green or white—but none are higher in the animal kingdom than the fishes. Although bioluminescence (in fungi) was known to Aristotle and studied by such notables as Francis Bacon and Robert Boyle, it was not until 1887 that the mechanism behind this phenomenon was discovered. In that year, physiologist Raphael Dubois extracted juice from clams that were graced with light. He discovered that the juice contained two substances which, when mixed, were responsible for the glow. One he named luciferin after Lucifer, the light bearer, and the other he called luciferase to indicate that it had the properties of an enzyme.

Recently, and under the aegis of the National Science Foundation, the pace of research in bioluminescence has quickened. This renewed interest stems from the discovery that the processes a firefly employs to convert chemical energy into light can provide a sensitive instrument for biologists probing the secrets of cell metabolism.

One of the men most deeply involved in current research on bioluminescence is Dr. William McElroy of Johns Hopkins University. With the assistance of Baltimore area school children, who were paid 25 cents for every 100 fireflies they collected, he was recently able to isolate luciferin, establish its structure, and synthesize it.

Dr. McElroy found that the firefly emits light extremely efficiently,

"Luminescence," *The Sciences*, Vol. 4 (6) (1964), pp. 7-10. Reprinted by permission of The New York Academy of Sciences.

producing approximately one basic unit or quantum of "cold" light for each luciferin molecule oxidized. This means that the firefly is able to convert almost all of the chemical energy of the bioluminescence reaction into light, wasting very little as heat. By comparison, an incandescent bulb dissipates most of its electrical energy as heat.

In the firefly bioluminescence results when luciferin combines with oxygen in the presence of luciferase and ATP—an energy-yielding compound. An unusually large amount of energy is liberated in this reaction, enough to convert the luciferin-luciferase complex from its lower energy ground state to an electronic configuration of higher energy, the excited state. The molecule in the excited state may return to the ground state by losing its energy as a photon of visible light. Researchers are finding that, by borrowing the firefly's system of creating light, they are able to measure minute quantities of ATP in the laboratory. With this extremely sensitive technique they are studying the role of ATP in the mechanism of muscle contraction, nerve and brain function, photosynthesis, and many other biological systems. The enzyme luciferase in addition to serving as a catalyst for the bioluminescent reaction, also appears to control the color of the light. This may be a clue to what goes on when the larva of the South American beetle, *Phrixothrix,* is disturbed and begins to crawl.

When the larva is at rest at night, it glows red at one end; but when it starts to move, 22 small green spots arranged along the body suddenly light up. With every light source ablaze, the larva's appearance strongly suggests its common name—the railroad worm. Recent studies have revealed that the color of bioluminescent light in many animals depends on slight alterations in the structure of luciferase (a protein). It may be, therefore, that the railroad worm uses one form of the enzyme when only glowing red, and brings a second form of this enzyme into play when it starts making tracks away from a disturbance.

Among the roster of organisms with night lights may be found bacteria (only salt water, aerobic types have been found glowing), toadstools, ocean worms, sea pansies, jellyfish, squid, sponges, crustaceans, snails, millipedes and fish. These bioluminescent animals employ various systems to convert chemical energy into light. Consider, for example, the single-celled, flagellated organism *Gonyaulax*—one of many organisms responsible for the "red tides" of the ocean, and the phosphorescent glow stirred up by the wake of a ship. When the water around them is disturbed, these creatures emit flashes of light lasting some one-tenth of a second.

Recently Dr. J. W. Hastings of the University of Illinois, working under an NSF grant, discovered luminescent crystalline particles within the bioluminescent organism, *Gonyaulax polyedra.* Isolated particles, referred to as "scintillons," can be made to emit a luminescent flash that resembles the flash of the living *Gonyaulax.* These puzzling scintillons react with neither the enzyme (luciferase) nor the substrate (luciferin) extracted from the organisms. Luminescence is triggered simply by increasing the acidity of the particle solution in the presence of oxygen.

The flashing of these isolated crystalline subcellular particles constitutes a previously unknown bioluminescent system. Although he has isolated a typical luciferin-luciferase system within this same organism, Dr. Hastings believes that the scintillons are responsible for the characteristic flash of the living *Gonyaulax*.

Dr. Hastings discovered the scintillons while investigating the biochemical mechanisms involved in various clock-like rhythms exhibited by *Gonyaulax*. When exposed to alternating 12-hour periods of light and dark, cultures of *Gonyaulax* emit about 60 times more light when stimulated at the middle of the dark period than during the light period. Also, the amount of luciferin and luciferase in each cell reaches a maximum at the middle of the dark period. Dr. Hastings found that this biological rhythm is inhibited by a certain chemical known to block RNA synthesis. Thus, the cell's ability to synthesize RNA may be a crucial variable affecting the biological clock mechanism of bioluminescence.

Bioluminescence apparently plays a significant role in the lives of many marine organisms. Specifically, it may affect migratory activities, or speed and direction of swimming under different conditions. With the aid of the bathyphotometer, a very sensitive instrument for measuring light, Dr. George L. Clarke (Woods Hole Oceanographic Institute) has obtained records of bioluminescent flashes at depths as great as two and one-third miles. A luminescence camera was used to photograph a rare jellyfish at a depth of 3,000 feet; the jellyfish provided all the illumination needed.

A VESTIGIAL MECHANISM?

Recent investigations continue to turn up still other chemical variants of the bioluminescent reaction. Dr. Frank Johnson (Princeton University) has discovered a new type of luminescent system in the jellyfish, *Aequorea*, which requires no oxygen or luciferin, as such, for the emission of light. In this system, a single protein component emits light in the presence of calcium. Using the light from this unusual bioluminescent system as a quantitative measure of the presence of calcium is the most sensitive method known for detecting trace amounts of calcium in various biological and other solutions.

However bioluminescence is produced by an organism, it may be that they are all carry-overs from a time many millennia ago when free oxygen first appeared in the atmosphere. A theory by Dr. McElroy and his colleague Dr. Howard Seliger (also at Johns Hopkins University) jumps off from the generally accepted assumption that life developed in the oceans before there was any oxygen in the air. The first organisms were therefore anaerobic, and the oxygen which was later freed from the water and soil would have been toxic to them. These primitive animals must have possessed an energy transport system, and this system was best suited for eliminating the oxygen by converting it to water. The conversion would liberate enough energy to excite organic molecules to emit light. Even after the evolution of aerobic animals, the oxygen-removal system was retained by some organisms as part of the over-all electron-transport system still needed by the body. This theory gains credence from a report that, in most cases studied, bioluminescence appears to be produced by a nonessential enzyme system.

But even if bioluminescence relies on vestigial mechanisms, the reaction promises to be of great aid to biologists. Because each flash is easily observed proof of the transfer and liberation of energy, researchers are finding the phenomenon an ideal tool for monitoring the vital process by which the body converts food into energy. Also, the development of highly sensitive devices for measuring the emission of light, may permit this enzyme-catalyzed reaction to be used as a very discriminating indicator of the effects of various drugs or chemical inhibitors of cell activities.

9

Life's Mysterious Clocks

Frank A. Brown, Jr.

One of the greatest riddles of the universe is the uncanny ability of living things to carry out their normal activities with clocklike precision at a particular time of the day, month and year. Why do oysters plucked from a Connecticut bay and shipped to a Midwest laboratory continue to time their lives to ocean tides 800 miles away? How do potatoes in

Frank A. Brown, Jr., "Life's Mysterious Clocks," *Saturday Evening Post* (December 24, 1960), pp. 18-19, 43-44, © 1960 The Curtis Publishing Company. Reprinted by permission.

hermetically sealed containers predict atmospheric pressure trends two days in advance? What effects do the lunar and solar rhythms have on the life habits of man? Living things clearly possess powerful adaptive capacities—but the explanation of whatever strange and permeative forces are concerned continues to challenge science. Let us consider the phenomena more closely.

Over the course of millions of years living organisms have evolved under complex environmental conditions, some obvious and some so subtle that we are only now beginning to understand their influence. One important factor of the environment is its rhythmicality. Contributing to this rhythmicality are movements of the earth relative to the sun and moon.

The earth's rotation relative to the sun gives us our 24-hour day; relative to the moon this rotation, together with the moon's revolution about the earth, gives us our lunar day of 24 hours and 50 minutes. The lunar day is the time from moonrise to moonrise.

The moon's arrival every 29.5 days at the same relative position between the earth and the sun marks what is called the synodical month. The earth with its tilted axis revolves about the sun every 365 days, 5 hours and 48 minutes, yielding the year and its seasons.

The daily and annual rhythms related to the sun are associated with the changes in light and temperature. The 24.8-hour lunar day and the 29.5-day synodical month are associated most obviously with the moon-dominated ocean tides and with changes in nighttime illumination. But all four types of rhythms include changes in forces such as gravity, barometric pressure, high energy radiation, and magnetic and electrical fields.

Considering the rhythmic daily changes in light and temperature, it is not surprising that living creatures display daily patterns in their activities. Cockroaches, earthworms and owls are nocturnal; songbirds and butterflies are diurnal; and still other creatures are crepuscular, like the crowing cock at daybreak and the serenading frogs on a springtime evening. Many plants show daily sleep movements of their leaves and flowers. Man himself exhibits daily rhythms in degrees of wakefulness, body temperature and blood-sugar level.

We take for granted the annual rhythms of growth and reproduction of animals and plants, and we now know that the migration periods of birds and the flowering periods of plants are determined by the seasonal changes in the lengths of day and night.

In a similar fashion creatures living on the seashore exhibit a rhythmic behavior corresponding to the lunar day. Oysters and clams open their shells for feeding only after the rising tide has covered them. Fiddler crabs and shore birds scour the beach for food exposed at ebb tide and retreat to rest at high tide. The reef heron, though living many miles inland, appears to know when low tide will occur and leaves home each day just at the proper time to take advantage of it.

Synodical monthly breeding rhythms, geared to particular portions of the year, phases of the moon, and times of solar day, are common among animals inhabiting the sea. These rhythms assure that the eggs and sperm of a given species will be available at the same place at the same time. Each species has its own characteristic breeding time, which is often so precisely scheduled that we can accurately predict its occurrence. If, for example, we should go to the water's edge in Bermuda about an hour after sunset during a three- or four-day period of a summertime full moon, we would witness within a few minutes the mating display of the Atlantic "fireworm." At that time the females swarm to the surface from their burrows in the coral rock and luminesce brilliantly until joined by the males. At the same location, just before midnight either three to four days before or two days after a new moon, the swarming of the males and females of the glassy transparent shrimp, *Anchistioides*, takes place.

Palolo worms of the Southwest Pacific swarm in huge numbers on the nights of the third quarters of the October and November moons, liberating their reproductive elements into the sea water just as the dawn breaks. The breeding behavior of a small California fish, the grunion, is also exquisitely timed. Just after the moment of high tide, on nights from April through June, when the tides are at their monthly highest, these fish arrive at the beach in large numbers and ride the waves onto the sand. The fish quickly dig pits into which they discharge their eggs and sperm. Thus the new generation is able to develop over the period of a month without being prematurely washed out by the surf of the ordinary high tides.

Reproductive rhythms also occur in certain seaweeds. *Dictyota*, a brown alga, produces eggs and sperm on a monthly schedule. All the plants in one area may be synchronized to one phase of the moon, while those in another area will be regulated to another phase. The particular phase appears to be determined in some manner by the local tides.

Lunar reproductive rhythms are not restricted to sea dwellers. The reproductive cycle of the human female, averaging exactly the synodical month, indicates that here, too, exist both solar and lunar rhythms.

Though it might appear that such rhythms are merely the responses of organisms to rhythmic changes in light, temperature or the ocean tides, this is far from being the whole answer. For when living things, ranging from the single-celled Paramecium to flowering plants and mammals, are removed from their natural habitat and placed under conditions where no variations occur in any of the forces to which they are generally conceded to be sensitive, they commonly continue to display the same rhythms they displayed in their natural environment. The fiddler crab, for example, normally darkens by day and pales by night, runs actively at low tide and rests at high tide. When removed from the beach to laboratory isolation from light, temperature and tidal changes, the crab continues to behave in synchrony with his fellows still free on the beach. The crab somehow possesses the capacity to measure accurately and simultaneously both solar-day and lunar-day intervals without the stimulation of light, temperature and tidal changes.

Seeds persist in their annual sprouting cycle under similar laboratory conditions. This persistent adherence to rhythms with sun- and moon-related periods under conditions in which the organism is isolated from any obvious manifestation of these time cycles strongly suggests that an inherent clock system is probably a universal attribute of life.

Although living clocks appear to function simply and precisely in their regulation of organisms in nature, they present baffling difficulties when they are studied in the laboratory. The inquiring biologist faces a problem comparable to that of an observer in space who tried to figure out the nature of man's artificial clocks by observing the activities of a coastal industrial town. In the daily activity rhythm, some persons would be early risers, others late. Some, the clam diggers, would appear to have a lunar-day timer. The employees of a factory with three equal shifts working around the clock, would appear to have no daily clocks. The general population would appear to have a seven-day clock reflecting no natural terrestrial period.

In studying the living clocks in nature we are confronted with a similar observational limitation; we can analyze the clocks only by observing the rhythmic phenomena they time. We must, in other words, work from what the clock does back to the clocks themselves. This sort of inference is simply illustrated in a study of the common fruit fly.

In its natural habitat, the adult fruit fly normally emerges from its pupal case about dawn. If this process is subjected to laboratory control, with the eggs being laid and allowed to develop in continuous darkness, the young flies will emerge at any time of the day. If the maggot-larvae hatched from the eggs are subjected to even a single light flash during this controlled period of darkness, however, the flies, when they emerge, will come out of their pupal cases at the same time of the day that they were exposed to the light flash. This suggests that fruit flies have operating twenty-four-hour clocks; under natural conditions the clocks of the developing flies are set to local sun time while they are still maggots and alert the flies for emergence at dawn. In much the same way, the lunar-day activity rhythms of such creatures as oysters and fiddler crabs correspond to the tidal times of their local shores.

The adaptiveness of the basic timing system may be illustrated with organisms as unlike as beans and bees. The leaves of beans, which rise and fall in a regular daily sleep rhythm when the plants are kept in a constant dim illumination, may be induced to rise momentarily from their lowered position by a brief light stimulus. This induced behavior will continue day after day at the same time, without further stimulus, if the plants are kept in the same environment. Similarly, honeybees trained to come to a sugar-water feeding station at one or two arbitrarily selected times of day, will persist in this same twenty-four-hour food-seeking schedule for a few days even if the food is no longer provided.

This adaptiveness of daily rhythms is most useful when living things are moved rapidly to a new time belt. When, for example, a person flies from California to England, he arrives in England with his physiological rhythms of waking, body temperature, blood-cell count and hormone secretion still adjusted to the local time of California. It takes at least eight or ten days for these physiological processes to adjust to the new local time. The various processes change at different rates; time of waking shifts fast, requiring only two or three days, while other rhythms shift more slowly. Hence there appears to be a period during which various bodily processes are shifting gears relative to one another.

Recent studies by Dr. Mary Lobban and by Dr. Janet Harker, both at Cambridge University, suggest some possible consequences of having our rhythms out of their ordinary relationships with one another. Doctor Lobban found evidence of stress in some human subjects who, during the protracted daylight of the arctic summer, lived by watches adjusted to indicate recurrent "days" of unnatural lengths. Doctor Harker, working with cockroaches, discovered she could produce tumors by transplanting a hormone-producing neural element, the subesophageal ganglion, from animals with their running-activity rhythms set to the usual time of day into animals whose rhythmic changes had been artificially reset (by reversing the natural light-dark cycle) to be twelve hours slow.

It is well established that some animals navigate by the sun, the moon or even the constellations, orienting themselves relative to these objects at an angle which changes systematically with the rotation of the earth. Birds or bees also alter their usual direction of orientation when their natural clocks are reset by cycles of light and darkness to indicate a different time zone. One can even predict the new direction of orientation from the interval by which the timing rhythm has been reset.

This was dramatically illustrated in a recent study by Dr. Max Renner of the University of Munich. Honeybees were trained on the East Coast of the United States to fly northwest to a feeding station at one P.M., Eastern Standard Time. The trained bees were then taken by airplane to the West Coast. The next day, in California, the bees went seeking food about ten A.M., Pacific Coast Time. They were still on Eastern Standard Time. But they adhered to their previously learned sun angle, and now with the morning sun flew off in a different direction—southwesterly. In both cases the sun was, so to speak, in their left eye.

Daily changes of both light and temperature are primarily responsible for resetting natural rhythms to local time. The twenty-four-hour rhythms in an organism's sensitivity to light and temperature facilitate this resetting process. If a plant, for example, is exposed to light during the hours of darkness (when it is sensitive to light), the plant will immediately reset its twenty-four-hour rhythm of light sensitivity. If the plant is then returned to its natural environment of uninterrupted periods of light and darkness, this adjusted rhythm will continue to be reset by a small amount each day until the plant's light-sensitive and light-insensitive periods match the appropriate periods of night and day. In a similar fashion a mouse's rhythm of light sensitivity is set so that its activity and its running occur at night.

Each species seems to utilize such characteristic sensitivity rhythms. It also seems probable that these same twenty-four-hour cycles of light and temperature responsiveness in some way assist living creatures to measure the changing lengths of night and day and thus adapt themselves to natural annual cycles.

When some animals and plants are kept under controlled conditions of unchanging light and temperature, their daily rhythmic activities are observed to occur, in some cases, slightly earlier, in others, a little later each day. This produces activity rhythms with periods which vary from the twenty-four-hour cycle. These latter rhythms also vary somewhat in their periods with changes in temperature and illumination and from one individual to another. Such variations from the twenty-four-hour cycle introduce a fundamental question. Are these variations the product of poor-quality living clocks which run fast or slow? Or are the clocks themselves precise—with the apparent inaccuracies ascribable to some other cause?

We think we have the answer to why the rhythms often appear to run fast or slow under these unchanging conditions. To the organism placed in the laboratory at a constant level of light and temperature these two factors will continue to have the most impact during the sensitive phase of its twenty-four-hour cycle of responsiveness to the environment. These two factors in effect will appear, therefore, to the organism to show a daily variation, but now the light and temperature cycles will seem to have become inverted. Thus, during the sensitive period of its cycle—which normally falls at night—it will interpret the increased effectiveness of the light and temperature as indicating daytime. Employing the same splendidly adaptive machinery it uses in nature to reset its rhythm until the sensitive portion comes to fall in the darker, cooler nighttime, the organism keeps resetting its sensitivity rhythm a little forward, or backward, regularly each day in a futile attempt to adjust to the illusory "day-night cycles."

This simple, reasonable hypothesis, compatible with all our current knowledge, makes it probable that the living clocks are always precise in their time keeping. The alternative interpretation—that the inaccurate rhythms persisting under controlled conditions reflect inaccuracies in living clocks—is most improbable in view of the precision of the clocks under natural conditions where such resettings would not occur.

BASIC CLOCK QUESTION

Scientists are reluctant to credit a phenomenon for which they see no plausible explanation. As a consequence, evidence for living clocks was for a long time essentially ignored by most biologists. Recently, as our knowledge has become more refined, the phenomenon of timed rhythms was encountered so frequently by investigators in so many areas of biology that the possession of clock systems by living things became tacitly accepted. The problem of the nature of the clock systems had then to be faced.

Man-made clocks are of two general types—those with intrinsic timing and those with extrinsic. Examples of the intrinsic type are the hourglass, the pendulum and hairspring-balance clocks. Intrinsic clocks possess independent timing capacity and are useful any time and any place. Extrinsic clocks, like the sun dial and the electric clock, have no independent timing capacity but depend upon an inflow of timing information. The sun dial depends upon the sun's shadow, the electric clock upon the sixty-cycle alternating current. Extrinsic clocks are sometimes referred to as repeaters.

The basic question concerning the clocks of living things is whether they are intrinsic or extrinsic or whether, perhaps, they are both. This question has long been debated by students of biological rhythms.

The intrinsic-clock hypothesis has been generally favored over the years. This seemed the simplest hypothesis to account for the persistence of behavior of rhythms in unvarying light and temperature—especially the apparent inaccuracies and individually differing periods of the rhythms, their adaptiveness and their persistence in organisms transported long distances eastward or westward.

The extrinsic hypothesis, on the other hand, was questioned because it demanded that living things be sensitive to still unidentified, subtle pervasive factors. Such an hypothesis was radically opposed to the universally accepted concept of "constant conditions" in the laboratory—which postulated that under controlled laboratory conditions we could truly isolate an organism from fluctuations of every factor of the environment to which the organism is sensitive. The organism was deemed insensitive to such factors as magnetic and gravitational changes.

Since the rhythms persist in meticulously controlled "constant conditions," the working hypothesis of most investigators has been that the living clocks are intrinsic. The lengths of their natural periods, it was thought, are inherited and a consequence of fully independent cyclic biochemical transformations which would someday be explained solely in terms of the principles of physics and chemistry. But every investigation based upon this assumption found the living clocks unorthodox in terms of any ordinary biochemical scheme. Though all ordinary metabolic processes are greatly speeded up or slowed down by raising or lowering temperature, respectively, the periods of the clocks seemed generally independent of temperature. Crabs, as indicated by their color change and running habits, continue to measure accurately the periods of the day and the tides whether they are kept at 54° F. or 77° F.; dried seeds, as shown by testing samples periodically, display the same annual rhythm in their capacity to germinate whether they are stored in a freezer at −8° F. or in an incubator at 113° F. Similarly, none of the drugs known to alter the rate or character of metabolic changes seem to interfere with the accuracy of the basic timer.

Clearly, if the timer is intrinsic, it is a most extraordinary mechanism. But this is exactly what one would expect of any good clock. And if the experimental conditions in which these rhythms persisted were really constant for the organism, the timer had to be intrinsic. On the other hand, if it were proved that laboratory conditions hitherto presumed constant for the organisms were really not constant and that the organisms continued to receive outside rhythmic stimuli despite laboratory controls, a potential timing signal would be available for an extrinsic clock. And such an extrinsic clock could account readily for all the observed properties of the rhythms, including temperature and drug immunities, and the long rhythmic periods which are the same lengths as the geophysical ones.

EXTRINSIC RHYTHMICALITY

It has recently become evident that organisms, even when hermetically isolated under so-called constant conditions, still derive information as to the geophysical rhythms from their environment. Such information must be transmitted by highly pervasive forces hitherto ignored by biologists. Let us briefly consider the evidence for this.

Oysters, collected in New Haven Harbor, Connecticut, were shipped to Evanston, Illinois. Kept in pans of sea water in a dark room, they continued for a time to open their shells widest when it was high tide in New Haven waters. By the end of two weeks the New England oysters had reset their rhythms to open their shells widest at the moon's zenith and nadir positions with reference to Evanston. The oysters maintained thereafter this new schedule throughout the month they were observed. The zenith and the nadir positions of the moon—the two lunar positions on opposite sides of the earth which give rise to twice-daily high tides—are the periods of the moon's maximum gravitational effects upon the atmospheric tides over Evanston; this same gravitational effect would produce high ocean tides if Evanston were a coastal city. Recently, from simultaneous studies of fiddler crabs collected from beaches with differing local tidal times, we have learned that these creatures are also able to reset their tidal rhythms of running activity to accord with lunar zenith and nadir, despite absence of any obvious cues as to these times. Obviously some subtle atmospheric fluctuation related to local lunar time is able to substitute for local ocean tides and reset the periods of maximum activity. The same factor must continuously signal the lunar periods.

Living things as different as fiddler crabs and potatoes continue indefinitely to display both solar-day and lunar-day rhythms in their metabolism while they are subject to constant conditions in a laboratory. These two rhythms co-operate to provide both species with a synodical monthly rhythm. Plainly, the artificially isolated organisms continue to derive a wealth of information about outdoor atmospheric rhythms. Some of the evidence available is quite fantastic.

The solar-day tides of the atmosphere are expressed in rhythms of barometric pressure. The atmospheric tide rises in the morning, reaching its highest point about ten o'clock, and then falls to its lowest in the afternoon. The daily rhythms of organisms, even when they are sealed off from such pressure changes, are somehow associated with these daily tides of the atmosphere and their regular modification by lunar influences.

Nature provided us with a ready means for discovering this relationship. The daily tides of the atmosphere in temperate latitudes are continuously distorted by large irregular, weather-associated pressure changes. We know that both potato plants and crabs follow some outside factor reflecting the daily atmospheric tides because the daily cycles in their rate of oxygen consumption continuously reflect significantly the unpredictable distortions in the daily pressure cycles. Since it is inconceivable that living things are provided with a detailed program of all the erratic weather changes which are to occur while they are sealed under conditions including unvarying light, temperature, humidity and pressure, we must conclude that information reaches them continuously.

All of numerous species of animals and plants which have been studied reflect, in their metabolic processes between five and seven A.M., the amount the barometric pressure changed between two and six o'clock that same morning. Their metabolism from five to seven P.M. reflects the amount the pressure changed between two and six o'clock that same afternoon. These times are highly specific; no comparable relationships are found at any other time of day.

In both winter and summer the atmospheric tide tends to rise in the morning; at the latitude of Chicago, the time of lowest tide occurs about two P.M. during the coldest months and about seven P.M. during the warmest months, and so the afternoon pressure tends to fall during summer and rise in winter. The metabolism of potato plants, even when they are sealed off from pressure changes, conforms to this annual pressure change.

A by-product of this study has been the astonishing discovery that the late-afternoon biological activity of nearly all living things, while only remotely related to mean daily barometric pressure of the same day, is intimately related to that of the second day thereafter. These organisms seem to be "predicting" the atmospheric-pressure trends. The biological explanation of the riddle is this: the afternoon pressure change which the organism's late-afternoon metabolism reflects is itself quite inexplicably tending to predict the barometric pressure trends two days in advance. Imagine the predicament of a meteorologist, sealed away like potatoes, and faced with the problem of weather prediction.

Fluctuations in the numerous factors in the earth's atmosphere are variously interdependent. The discovery that the metabolism of living things, even under hermetic seal, reflects erratic changes in such rhythmic environmental factors as outdoor air temperature, cosmic radiation and general background radiation was, therefore, not surprising. Collectively, these relationships, continuing year after year, compel us to conclude that the organisms, even in so-called constant conditions, are not fully shielded from their rhythmic geophysical environment.

Within the past year my associates and I have implicated magnetism as one subtle factor related to the rhythms. Terrestrial magnetism is known to fluctuate rhythmically with the solar and lunar periods. Additionally, the earth's magnetic axis, at an angle with its polar axis, wobbles as the earth rotates and produces a movement of the magnetic field in relation to the polar axes. Snails, when oriented geographically, were found to display solar- and lunar-day rhythms in their tendency to veer from a true southward path, even while in presumably unchanging conditions. Experiments with magnets further proved the snails could perceive very weak magnetic fields. In addition, the snails' response to a bar magnet showed both solar and lunar rhythms.

The snails were able also to distinguish directions of magnetic fields and, therefore, they possess a magnetic compass. The snails' perceptive system for a magnetic field behaves like two rotating "directional antennae," the rotation of one is related to the sun, the other to the moon. For fields of equal magnetic strength, the field parallel with the snail's body was most effective when the sun or moon was above the horizon, while a field at right angles was most effective under other conditions. Hence, the magnetic receiver behaved like a living compass geared in with the living-clock system. This compass may serve as a navigational instrument.

These magnetic-field studies have introduced a subtle and pervasive geophysical factor with which biologists must now reckon. It seems highly probable that other animals will be found similarly armed with both a clock and a compass. We have, furthermore, experimental evidence suggesting that both flatworms and snails perceive changes in electrostatic fields, the fields surrounding electrically charged bodies. And, as with magnetic fields, the response seems to be regulated by the living-clock system.

The weight of all the evidence suggests that living clocks depend upon some universal-time, geophysical rhythm—one with simultaneous world-wide changes. Magnetic and electrostatic sensitivities support this theory, since these forces are known to fluctuate on a universal scale. If living things truly possess such a universal timer, they have always available what man terms Greenwich time and uses for purposes such as navigation and astronomy—a means for pinpointing their location on the earth's surface. Interestingly, studies of bee, bird and fish navigation have proved that these creatures are acutely aware of the heavens.

Experimental evidence suggests, therefore, that life, time and space, in the range of their terrestrial dimensions, are very intimately inter-related. It appears that the forces regulating the life processes are de-pendently related to their counterparts of the outside physical environ-ment. The living organism is a diminutive oscillating system with periods paralleling those of the physical environment.

What kind of timing system did nature fit into the microscopic dimen-sions of single cells—a timer which could reproduce so unerringly the long natural periods?

Evidence suggests the primary timing system to be the movements of the sun, moon and earth. Nature provided means by which this timer could simultaneously serve the rhythmicalities of both living organisms and their environment. Ingeniously the timing bridge to living systems was fashioned, not in terms of such variable and biologically potent forces as light and temperature (to which organisms must respond in spe-cifically adaptive fashions), but in terms of more stable forces demanding little or no specific adaptive response and simultaneously so pervasive that no living thing would ever normally be deprived of their influence. Only with such provisions could living clocks become the loyal servant rather than the domineering master of life.

10

Avian Adaptations

Birds are doubtlessly the most highly specialized of the vertebrates. Wings and feathers, two remarkable adaptations by themselves, have combined with other, more subtle changes to produce a highly efficient

"Avian Adaptations," *The Sciences*, Vol. 5 (7) (1965), pp. 20-23. Reprinted by permission of The New York Academy of Sciences.

flying machine. In almost every conceivable way, the avian body is "designed" for flight, incorporating lightness, strength, and efficiency into a rigid, compact body with a low center of gravity.

The most distinctive characteristic of birds is their feathers, which among other functions, insulate the bird from the elements, streamline its body, and provide a lifting surface over the wing. Feathers are as varied in structure as the jobs they perform, but the long tail or wing feather is usually considered typical. It consists of a central stem, or rachis, and a broad portion or vane. The vane is composed of small branches or barbs, with numerous overlapping small barbules. Tiny hooks lock the individual elements of the feather into a sturdy, flexible unit. If a feather should become disarranged, preening by the bird locks the elements back into place.

THE FRAMEWORK

A comparison of the bird's skeletal system with other, more generalized vertebrate skeletons, shows how specialized the bird's has become. As the bipedal form of locomotion freed the forelimbs for modification into organs of flight, the loss of some bones followed, with the fusion of others. As illustrated in *Flight* (Life Science Library, 1965) the large bones became hollow, and strengthened with internal struts. Air sacs, extensions of the bird's extensive respiratory system, invaded some of the bones, adding to their buoyancy.

In flight, the body of the bird hangs from the wings, an arrangement which is reflected in the strong shoulder girdle and rib cage. Unlike those of most other vertebrates, the ribs of birds have no cartilage, but are fully ossified and connect the backbone with the sternum, or breastbone, forming a rigid cage. The backbone itself is fused for most of its length, with a small freely movable tailpiece, or pygostyle, which controls movement of the tail feathers.

THE FLIGHT MECHANISM

Changes in the skeletal system have produced forelimbs that serve efficiently as wings. As described by Wesley E. Lanyon in *Biology of Birds* (The Natural History Press, 1964) most of the bones of the hand have become fused, with the loss of the first and fifth digits. The second digit may be moved independently, and, along with the feathers attached to it, it is an important structure in flight.

The breastbone of all flying birds is provided with a large keel, which serves for attachment of the massive wing muscles. In general, the size of the keel is an indication of wing power, and flightless birds, such as the ostrich, lack this adaptation.

Undoubtedly because of the need for a low center of gravity, both the muscles for raising, as well as those for lowering the wing are located on the keel, eliminating all large, weighty muscles from the back. The overlying breast muscle, *pectoralis major*, is attached to the humerus, or upper wing bone, and serves to pull the wing downward. Underlying the *pectoralis major* is the *pectoralis minor*. A tendon extends from this muscle, passing over the shoulder to its insertion on the upper side of the humerus. Acting by a pulley-type mechanism, a contraction of the *pectoralis minor* elevates the wing.

ENERGY FOR FLIGHT

Skeletal and muscular systems alone, of course, will not provide power for flight. Birds have evolved extremely efficient mechanisms for providing themselves with fuel and oxygen. Their lungs, for example, are unlike those of other animals; they are relatively inelastic and have no diaphragm to help bring in the air.

A number of large thin-walled air sacs are situated throughout the body, among the internal organs and muscles, and within the hollow bones. Besides invading the wing bones, sacs usually extend into the femur (the large bone in the leg), the ribs, and also the vertebrae. In screamers and hornbills the air sacs are so extensive that they penetrate even into the pygostyle, the tips of the wing bones, and the toes. The air sacs are connected to the lungs by rather large diameter tubes, where they meet with a number of smaller, interconnecting passageways. Lungs of birds, therefore, do not have dead end spaces, such as do the lungs of mammals, for instance.

EFFICIENT RESPIRATION

Breathing is accomplished by muscular movement of the thoracic region, and is aided by wing movements during flight. These movements force air in and out of the air sacs, thereby continuously ventilating the lungs. Unlike lungs with dead spaces, the air in the lungs of birds is completely changed during each respiratory cycle.

The transfer of oxygen and carbon dioxide occurs in the lungs themselves, but the air sacs are not entirely without physiological function. When large amounts of heat are generated, as in flight, the air sacs aid in cooling the bird. Since they have no sweat glands, birds must rely on evaporation from these moist internal sacs for cooling.

In response to the high respiratory requirements imposed by flight, the avian heart is relatively larger in size, beats faster, and pumps more blood per unit time, than the mammalian heart. Complete separation of oxygenated and unoxygenated blood is maintained by the double circulatory system characteristic of all homoiotherms ("warm-blooded" animals). According to Josselyn Van Tyne and Andrew J. Berger in *Fundamentals of Ornithology* (John Wiley's & Sons, Inc., 1959) the basal heart rate of birds varies from one species to another, but is generally high; 135 beats per minute in the mourning dove, to 615 in the ruby-throated hummingbird.

REDUCTION IN WEIGHT

Economy of weight must be maintained in spite of the high fuel consumption needed for flight. This apparent dilemma has been resolved in the highly efficient avian digestive system, which digests food rapidly, and immediately eliminates wastes. Experiments performed on song birds have shown that artificially stained food (grain, fruit or insects) passes through the digestive tract in about one and one-half hours. Various fruits have been shown to pass through the tract of a cedar waxwing in from 16 to 40 minutes.

The horny bill and muscular stomach, or gizzard, have taken the place of teeth in seed and vegetable-eating birds, serving to mechanically break down the food. In carnivorous and carrion feeders, the gizzard is poorly developed. Bones, fur, and feathers are regurgitated from the mouth in pellet form, without burdening the rest of the system. When the barn-owl, for instance, preys on small mammals, it swallows its prey whole. A neat pellet, consisting of bones and fur, is later ejected from the mouth. A short large intestine rapidly eliminates digestive wastes.

Adaptations resulting in weight reduction have involved every part of the avian body, including the urinary and reproductive systems. Most adult female birds have only a single (left) functional ovary. The rudimentary right gonad remains as a potential ovary, testis, or ambisexual organ. Birds also have no urinary bladder, thus eliminating the weight of stored urine. Rather, the concentrated urine, high in uric acid content, is mixed with the feces in the common urogenital chamber, or cloaca, and voided in the semi-solid state.

NERVOUS CONTROL

The nervous system has also changed, in keeping with the specialized needs of an aerial way of life. Associated with the importance of equilibrium and coordination in flight, the cerebellum is highly developed. Also well developed are the semicircular canals, which help to provide the equilibrium needed in flight. Greatly enlarged optic lobes are located at the sides of the brain, rather than roofing the midbrain as in reptiles and mammals. Eyes of birds are disproportionately large, and are not spherically shaped, as in man. Their flattened shape saves considerable space and weight, with no loss in optical efficiency.

Of course, there have been many variations upon the basic theme of bird structure. Numerous variations in wing and body structures coincide with particular flying abilities; soaring and gliding as well as powered flight (See "Bird Flight," THE SCIENCES, February 15, 1965). Their flying ability made the birds the masters of the sky for centuries before man's machines invaded their realm. Even in this time of supersonic speeds, though, the near perfection of birds is a source of wonder.

11

Blood

WHAT ARE THE MAIN PARTS OF BLOOD?

Blood is a tissue made up of cells in suspension and of plasma containing substances in solution. Forty-five percent of blood volume consists of the formed elements (red cells, white cells, and platelets). Fifty-

From *Blood and the Nation's Health* (1964), pp. 1-16. Reprinted by permission of the American National Red Cross.

five percent of blood volume is composed of plasma, which consists mainly of water, some proteins, and the various mineral salts necessary to life.

HOW IS BLOOD MANUFACTURED?

Blood is assembled by the body from many different sources. With the exception of injections that may be necessary for treatment, all constituents of blood ultimately come from substances taken by mouth.

The plasma is formed from water, proteins, and salts, all of which are absorbed from the digestive tract. The proteins are modified by the metabolism of the body into the type needed for the human species.

The cells of the blood come from diverse sources. The various organs and tissues that collaborate in the manufacture of blood cells are known as the hemopoietic (blood-forming) system. This includes the bone marrow, spleen, lymph glands, stomach, liver, and the reticulo-endothelial system (a network of special tissue cells plus the lining of the blood vessels). The reticulo-endothelial cells are widely distributed throughout the body, but the most important sites are the lining of the bone marrow and spleen. They are phagocytic; that is, they can ingest micro-organisms and foreign particles of all sorts, thus removing them from the circulating blood.

WHAT ARE THE GENERAL FUNCTIONS OF THE BLOOD IN THE BODY?

Blood, a complex fluid serving many purposes in the human body, preserves the internal environment required for normal activity of the living cells. Following are some of its main functions:

Respiratory. Blood transports oxygen from the lungs to all the body tissues, and simultaneously carries carbon dioxide from these tissues to the lungs, where it is expired. (External respiration.)

Nutritive. Blood conveys food materials from the alimentary canal and food depots to all the tissues of the body.

Excretory. Blood assists in the removal of waste products of metabolism by conveying them to the kidneys, where they are excreted in the urine.

The maintenance of the water content of the tissues. Fluid lymph, containing oxygen and food materials, leaves the vascular channels and comes in contact with the tissues. Here it picks up carbon dioxide and other waste products and then flows back into the vascular channels. (Internal respiration.) The complex chemical processes of the body are enabled to take place because of the high dissolving and ionizing property of water in the blood and lymph.

Regulation of body temperature. The body owes its ability to regulate temperature largely to the water content of blood and of the tissue fluid. Heat from the deeper regions of the body is brought to the skin and lungs by the blood stream and dispelled.

Protective and regulatory. Blood and lymph contain complex chemical substances such as antibodies, antitoxins, and lysins—all of which protect the body against injurious substances. The circulating blood also brings hormones from the ductless glands into direct contact with the tissues that respond to such stimuli.

HOW MUCH BLOOD IS IN THE BODY?

The average healthy individual has a blood volume equal to about 8 percent of his body weight. Thus the mean blood volume for a person weighing 110 pounds would be 4,400 ml.; for a person weighing 150 pounds, it would be 6,000 ml.; for a person weighing 200 pounds, it would be 7,600 ml. As 1,000 ml. is equal to 2.1 pints, it will be easy for one to estimate the number of pints of blood in his body. The volume for men will be slightly higher than that for women of the same weight because men have an agerage of 7½ percent more red cells than do women.

The amount of blood in the human body has been the subject of careful study. The methods used to calculate blood volume are based on this fact: When a known amount of concentrated substance is introduced into the blood stream, the extent to which the concentrate is diluted is a measure of blood volume. Substances used must be harmless in small quantities and easily identifiable in blood samples. Depending upon the type used, they attach themselves either to the red cell or to a plasma protein. Red cell volume has been measured by tagging the red cells with radioactive molecules; plasma volume has been measured by using a harmless blue dye. Information gained in this way can be used to calculate the whole blood volume.

The blood volume may vary within certain normal limits, depending upon the needs of the body. At rest, the circulating volume is at a minimum. But the blood volume may be increased by several conditions, including hot weather, high altitudes, muscular exercise, emotional excitement, and pregnancy. On the other hand, an abnormal decrease in blood volume may occur during anemia, hemorrhage, loss of plasma due to extensive burns, or by various forms of dehydration.

WHAT ARE RED CELLS?

Red cells, or erythrocytes, are small, solid, disc-shaped particles whose main function is to transport oxygen from the lungs to the tissues and to transport carbon dioxide from the tissues to the lungs. The red cells contain hemoglobin, a chemical substance that has an amazing affinity for oxygen and carbon dioxide.

Compared to other cells in the body, red cells are incomplete and cannot reproduce themselves because they lose their nuclei shortly before being released from the bone marrow into the blood stream.

However, they are considered to be "alive" in the sense that they are able to perform their functions in the body for as long as 120 days. After that time they wear out and are then removed from circulation and destroyed by the spleen. The various components of protein and iron are salvaged for reuse by the body. Red cells are created in vast numbers, mainly in the marrow of the short, flat bones of the body. It is estimated that they are worn out and removed from the circulation at the rate of 10 billion red cells an hour. The means by which the bone marrow must produce this same amount in the same period of time is part of the marvelous balance of supply and demand carried on by the normal physiology of the body.

Red cells appear fragile in structure under the microscope but are actually very durable. They must be able to withstand a good deal of hammering about while being pumped through the blood vessels, and are able to squeeze through a capillary, which has a smaller diameter than the cell itself. In order to do this, the red cells must fold and bend in a flexible manner and be able to repeat the process many times.

While in the lungs the red cells are exposed to oxygen for only a brief time, but, owing to a chemical balance in the surrounding plasma, they become saturated with oxygen in 1 second. These oxygenated cells are then carried from the lungs to the heart and pumped out into the body. In the tissues, a delicate chemical change takes place in the plasma, and the oxygen is released for use. The carbon dioxide, created by the metabolism of the body cells, is picked up immediately by the red cell in exchange for oxygen and carried to the lungs. Here, another chemical change takes place in the plasma, a change enabling the red cell to release the carbon dioxide and almost instantly pick up more oxygen. This cycle is constantly repeated.

Red cells are very small, measuring about 7.5 microns in diameter and 1.95 microns in thickness. (A micron is about 1/25,000 of an inch.)

It would require approximately 3,000 red cells lined up in their widest diameter to cover the space of an inch. Yet, because there are so many red cells in the human body, they would encircle the earth four times if lined up in a beadlike chain. In spite of the smallness of the individual red cell, the surface area of the combined cell mass is very large. In a man of average size, the surface area of the red cells represents a space as large as the surface of a football field. Because one-fourth of the circulating blood is in the lungs at any one time, a combined cell surface area of 1,200 square yards is available to air. In 1 second, about 370 square yards of red cell tissue surface is exposed to the air, binding the oxygen to the hemoglobin. Only through these unique properties of the red cell, can man— with his relatively large size and weight—obtain enough oxygen to satisfy the needs of his complex system. From the heavy work of the muscles to the delicate functions of the brain, all cells and tissues depend on oxygen for life.

WHAT ARE THE WHITE CELLS?

The white cells, or leukocytes, are the protective cells of the blood stream. They are two or three times as large as the red cell and possess a nucleus. In a normal person, there are about 7,000 white cells per cubic millimeter° of blood (or about one white cell to 600 or 700 red cells).

There are several varieties of white cells, and each variety has a different function. When a drop of blood is placed on a glass slide, spread into a thin film, and allowed to dry, it may be stained with a dye so that each type of white cell has a distinctive appearance and color. White cells may thus be classified into two major groups: those that have easily visible granules in the cytoplasm (the body of the cell exclusive of the nucleus) and those that do not.

The most common type of white cell in the circulating blood has granules and is thus called a granulocyte. This variety comprises 60 to 70 percent of the white cells. The granulocytes have the ability to migrate, like an amoeba, along the wall of a blood vessel and out of the capillaries into the body tissues, to fight bacteria. Also like an amoeba, they are able to engulf foreign substances. (This property is common to the granulocytes, monocytes, and reticulo-endothelial cells—all sometimes referred to as phagocytes.) When the body is threatened by infection, the granulocytes quickly gather at the point of invasion and set up a first line of defense. As an example, when you prick your finger and the bacteria enter and start to multiply, the body will mobilize many white cells at that

° A cubic millimeter is approximately 1/16,400 of a cubic inch.

point. They can sometimes be seen as a yellow accumulation called pus.

Lymphocytes, a second type of white cell, comprise 25 to 35 percent of the white cell population. These cells—formed by the spleen, lymph nodes, and other lymphoid tissue of the body—do not appear to be so aggressive in combating acute infection, but cluster in the tissues where chronic infection exists. There they form a barrier against the spread of infection to other parts of the body. Lymphocytes may undergo certain chemical changes that are protective in nature, and they may have some function in the development of immunity.

Monocytes, a third type of white cell found in the blood, are larger than the other white cells and relatively few in number. Like the granulocyte, they have the ability to migrate to the site of infection and ingest bacteria. Like a lymphocyte, they tend to wall off the infected area. During the healing process, they are capable of growing into another type of tissue repair cell, strengthening the weakened area.

The disease of leukemia is an abnormal, unrestrained overgrowth of white-cell-forming tissue. In other diseases, there may be an increase or decrease of white cells in the circulating blood. By obtaining a laboratory count of the number of white cells in a cubic millimeter of blood, a doctor has a valuable clue as to the state of health or disease of the body.

WHAT ARE PLATELETS?

Platelets are small, colorless, cell-like bodies that have an important function in the clotting of blood. They are a source of thromboplastin, a substance that is one of the links in the chain of clot formation. Platelets are liberated into the blood stream as fragments of a large parent cell in the bone marrow. They are smaller than the red cell and fewer in number (one platelet to 10 to 20 red cells). The normal range in platelet counts is quite wide, varying from 200,000 to 400,000 per cubic millimeter of blood.

WHAT IS PLASMA?

Plasma is the fluid part of the blood in which the red cells, white cells, and platelets are suspended. It is composed of 92 percent water and 7 percent proteins; the remaining 1 percent consists of fat, carbohydrates, and many mineral salts necessary for life. It also contains hormones, vitamins, and enzymes.

Many of the plasma proteins have specific uses in the treatment of disease. The most well known of these plasma derivatives are gamma globulin, serum albumin, and fibrinogen. Fresh frozen plasma is also prepared for the treatment of certain bleeding problems, especially hemophilia.

HOW IS PLASMA OBTAINED FROM WHOLE BLOOD?

Plasma is separated from whole blood by centrifugation; the red cells, being heavier, settle to the bottom of the blood-collecting container. The plasma can then be drawn off into separate containers and processed as fresh frozen plasma or sent to commercial firms for fractionation into specific derivatives.

WHAT ARE BLOOD DERIVATIVES?

Blood derivatives are those substances that can be separated from whole blood and used for specific purposes. Plasma itself is a component of whole blood. From the plasma there are a number of proteins that can be separated, and these fractions are usually called derivatives. Serum albumin, which in the body maintains plasma volume, is used for shock, low blood protein, and edema (the loss of water from the blood stream into the tissues). Antibodies against disease are concentrated in the gamma globulin. Fibrinogen is one of the proteins essential for the formation of a blood clot. In addition to serum albumin, gamma globulin, and fibrinogen, a number of other plasma proteins are under study. These may prove valuable additions to the derivatives mentioned above. The red cells left in the bottle after the withdrawal of plasma can also be used to great advantage in certain diseases.

WHAT MAKES BLOOD CLOT?

The clotting of blood is the result of a delicate and complex series of biochemical events, some of which are not fully understood. This mechanism must satisfy two rigorous requirements if life is to be sustained: (1) blood must never clot while it is performing its functions within the intact circulatory system; (2) blood must always clot when any damage occurs that causes a break in the blood vessels. The body must be able to vary this complex response to bleeding ranging from a slight cut to a massive hemorrhage.

When tissues are damaged, thromboplastin is released from the nearby cells and platelets. This initiates a chain of reactions in which calcium plays an important part. The end result is that the soluble protein (fibrinogen) is converted to a gelatinous solid (fibrin). Fibrin forms in threadlike strands, making a webbed mesh in which the sticky platelets, red cells, and white cells are trapped, forming a jellylike clot. As the platelets disintegrate, they cause the fibrin web to shrink and have a constricting action on the walls of the torn blood vessel, causing it to clamp down and narrow the tear through which blood is escaping.

This knowledge of clot formation is applied in the collection of blood for transfusions. The calcium, which plays a key role, is inactivated when it is mixed with a citrate solution in the blood container during collection.

WHAT IS AN ANTIBODY?

An antibody is a substance in the plasma that reacts in a highly specific way with a foreign substance (called an antigen) when it is introduced into the body. Although this reaction is usually protective, it may sometimes result in injury to the body.

As an example of its protective function, if the body is invaded by a virulent strain of bacteria, two main lines of defense are set up. The white cells attempt to wall off and engulf the invaders; the bacteria, being a foreign substance, are antigens, and stimulate the reticulo-endothelial cells of the body to produce an antibody that will assist in repelling them. This antibody, contained in the globulin fraction of the plasma, may act on the bacteria in one of several ways. It may dissolve them; it may cause them to clump so that they cannot circulate freely through the blood stream; it may soften their protective membrane and inactivate them so that they will fall easy prey to the phagocytic white cells.

So it is that this type of antibody forms a protective agent against disease. Furthermore, as most of us are exposed to a large number of disease-causing microorganisms during our lifetime, we develop a concentration of various antibodies that may remain in the blood stream for a long time, even after we are well.

If we donate blood, the globulin fraction containing these protective substances can be separated from the rest of the plasma components and concentrated to about 25 times its normal strength. This concentrated substance, called gamma globulin or immune globulin, can then be injected into others to help protect them against certain diseases.

The antigen-antibody reaction also has an important application in giving blood transfusions. Red blood cells, if they are not the proper group and type, may act as antigens in the blood stream of the recipient. In this case, oddly enough, the antibodies in the A, B, AB, and O groups do not have to be developed by the introduction of red cells but exist in the blood stream in the natural state. In contrast to this, the antibodies to the Rh factor do not exist in the natural state and must be developed by a transfusion of incompatible Rh-type cells. In the case of the ABO groups or the Rh types, the incompatible antigenic red cells are attacked by the circulating antibodies and caused to clump, or agglutinate, in the blood stream. If this reaction is strong enough, the red cells may be broken up, or hemolysed, by the antagonistic antibody. If enough of the transfused, incompatible red cells are clumped or broken up in the recipient's body, they have a damaging effect on the tubules of the kidney, and serious illness or even death may result from the inability of the kidney to excrete waste products. The steps by which these hazards are avoided will be discussed in a later section on laboratory work.

WHAT ARE BLOOD GROUPS?

Blood groups are inherited patterns into which human blood may be divided for scientific purposes. There are four major blood groups: A, B, AB, and O.° Groups A, B, and O were discovered by Dr. Karl Landsteiner in 1900, and a fourth, AB, was described by another scientist in 1902. Although the percentage of people belonging to each group tends to vary in different countries (as do other inherited characteristics, such as color of eyes and hair), the following distribution represents the general spread in this country: 45 percent—group O; 40 percent—group A; 10 to 12 percent —group B; 3 to 5 percent—group AB.

About the turn of the century, there was great interest in learning how to use blood transfusions as part of the practice of medicine; but doctors were held back by a forbidding obstacle: while about half the transfusions given to treat illness had a remarkable therapeutic effect, the other half seemed to make the patient much worse and sometimes resulted in death.

In seeking the clue to this riddle, Landsteiner performed a series of tests in the course of which he placed the red cells of one person in suspension in the serum of another person. From this crucial experiment, he noted that in a number of the combinations of red cells and sera, the red cells remained undamaged and freely suspended; in other combinations, the red cells were clumped together in sticky clusters—with resultant damage to the cells. From this evidence, he deduced that certain combinations

°There are a number of other groups that are of scientific and legal interest and are of importance in giving transfusions.

of cells and sera were incompatible and that it was these unfortunate combinations that were causing illness and death in some patients following transfusion (transfusion reaction).

Further investigation of the factors causing clumping, or agglutination, of the red cells when exposed to incompatible sera revealed that there are two main antigenic substances (agglutinogens) in the red cells and two main antibodies (agglutinins) in the plasma. The antigens in the red cells were named A and B, and the antibodies in the plasma were given names to correspond with the group of red cells that they would agglutinate. Therefore, the plasma antibody causing group A cells to clump was called anti-A; the plasma antibody causing group B cells to clump was called anti-B. As noted in the discussion on antibodies, the anti-A and anti-B substances are contained in the globulin protein of the plasma. These basic facts enable us to understand the four simple combinations that are the bases for the major blood groups:

1. *Group A blood* has A substance in the red cells, and anti-B substance in the plasma.

2. *Group B blood* has B substance in the red cells, and anti-A substance in the plasma.

3. *Group AB blood* has both A and B substance in the red cells, and neither anti-A nor anti-B substances in the plasma.

4. *Group O blood* has neither A nor B substance in the red cells, and has both anti-A and anti-B substances in the plasma.

It will be noted that each blood group is named for the type of antigenic substance that is an inherited characteristic of the red cell.

HOW ARE BLOOD GROUPS DETERMINED
IN THE LABORATORY?

Blood groups are determined in the laboratory by a simple technique utilizing the known facts about the A and B substances in the red cells, and the anti-A and anti-B substances in the plasma. On the left side of a clean glass slide, the technician places a drop of serum known to contain anti-A substance; on the right, a drop of serum known to contain anti-B substance. He then places a drop of blood (obtained from the person whose group he wishes to determine) into each of the specimens of anti-A and anti-B sera. After a minute or two, the technician can observe one of four possible events take place by which he can determine the blood group:

1. If the anti-A serum alone causes the red cells to clump, the blood sample is labeled *group A.*

2. If the anti-B serum alone causes the red cells to clump, the blood sample is labeled *group B*.

3. If *both* anti-A and anti-B sera cause the red cells to clump, the blood sample is labeled *group AB*.

4. If *neither* anti-A nor anti-B serum causes the red cells to clump, the blood sample is labeled *group O*.

The clumping, or absence of it, is clearly visible to the naked eye in a few moments. Thus, in a well-organized laboratory the technician can determine the groups of a large number of samples in a few hours' time.

For safety, the results of blood group determination are checked in the laboratory in another procedure called proof of blood group.

This utilizes samples of known group A and group B red cells, against which samples of the unknown serum are tested. Once again, four observable results may be noted: the group A cells alone may be clumped, the group B cells alone may be clumped, both group A and B cells may be clumped, or no clumping at all will occur. One can easily work out the blood group that would occur with each of these events.

Still another use is made of these facts when the bottle of blood, properly identified as to group, reaches the hospital and is ready to be transfused into the injured or ill patient. Even though the blood is the same group as the patient's, another precaution must be taken to ensure that bloods of donor and recipient are compatible. This is a laboratory test, very similar to those described above, known as crossmatching. A drop of the donor's red cells is mixed with a drop of the recipient's serum; this is known as the major side of the crossmatching test. The mixture of recipient's cells with donor's serum is known as the minor side of the test. If agglutination occurs on the major side, the blood is incompatible and must never be given because the donor's cells would be agglutinated and hemolyzed in the recipient's blood stream, causing dangerous transfusion reaction. If agglutination occurs on the minor side, as it will when group O blood is given to A, B, or AB recipients, it does not mean that the blood cannot be given. At the present time, however, it is the practice to give group-specific blood (group A to group A recipients, B to B recipients, and so on) wherever possible and to use group O donors as universal only in emergencies.

HOW ARE BLOOD GROUPS INHERITED?

Blood groups are inherited as dominant characteristics according to the Mendelian law: for every inherited characteristic, including blood group, there is a pair of genes, one contributed by each parent. The blood group that a child may inherit is therefore dependent on the combinations resulting from genes contributed by both parents. Owing to intermarriage of people with different blood groups, a variety of combinations can result; but if the parents' blood groups are known, those possible for the children can be predicted.

WHAT ARE THE MEDICOLEGAL IMPLICATIONS OF BLOOD GROUPS?

Blood groups are inherited and never change. For this reason, they may have legal importance in identifying bloodstains or determining parentage. But the evidence so provided is useful only in a negative sense.

For example, if a murder suspect had his clothing stained with group A blood, and the victim was of group O, this is evidence that the suspect was not stained by the victim's blood. However, even if the stains proved to be group O, it still would not be conclusive evidence, for the suspect may have had his clothing stained with the blood of any person who was group O.

This logic also applies to paternity cases. The determination of paternity in disputed cases is very complicated. Such cases must be studied by experts in forensic medicine.

WHAT IS THE RH FACTOR?

The Rh factor is an inherited antigenic substance in the red cells (similar in nature to the group A and B substances) that occurs in 85 percent of the white population of this country. Those who possess this factor are said to be "type Rh positive." Those who do not possess it are "type Rh negative." It occurs in about the same percentage in all blood groups; that is, of 100 group A bloods, approximately 85 will be Rh positive and 15 Rh negative; of 100 group B bloods, approximately 85 will be Rh positive and 15 Rh negative. These same percentages hold for all four blood groups.

The Rh factor was named in 1940 by Landsteiner and Wiener, who were doing work with the red cells of the rhesus monkey. They discovered that the antiserum that agglutinated the cells of the rhesus species also agglutinated 85 percent of the donors they examined; it failed to agglutinate the other 15 percent. The word rhesus was shortened to Rh in discussions of this new factor and thus entered the literature. In 1939 Levine and Stetson reported a severe transfusion reaction in a woman delivered of a dead baby, and discovered that her blood would agglutinate 80 percent of donors who were of her own blood group. They assumed that the infant had inherited from the father a blood factor that was not present in the mother's blood. Small quantities of the fetal red blood cells had seeped through the placental membranes and caused antibody production in the mother. The brilliant scientific work by which these groups of research workers correlated their separate findings and laid the foundations for the important work on the Rh factor is worthy of additional reading.

WHAT IS THE SIGNIFICANCE OF THE RH FACTOR?

The Rh factor is of significance in blood transfusion and may be significant in childbirth. The Rh substance can cause a reaction if injected into the blood stream of a person who is Rh negative; that is, his body will have a tendency to break down the Rh-positive cells. This may clog the kidney with the residue of broken-down red cells and, if severe, can result in death. However, the first tranfusion may not cause this reaction because the recipient may become only sensitized; in other words, he develops anti-bodies—but not enough to produce severe symptoms. However, having been sensitized, he might suffer a severe reaction from subsequent transfusions.

In pregnancy the Rh-positive child of an Rh-positive father may be carried by an Rh-negative mother. In a small percentage of these cases, Rh-positive cells from the infant's blood stream cross the placental barrier membrane and seep into the mother's circulation. Because these cells of the infant carry an antigenic substance, Rh, they may evoke in the mother's body an antibody response against the cells. This has little effect on the mother because the amount of the infant's cells in her blood stream is very small compared with the volume of her circulating blood. However, if the antibodies to the Rh-positive cells generated by the mother are carried back into the blood stream of the infant, they may do a great deal of damage. The concentration of the antibodies in the small body of the infant is so great that it may damage a large percentage of the red cells. Depending on the degree of severity with which this happens, the infant at birth may be merely jaundiced, a condition that may clear up in a few days; he may be quite ill, and to save his life may require an exchange transfusion (removal of baby's blood and simultaneous replacement with Rh-negative blood). In a very few cases, the baby is born dead.

Because the Rh factor has received a great deal of publicity during the past few years, many women fear the possibility of giving birth to an infant affected by hemolytic disease of the newborn (erythroblastosis). Actually, much of this apprehension is unfounded. It should be understood that Rh is a normal inherited characteristic, just as color of eyes and hair. Again, marriages with an Rh-negative woman and an Rh-positive man may occur in approximately 13 percent of marriages (15% x 85% = 13%). Most women who are Rh negative do not produce anti-Rh antibodies, and those who do usually have at least two babies that are unaffected. Even in marriages with an Rh-negative woman and an Rh-positive man, only 1 in about 26 has an infant affected, and many of these children only mildly so. With the present knowledge about blood, there is a much better outlook for detecting any Rh incompatability and treating the affected infant.

CAN BLOOD OF DIFFERENT RACES BE USED INTERCHANGEABLY IN TRANSFUSIONS?

Yes. Although there are differences in the percentages of blood groups and types among the various ethnic groups, the structure and function of blood cells and plasma are essentially the same among all peoples and, with due regard for group and type compatibility, may be used interchangeably throughout the human species.

CAN ANIMAL BLOOD BE USED FOR HUMAN TRANSFUSIONS?

No. Blood is highly species-specific. Red cells injected from one species to another act as a foreign protein and therefore undergo rapid agglutination and hemolysis, with the consequent transfusion reaction causing damage or death to the recipient.

CAN BLOOD BE MADE SYNTHETICALLY?

No. Blood can be produced only in the body and cannot be made synthetically. The oxygen-carrying red cells needed to sustain life must be produced in the body or given to it via transfusion.

Fortunately, however, some substances can be used in limited amounts per patient in place of plasma. They are called plasma volume expanders or plasma extenders. Among these is Dextran, a carbohydrate material adjusted to a molecular size similar to that of a molecule of albumin. It should be emphasized that blood is a fluid for which there is no substitute. The synthetic plasma volume expanders have a valuable role in preventing death from shock for the first few hours after injury until whole blood becomes available.

III

The Structure and Function
of Higher Plants

12

Photosynthesis

Johannes van Overbeek
Harry K. Wong

The most important function of a leaf is *photosynthesis.* This term comes from the Greek word *photos,* meaning "light," and *synthesis,* which means "putting together." In photosynthesis, carbon dioxide and water are put together to make sugar and starch, using energy from light. A few simple experiments can convince us that this is true. You can cut your name in a piece of aluminum foil. Use the foil to cover one of the two primary leaves of a young bean plant growing in a pot. Let the plant photosynthesize for a few days by keeping it under the same good conditions under which it grew before you started the test. Now, cut off both leaves and plunge them into boiling alcohol. (Caution: Do not boil alcohol over an open flame.) You will notice that the green pigment dissolves in the alcohol. The decolored leaves should then be removed from the boiling alcohol and placed in a shallow dish containing a dilute solution of iodine in potassium iodide. After a while, you will notice that the leaf that remained uncovered turns blue. This indicates the presence of starch. In the other leaf, only your name appears in blue. Starch was formed only in the portion of the leaf that received light.

Another test can be made under a tightly sealed Bell jar. A large pickle jar will do, too. In the jar is placed a dish with sodium hydroxide solution, which will capture the carbon dioxide out of the air. Let a bean plant remain in the sealed jar in the light for a few days. When the plant is removed from the jar and the leaves tested for starch with the iodine test, no starch will be found. This time carbon dioxide was lacking. To provide a control for the experiment, put a bean plant in another jar with-

Johannes van Overbeek and Harry K. Wong, "Photosynthesis," *The Lore of Living Plants,* National Science Teachers Association, Vistas of Science No. 18 (New York: Scholastic Book Services, 1964), pp. 12-28. Reprinted by permission.

out sodium hydroxide. The leaves of the control plant should have starch in them at the end of the test.

CHEMISTRY OF SUGAR

We have seen that during photosynthesis a plant must have light and carbon dioxide in order to form starch. For a deeper understanding of photosynthesis, we must go to the level of atoms and molecules again. Starch is simply many molecules of sugar put together end to end in a chain-like arrangement. The sugar molecule is built of atoms of carbon, oxygen, and hydrogen. The hydrogen (H) and the oxygen (O) occur in the same proportions as in water (H_2O). On the surface it appears that sugars (CH_2O) are composed of carbon (C) and water. This is why the class of chemicals to which sugars belong is known as *carbohydrates*, from the Latin *carbo* (coal), and the Greek *hydor* (water): coal combined with water. Starch is a carbohydrate and so is cellulose. When the sugars are linked together in one way, a coil, starch, results. When the sugars are linked together in a slightly different way, the straight chain of cellulose results. You see starch every day in bread and potatoes; you see cellulose in the cotton of your handkerchief.

Early experimental scientists did not know the chemical composition of sugar. Nor did they know the fundamental significance of sugars in nature. Jan Baptista van Helmont, a physician and chemist who lived from 1577 to 1644 near Brussels, was one of the first to experiment with plants. He placed in a pot a certain quantity of earth which, when highly dried, weighed 200 pounds. A willow branch weighing five pounds was then set in this pot that was protected from dust by a cover, and watered daily with rainwater. In five years' time the willow had grown large and strong and had increased in weight by 164 pounds. The earth in the pot, when once more dried, showed a loss of about two ounces. Van Helmont concluded from this experiment that the considerable increase in weight in the plant had been gained entirely at the cost of the water, and, consequently, that all the materials in the plant, though distinct from water, nevertheless came from it.

CHEMISTRY OF PHOTOSYNTHESIS

Van Helmont did not realize that plants take up carbon dioxide from the air. The chemical symbol for carbon dioxide is CO_2, signifying that each molecule is composed of one atom of carbon and two atoms of oxygen. There is only 0.03 percent of this gas in the atmosphere. It is put in the air continuously by respiration, as well as by combustion and decomposition of wood, gasoline, and other natural products. It is removed from the air by plants and built again into natural products via photosynthesis.

After physicists had learned to make radioactive atoms, biologists used them to trace the paths of chemical elements through the plants. When photosynthesis was studied in this way, some interesting new information was obtained. This information can be written in chemical shorthand:

$$CO_2 + 2H_2O \xrightarrow[\text{chloroplast}]{\text{light}} (CH_2O) + O_2 + H_2O$$

carbon   water   carbo-   oxygen   water
dioxide   hydrate

You will notice that the equation is balanced. There are equal numbers of the same atoms on each side of the arrow. The equation signifies that carbon dioxide and water yield carbohydrate, oxygen, and water in the leaf. A carbohydrate is represented in the equation by (CH_2O). More accurately, this should be $(CH_2O)_n$. The n indicates that carbohydrate molecules are multiples of CH_2O. For ordinary sugar with its 12 carbon atoms, n would be 12. For simplicity, we will ignore the n in this discussion.

The carbon atom from carbon dioxide becomes incorporated into carbohydrate. The oxygen in the carbohydrate comes from carbon dioxide. On the other hand, the free oxygen formed during photosynthesis is liberated from water. The hydrogen in the carbohydrate also comes from water. Notice that in photosynthesis water is consumed as well as produced.

The release of oxygen during photosynthesis can be easily demonstrated with a branch of *Elodea*. This branch is put in a tall glass jar* with the cut end of the stem up and the top down. When left undisturbed in strong sunlight, bubbles come from the stem and rise to the surface. These are oxygen bubbles. The gas can be trapped in a test tube and identified.

DUAL NATURE OF PHOTOSYTHESIS

The convenient equation of photosynthesis that was just shown is known as an over-all equation. It indicates what products go into a reaction and what finally comes out. It tells nothing of what goes on in between. The mechanism of photosynthesis is far, far more complicated than this simple equation indicates. There are two main steps. The first step needs light and can be called photosynthesis proper. During this phase, oxygen is liberated and light is required to liberate the oxygen from water. However, no carbohydrates are formed as yet. Only intermediate

*Of water. (Ed.)

chemicals result; these are loaded with the sun's energy. These chemicals are then used in the second step, which does not require light, and is sometimes called the "dark reaction." This second major step, during which carbon dioxide is turned into carbohydrates, has recently been worked out in great detail by Professor Melvin Calvin, of the University of California. In 1961, he received a Nobel prize in chemistry for this feat.

BREAKTHROUGH

The first step involving the reactions that require light is just now beginning to be understood. For many years, scientists had tried to make photosynthesis work outside of the cell, but they succeeded only in making chloroplasts produce oxygen in the light. Carbohydrates were not formed. The major breakthrough finally came when Professor Daniel I. Arnon and his co-workers at the University of California succeeded for the first time in causing chloroplasts to photosynthesize outside of the cell. They found new ways by which the cell could be broken down more gently.

Dr. Arnon's work proved that the whole process of photosynthesis takes place exclusively in the green bodies of the cell, the chloroplasts. Not only do the light reactions take place there, but also the dark reactions.

When the electron microscope became available, it disclosed in great detail a number of tiny bodies inside cells. When our knowledge of biochemistry was combined with the knowledge of electron microscopy, it was found that the vital functions of life are located in these special bodies, which are called *organelles*. We now recognize that in a cell, organelles perform certain jobs, just as the organs of the human body have special functions.

ENERGY CONVERTERS

There are two types of organelles whose function it is to convert energy from one form to another. The *chloroplasts* convert light energy to the chemical energy of food. The *mitochondria* change the chemical energy of food to the chemical energy of ATP. The full name of this chemical is *adenosine triphosphate*. It has three phosphate groups. ATP is a magic word in the biological world. Just as money is necessary in the economic world, ATP is the currency used in metabolic activity. Nothing gets done inside the plant or animal unless ATP is available.

ATP is made from food in the mitochondria of your active cells. The oxygen of the air you need for respiration is used by the mitochondria to slowly oxidize the food. And during this process of *oxidation,* the stored energy of food is changed to the quickly available energy of ATP. This is the essence of respiration. You eat because you need ATP. When you jump quickly, it is ATP energy that makes you move. It would take far too long to extract the needed energy from sugar for immediate use.

When ATP is formed, one of its phosphate groups, the last one in the molecule, is pushed into the rest of the molecule like a loaded spring in a BB gun. The ATP molecule is loaded indeed! Loaded with energy that can be made available instantly.

For many years it was thought that the mitochondria were the only organelles that could make ATP, but Dr. Arnon discovered in 1954 that chloroplasts could do it too. It is now generally accepted that plants can generate ATP in two ways: by photosynthesis and by respiration. Photosynthesis takes place in the chloroplasts, and respiration in the mitochondria. Man and the animals, however, can only generate ATP by one process, by respiration in the mitochondria. Strictly speaking, there is another process, called *fermentation,* that also yields ATP. In fact, this is the only way in which fermenting yeast cells can obtain ATP.

You may be surprised to find out that the ATP of humans, animals, and plants is the same, and that these organisms have comparable mitochondria. The chemistry of respiration is the same in all living things. The reason for this appears to be that all living things are built on one and the same pattern.

PHOTONS AND ELECTRONS

The brilliant work of Dr. Arnon and his associates has helped clarify the way chloroplasts make ATP. To understand what happens when light strikes chlorophyll, let's first consider the nature of light. Light can be pictured as a stream of bullets, tiny energy packages called photons. The sun shoots a stream of these at us all the time. During photosynthesis, the stream of photons hits the chlorophyll inside the chloroplast. When photons hit chlorophyll, the impact throws electrons ($e-$) out of their "track." These electrons may fall back into their track or they may be captured by other molecules—either other molecules of chlorophyll or other kinds of molecules just right for the capture of electrons. Still different molecules may then capture these electrons and the electrons may wander farther and farther away from home.

When an electron is knocked out of the chlorophyll molecule by photons, a hole is left in the molecule. Electrons have a negative charge, and so the more electrons that are shot out of the chlorophyll, the more electrically unbalanced the chlorophyll becomes. It becomes electrically positive ($+$). Such a positive charge attracts negative electrons to it; soon electrons start flowing back into the chlorophyll molecule. What we have is an electron pump: electrons leaving chlorophyll and electrons returning to it. In other words, there is an electric current going around inside the chloroplast. What actually happens in a leaf during photosynthesis is that the light energy of the stream of photons is converted to the electrical energy of a stream of electrons. In the chloroplast this electrical energy produces ATP.

In recent years, we have learned many details about how the photosynthetic process goes on inside the chloroplast. Some of our understanding is still based on guesswork; yet the outlines are becoming clear. The theory of electron flow as a result of light rests on strong experimental evidence. For instance, scientists took a dried film of the light-catching organelles of photosynthetic bacteria (something like the grana of higher plants) and tried to pass an electric current through it. The resistance of the film was so high that little current passed through in the dark. However, upon illumination of the film, current passed through readily. In other words, only when light was shining on it did there appear to be free-moving electric charges in the photosynthetic apparatus.

ELECTRON CARRIERS

Another part of photosynthesis that is fact and not fiction is the presence of *electron carriers*. These are the compounds that conduct the electron toward chlorophyll to fill the positive holes. There are also electron carriers that conduct the highly activated electron away from chlorophyll. *Cytochrome* is an iron protein that conducts electrons toward chlorophyll. *Ferredoxin* is another iron compound that carries electrons away from chlorophyll. The properties of the electron carriers are determined by their electrical characteristics. You will note that cytochrome in the chloroplast has a potential of $+0.4$ volt, while ferredoxin has a potential of -0.4 volt. In other words, during photosynthesis there is a potential difference of 0.8 volt between cytochrome and ferredoxin. Thus an uphill current flow occurs during photosynthesis.

PUTTING ELECTRONS TO WORK

Energy of an electron flow can be converted to chemical energy of ATP. Electrons can do more. When an electron combines with a molecule, chemists say that the molecule that accepts the electron is *reduced*. The extra negative charge often attracts a proton. A proton is nothing but a positively charged hydrogen atom (H^+). Protons are found in water and are available throughout a plant. The highly activated electrons in photosynthesis can do many things, although usually not all in the same plant. For example, in photosynthetic bacteria that live in the mud of ocean bays, a highly energized electron can combine with a proton and form ordinary molecular hydrogen (H_2). Then in some of these bacteria and in some blue-green algae, the highly charged electrons of photosynthesis can reduce free nitrogen of the air (N_2) to ammonia (NH_3). This process is known as *nitrogen fixation.*

All plants need nitrogen, yet the vast pool of nitrogen gas in the air is not available to many higher plants. They can use only nitrogen *compounds* such as ammonia. Lower forms of plant life, such as blue-green algae, pave the way for the growth of higher plants by producing ammonia from nitrogen of the air. Blue-green algae enrich rice fields, fertilizing this crop free of charge.

When a volcanic island blows up and all life is destroyed, the first thing to establish itself after the island has cooled off are these pioneers, the blue-green algae. The ammonia they produce from the nitrogen of the air makes possible the subsequent growth of other plants. Even in Antarctica, blue-green algae carry on their work using the high-powered electrons made in photosynthesis.

In higher plants, the high-powered electron is used another way. Here, the reducing power of the electron is preserved in a compound known as triphosphopyridine nucleotide, or TPN, for short. TPN resembles the molecule of ATP. Both have the adenine base, both have ribose sugar, and both have phosphate. That is just the bulk of the molecule. The "business ends" of the two molecules differ greatly. ATP, as you will recall, has a high-energy phosphate bond (the coiled spring) at its end. TPN has a nicotinamide group with a positive charge at its end. This charge attracts the electron from photosynthesis. Ferredoxin, the electron carrier, hands over its charge to TPN. TPN then becomes negative and at the same time attracts a proton, forming TPNH, the reduced pyridine nucleotide. TPNH, in turn, can reduce other chemicals; for example, carbon dioxide to carbohydrate.

Now let us turn to another aspect of electron flow. The very fact that a potential difference exists and that electrons move implies that work can be done. Early physicists who studied electricity recognized the fact that electricity behaves much like water. Electric potential is very much like the potential of water locked in a lake high in the mountains. When allowed to run downhill, the water can do work: move heavy boulders, turn millwheels and electric generators. Similarly, when electrons run downhill they can do work. In the living cell, the most spectacular thing they do is operate the mechanism that produces ATP. This mechanism compresses the spring at the end of the ATP molecule when it puts a molecule of inorganic, free phosphate on the end of ADP (adenosine diphosphate). ADP has only two phosphate groups instead of the three of ATP.

$$\begin{array}{ccccc} \text{ADP} & + & \text{P}_i & \longrightarrow & \text{ATP} \\ \textit{adenosine} & & \textit{phosphate} & & \textit{adenosine} \\ \textit{diphosphate} & & (\textit{inorganic}) & & \textit{triphosphate} \end{array}$$

Exactly how flowing electrons accomplish this conversion of energy is not yet clear, but the process certainly involves the membranes of the organelles (the grana). Photosynthesis, respiration, and most biochemical reactions are intimately tied to the minute structures of the cell. Studying these reactions without taking into account the function of the fine, delicate structures of the cell does not give a full understanding of life's processes. It is very much like trying to understand the operation of an automobile engine by considering only the reaction of burning gasoline.

ASSIMILATORY POWER

Remember that a stream of photons (light) sets in motion a flow of electrons inside the grana of the chloroplast. The chloroplast, then, is much like the photocells used in spacecraft and in cameras. In plants, as a result of this electron flow, a substance with strong reducing power, TPNH, is formed and also a substance with a high-energy content, ATP. These two are the only direct products of photosynthesis proper. They contain the energy of trapped light. Together, TPNH and ATP are called assimilatory power. With the aid of these two substances, the cell can carry out many reactions without requiring any more light. The most important of these reactions is the reduction of carbon dioxide to sugar and starch. This is often referred to as the Calvin cycle after Professor Melvin Calvin who, with his associates, worked out this mechanism in painstaking detail.

The sugar-phosphate combination formed in photosynthesis is not an ordinary sugar of 6 or 12 carbon atoms, but one with only 5. It has become supercharged by combining with the energy compound ATP, and a 5-carbon sugar *di*phosphate results. This compound is so reactive that it can combine with carbon dioxide of the air. It may be that an intermediate 6-carbon molecule is formed that is so unstable it breaks down immediately into two 3-carbon molecules of PGA, or phosphoglyceric acid. At any rate, PGA is the first stable compound found with carbon dioxide built into it.

Now the reducing compound TPNH and more ATP enter the cycle

and reduce the acid (PGA) to a 3-carbon sugar. Two 3-carbon sugars are converted to 6-carbon sugar. At this stage, these sugars are still combined with phosphate. These can yield starch and sucrose or undergo further modification to again yield the 5-carbon sugar phosphate with which we started. The cycle goes around and around as long as ATP, TPNH, and CO_2 are fed into it. The result is stable energy-storage products, the foods starch and sugar, that figure so prominently in animal and human nutrition.

PHOTOSYNTHESIS IN HIGHER PLANTS

Until very recently, photosynthesis was not sufficiently understood to enable us to describe the process in any detail. Two or three years ago, it would not have been possible to put together very many pieces of this jigsaw puzzle. The pattern is still not complete, but the outlines are clear. It is now even possible to follow in higher plants the course of an electron during photosynthesis. Chlorophyll acts as a pump, operated by the energy of light. Chlorophyll pumps an electron "uphill" from cytochrome and delivers it to ferredoxin which, in turn, hands it over to TPN. With the addition of a proton (H^+) from water, TPNH is formed. Where did the cytochrome obtain its electron? Higher plants get theirs from water. The electrons of water have a very low energy content, a potential of only $+0.8$ volt, and must be pumped uphill. Recently it has become clear that another pigment, probably chlorophyll b, delivers the electron to another carrier, *plastoquinone*.

Plastoquinone is not an iron compound like cytochrome and ferredoxin. It is related to Vitamin K. By the way, the nicotinamide of TPN is nothing but a vitamin-B compound. These vitamins are working parts of the plant. Plants can make these compounds, but animals cannot. That is why you need vitamins in your diet.

After plastoquinone receives an electron from water charged by chlorophyll b and light, it turns over its electron to cytochrome. On this "downhill" run, the electron flow furnishes the energy to operate the ATP-producing mechanism. The electron flow is coupled to the ATP-producing mechanism, the way the generator that charges the battery in a car is coupled to the engine. This downhill run from plastoquinone to cytochrome may not be the only place where ATP is generated. There may be as many as two additional sites where the generation of ATP is coupled to photosynthetic electron flow.

Let us return to the water from which the electron came. Water normally is dissociated to a certain degree into protons (H^+) and hydroxyl ions (OH^-).

$$H_2O \rightleftharpoons H^+ + OH^-$$

It is this proton that is used in the production of TPNH.

$$2e^- + TPN^+ + H^+ \longrightarrow TPNH$$

The OH^- ion is robbed of its electron by the pull of the chlorophyll-*b* electron pump and the rest goes to oxygen and water.

$$4OH^- \longrightarrow 4e^- + 2H_2O + O_2$$

Photosynthesis is the source of most of the oxygen of the air. Oxygen is a mere by-product of the process, but its production changed the course of evolution. It made possible the development of creatures like ourselves, dependent on the oxygen of the air.

13

Respiration

William A. Jensen

THE RELEASE OF ENERGY

Photosynthesis results in the conversion of light energy to chemical energy. This chemical energy is incorporated into the bonds of synthesized compounds, primarily six-carbon sugars. The energy present in such compounds is essentially stored energy, which can be released only by breaking the chemical bonds that hold the molecule together.

The energy present may be released by breaking all the bonds at the same time. This type of energy release occurs when a piece of wood burns. An indication of the amount of energy involved is given by the heat and light evolved during the combustion. Biological systems effect the release of energy in a similar yet far more subtle way. Each bond may be broken individually, and the released energy is then trapped by suitable receptors in ways that permit the future transfer of this energy to other compounds.

The receptors of the released energy are the same as those involved in energy transformations in photosynthesis: ADP and PN. The energy-rich compounds that result are also the same as in photosynthesis: ATP and PNH_2.* These compounds are extremely important to the cell. They are the negotiable energy currency of the cell, the currency that must be available for investment in the building and maintenance of the cell.

The systematic breakdown of a molecule such as glucose is a complex undertaking, and in the cell it is accomplished by scores of reactions. Each of these reactions is controlled by a specific enzyme, and the entire process involves many enzymes acting in teams.

ENZYMES

Enzymes have been termed organic catalysts and this is an accurate, if limited, statement. A catalyst can be defined as a compound that speeds up a chemical reaction and yet remains unchanged at the end of the reaction. In the case of the enzyme *amylase*, the reaction that is catalyzed is the breakdown of starch to individual glucose molecules. Some breakdown would occur, if enough time were available, without the presence of amylase. But in the presence of amylase the reaction is rapid and large amounts of glucose appear. Amylase does not change the course of the reaction. Moreover, although amylase is involved in the reaction, it is unchanged at the end of the reaction.

Enzymes lower the activation energy of reactions in which they are involved. Molecules will break down if their energy is increased to a point where the molecules are no longer stable. The energy needed to achieve this point is called the *energy of activation*. As the temperature is raised and more energy is available, the reaction rate increases. Enzymes, by lowering the activation energy of the reaction, permit reactions to occur at normal environmental temperatures. How enzymes are able to permit such reactions is unknown.

All enzymes are proteins. They are, with few exceptions, large molecules composed of hundreds of amino acids. The amino acids are joined together in long, elaborately coiled chains. Some enzymes consist solely of proteins, while many consist of two parts. The larger of these two parts is inevitably a protein molecule. This does not mean that all proteins are enzymes; but a part of every enzyme is a protein. The second part, called the co-enzyme, may be a metal such as iron, manganese, or copper, or a vitamin such as thiamin, riboflavin, or nicotinic acid. When an enzyme consists of two parts, both parts must be present for the enzyme to func-

* Reduced di or triphosphopyridine nucleotide. (Ed.)

tion. The fact that enzymes are proteins and therefore highly complex molecules means that most enzymes are easily damaged. Any treatment that will break down or alter (denature) proteins will destroy the enzymes' activity. Thus, while an increase in temperature will increase the rate of an enzymatic reaction, too high a temperature denatures the protein and the enzymatic reaction ceases. Any number of other changes in the immediate environment of the enzyme molecule may result in the loss of activity.

The enzyme molecule is believed to combine with the substrate molecule. This combination is short-lived and, when it breaks up, the enzyme molecule remains intact while the substrate molecule is changed. Enzymes are highly specific. This specificity is believed to be based on the spatial configuration of the surface of the enzyme molecule. Enzymes can be inhibited by compounds that closely resemble the substrate but that are inactive in the reaction. A well-known and important example of this type of enzyme inhibition involves the enzyme *succinic dehydrogenase*, which acts on the substrate succinic acid. Another compound, *malonic acid*, closely resembles succinic acid but is different enough so that the enzyme while combining with the malonic acid does not change it. The malonic acid, however, occupies the reactive site on the enzyme molecule and prohibits the attachment of succinic acid. This type of inhibition is termed *competitive inhibition*. Other types of enzyme inhibitors act by combining or changing various parts of the enzyme molecule so that the reactive site is destroyed. A large number of enzyme inhibitors have been discovered and their use has led to the elucidation of many aspects of enzyme action.

Each enzyme mediates only a limited number of reactions—in most cases, only one. Thus, an enzyme involved in a reaction that results in the loss of a hydrogen atom from one compound is different from an enzyme involved in a similar type of reaction with a different compound. Consequently, there are hundreds of enzymes in the cell, each acting on a specific compound or substrate. To understand the functioning and growth of a cell, we must understand the factors controlling enzyme formation.

A formidable body of information indicates that enzyme synthesis is controlled by genes. Many of the details of the nature and method of this control are now understood.

A feature of many enzymes is that they function in teams. In such an arrangement, the end product of one enzymatic reaction becomes the substrate for the next enzyme in the series. This pattern can be repeated dozens of times. The CO_2-fixation cycle discussed in relation to photosynthesis is an example of enzymes working in a team. Similar arrangements of enzymes are found in the breakdown or respiration of carbohydrates.

RESPIRATION

Respiration is the biologically controlled breakdown of energy-containing substances, such as carbohydrates, fats, and proteins, with the release of energy. As such, it is the reverse of photosynthesis, in which energy is used to synthesize compounds. The major pathway of respiration in the cell can be broken into two parts: (1) *glycolysis* and (2) the *Krebs cycle*. In the first part, glycolysis, glucose is eventually split into two pyruvic acid molecules, each having three carbon atoms. At this point, the second part of respiration begins; and after one carbon is removed, the remaining two-carbon compound enters the Krebs cycle. During the Krebs cycle, the two-carbon compound is converted to CO_2. This part of respiration is a cycle because the reactions are organized so that the chemical compound *oxalacetic acid,* which accepts the two-carbon piece entering the cycle, is regenerated at the end of the cycle and can accept another two-carbon piece.

The two parts of respiration differ in a number of important features. In the absence of oxygen, glycolysis can occur but the Krebs cycle cannot function. If no oxygen is present, the pyruvic acid produced at the end of glycolysis is converted, with the loss of one carbon atom, to ethyl alcohol. In this case, the process is *fermentation.*

Another important difference between glycolysis and the Krebs cycle is the amount of energy made available to the plant cell in the form of ATP molecules. The important consideration is not the total number of ATP molecules formed but the net number available at the end of the reactions. This is because some energy in the form of ATP must be invested if the reactions are to occur. During glycolysis, only two ATP molecules are obtained per glucose molecule respired, while in the Krebs cycle the net gain is 38 ATP molecules per glucose molecule.

ANAEROBIC RESPIRATION

$$C_6H_{12}O_6 \longrightarrow 2C_2H_6O + 2CO_2$$

This equation is the over-all reaction for fermentation. It states merely that one molecule of glucose is converted to two molecules of ethyl alcohol and two molecules of carbon dioxide. This is the merest outline of the reactions involved. These reactions show a minimum of some ten steps between glucose and ethyl alcohol.

The first step in fermentation is the addition of a phosphate to the glucose molecule. Shortly after, a second phosphate is added. These steps are carried out at the expense of two ATP molecules. The end product is a six-carbon sugar with two phosphates attached, called *fructose-1, 6-diphosphate*. This is split into two three-carbon compounds and, in the reactions that follow, two ATP molecules as well as two PNH_2 molecules are generated—one each per three-carbon compound. As the reactions continue, pyruvic acid is produced, which results in the formation of an additional ATP per three-carbon fragment. Finally, as a necessary consequence of the absence of oxygen, the electrons from the PNH_2's are used to produce ethyl alcohol. This final reaction results in the formation of one CO_2 per pyruvic acid molecule.

If a balance sheet is compiled to show the energy of the compounds involved, it will show that, for each glucose molecule used, four ATP molecules and two PNH_2 molecules are produced at the expense of two ATP molecules and two PNH_2 molecules. The net gain is thus two ATP's. There is considerable energy remaining in the ethyl alcohol—energy that can be released only by different metabolic pathways.

The basic reactions involved in anaerobic respiration show only the fate of the carbon atoms and the net changes in ATP. The first stages of anaerobic respiration are very similar to part of the CO_2-fixation cycle of photosynthesis. The direction of the reactions is reversed in the two processes. Except for this and differences in the details of the steps, the reactions from fructose-1, 6-diphosphate to PGA are essentially the same.

The entire process of fermentation can be carried out in the complete absence of oxygen. Fermentation is the major energy-producing system of many micro-organisms. Commercially, the most important of these organisms are the yeasts. The production of alcohol through fermentation has been discovered by almost every civilization, and the art of making alcoholic beverages has been practiced for centuries.

AEROBIC RESPIRATION

$$C_6H_{12}O_2 + 6O_2 \longrightarrow 6CO_2 + 6H_2O$$

In the presence of oxygen and the necessary enzymes, the breakdown of glucose is complete and occurs as outlined in the equation above. For every molecule of glucose used, six molecules of CO_2 and six molecules of H_2O are produced. During the course of this reaction there is a net production of 38 ATP molecules produced and made available to the plant.

Aerobic respiration, as noted earlier, can be described as having two parts. During the first part, the glucose molecule becomes involved in a set of reactions that yields two pyruvic-acid molecules. This part is identical to the similar reactions that occur in anaerobic respiration. At this point, however, the fate of the pyruvic acid differs depending on the presence or absence of oxygen and the appropriate enzymes.

In the presence of oxygen, a carbon atom is removed from the pyruvic acid and an activated two-carbon compound is formed. This compound unites with a four-carbon compound, *oxalacetic acid*, forming citric acid, which contains six carbon atoms. Then, through a series of reactions, two molecules are released and oxalacetic acid is formed. For each CO_2 molecule produced, six ATP molecules are made, so that, for each two-carbon fragment entering the cycle, 12 ATP molecules are made available to the cell.

The total energy relations in aerobic respiration are more involved. The aerobic cell receives more energy from the first part of respiration than does the yeast cell for the same series of reactions. This results from the fact that in the yeast cell the PNH_2 that is produced is used later in the formation of alcohol. In the aerobic cell, the energy of this PNH_2 is converted to three ATP molecules. Thus the net gain of ATP in the yeast is two ATP molecules, while in the aerobic cell it is eight ATP molecules per glucose molecule. An additional six ATP molecules are gained between pyruvic acid and the Krebs cycle. The total number of ATP molecules produced per glucose molecule used is 38 (8 + 6 + 24 = 38). Aerobic respiration is thus a much more efficient process with regard to energy release than is fermentation.

DIRECT OXIDATION PATHWAY

The major pathway of aerobic respiration appears to be through glycolysis and the Krebs cycle. Another pathway, known as the *direct oxidation pathway* or the *pentose phosphate shunt mechanism*, is known to exist in both plants and animals. More involved in some ways than the glycolysis-Krebs-cycle reactions, it has the same over-all equation:

$$C_6H_{12}O_6 + 6O_2 \longrightarrow 6CO_2 + 6H_2O$$

The first steps are the same as in glycolysis, but one CO_2 and a five-carbon sugar are then formed. This sugar is broken down through a rather complex set of reactions involving a number of three-, six-, and seven-carbon compounds. Ultimately, for every six glucose molecules entering the cycle, six five-carbon sugars, six CO_2 molecules, and 12 PNH_2 molecules are produced. The energy of the PNH_2 can be converted to 36 ATP molecules. The reaction is, therefore, nearly as efficient as the glycolysis-Krebs-cycle pathway. The five-carbon sugars produced are important in the synthesis of ATP and various other cellular constituents. Moreover, these same reactions play a very important role in the CO_2-fixation cycle of photosynthesis.

ELECTRON TRANSFER AND OXYGEN UPTAKE

The presence of oxygen is necessary for aerobic respiration to take place. The uptake of oxygen during respiration is a consequence of the transfer to oxygen of electrons from the various compounds involved in the metabolic breakdown of glucose. This transfer of electrons results in a reduction of oxygen gas to water. The fact that electrons have varying amounts of energy was stressed in the discussion of photosynthesis. During photosynthesis, electrons are raised to higher energy levels and their energy is ultimately incorporated into the bonds of carbohydrate molecules. During respiration, electrons pass through a series of reactions that take them from high energy levels to lower energy levels. At the lowest level, the electron combines with oxygen and H^+ ions to form water. At the intermediate levels, the energy released is transformed into high-energy phosphate bonds by the conversion of ADP to ATP.

At six places in the glycolysis-Krebs-cycle pathway, a pair of electrons is released. These electrons are accepted by PN, which becomes PNH_2. Then, through a series of cyclic reactions, the electrons move down a series of compounds. During this passage, the electrons lose energy and ATP molecules are formed. The compounds involved in these reactions are PN, a *flavo-protein*, and a series of *cytochromes*. The latter contain iron. The final step in the electron-transfer system is the reduction of O_2 to water mediated by the enzyme *cytochrome oxidase*.

THE METABOLISM OF FATS AND PROTEINS

This discussion has stressed the metabolism of carbohydrates, and glucose in particular; however, most of the compounds present in the cell can be respired. Most types of carbohydrates can be and are used. Similarly, fats and proteins may also be respired.

Both fats and proteins can undergo a series of reactions that eventually reduce them to two-carbon fragments, which can enter the Krebs cycle. The utilization of fats and oils supplies much of the energy used during germination. Fats are a highly efficient means of storing energy, since on a comparative-weight basis they have more stored energy than the carbohydrates.

Proteins can be utilized as an energy source, but they are not normally used in this manner. In general, only after other energy sources are exhausted are the proteins respired.

SITE OF RESPIRATION IN THE CELL

The fact that the chloroplasts were the site of photosynthesis in the cell was known long before the process was understood. Conversely, the mechanism of respiration was known in considerable detail before the site of the process was determined in the cell.

The major breakthrough in the search for the site of respiration in the cell came with the development of the methods of cell homogenization and separation of cell parts by differential centrifugation. During differential centrifugation, the solution containing the cell parts is rotated rapidly at varying speeds. The parts separate because the heavier parts settle to the bottom of the tube first and then the lighter ones follow. . . .

From studies like these and from other lines of evidence, it has been established that the enzymes of the Krebs cycle are found associated with the mitochondria. The enzymes of glycolysis, on the other hand, are found primarily (although not exclusively) in the soluble portion of the cytoplasm.

The localization of the enzymes of the Krebs cycle in the mitochondria was one of the first and greatest discoveries using cell fractionation procedures.

14

Photoperiod

Arthur W. Galston

We now know that the flowering of many angiosperms is controlled by two major factors of the environment, photoperiod and temperature. The discovery of photoperiodism by Garner and Allard in 1920 was the accidental result of an attempt to propagate a mutant type of large-leaf tobacco, called Maryland Mammoth, which had arisen by chance as a

Arthur W. Galston, THE LIFE OF THE GREEN PLANT, SECOND EDITION, © 1964. Reprinted by permission of Prentice-Hall, Inc., Englewood Cliffs, N. J.

single individual in a field of other tobacco plants. As the season progressed, the original type flowered profusely, but the Maryland Mammoth did not. Wishing to obtain seeds of this valuable new type and fearful that the plant might not flower before the autumn frost, these investigators removed the plant from the field and transferred it to the greenhouse. Despite every urging, however, the plant steadfastly refused to initiate floral organs until approximately mid-December, many months after the normal plants had completed seed production successfully. When the seeds of the self-pollinated Maryland Mammoth type were planted in the field the next year, this behavior pattern was repeated, i.e., the plants grew vigorously in the field, failed to flower together with the original type, but did flower when removed to the greenhouse and maintained until about Christmas time.

An analysis of the various factors that could possibly be responsible for this behavior finally led Garner and Allard to the inevitable conclusion that the plant was flowering only during the very short days characteristic of the northern hemisphere at Christmas time. They discovered that flower initiation could be induced at will by transferring Maryland Mammoth plants to special chambers in which the length of day could be artificially shortened. They named this response of plants to length of day *photoperiodism*. Maryland Mammoth tobacco, which flowers only if the day length is reduced below a certain critical value, was called a *short-day plant*. Other plants of this type are soybeans and chrysanthemums. Another class of plant is the *long-day* type, such as spinach and certain cereals, in which flowering occurs only if the day length exceeds a certain critical value. Finally, there is a class of plants called *day-neutral plants* in which photoperiod does not exert a major effect on the time of flower initiation. An example of this type is the tomato plant, in which floral primordia are initiated at particular nodes when the plant has obtained a particular size. This situation is not amenable to control by photoperiod, although the tomato may be induced to premature flowering by certain synthetic chemicals that are related to auxins.

In the years since 1920, considerable work has been done to determine how photoperiod exerts its effect on the flowering of the plant. It has been unequivocally demonstrated that the leaf is the receptor for the photoperiodic stimulus. For example, if a single leaf of a Maryland Mammoth tobacco plant is enclosed in a black bag and given the appropriate short photoperiod required for floral initiation, the terminal bud some distance away from the leaf will initiate floral primordia. This separation in space of the photoperiodic receptor (leaf) from the region of response (bud) makes it necessary to postulate some connecting link between the two. Since it can also be demonstrated that a plant or plant part exposed to a short day can transmit its florally initiated state to a receptor plant or plant part maintained vegetatively on a long day, it is clear that some hormonal substance, tentatively named *florigen*, is produced in the photoperiodically stimulated leaf. This stimulus can be transmitted from a donor plant to a receptor, provided there is tissue union between the two grafted plants. The transmission of the stimulus is prevented by steam-girdling of the petiole or by other means of interrupting phloem transport. These facts clearly imply the production in the photo-induced leaf of a yet unknown substance, which is transported via phloem to the terminal bud, where it influences the meristem to favor the production of floral primordia rather than vegetative organs.

Recently it has become clear that many long-day plants may, if supplied with gibberellin, initiate floral primordia under an otherwise unfavorable photoperiod. In this group of plants, there appears to be some connection between gibberellin and florigen. Gibberellin, however, does not promote flowering in short-day plants. Since there is very good evidence from grafting experiments that the florigen of long-day and of short-day plants is at least functionally equivalent, if not chemically identical, the exact nature of the relation between gibberellin and florigen is not clear. In still other plants, such as the pineapple and the litchi, floral organs can be initiated by the application of certain synthetic auxins. In the series of events leading to the production of reproductive organs, therefore, various substances may well become limiting in different plants. This substance may be gibberellin in some plants, auxin in other plants, and perhaps additional, possibly unknown, substances in still other plants.

One interesting generalization that has developed out of the study of these photoperiodic phenomena is that most plants respond not to the length of the light period but to the length of uninterrupted darkness. Thus, a so-called short-day plant is really a "long-night" plant that requires an uninterrupted dark period of a certain minimal duration for the initiation of its floral primordia. In the same way, a long-day plant is in reality a "short-night" plant, that is, a plant that will flower only if the night period is not longer than a certain critical maximum.

The effective period of darkness can be interrupted by the simple expedient of making it a bit too short (even a few minutes will do), or by interposing a brief flash of light in the middle of the dark period. For example, in the short-day cocklebur plant, flowering will occur in a regime of 15 hours of light and 9 hours of dark. If the 9-hour dark period is shortened appreciably, to about 8½ hours, flowering will not occur. But one single cycle of exposure to 15 hours of light and 9 hours of dark will suffice to induce the plant to initiate floral primordia, even though photoperiods unfavorable for floral initiation are immediately re-imposed. Such a phenomenon is referred to as *photoperiodic induction*. If the single long dark period of 9 hours is interrupted at its midpoint by a flash of light, the plant will not flower. Certain chemical processes that are very sensitive to minute quantities of radiant energy must thus be proceeding in darkness in the leaf. If a quantum of absorbed light impinges on the course of these reactions, the entire sequence of events is wrecked and the plant must start over again. With the long-day plants, the situation is just the reverse, i.e., the interruption of an unfavorably long dark period by a brief flash of light will lead to floral initiation. These two types of plants seem to possess the same kind of photoperiodic mechanism, but they somehow work in reverse fashion.

By the use of the action spectrum technique, it is possible to obtain some notion of the wavelengths of light that are effective in interrupting or promoting flowering when administered in short flashes. We should mention here that the same kind of light that inhibits the flowering of short-day plants will promote the flowering of long-day plants. Recent experiments with monochromatic light have revealed that many types of plants respond best to red light in the region near 660 mμ. It has also been surprising to find that the effect of red light may be instantaneously and completely negated by the subsequent application of what is called near-infrared light, or "far-red" light, in the region of 730 mμ. These experiments indicate that there is a pigment in plants present in two forms, a red-absorbing form and a far-red-absorbing form. In the short-day plant, the absorption of red light in the middle of the long inductive dark period leads to a negation of flowering, while the absorption of far-red after the red leads to the repromotion of flowering.

The control of flowering thus appears to be a resultant of the ratio of the two forms of this pigment in the plant. So far, we do not know exactly what this pigment is, although extracts of it that show reversible spectral changes on irradiation have been obtained from several plant tissues. For example, the administration of red light has resulted in a decreased absorption of red near 660 mμ and an increased absorption of far-red near 730 mμ, whereas administration of far-red has resulted in the reverse changes. Our best guess is that this light treatment is causing a reversible chemical change in the effective pigment molecule and that these changes are determining the course of development of the plant. The yet uncharacterized protein pigment has recently been named *phytochrome*.

The discovery of the existence of this reversible photoreaction governing flowering has clarified several other perplexing problems in plant physiology. For example, it is well known that the germination of many seeds is affected greatly by light. Seeds of the Grand Rapids variety of lettuce will not germinate at all when placed in darkness on moist filter paper at room temperature, but the administration of minute quantities of red light will result in prompt germination. If the red-light-treated seeds are promptly irradiated with far-red, the effect of the red is completely canceled out and the seeds remain dormant. Here again, the growth of the plant is apparently controlled by a two-way switch mediated by the unknown red-far-red pigment. With other seeds, such as the California poppy, germination is inhibited by light. Here, too, the red-far-red system is involved; red light promotes and far-red inhibits germination. The inhibition, rather than promotion by white light in these seeds, is the result of a reverse differential sensitivity to the two regions of the spectrum.

We have already mentioned that the germination of certain seeds can be greatly promoted by the plant growth substances gibberellin and kinetin. Indeed, a portion of the light response of these seeds may be interpretable in terms of the alteration of the levels of such substances within the seeds. This, however, has not yet been experimentally demonstrated.

The same controlling red-far-red morphogenetic photoreaction can be seen to operate in *etiolation* (growth in darkness) of stems and leaves. A seed germinated in total darkness gives rise to a seedling with a very long, slender, unpigmented stem and to scale leaves that never expand greatly. If we analyze the visible spectrum in terms of its ability to transform the etiolated plant into a normal plant, we find that red light is again most effective and that its effect can be prevented by far-red light administered after the red. The exact nature of the response, however, depends on the tissue. If the red light is given to stem tissue, that stem will then be greatly inhibited in its growth, but a leaf exposed to the same red light will be promoted in its growth. The responses of both stem and leaf will be completely prevented by the application of far-red light after the red. Therefore, we see that the response to visible radiation is pre-determined by the differentiation processes that have given rise to the specific types of cells.

The red-far-red morphogenetic photoreaction described above is certainly of great importance in the life of the plant, affecting such diverse processes as the germination of seeds, the growth of roots, stems, and leaves, and the initiation of floral primordia. Clearly, increased knowledge of the nature of phytochrome and of its mode of action is greatly needed and must be an important aim of research in plant physiology.

15

Growth Hormones

Arthur W. Galston

In addition to the water, light, carbon dioxide, and various other materials absorbed by a plant from its environment, other chemicals are re-

Arthur W. Galston, THE LIFE OF THE GREEN PLANT, SECOND EDITION, © 1964. Reprinted by permission of Prentice-Hall, Inc., Englewood Cliffs, N. J.

quired for plant growth. These substances, called *hormones*, are generally needed in only infinitesimally small quantities, and in most instances they are produced in adequate amounts by the plant itself. By appropriate experimental techniques, we can deplete their supply in the plant, demonstrate their existence, and deduce a great deal about their nature. A hormone is a substance produced in very small quantities in one part of an organism and transported to another part where it produces some special effect. Two major classes of growth-regulatory hormones have been shown to exist in most, if not all, higher plants. These are the *auxins* and the *gibberellins*, to which we now turn our attention.

THE AUXINS

The auxins are a group of substances produced by the growing apexes of stems and roots. They migrate from the apex to the zone of elongation, where they are specifically required for the elongation process. If the tip of a rapidly growing stem is removed, the growth in the region below the cut will slow down very quickly, and within several hours or days, depending on the type of plant, it will come to a complete halt. If the removed tip is replaced, growth of the stem continues almost normally, showing that some influence emanating from the tip is conducted across the wound to the growing cells. If the tip is placed on a block of gelatin or agar for a period of several hours and the block without the tip is then transferred to the cut stump of a decapitated stem, the block will partially substitute for the tip in facilitating growth of the subjacent regions. From this experiment, we deduce that a substance, called *auxin*, moves from the tip to the block and from the block down to the base. Extensive chemical work of the last several decades has revealed the existence of many substances with auxin activity. Several of these have been isolated in pure form and have been shown to be native plant growth hormones. The most common of these substances is the simple material indole-3-acetic acid, which is probably derived from the amino acid tryptophan. . . .

The amount of auxin in any plant tissue may be determined by extraction with some solvent, followed by the application of the extract to some tissue that will respond quantitatively to the auxin contained in it. Normally, the tissue is placed in diethyl ether at a temperature near 0°C and gently shaken for a period of 2–4 hours. This ether extract is then concentrated and, when reduced to a small volume, is incorporated into an agar block that is then placed asymmetrically on the decapitated stump of the auxin-sensitive organ. Traditionally, the leaf sheath, or *colepotile*, of dark-grown oat plants has been used. In this plant, the asymmetrically placed auxin enhances the growth of the tissue only directly below it. This unequal growth on the two sides of the coleoptile causes a curvature of the organ that is directly proportional to the amount of auxin incorporated into the block. Thus, to determine quantitatively the amount of auxin in an unknown organ, the extract is made, the curvature is measured, and this curvature is compared with curvatures produced by known quantities of auxin in another experimental series. This technique of using the response of an organism to measure the amount of a chemical in an extract is called *bioassay*.

The curvatures produced by the unilateral application of auxin to plants bring to mind the curvature of various plant organs toward or away from light or gravity. In fact, we now know that such curvatures (called *tropisms*) are due to the asymmetrical distribution of auxin in the organ involved. For example, if an oat coleoptile is subjected to a low intensity of unilateral light, it will curve toward that light (*phototropism*). This curvature results from the fact that the side near the light has had its growth somewhat depressed by the light while the growth on the side away from the light has been accelerated. If the tip of a unilaterally ex- posed coleoptile is removed and the amount of auxin of the two halves (light and dark) assessed by the curvature test described above, invari- ably the side away from the light will have about twice as much auxin in it as the side toward the light. Plant physiologists have therefore concluded that light acts in producing curvature by affecting the distribution of auxin in the organ; this auxin concentration, then, controls growth.

Similarly, a stem laid prostrate can be shown, after some time, to ac- cumulate more auxin on the lower surface than on the upper surface. This results in an accelerated growth below and an ultimate curvature upward (*geotropism*). The growth downward of a prostrate root is a consequence of the different auxin sensitivity of the root. In the prostrate root, as in the prostrate stem, auxin accumulates below, but since in the normal root the auxin concentration is already optimal, or supraoptimal, this greater concentration of auxin on the lower side leads to depressed growth, and thus to a downward curvature of roots. . . .

So far we have been discussing only those aspects of auxin action per- taining to cell elongation. Auxin may also initiate or promote cell division. For example, in tissue cultures of normal cells excised from stems or roots, cell division is entirely dependent on the application of auxin to the me- dium. Similarly, the initiation in the spring of cambial activity in trees can be shown to be controlled by auxin diffusing downward from develop- ing buds. In addition, the formation of branch roots and adventitious roots from the pericycle region of stems or roots can be initiated by the application of auxins. In this mitosis-inducing activity, auxin apparently works together with other substances such as the constituents of nucleic acids. In fact, a substance called *kinetin* has been isolated from autoclaved yeast nucleic acid and has been shown to be active in promoting cell division of plant cells in the presence of auxin. Substances resembling kinetin in chemistry and physiological action have been shown to occur in seedlings, dividing cells, fruitlets, and in coconut milk and other liquid endosperms. Such substances are referred to collectively as *kinins.*

In addition to its roles in promoting cell division and cell elongation, auxin has other correlative effects on the growing plant. For example, auxin determines whether the apical bud or a lateral bud on a stem will develop. In the intact stem of many plants, only the apical bud can grow. Removal of the apical bud, however, results promptly in the growth of one or several of the buds lower down. If the tip is removed and the cut surface covered with an auxin paste, the buds lower down will continue to be inhibited. From this type of experiment, it has been deduced that auxins inhibit lateral bud growth. . . .

Auxins are also important in regulating the fall of leaves and fruits from plants. A leaf blade is attached to a stem by means of a petiole that persists during the growing season but falls off at some time later in the year. As long as the leaf blade produces adequate quantities of auxin, the attachment of the petiole to the stem is firm. If, however, the leaf blade becomes deficient in auxin production, the petiole forms at its base a special layer of cells called the *abscission layer,* which is mechanically so weak that the leaf blade is easily caused to fall from the plant by a breeze or by mechanical irritation.

This knowledge has been put to good use in agriculture. For example, where it is desirable to retain leaves or fruits on a tree (as in apples and oranges), it is merely necessary to spray the tree with a dilute solution of 2,4-dichlorophenoxyacetic acid or some related auxin. This simple process has saved millions of dollars for orchardists whose fruits normally fall off the tree when they are not yet ready for harvest. Similarly, by the production of chemical analogs that antagonize the action of auxin, leaves or fruits can be causd to fall prematurely from a plant. This fact greatly aids mechanical cotton picking, for instance. . . .

In the pineapple plant, one auxin, *a*-naphthaleneacetic acid, has the remarkable effect of promptly inducing the onset of flowering. Although the mechanism of this effect is obscure, its value in pineapple agriculture is obvious. The plants can all be grown to a uniform size and naphthaleneacetic acid applied at any desired time. The fruits will then develop uniformly, making mass methods of harvest possible. . . .

In another important economic activity, auxin is applied to the pistil of the flower to produce artificial, or *parthenocarpic* fruits. Normally, most fruits are formed as a result of pollination and fertilization of the ovary of the flower and of the subsequent growth stimulation produced in the ovary by the fertilization process. If, however, no pollen reaches the pistil, the development of the ovary into a fruit can be stimulated by the application of fairly large quantities of auxin-type materials. . . .

One final aspect of auxin action should be noted here. . . . In a lawn containing dandelions, the application of 2,4-D kills the dandelions while leaving the grass intact. Similarly, the application of 2,4-D to a cornfield containing the noxious bindweed will kill the bindweed, leaving the corn intact. As a result, chemical weeding has been substituted for the laborious, injurious, and expensive practice of mechanical cultivation. The savings from such practices are incalculable. . . .

THE GIBBERELLINS

Another group of important plant growth hormones, also discovered through a series of accidents, is the gibberellins. . . . Gibberellic acid, when applied to plants, produces tremendous hyperelongation effects on stems. . . . At the moment, the most important agricultural use of the gibberellins is in the grape industry, where the application of gibberellins to seedless grape clusters results in the retention and development of a greater number of grapes, and in fruit much larger than normal. For a relatively small expenditure of time and money on the chemical, the farmer obtains a much larger crop. Gibberellin is also useful in celery growing, where it produces larger, more succulent plants in a shorter time. It can also be used to stimulate seed germination and growth of early seedling grass, including the barley that is used as malt in the brewing industry. Its potential in agriculture is very great, and is only now beginning to be explored.

16

The Agricultural Sciences

R. E. Geyer

The harvest from 311 million U.S. crop acres and many more millions of acres of pasture fed 92 million Americans in 1910. Today, fewer acres provide an even greater supply of food for nearly 200 million.

Our abundance of food, more appetizing, nutritious, and convenient today than ever before, can be attributed in large part to progress in the

R. E. Geyer, "The Agricultural Sciences," *BioScience*, Vol. 15 (1965), pp. 349-353. Reprinted by permission of the COMMISSION ON EDUCATION in Agriculture and Natural Resources, Agricultural Board, Division of Biology and Agriculture, National Academy of Sciences—National Research Council.

agricultural sciences. The animal, plant, and soil sciences, food science, agricultural engineering, and other biological and physical disciplines have made it possible to produce more and better food. Agricultural economics and other areas of social science have contributed to maximizing return on investment in agriculture, whether the investment has been in production goods or human resources.

The agricultural sciences are products of the synthesis of evolving disciplines characteristic of the world of science. Through free exchange of ideas, concepts, and research-derived principles, the agricultural sciences have emerged as distinct entities from the biological sciences, mathematics, physics, chemistry, and the social sciences, during the past century. Though now highly developed and rapidly maturing, the agricultural sciences continue to serve as a vehicle for exploring new areas and catalyzing an onrush of changing technology as new problems are encountered.

Increasingly, agricultural research is delving into the nature of life itself. Work in progress on blood antigens offers hope that we may learn more about the manner in which hormones and genes act in the formation of those antigens. Basic studies in plant physiology are leading ever closer to an understanding of the processes in photosynthesis. Agricultural scientists are studying viruses to learn how they develop, mature, and reproduce themselves.

Although the relationship of the agricultural sciences with the biological sciences is particularly close, the importance of the physical sciences should not be minimized.

Further, all life exists in time and space within an environment of land, water, air, climate, and other components, both animate and inanimate. It is man's challenge to make productive use of living things within their environments, as those environments currently exist or as they may be modified. This, then, is the broad realm of the agricultural sciences. The principal architect in this realm is the agricultural scientist. He may be an animal geneticist, physiologist, or behavioral scientist; or he may be a plant geneticist, pathologist, virologist, horticulturist, or agronomist. He might also be a biochemist, microbiologist, entomologist, agricultural engineer, agricultural economist, or yet another one of the many kinds of biological, physical, or social scientists. Use of the term "agriculturalist" to describe him is no longer appropriate except in a generic sense.

THE PRINCIPLE OF INTERACTION

Regardless of his specialty, the agricultural scientist is affected by the principle of interaction, probably to a higher degree than any other scientist. There is a natural and necessary interaction among the agricultural sciences, and between agriculture and cognate disciplines.

Agricultural scientists cannot improve crop varieties, for example, without using and perhaps advancing our knowledge of plant genetics. But a superior variety cannot produce to its inherent capacity unless advances in soil chemistry and soil physics make possible advanced soil fertility practices which will, in turn, provide better nutrition for the improved strains of crops. Similarly, greater milk output, to use an example, depends on improved genetic potential of dairy cattle. This potential will not be realized, however, unless nutritional requirements as well as physiological responses of the dairy cow are thoroughly understood.

It is only after scientists have improved yields from crops *and* animals and have studied pertinent economic factors that we can produce larger quantities of commodities such as milk at a lower cost per unit. Even then this opportunity will be denied unless agricultural scientists provide the means to control insects and diseases which attack plants and animals and impair the flavor or quality of milk or of the many food products which include milk as an ingredient.

INTERACTION IN AIR POLLUTION STUDIES

Air pollution studies provide still another example of interaction involving agricultural scientists. Contaminated air causes more than poor visibility, unpleasant odors, eye and throat irritations, and ash deposits on buildings and cars. It also injures vegetation—to the extent of 10 million dollars annually in just one metropolitan area.

A team of plant pathologists at Rutgers University learned that airborne fluorine damaged the foliage of peach trees and more than 30 other kinds of vegetation in a certain industrial area. Recently, they identified aldehydes as a toxic component of the air pollutants being studied.

Agronomists and horticulturalists at Rutgers are assisting the pathologists in developing cultural and chemical control practices. Chemists are making further identification of atmospheric compounds. Meteorological data have made possible correlations among the concentrations of the pollutants and several atmospheric factors, including wind speed and direction, and barometric pressure.

Preventive anti-oxidant sprays are being tested. Geneticists and plant breeders are at work on the development of plant varieties that are resistant to air-borne phytotoxins, since species and varieties have been shown to vary in degree of susceptibility to pollutants. Plant physiologists are seeking to explain the mode of action of the toxins' activities in plants.

Perhaps soon, as the plant pathologist leading the Rutgers research team proposed before the Senate Subcommittee on Air Pollution, a research center will be formed to serve the Eastern United States by bringing together "sufficient diversification of skills . . . to allow delving deeply into this 20th century challenge."

THE AGRICULTURAL DISCIPLINES

A scientific discipline, to deserve the title, should be a distinct field of objective investigation which develops a systematic body of verifiable facts and general laws. While agricultural disciplines such as animal science and plant science rely heavily upon knowledge from other fields of science, they also meet these criteria. It is not argued, however, that agricultural engineering, to use an example, is *agriculture* and not *engineering*, or that agricultural economics is *agriculture* and not *economics*. The important point is that agricultural engineering, agricultural economics, and other disciplines exist as distinct entities to contribute to agricultural progress.

In this paper, we explore the nature, achievements, and challenges of six such disciplines—soil, plant, animal and food sciences, agricultural economics, and agricultural engineering. *This is not claimed to be a complete list of scientific disciplines devoted entirely to agriculture.* Some would subdivide our categories. Plant science, for example, includes (agronomic or field) crop science, as well as the study of horticultural (fruits, vegetables, ornamentals) and range crops.

Some would argue that forestry should be a part of plant science, or at least be included in the agricultural sciences, and cite such justifications as the large acreage of farm woodlots. We are content to acknowledge that forestry is closely related to agriculture—especially because of the concept of multiple land use, and because of common interests in several disciplines including soils, microbiology, and economics—and we are content to state that the significance of this relationship transcends any possible importance of defining forestry as a part of, or separate from, agriculture. We have merely elected not to include forestry in this paper.

Similarly, animal science can be divided into meat animals, dairy, poultry, and horses and—expanding beyond traditional agriculture—can include fish and wildlife. We have chosen not to include these two areas which, from an agricultural viewpoint, have a relationship to animal science somewhat similar to forestry's relationship to plant science. Animal science and veterinary science overlap to the extent that each is concerned with the physiology and pathology of large, domestic animals. But animal science is concerned with many other aspects of large, domestic animals and veterinary science, of course, also includes pets and laboratory animals. Again, we have chosen not to discuss veterinary science.

There are other classifications of the agricultural sciences in addition to the one which we have selected. One example is seen in the field of agronomy, which is a mechanism for combining two closely related disciplines—(agronomic or field) crop science and soil science.

Finally, it is not intended to minimize, by omission, other disciplines which contribute heavily to agricultural research but which are not oriented *exclusively* to agriculture. Examples are biochemistry, entomology, plant pathology, microbiology, and meteorology, each of which occasionally has the adjective "agricultural" preceding it. Economic entomology, for example, is readily identifiable; it concerns itself with beneficial as well as harmful insects, has its own society, and publishes a journal.

SOIL SCIENCE

Soil scientists are responsible for leadership in the never-ending battle of rebuilding, maintaining, improving, and conserving our nation's soil.

A considerable portion of the knowledge of soil science involves the application of chemistry, physics, microbiology, and geology to the biosystem we call soil. The contribution of the basic sciences is seen in the phenomenon of cation exchange, discovered years ago. It was soil scientists, with strong training in physical chemistry, who explored the nature of the exchange phenomenon and built a background of basic information which has made important contributions to our understanding of the function of synthetic exchange materials. As a consequence of their investigations, we have new understandings of the mechanisms involved in nutrient absorption by both plants and microorganisms.

Specialized fields such as soil genesis and soil classification, though rooted in fundamental science, have developed a large body of knowledge which is unique to soil science. An illustration of the use of knowledge about soil classification is seen in interpretations from soil classification surveys. These can be used to predict productivity, erodability, suitability for irrigation or drainage, fertilizer and lime requirements, and best uses —including crops, wildlife, and forests.

In recent years soil scientists have been refining methods of examining the soil and defining the reactions that go on within it. The importance of the diffusion process in physical-chemical mechanisms in the soil has resulted in research on the movement of ions, liquid, and gases in the soil.

As soil scientists work toward complete understanding of the earth's land surface mantle, they encounter special kinds of soil problems such as irrigation and reclamation of saline and alkaline soils. Others include the problems associated with the soils of forests, watersheds, wildlands and deserts, and the complex variations in soils induced by different climates, vegetative covers, and underlying parent rocks.

PLANT SCIENCE

Plant scientists, often in cooperation with other scientists, have made it possible to control epidemics of plant diseases, insect attacks, and severe weed competition. They have developed plant varieties adapted to specific environments and have determined plant nutritional needs so that yields could be increased far above those believed possible a few decades ago.

Plant scientists have added to our pleasures. The discovery of the influence of the length of night on flowering plants makes it possible for us to enjoy floral plants any time of the year instead of only during a certain season. Plant scientists now are engaged in isolating and identifying the enzymes and hormones responsible for flowering and other developmental processes.

Years ago, plant scientists produced hybrid corn. Today, studies in biochemical genetics of corn and other crops are leading to a much clearer idea of how genetic material functions in transmitting a cell's likeness to new cells. Scientists are studying subcellular differences which cause certain plant strains to be susceptible to diseases and some weeds to be resistant to herbicides.

Plant science research illustrates the fact that the solution of many of mankind's basic problems often derives from the efforts of scientists in rather diverse fields of interest. Two such fields that are important to plant science are biochemistry and biophysics. Although photosynthesis cannot yet be carried out continuously in entirely artificial systems, we do have increasing knowledge of how the process operates. Biophysicists have studied and largely explained the intricacies of the energy transfer. Biochemists have traced the chemical pathways involved. Plant physiologists and other plant scientists have contributed through their knowledge of cell structure and function. The pioneers of future discoveries concerning photosynthesis may represent any one of several areas of science or a combination of them.

ANIMAL SCIENCE

Man's dependence upon animals as sources of food, fiber, and power traces to the earliest chronicles of history. Despite the revolution in power sources in the well-developed countries of the world, animals are perhaps more important to the health and welfare of mankind today during any earlier period.

Foods of animal origin provide high quality protein together with vitamins, minerals, and associated dietary factors. Meat, milk, and eggs not only contribute much to the health of our nation but also to that of many other peoples who are considered to be the best fed populations of the world.

Wool, mohair, leather, and other fibers have long been staples of our American economy. Although the horse no longer provides our power and transportation, its popularity for recreational activities is at an all time high.

Animal science embraces all the disciplines in the biological and physical sciences which influence animal life. The principles underlying these disciplines have been employed to select and breed increasingly more desirable animals, to better understand reproductive physiology and thereby improve fertility and enhance productivity, and to provide well balanced and adequate rations which have decreased death losses of the young and provided the nutrients for fast and efficient growth and production.

One agricultural research project has determined that a riboflavin deficiency in chicken eggs is caused by an autosomal recessive gene, and studies are under way to determine the mechanism by which the gene produces its effect. Another searches for the neural factors which control pituatary functions that are related to ovulation in the female. Still another seeks to learn the amount and seasonal fluctuations of thyroxine production in a cow, and the effects of thyroxine injections.

All are exploring fundamental questions that, when answered, will result in more and better animal products at lower cost.

FOOD SCIENCE

Food science is important at every step in food processing, beginning with the raw product and terminating with consumer acceptance of the purchased commodity. Food science is increasingly being considered a part of a broader field of nutritional sciences, consisting of nutrition and dietetics as well as food science.

The food scientist uses the principles of chemistry, genetics, microbiology, physics, mathematics, and engineering in evaluating the quality attributes of foods. These include flavor, color, texture, nutritive value, and wholesomeness. He studies food processed by various methods such as heating, freezing, dehydration, fermentation, or irradiation.

The principles of biochemistry are employed to preserve or enhance natural or desired flavor, color, or physical characteristics of foods. For example, enzymes tenderize meat and clarify juices. Natural anti-oxidants prevent deterioration in flavor. Chemical reactions are manipulated to enhance the ripening and produce the desired color of fruit.

The food scientist uses controlled microbiological fermentations in the production of cheese, beverages, and other fermented foods. On the other hand, he prevents microbial spoilage and minimizes loss by judicious application of appropriate physical principles such as refrigeration, heat, drying, salting, smoking, and atmosphere control.

Proper incorporation of additives in the form of minerals, vitamins, and amino acids improves the nutritive quality of foods. Conversely, exclusion of objectionable materials such as pesticide residues, hormones, antibiotics, and toxins protect the safety of our foods.

AGRICULTURAL ECONOMICS

Agricultural economics is a social science, a specialized branch of economics. Its subject matter is concerned with the principles of economics as related to the problems of agriculture.

The work of agricultural economists encompasses problems involving production economics, agricultural business management, land tenure, credit, appraisal, resource conservation and development, marketing and pricing, interregional and international trade, industrial structure and competition, and agricultural policy. Agricultural economists integrate technology, public policy, and business principles in the development of information to assist producers, consumers, and policy makers in making decisions.

Agricultural economists are particularly concerned today with:

1) The continuing disequilibrium between agricultural and nonagricultural industries, manifested by low returns for resources employed in farming. Agricultural economists are identifying optimum methods of producing commodities and are identifying regions with greatest competitive advantage in producing various commodities.

Cost and return analyses generate information which is helpful to farmers and managers of marketing firms in deciding what and how much to produce, what combination of resources to use in production, and the location and scale of production units.

Increasingly, the efforts of many agricultural economists are concerned with economics of land use and development of natural and biological resources in an ever-broadening context. How can our land resources—agricultural land not needed at this time for traditional agricultural use, and forest and wildlands which are not being utilized most efficiently—be used best for recreation, wildlife, conservation, and forestry? How can human resources be developed to provide managerial proficiency for modern farms and yet provide flexibility for nonfarm employment?

2) A second major problem concerns the processes of change in agriculture and impediments to change. Why are changes in the number and size of farms and marketing firms necessary? What factors determine the rate of change? What is the relationship of size to efficiency? How is competition affected by ownership patterns and industrial structure?

3) A third major area is public policy. Many studies currently under way seek to identify the effects of alternative policies and programs upon resource use and incomes in agriculture. Other studies are concerned with policies designed to conserve and develop resources.

The basis for many of these studies is research which seeks to determine how and why the economy functions as it does, and what the implications are for resource use and income distribution to and within agriculture. This research seeks to provide a factual basis for public policy decisions by determining the consequences of changes in economic and institutional conditions.

4) The structure of international competition and the possible role of U.S. agriculture in trade with and development of foreign countries is receiving new emphasis by agricultural economists.

AGRICULTURAL ENGINEERING

Agricultural engineering recognizes and solves engineering problems connected with agriculture. Since agriculture is founded on biological systems, agricultural engineering is, in effect, the engineering of biological systems—the application of the laws of physical science to the control of biological reactions. Its practice involves solution of problems in plant and animal environmental control, planting, harvesting, transport, processing, and storage of food and natural fiber, and the creation and optimization of automated agricultural systems.

A distinguishing feature of the agricultural engineer's education is the combination of basic biology and agriculture studies with his engineering studies, so that he can understand the scientific foundations involved in the biological systems of agriculture and can put them to work. This includes the engineering phases of soil and water management, sources of energy for agriculture, the functional requirements of plant life as related to agricultural machines, the functional requirements of farm animals as related to housing and environmental control, engineering factors involved in transport, processing, and storage of biological products, and integration of agricultural machine systems through mathematical interpretations and analogies.

Agricultural engineers specify power requirements for the machines and processes of agriculture and develop functional and mechanical requirements of the machines; design water systems to meet the needs of plants, animals, and rural people; develop engineering methods for increasing the value of food and fiber through processing; and design transport methods and materials-handling procedures.

The principal challenge to the agricultural engineer today is to create more powerful and efficient agricultural production systems. Tomorrow's challenge will be similar, but the techniques employed will be more sophisticated.

THE CHALLENGE OF COMING DECADES

The challenge to our agricultural sciences for the future is no less dramatic than it has been in the past. Our U.S. population is growing at the rate of about 2% per year. At the moment, this is an increase of one person every 11 seconds, 8000 more mouths to feed each day. By 1980, our population may reach 245 million persons.

World population presently numbers about 3.1 billion. It is expected to double by the year 2000. This means that there will be as many additional people on earth at the end of each 3-year period between now and the end of this century as presently live in the United States.

Moving from a world in which scarcity is the predominate pattern to a world in which freedom from hunger may at long last prevail is the challenge which faces this and succeeding generations. Dr. J. George Harrar, President of the Rockefeller Foundation, has stated: "We range in our agricultural practices throughout the world from those which approach automation on the one hand to the other extreme which reflects only that there has been little or no change from antiquity. There are situations which require only two man-days to produce an acre of rice under total or semi-total automation versus 259 to 400 days in areas where work is all done by untrained manpower; there is tremendous power in scientific agriculture applied gradually and as rapidly as is compatible with situations. It can contribute enormously to the future food supply of the world even in the face of a rapidly increasing population.[*]

[*]Harrar, J. George, Barriers to Nutritional Optima, International Symposium on the Role of Food in World Peace, The Ohio State University, Columbus, Ohio, May 1, 1962.

17

Tree Ferns

Henricks Hodge

Beautiful though they are, the lowly ferns that decorate our temperate woodlands give little idea of the size that some of their giant cousins attain. The tree ferns of the tropics stand head and shoulders above all other members of the great fern group. Some of them raise their slender trunks to a height of 60 feet—about the equivalent of a 6-story building.

The 300 or more species of living tree ferns inhabit the cooler temperature situations of the tropics and subtropics. They thrive especially well on lush, rain-swept mountain slopes where the torrid climate is tempered by elevation. There they may form small forests, particularly on abandoned agricultural land.

Tree ferns may be found growing as high as timber line, which in the tropics may lie above 10,000 feet. Seemingly the rainier the climate the better these giant ferns like it. They are at their best in that montane belt where the cumulus clouds sailing in from the surrounding lands, impinge upon the mountains, saturating them with mist or rain and forming what have been fittingly called the "weeping woods." It makes little difference whether the habitat be in Hawaii or the West Indies, in the Andes or the distant Himalayas, for the conditions are essentially the same the tropical world around. In these areas, the traveler will see tree ferns in all their grandeur, silhouetted as often as not in the fog, their delicate crowns conspicuous among the surrounding mass of vegetation.

Some tree ferns have wandered out of the confines of the tropics into the temperate zone. In the mild oceanic climate of New Zealand, for instance, they grow even in sight of glacier ice. From that temperate land has come *Cyathea medullaris*, a tree fern that can stand even a few degrees of frost. This enables it to be grown in certain favored sections of

W. H. Hodge, "Tree Ferns," *Natural History,* Vol. 65 (1956), pp. 88-92. Reprinted by permission.

the United States, such as California and Florida. On our Pacific Coast it can be seen in San Francisco's Golden Gate Park, where the Pacific fogs, as they roll in, apparently give these alien ferns a welcome taste of their native atmosphere.

RESEMBLE SMALLER COUSINS

Tree ferns resemble their more familiar lowly cousins of our woodlands except for their over-size dimensions and certain technical differences known only to fern specialists. The stems of most ferns are short underground structures called rhizomes, usually lying in a horizontal plane. However, the stems or rhizomes of tree ferns grow stiffly erect to form a tough, fibrous trunk.

Tree fern trunks are not to be compared to tree trunks. They lack the solid woody cylinder and growth layer (cambium) typical of the trunks of most trees. The tree fern trunk is incapable of growth in girth and grows slowly only in length from a single terminal bud. The giant leaves or fronds are at first tightly coiled in the bud in the form of elegantly designed "fiddleheads" or croziers, as the reader may have observed among our common woodland ferns. The "fiddleheads" uncoil progressively, producing new whorls of leaves, and with each successive season, the gigantic green crown of the tree fern rises higher and higher.

Curiously, multitudes of tiny, aerial roots often grow down over parts of the trunk, covering it with an interlacing network. This serves as a wonderful footing for the growth of tropical air plants. As a result, tree fern trunks often look like green ferneries, cloaked as they are with mosses, tiny ferns, and similar plants.

In their arborescent form, at least, our existing tree ferns are perhaps our closest approach to those distant ancestors which, in the age of coal, first gave the earth a green cloak of forests. Most of the arborescent fernlike plants of those ancient times were the so-called "seed-ferns" (Pteridospermae). Where coal was being formed, these were more abundant than the tree ferns. Some of these fern allies of long ago reached a height of 100 feet. There were, at the same time, true ferns of arborescent habit in those days, though none of them can be included in any modern family.

KINDS AND USES

The family that includes most of the living tree ferns is the Cyatheaceae. Another family, the Dicksoniaceae, includes most of the near-temperate species, all of the southern hemisphere ones of Australasian origin, and also the genus *Cibotium*, which includes two Mexican species. These latter are commonly grown in the United States as display plants for hotels and the like. They have pale green, much divided leaves, which are several feet long. They are sold before the trunks have begun to assume tree form.

Orchid fanciers in the tropics have long recognized the value of tree fern trunks and often cut them to length and hang them up as supports on which to grow their exotic specimens. Fern trunks are termite resistant and make practically indestructible posts. Many a simple tropical dwelling stands on them. Long ago, the fierce Carib Indians of the Lesser Antilles found another use. They noted that dried tree fern trunks made fine tinder and used it as their standard material for carrying fire from place to place. Dried fern trunk will burn for hours, very conveniently without smoke or visible flame. The Caribs called it *wâtu hakuiyâ*, meaning "voracious fire."

But of all the uses of the giant ferns, the one that seems most fitting is their utilization as ornamentals in horticulture. No botanical garden would consider its conservatory complete without at least one arborescent fern. Many a home owner in the tropics and subtropics feels the same way about these lovely plants. Certainly few species can offer anything comparable to the lacey tracery of their magnificent leaves.

Next time you see one of these splendid plants, imagine a whole forest of them, on one of those breathtaking mountain slopes in the tropics, amid swirling mists and tumbling torrents. If you visit such a region on your next vacation trip—perhaps the Luquillo Mountains of Puerto Rico, Jamaica's Blue Mountain Peak, or the knife-edged ridges of Hawaii—you will be able to conjure up a good impression of what a good pteridophyte forest would have looked like eons ago, when the coal beds were being laid down for races yet unborn to burn in their hearths in climates too cold for tree ferns.

18

Of Molds and Men

Richard N. Shoemaker

Osiris looked down from the sky and saw Man bent under the weight of his troubles. With a smile of compassion the god handed down the gift of fermentation.

That is a Fourth Dynasty Egyptian myth. But primitive man did lighten his load with fermentation. He fermented everything that could be fermented. He made beer and wine from grasses, roots, trees, berries, honeys, pine cones. He even fermented fish.

Then he applied the heavenly skill to the brewing of other beverages: beers from cereal grains, wines from grapes, meads from honeys. Spiced date wine and Tequila-like spirits of cactus became passé. Every man began to insist on "brand names" like *Latium* of the House of Lucius Titus— a full-bodied red wine that was shipped all over the world.

In the 1950's, Captain Y. P. Cousteau and his crew from the French Navy's Undersea Research Group sampled some Titus Latium (vintage 230 B.C.) which they recovered from an argosy in the harbor of Marseilles. Their comment was dry: "The Third Century Before Christ was not a good vintage century." Apparently there was more method than madness in the ancient practice of diluting wine with water.

The ancients cherished the gift of fermentation and even fought wars for the best vineyards. Religious cults sprang from the grape.

Somewhere along the line early man realized that fermentation did more than make his head whirl. The chance contamination of wine by bacteria pointed up the possibilities of other products. Vinegar, for instance. This sour liquid could be carried by the legionaires and mixed with the water of foreign lands. Undiluted, it could be used as an astringent. According to Pliny, vinegar was also used to convert lead into a white pigment.

Richard N. Shoemaker, "Of Molds and Men," *Yale Scientific Magazine,* Vol. 31 (1957), pp. 2-6. Reprinted by permission.

Other fermentations proved extremely useful. Linen was made from flax fibers retted by bacteria in stagnant water. Meats, fish and certain vegetables were preserved by the action of one kind of bacteria against the growth and activity of harmful bacteria. Dye was made by fermenting the indigo plant. Coffee and cocoa are still fermented to separate the bean from the pulp. Arrow poisons, hypnotics and soporifics were extracted from fermented decoctions of herbs, roots and mushrooms. And cheeses were made from the fermented milk of camels, ewes, goats, llamas, yaks, mares, caribous, cows, water buffalos, and a long list of other mammals.

Crusaders returning from the seraglios of the Holy Land told wild tales of dancing girls, wines, medicines and riches beyond expectation—hoping to kindle interest in more crusades and foment an escape from medieval monotony. Tales of the "chalice" endowed with miraculous medical cures, the "Philosopher's stone" that commuted baser metals to gold, the "Mithradaticum," a universal antidote, sent alchemists scurrying to their cells to mix, distill, percolate, extract and ferment everything within reach. Some of their formularies make the witches brew of Macbeth look like a housewife's recipe for pink lemonade.

Reports on the potency of his "ferments" boosted the alchemist's standing in society. He reached his zenith about the time the Bubonic Plague was decimating Europe's populations in the Fourteenth Century. Promulgating such theories as "poisons counteract poisons" and attributing disease to a "malevolent admixture of the elements," the alchemist did neither medicine nor fermentation much good.

Over the next three hundred years, man gained greater knowledge of the world around him. But knowledge and understanding are not synonymous. Even after the little Delft microscopist van Leeuwenhoek demonstrated "animalcules" in his teeth in 1687, no one suspected their nature or importance until 1732, when Boerhaave examined the "schmutzdecke" of vinegar. He postulated that living organisms changed it into sour wine (vinaigre).

One hundred five years later Kützing confirmed Boerhaave's observations by actual studies of the minute blobs of life responsible for vinegar formation. But Kützing's revelation was ignored by most scientists for almost 40 years. The world was not ready to acknowledge the role of microbes in fermentative change.

It took a chemist with a flair for public relations to hammer home the message of the microbes. Louis Pasteur not only developed the bacterial concept of disease, but established the principle that fermentation is a process brought about by living cells. Though his definition of fermentation ("life without air") is not correct, he got the essential idea: fermentation is life.

In 1878, Lister diluted sour milk to isolate lactic acid bacteria and prove that they caused the milk to sour. Three years later, Charles E. Avery ventured into industrial fermentation to manufacture lactic acid.

Although yeast, vinegar and alcoholic beverages had been produced on an industrial scale for decades, Avery's enterprise made him a father of industrial fermentation.

Alcohol had been distilled on a small scale from wines and beers since the Middle Ages. This was uneconomical—especially for industry. The Industrial Alcohol Act of 1906 legalized the quantity production of *denatured* alcohol for industrial purposes. The act also declared such alcohol tax free. As a result of this legislation, more than 100 million gallons of tax-exempt alcohol go to market each year—mostly for industrial consumption.*

From 1906 on, industrial fermentation grew like Topsy. World War I gave it new impetus. Britain wanted to blast the Kaiser out of Europe with an explosive called cordite. The Kaiser, in turn, sought to widen the English Channel from Calais to the Irish Sea with nitroglycerine.

Both lacked the necessary means. Britain needed acetone to manufacture cordite; Germany lacked glycerine to make nitroglycerine. Almost simultaneously, both found fermentation the key to their production problems. Glycerol could be made by fermenting molasses; acetone by fermenting corn. The British process proved more successful.

Acetone, a commercial solvent, was also used as dope to stretch and tighten the canvas on the wings of German Fokkers and British flying jennies. The Germans were hamstrung by embargoes and blockades and concentrated their war efforts on developing a synthetic rubber. The production snag in the German program was butadiene, the starting material. There wasn't any.

So Kaiser Wilhelm's scientists fermented butanol which, in turn, was converted to the diene. Here was a picture in irony: the British were making acetone by fermentation and throwing away the by-product butanol desperately needed by the enemy. The Germans were using the same fermentation and discarding acetone!

Henry Ford's mass production of flivvers brought butanol back into business after World War I. The fermentation-derived chemical was used as a solvent in the red, black, green and yellow lacquers on the automobiles of the era.

Fermentation was pushed further along when Italy slowed the flow of concentrated lemon juice and citrate of lime shortly before the war. These products were used in America for the commercial production of citric acid. A Brooklyn firm of manufacturing chemists, Chas. Pfizer & Co., Inc., was one of the larger importers of this raw material. The firm thought about making its own lemon juice. Lemons, however, do not grow in Brooklyn. Pfizer chemists tried fermenting sugar. (Sugar beets don't grow in Brooklyn, either, but they could be freighted in from the West.)

---

*Filtering it through bread does not make it drinkable.

Hairbreadth controls were developed; intricate steps and ingenious methods were devised. Fermentation, long an art, became a science overnight. Sugar was converted by man and by mold into citric acid.

By 1923 Pfizer was producing citric acid commercially, by fermentation. A constant source of supply was assured. A saving of more than 75 per cent was realized on the price of citric. Then came Prohibition—and a nation-wide preoccupation with bathtub gin. For some reason, industrial fermentation sat out the next decade.

In 1934, Reichstein and Grüssner synthesized vitamin C. Sorbose, a necessary starting material, was not readily available. Industrial research teams then developed a method of converting sorbitol into sorbose by fermentation. This was the crucial hurdle in vitamin C production. The method was a boon to humanity in general and to the British Navy in particular. His Majesty's seamen had sucked lemons since Nelson's time to ward off scurvy, a vitamin C deficiency disease.

The citric acid process later paved the way for riboflavin (vitamin B-2), vitamin B-12, and as-yet-undefined growth factors like Vigo-fac, a farm animal growth stimulant.

In terms of health and well-being, these achievements are overshadowed by fermentation developments since 1941. Work was begun that year by the Northern Regional Research Laboratories in Peoria, Illinois, and by Merck, Squibb and Pfizer on mass-producing Sir Alexander Fleming's discovery, penicillin. Eventually, the entire U. S. drug industry was enlisted. Research on the first "miracle drug" had the unlimited backing of the governments of the United States and England. The lives of their soldiers were at stake.

The *Penicillium* mold, resembling the exotic microorganism that makes Roquefort cheese, was grown in flasks that looked like milk bottles. Production, however, was slow and uneconomical. Large volume production was the only answer. Giant tanks were built to hold the fermentation liquor. Ship-sized propellers were designed to churn the broth into a frothy maelstrom. Sterile air was sent bubbling through the brew. This was submerged fermentation. It worked.

But there were other problems. The mold originally used for the production of the first penicillin didn't grow too well in tanks. It preferred the undisturbed surface growth in bottles. So the search began for a mold that could live and reproduce in the turbulent tanks.

In 1943, three government scientists, Raper, Alexander and Coghill, obtained an cantaloupe from a Peoria market. From it they isolated a mold called *Penicillium chrysogenum,* which proved adaptable to the submerged-culture techniques. The new mold stepped up penicillin production.

But even this was not enough. Demerec, working at the Carnegie Institute in Cold Spring Harbor, Long Island, bombarded the *P. chryso-*

genum mold with X-rays, hoping to mutate it so it would produce greater quantities of the drug. This worked. Still Demerec wasn't satisfied. He tried chemicals, heat, more X-rays, and ultra violet rays. Out of this electro-chemical whirligig eventually came a culture that produced more than a thousand times as much antibiotic as the original mold. Penicillin got to Normandy by D-day.

The Demerec method has been used by industry ever since.

Industrial scientists then began looking for other microscopic forms of life to make more antibiotics. Waksman found Streptomycin. Bartz isolated Chloromycetin. Duggar discovered Aureomycin. Finlay and other Pfizer researchers turned up Terramycin.

Strange new names were added to the lexicon and the man on the street began talking about Terramycin, Tetracyn, Sigmamycin*, Magnamycin, Viocin, Ilotycin and the like. The era of antibotics was here.

At the same time, the medical profession began paying closer attention to hormones from the adrenal cortex—regulatory chemicals from glands no bigger than a pullet egg. Merck and Co. developed a method for synthesizing cortisone by a thirty-odd step process, proof that science was not dependent on the animal body for its regulatory chemicals.

Upjohn, Pfizer, and others developed methods for converting a readily available chemical, Reichstein's Compound "S", into one of these hormones by means of molds. This was hydrocortisone.

Prednisolone was another giant step in steroid research. Also made by fermentation, prednisolone is from four to five times more potent than natural compounds.

Many antibiotics and hormonelike steroids have gone to market since 1952. Fermentation-produced chemicals like itaconic and kojic acids have been made available to industry. Microbes have been coaxed to make the basic amino acid, l-lysine, an essential "building block" of proteins. . . .

Cultivation of plant tissue by submerged fermentation is still a laboratory curiosity. But some day, submerged culture techniques may give us— at lower cost, on a year-round basis—plant alkaloids, botanical extracts, and medicinal and agricultural chemicals heretofore dependent upon climatic whims and seasonal changes.

Three basic types of fermentation processes are in use today.

In many parts of the world, flax, hemp, jute and ramie are still retted —the bast fibres are separated from the surrounding stem tissues by uncontrolled or natural fermentation. The plants are simply exposed to the weather (dew-retting) or placed in ponds or streams (water-retting), where bacteria ferment them. Natural fermentation is also used, with some refinements, in the commercial production of preserved foods like pickles, sauerkraut and olives.

*Now called Signemycin. (Ed.)

Beers, wines and liquors, on the other hand, are made by a semi-controlled fermentation process. Braumeisters,* wine makers and fermentologists in the alcohol, whisky, solvent, yeast and related industries would probably not take kindly to this label. The term "semi-controlled" is used here strictly as a comparative. These processes *are* controlled—but the controls generally are not so rigid as those used in the chemical and pharmaceutical industries.

Habitués of Morey's know there are many kinds of beer. Lager, pilsner, bock, ale, stout and porter are domestic favorites. Each has a different character. However, all are made by essentially the same process. The differences in flavor are determined by the strains of yeast used, type of water, fermentation temperature, quantity and quality of hops, methods of malting, and so on.

In controlled fermentation, the tanks may be jacketed, glass lined, and equipped with spargers, impellers, heating and cooling coils, electronic foam control apparatus, heat regulators, rotometers, exhaust valves, baffles, sight glasses and sampling tubes. The media in which selected organisms are grown to produce antibiotics and other fermentation chemicals is compounded to insure the optimum balance of essential inorganic ions, trace elements, buffering salts, growth factors, precursors and nontoxic defoaming agents.

Care is taken to maintain the proper ratio of available nitrogen and carbon in the raw materials used as nutrients. The inoculum, although preformed, must contain a specific quantity of actively proliferating cells at a definite stage in their growth cycle.

The sequence of events applies in nearly all controlled fermentations. The variables, of course, are the organisms, media, fermentation time and extrinsic factors such as heat, air supply, pH.

A specially-selected pure-bred microorganism is aseptically grown on a solid agar medium containing elements which favor the production of spores, the "seeds" of the mold. At maturity, these spores are washed from the mold with a sterile detergent-containing solution and microscopically counted. Appropriately diluted aliquots of the spore suspension are inoculated into small flasks containing sterile media. This encourages active growth and reproduction of the mold.

The inoculated flasks are then shaken for a predetermined length of time so the mold can grow. This vegetative growth, called mycelium, assumes the form of small balls. It reproduces itself by fragmentation. The mycelial balls are aseptically transferred to small containers called "seed tanks," in which the process is repeated—but on a much larger scale. This is staged fermentation.

---

*Education's debt to fermentation—Vassar was founded by a Braumeister who wanted "to build and endow a college for young women which shall be to them what Yale and Harvard are to young men." *Sic transit gloria mundi.*

From the time the inoculum is introduced into the seed tanks until the end of the fermentation, the operation is rigidly controlled. When the growth of mold is optimum in the seed tanks, their contents are pumped into production fermenters containing sterile production medium.

The vast quantities of production broth must be "cooked" enough to kill contaminating organisms without affecting the nutrients in the medium. Sterile air, or air mixed with other gases, is introduced into the fermenters at a carefully-controlled volume. Fermentation temperatures are also rigorously controlled. As metabolism progresses heat is evolved—and heat often destroys the end product. Likewise, pH (hydrogen ion concentration) must be kept in check. pH values far below or much above the optimum tend to cut yields.

How the fermentation medium is agitated also directly influences the yield. Agitation must uniformly distribute air and nutrients to the growing mold. It must not allow toxic metabolic products to accumulate and reduce the yields by "poisoning" the ferment.

Progress is measured periodically by sampling. This involves pH, mycelial volume and sugar or protein concentration tests. Nutrients, defoaming agents, buffering compounds, precursors and other agents are added as tests indicate, and elaborate precautions are taken to maintain sterility.

When it is no longer economically feasible to continue the fermentation, the liquor containing the product is separated from the vegetative growth and insoluble ingredients. The extract is crystallized and made into the various forms in which it is packaged.

There are other types of fermentations: production of enzymes, chemical transformations by microbes, manufacture of cheese, industrial and human waste disposal, and many others. They add weight to a truism: That fermentation chemistry is indispensable to human well-being.

Without highly-developed controlled fermentation techniques, antibiotics would still be laboratry curiosities. Citric, kojic, gluconic, itaconic, oxalic acids; vitamins, hormones, steroids and a long list of chemical intermediates used by industry would be rare and costly. The methods for producing chemical "building blocks" economically would not exist.

In the years ahead, the gift of Osiris may be expected to loom even larger as the key to better living.

IV

Nutrition, Health, and Disease

19

Food, Facts and Fads

Gladys Cook
May Foley

FREQUENT QUESTIONS ABOUT FOODS

ABOUT MILK

▶ *Must we use raw (unpasteurized) milk? Some people tell us that milk has lost much of its nutritive value as a result of pasteurization.*

ANSWER: No. There are some slight nutritional losses as a result of pasteurization. However, it's worth the insignificant nutritive losses to have the protection that pasteurization gives against certain milk-borne diseases.

▶ *Do adults need milk?*

ANSWER: Yes. Adults, as well as children, need the nutrients found in milk. It is the best and most reliable single source of calcium, which is needed by everyone. Milk is recommended for adults because it provides nutrients needed for maintenance of bones and teeth and for other body functions, such as normal clotting of the blood in healing, and regularity of the heart action. Milk is also a valuable source of good quality protein, riboflavin, and many other elements.

▶ *Does yogurt have more nutritional value than milk?*

ANSWER: The food value of yogurt is the same as that of the milk used to make it. It is a form of fermented milk. Usually it is made from whole milk. Sometimes powdered milk is added; if so, the yogurt will

Gladys Cook and May Foley, "Food, Facts and Fads," *Leaflet No. 308,* The Co-operative Extension Service, University of Massachusetts, Amherst. Reprinted by permission.

have more protein, vitamins, and minerals. The therapeutic value of the lactic acid organism used in making yogurt is a different matter and must not be confused with the nutritive value.

ABOUT BREADS

▶ *Is white bread "harmful?"*

ANSWER: The relative value of whole wheat versus white bread is an example of an area where the faddist is responsible for much confusion and exaggerated misrepresentation. It is true that from a point of view of nutritive values, whole wheat flour is superior to white flour. However, people do not live on bread alone. Furthermore, much white bread in this country is enriched and has milk solids added. Some people cannot digest the roughage from whole wheat and they must eat white bread. White bread is not harmful or poisonous, nor is bleached flour harmful.

▶ *Is there any advantage to using "special" breads, such as gluten, high protein, and low starch?*

ANSWER: The chief appeal of these products is their alleged low calorie content. However, unless the necessary information is given on the wrapper there is no way of knowing how much lower the caloric value is than that of regular bread.

No doubt in many instances the value of reduced calorie content is out of line with the increased cost of these special breads.

ABOUT VEGETABLES

▶ *Do raw vegetable juices, called "liquefied vegetables," have life-giving properties not present in the vegetables themselves?*

ANSWER: Whether raw vegetables are eaten in salads, in sticks or pieces, or in juice form, they are valuable, but the liquefied form has no special virtues. Cooked vegetables are also valuable sources of certain vitamins and minerals, if the juice is eaten and if not cooked too long a time.

▶ *Is it true that there is no use trying to eat a balanced diet because much food is devitalized, demineralized, and unfit for consumption because of poor soil?*

ANSWER: Poor soil reduces yield more than it reduces nutrient content of the food. Furthermore, people are not likely to eat food grown in only one type of soil, and the various soil deficiencies here and there would not affect the average person.

ABOUT "MIRACLE" OR "WONDER" FOODS

▶ *Is it true that food, such as blackstrap molasses, wheat germ and yeast, can correct menopausal difficulties, induce sleep, prevent nervousness, correct baldness, restore original color to hair, help digestion, and prevent changes due to old age?*

ANSWER: These so-called miracle foods have no unique virtues, no magical powers. Certain special foods, such as wheat germ, brewer's yeast, and blackstrap molasses, do contain a generous amount of some vitamins and/or minerals or other nutrients. But, these nutrients are also found in many common foods and often in a more palatable form.

ABOUT FOOD SUPPLEMENTS

▶ *Are food supplements safe to use in place of less pleasant medicines?*

ANSWER: The so-called food supplements so widely advertised today are not harmful in themselves. However, with some of them, danger lies in the faith which customers may place in exaggerated or unwarranted claims made for their therapeutic value. This is especially true when the material is represented as providing adequate treatment for such diseases as cancer, arthritis, and pneumonia, which need prompt medical attention. No serious disease or physical disability should be treated by the patient without the advice of a qualified physician.

Fortunately, authorities are working hard to restrain such dangerous misrepresentation. However, until, and during the course of an investigation, considerable time may have elapsed, and as a result of highly effective sales promotion, large quantities of such products may have been sold. Vitamins, minerals, and other food elements claimed to be in many "supplements" are also in common foods and can be adequately provided in a well-balanced diet.

ABOUT REDUCING AIDS

▶ *Will reducing aids allow weight loss while eating normally?*

ANSWER: Overweight is the result of eating more food than the body requires. Weight reduction can be accomplished only by eating less than the body needs. These reducing aids are generally useless. Many are merely vitamin and mineral mixtures, sweetened skim milk powder concentrates or fillers.

▶ *Are weight-reducing drugs safe?*

ANSWER: Some are harmless, most are useless, and many are dangerous. Fortunately most drugs are available only on prescription. Drugs to lessen appetite should be used with caution. No drug should be taken without the advice of your physician.

SOME MISINFORMATION ABOUT FOODS, DIETS

▶ *"Food cooked in aluminum is poisonous and causes cancer."*
The American Medical Association and other authorities have proved that there is no danger involved in using aluminum cooking utensils. Many common plant foods contain aluminum which is absorbed from the soil. This fact does not stop us from eating these foods. Physicians use aluminum compounds in the treatment of ulcers.

▶ *"A good way to reduce is to omit breakfast."*
Reliable studies show that a reducing plan including a well-balanced breakfast is more successful than one which omits breakfast. The individual feels better, has less fatigue, is more alert, less hungry and less tempted to "nibble" before lunch time. Everyone, including "weight-reducers," needs to replenish the body with vitamins, minerals and protein, as well as energy, after a 10- to 12-hour fast. Surplus body fat can supply some of the energy but not the other nutrients.

▶ *"Overweight is due entirely to heredity."*
Some authorities believe that in certain cases there may be inherited body disorders which may account for a family tendency to put on weight. Regardless of the cause, the overweight person is eating more than his body needs—he must eat less, or foods lower in calories, to lose weight.

In some instances there may be common family traits of unusually good appetites, easy-going temperaments, perhaps combined with a preference for sweets and high-fat foods.

▶ *"Dark bread has fewer calories than white bread."*
Generally speaking there is very little difference in the caloric value of regular white bread and dark bread. Some dark breads containing raisins or made with molasses may have a few more calories than plain white bread.

▶ *"Eat all the 'reducing bread' you want."*
If the so-called "reducing breads" have any worthwhile nutritive value, they will contain calories. Unfortunately, the composition of many of these breads is not given on the wrapper; therefore, the

caloric value is unknown. In cases where the composition is given, the caloric value is usually only slightly less than regular bread.

▶ *"Water is fattening."*

Water has NO caloric vaiue. There is nothing in water that can change to fat and be stored in the body. A person will weigh more if weighed immediately after drinking a large quantity of water, but if the body does not need all this water, the excess will be excreted shortly. In certain diseases of the kidney and heart, excess water may be retained in the body. If you feel that you aren't overeating, but are gaining weight, you should see your physician.

▶ *"Toast has fewer calories than untoasted bread."*

Toasting does not reduce the number of calories. Toasting does slightly reduce the water content, and so weight for weight, a pound of toast actually has a few more calories than a pound of untoasted bread.

▶ *"Homogenized milk is 'richer' in fat than unhomogenized milk."*

The fat content is not changed when milk is homogenized. Homogenization divides the fat into fine particles which remain equally distributed throughout the milk. This gives the impression of "richer milk."

▶ *"Margarine has fewer calories than butter."*

Margarine and butter have the same caloric value. Vegetable oils from which margarine is made have the same calorie content as animal fat.

▶ *"Grapefruit aids reducing."*

Grapefruit contains sugar, vitamins, minerals, and citric acid. None of these in any way removes or helps to remove fat from the body. Although grapefruit is not as high in caloric value as some fruits, it does contain calories.

▶ *"Sugar is not as fattening as starch."*

One ounce of sugar has essentially the same number of calories as one ounce of starch.

FOR FURTHER INFORMATION WRITE:

Extension Service, University of Massachusetts, Amherst, Massachusetts.
State Public Health Department, State House, Boston, Massachusetts.
Human Nutrition Research Branch, U.S. Department of Agriculture, Washington, D.C.

Pure Food and Drug Administration, Washington, D.C.
American Medical Association, Bureau of Investigation, 535 No. Dearborn Street, Chicago, Illinois.
American Dietetics Association, 620 No. Michigan Ave., Chicago, Illinois.

20

Horizons in Dentistry

George C. Paffenbargar

The primary task of dentistry is not to extract and replace teeth, but to preserve them. Consequently, dental research centers around the saving of teeth. Of course, research on prevention of the loss of diseased teeth and surrounding tissues is necessary, but what is even more important is the research on preventing dental diseases. This means that dental research should be concentrated on the treatment and prevention of (1) dental caries—a breaking down of the hard tooth tissues, (2) periodontal disturbances—loss of the tissues that support the teeth, and (3) malformations—deformities of the oral tissues, and (4) conditions which are the aftermaths of (1), (2), and (3). There is no inkling, on the scientific horizon today, of major changes in these public responsibilities of dentistry.

How is dental research accomplishing the foregoing tasks, and how can it become more effective?

RESEARCH ON FLUORINE AND DENTAL CARIES

The discovery that proper amounts of a trace element, fluorine, in the diet can influence the development of a body organ to make it disease-resistant—in this instance, the tooth—is an unparalleled achievement in

George C. Paffenbargar, "Horizons in Dentistry," *Frontiers of Dental Science,* George C. Paffenbargar and Sholom Pearlman, eds., Vistas in Science No. 3 (Washington, D.C.: National Science Teachers Association, 1965). Reprinted by permission.

disease prevention. Heretofore, practically all of the really preventive measures for the control of disease have been useful on *acute* diseases only. The *chronic* diseases have been, and are, strikingly resistant to preventive measures. The reduction of dental decay by proper amounts of fluorine, which do no harm to the body, has been repeatedly demonstrated. Yet no one knows precisely the manner in which fluorine acts. This must still be explained, and that explanation will probably come from intensified research on calcified tissues.

Some hints have been uncovered that ions other than fluoride, such as ammonium, sodium, and stannous (tin), may play a potent role in caries prevention. These leads should be relentlessly pursued.

CALCULUS RESEARCH

Much of the loss of teeth among older people is caused by the wasting away of the bone and the gums that support the teeth. Much of this loss of the investing structures is caused by the deposition of unwanted, hard deposits called dental calculus, mostly on the necks of the teeth. Today, the only treatment available is removal of the calculus. What is needed is intensive research in how calculus forms so that preventive measures may be designed.

BACTERIAL PLAQUE RESEARCH

The soft deposits on teeth—the *plaques*—are as undesirable as the hard deposits because they harbor bacteria that are thought to help break down the tissues which hold the teeth in place. What are these plaques? Why do some harden to form calculus while tooth decay occurs under others? Why do some individuals have extensive plaques while others have small plaques or relatively harmless ones? These are just examples of some of the problems that you yourself may solve sometime should you decide to make a career of dentistry.

RESEARCH ON SALIVA

The teeth are constantly bathed in saliva—why don't they dissolve in it? Because the saliva contains dissolved salts that keep the teeth from going into solution. Generally there is a balance in the solubility relationship in the enamel-saliva system with salts being replaced by the saliva at just about the same rate as they are being dissolved into it. However, imbalances occur all too frequently, causing enamel dissolution or the precipitation of calculus. If balance could be maintained at the proper level, much of what we know as dental disease would not exist. Who is going to discover the how and whys of such dental disharmonies—perhaps you, a potential dental scientist?

RESEARCH ON ORAL HYGIENE

What evidence is there that brushing teeth keeps them from decaying or stops the formation of calculus? Dentists have recommended oral hygiene as a preventive measure for decades, yet what few data there are indicate that the loss of teeth, at least the loss in young people, has been on the increase.

How can this trend toward increase in dental caries be reversed and be made to go downhill? Progress can be made principally by research on the treatment and the prevention of dental caries in the younger age groups; also, perhaps, by better oral hygiene on the part of the individual. Some data are available showing a direct relation between oral hygiene and tooth decay. Here again, field research and analysis have proved very effective, just as they did in the discovery of the relationship between fluorine and dental decay.

RESEARCH IN DENTAL MATERIALS

Most of the tissues of the body can restore themselves or fill in gaps caused by injury. When tooth tissues—enamel and dentin—are lost, they are not repaired or replaced. So much of dental therapy is unique. Why? Because much of modern dentistry involves the replacement of hard and soft oral tissues, lost by disease, with relatively inert materials. This surgical and *prosthetic* therapy must be biologically safe, mechanically efficient, and lifelike. Some of this treatment is largely reparative, such as artificial dentures; but much of dental treatment is preventive. The treatment of small cavities in teeth arrests decay and retards and prevents tooth loss.

Since much of dental therapy involves the making of restorations of lost tooth structures (operative dentistry) and replacements of missing teeth and tissues (prosthetic dentistry), research on the materials used in the treatment is imperative. The preparation of standards for these dental materials—standards that define the materials by physical and chemical tests—is an important part of the science of dental materials.

Another important aspect of dental therapy is relating laboratory research on dental materials with clinical research. . . .

Among the suggestions for needed research in dental materials is the development of insoluble, decay-preventing, adhesive cements and filling materials with the necessary physical and esthetic qualities.

The need for dental research is evident. It is startlingly significant that there are almost one-half as many dentists as there are physicians and surgeons for the rest of the body. This is just an "around-the-corner" way of saying that dental disease is nearly universal.

It appears that the incidence of dental disease is increasing and that dental defects are developing faster than dentists can correct them now or in the future. Since the incidence of dental defects seems to be pyramiding, it is neither economically feasible nor practically sound to try to cope with the situation merely by increasing the number of dentists. This indicates that only by the additional control and preventive measures that research may provide can dentistry hope to cope with dental disease.

21

Rats, Bats and Human Diseases

The recent occurrence of six cases of human plague—one of them fatal—in two of our western states is a timely reminder of the significance of the zoonoses to outbreaks of human disease. Zoonoses—singular, zoonosis—are diseases of animals secondarily transmitted to man. Two of the most deadly zoonoses and perhaps most widely feared, are the plague, and rabies.

Not since 1924, when there were 41 cases of plague with 36 deaths in Los Angeles, California, have so many cases been reported in one year in the United States. Throughout the world, the number of plague cases recorded for 1964—almost 1500—far exceeded the number recorded in 1963. Although an epidemic in Tanzania accounted for much of the increase, there were also more cases in Vietnam. Other countries seriously afflicted with plague in 1964 include Ecuador, Peru, Brazil, and India.

"Rats, Bats and Human Diseases" *The Sciences*, Vol. 5(7) (1965), pp. 24-28. Reprinted by permission of The New York Academy of Sciences.

WILD RODENT PLAGUE

The six Americans stricken all had what is known as sylvatic plague, because they acquired their infection from woodland or prairie animals. Prairie dogs, or rather their fleas, were deemed responsible for transmitting the disease to five of the victims. These American burrowing rodents are related to marmots and live in colonies on our western prairies.

In the woods and prairies of 14 of our western states, fleas convey the plague bacillus from one wild rodent to another. Bitten by one of these infected insects, a human being usually acquires plague in its bubonic form—so-called because of the swelling, or bubo, which appears. Sometimes the plague bacilli escape from the enlarged lymph node underlying the bubo and reach the lungs. In this way, bubonic plague is converted into pneumonic plague, a fulminating form which can be transmitted directly from one human being to another.

When large numbers of the bacilli are present in the blood—septicemic plague—fleas can spread the disease from man to man. The dark spots on the skin, due to hemorrhages, just beneath the surface, gave to this malady its dread-ridden name, the Black Death.

URBAN PLAGUE

Outbreaks of human plague acquired from wild rodents, occurring as they usually do in sparsely populated regions, do not readily grow to epidemic proportions. However, different species of rodents occupy overlapping territories.

The fleas of wild rodents dwelling in areas remote from human habitations can infect only a few domestic rats and wild rodents living in rural and suburban areas, or can initiate an epizootic outbreak. Their fleas, in turn, can transmit the disease to urban rats, and theirs, in turn, to urban dwellers of the species *Homo sapiens*.

It is possible for a single case of pneumonic plague in a crowded section of a city to initiate an epidemic of major importance. In the Los Angeles epidemic of 1924, 17 of the victims were members of a single family. Other victims included neighbors, nurses, an ambulance driver, and a priest who had visited at the home of one of the patients. During the 18 months following the epidemic, health officials carried out a "campaign of quarantine, disinfection, rat and flea eradication, and ratproofing buildings" at a total cost of about four million dollars (*Journal of the American Medical Association,* October 11, 1965).

A larger plague epidemic ravaged San Francisco during the world-wide outbreak which lasted from 1895 to 1905. In four years, 121 people were stricken with the disease and 118 lost their lives.

FURRED AND FEATHERED HOSTS

The great San Francisco earthquake and fire of 1906 which followed on the heels of the epidemic, drove the plague-harboring urban rats out of the city along with the exodus of people. Soon ground squirrels nearby became plague-ridden. The enzootic area gradually spread northward and eastward, and invasion of the plains states east of the Rocky Mountains began a quarter of a century ago.

Even if the enzootic were limited to ground squirrels, its eradication would be formidable. But the problem is one of far greater scope, for it is now known that plague occurs naturally not only in over 200 species of rodents, but also in rabbits and hares as well.

Wild-rodent plague is remarkably persistent in certain areas. Persistent plague foci are perpetuated, not by the highly susceptible hosts, but by hosts which are rather resistant to the disease. Animals which hibernate may acquire infection just before they turn in for their long winter's sleep. During this time, plague takes on a peculiar latent form and does not flare up until the animal has emerged from the dormant state. In this way, plague can persist over the winter in a hibernating species.

Other animals known to be instrumental in transmitting plague to human beings are camels, cats and shrews. By carrying infected rodents and their fleas from one place to another, birds of prey may spread the disease. These birds, although resistant to the disease, are sometimes infested with fowl fleas containing plague bacilli.

THE DEADLY FLEA

Rodents are not really transmitters of plague to man; they are, in a sense, its victims. The real vector is the flea. These tiny arthropods commute from host, where they partake of several blood meals daily, to the animal's nest or burrow, where eggs are laid and larvae develop. The proportionate time spent at each location varies with the species and climatic conditions.

Plague bacilli have been discovered in about 100 different species of fleas throughout the world. In the rat flea, *Xenopsylla cheopis,* and the ground squirrel flea, *Hoplopsyllus anomalus,* multiplication of the bacilli occurs in the mid-gut which becomes "blocked" with blood and bacilli. In desperation, the flea goes from host to host in rapid succession, regurgitating part of the deadly mass into each new puncture wound. "Blocked" fleas are believed to play a key role in enzootics, although ordinary fleas may keep epizootics going.

In rodent burrows, fleas escape the rigors of climatic change. And even though the normal inhabitants of such burrows are destroyed, the fleas in and around them can remain infective for many months. The flea is truly a reservoir of plague.

Although suspect for some 15 years, insectivorous bats of the United States are now known to be a natural reservoir for the rabies virus, and may harbor other zoonotic viruses as well. Perhaps it was not without good cause that, throughout recorded history, bats have been regarded as revolting creatures of ill omen.

Five people in the United States died of rabies following actual bites or other close contact with bats during the 1950's. By 1960, rabies virus had been found in naturally infected bats in 31 states. Twenty-four species of bat native to the United States have been incriminated.

For many years rabies enzootic in the vampire bats of South America has taken its toll in lives of both human beings and livestock. This is the first species of animal known to have the capacity to harbor rabies virus in its saliva in the absence of other signs of the disease. There is support for the view that this symptomless carrier state may also occur in other species of bats and in lemmings, ground squirrels, fowl and other animals as well.

This concept of inapparent rabies infections has spilled over into the field of human medicine. Human rabies was formerly believed to be consistently fatal. In recent years there is some suggestive evidence that "man may be subject to subclinical rabies or recover from an overt clinical infection." (See S. E. Sulkin, *Progress in Medical Virology,* Vol. IV, Hafner Publishing Co., New York, 1962.)

"RESERVOIRING MECHANISM"

The predilection of certain human viruses for the fat tissue of animals was a suggestion to investigators that the interscapular brown fat, so prominent in hibernators, might serve as a reservoir for the rabies virus in hibernating species of bats. Some bats hibernate in winter while others escape its rigors by migrating to warmer climates.

The hunch was a good one, for rabies virus was actually found in the brown fat of native American wild bats. In the laboratory, strains of rabies virus of bat origin often seemed to prefer the brown fat, multiplying in it at a much faster rate than in brain or salivary gland. In other words, some strains of bat virus are lipotropic rather than neurotropic.

There is still another "reservoiring mechanism." When bats hibernate the virus stops proliferating. Hibernation seems to put the virus into "cold storage." The virus, like the bat, is in a dormant state and does not actively proliferate until after arousal of the animal.

Rabies epizootics among wild animals are prone to occur where bat caves are numerous. Vampire bats are not hesitant about biting various animals and man. But no one has observed insectivorous bats in the act of biting foxes or other wild animals in nature or in the laboratory. The route of transmission of the infection from this kind of bat to wild animals was a riddle.

Then it was discovered that some species of bats excrete the virus either in urine or guano. It is also kown that the virus can enter the body through breaks in mucous membrane as well as through breaks in the skin. In fact, "men can contract rabies merely by walking into a cave inhabited by infected bats" (*Medical World News*, August 27, 1965).

Recently, animals in screened cages have been placed in bat caves and they, too, have contracted the disease. One fox became infected after only 10 hours' caged sojourn in a bat cave. So attempts are being made to gather the virus in caves directly from the air where it is believed to be suspended in an aerosol form.

22

Cancer

WHAT CANCER IS

1. *What is cancer?*

Cancer is a group of diseases in which there is uncontrolled and dis-

From *Answers to 101 Questions About Cancer* (1949, revised April, 1965). Reprinted by permission of the American Cancer Society, Inc.

ordered growth of abnormal cells which, if unchecked, will cause
death.

2. *How do cancer cells behave differently from normal cells?*

Normal cells grow in an orderly way to form the body or to repair
worn or damaged tissue. Cancer cells grow in a disordered way and
produce useless tissue. They deprive normal cells of nourishment, dis-
place and destroy them and, if unchecked, spread to other parts of
the body.

3. *Are all cancers alike?*

No. There are many different types of cancer, arising in different parts
of the body, growing at different rates and differing in their response
to treatment. Cancers are alike in that they grow and spread and, if
not treated, cause death.

4. *How does cancer spread in the body?*

Cancer cells grow into surrounding tissue or are carried by lymph and
blood vessels to colonize in other parts of the body. This spread is
called metastasis.

5. *How fast does cancer grow?*

There is not set rate of growth. Some types grow more in a few weeks
than others do in several years.

6. *Is Hodgkin's Disease a form of cancer?*

Yes. It is a disease in which there is uncontrolled growth of abnormal
cells arising from the lymphatic system.

7. *Is leukemia a form of cancer?*

Yes. It is a disease in which there is abnormal growth and development
of immature white blood cells.

8. *What is a tumor?*

A tumor is a swelling or lump. It may consist of an excess of normal
tissue or fluid, as in a cyst, or abnormal new growth.

9. *Are all new growths cancerous?*

No. New growths are of two kinds: 1) benign (seldom endangering
life or health) and 2) malignant or cancerous.

10. *What is the difference in behavior between a benign and a malignant
growth?*

A benign growth does not spread to other parts of the body as does a
malignant growth. A malignant growth (cancer), if unchecked, will
spread and cause death.

11. *Can one have cancer without noticeable symptoms?*

Yes. In their early stages some forms of cancer may give no warning to the patient, but may be detected by a physician in a routine health checkup.

12. *Do lower animals develop cancer?*

Yes. Cancer is found in all forms of life.

13. *Can the results of cancer studies on animals be of any help to human beings?*

Yes. Since cancer exists in all forms of life, scientists believe that better understanding of the disease in human beings will be furthered by animal studies. Important medical discoveries have been made or confirmed through animal experiments. Such research has saved countless human lives.

WHAT CAUSES CANCER

14. *What causes cancer?*

The basic causes are unknown, although certain conditions that may lead to cancer have been identified. Repeated injury to the cells is a factor. Such damage may result from overexposure to the sun, excessive radiation and contact with certain chemicals. Some forms of cancer in animals have been caused by viruses. Research to find the basic causes of human cancer is under way in many fields of science.

15. *Is cancer contagious?*

No. There is no recorded case of anyone having "caught" cancer from a patient, however closely they have been in contact.

16. *Does cigarette smoking cause lung cancer?*

Most physicians and scientists who have studied the problem believe that cigarette smoking is the principal cause of lung cancer. The U.S. Government's 1964 report on "Smoking and Health" affirms this belief. Lung cancer death rates are ten times as high among regular cigarette smokers as among those who never smoke. Among two pack-a-day smokers the rate is 20 times as high as among nonsmokers. The American Cancer Society's study of thousands of people showed that lung cancer rates increased directly with the number of cigarettes smoked; and those who stopped smoking had a lower death rate from lung cancer than those who continued to smoke. Cancer-causing substances are present in tobacco smoke. Autopsy studies of men who have died from a variety of diseases reveal that lung tissues were damaged in proportion to the number of cigarettes smoked. In addition, studies show that smokers have a higher incidence of cancers of the mouth, throat, and bladder than nonsmokers.

17. *Do filter tips prevent lung cancer?*

There is as yet no proof that filters reduce the lung cancer hazard in smoking. While the value of smoke filtration is undetermined, some filters do reduce the tar and nicotine content. Some scientists believe a decrease in intake of tar, either by filtration or reduced smoking, reduces the risk.

18. *How can one best protect himself against lung cancer?*

By avoiding known risks. Chief of these is avoiding cigarette smoking. The more cigarettes one smokes, the greater the risk of developing lung cancer. Nonsmokers have a low rate of lung cancer.

19. *Does air pollution bear any relation to lung cancer?*

The fumes, dusts and exhausts in the air have been under suspicion and are the subject of much research. The evidence suggests that air pollution is a relatively minor factor in the causation of lung cancer. The lung cancer death rate is somewhat higher in cities than in rural areas, but this difference is small when compared with the difference between cigarette smokers and nonsmokers.

20. *Does heavy drinking of alcoholic beverages increase the risk of cancer?*

Statistical studies show a greater incidence of mouth and throat cancer in heavy drinkers of alcoholic beverages who also smoke.

21. *Can cancer of soft tissue be caused by a bruise or injury?*

A single or an occasional injury to soft tissue, such as the breast, has not been known to cause cancer.

22. *Can eating any single food or combination of foods cause cancer?*

No. But a marked lack of some food elements (as in protein or certain vitamin deficiencies) may be related to certain types of cancer.

23. *Is cancer hereditary in human beings?*

No, but there may be inherited *susceptibility* toward certain types of cancer. Present knowledge on this point does *not* justify fear or a hopeless attitude. However, a record of cancer in one or both parents makes it especially important for their children to have annual health checkups and be alert to any danger signal that may mean cancer.

24. *Can repeated overexposure to the sun cause skin cancer?*

Yes. Cancer of the skin occurs often in fair-skinned persons who have been repeatedly exposed to the sun's rays over long periods of time. Dark-skinned people and those who tan rapidly and easily are less susceptible to the harmful effect of too much sun exposure.

25. *Can hemorrhoids turn cancerous?*
No. But hemorrhoids (piles) may bleed and occur in the presence of a bowel cancer. This may obscure the significance of the Danger Signal: rectal bleeding. Such bleeding, therefore, should always be brought to the attention of a physician.

26. *Can one's attitude toward cancer influence the course of the disease?*
Yes, in the sense that if one is unwilling to seek early medical attention or to accept proper medical treatment for cancer, the effects can be fatal.

27. *Does cancer usually develop in persons with poor general health?*
General health seems to have no relationship to the onset of cancer. This means that even people with no signs of ill health should get regular periodic medical checkups.

28. *Can radiation cause cancer?*
Yes, but not when radiation is properly used in the practice of medicine or dentistry. X-rays and other forms of radiation used by untrained people can be dangerous. Under such circumstances overexposure to x-rays or to by-products of atomic energy may contribute to the development of cancer, especially leukemia.

29. *Is there a connection between atomic bomb explosions and cancer?*
Some of the radioactive material, such as strontium 90 resulting from an atomic bomb explosion, settles to the earth (fallout) and may eventually get into the body. If a large enough quantity of such material is present over many years, cancer of the bones and/or blood-forming tissue may occur.

30. *Is cancer a disease of civilization?*
No. Cancer is found in all cultures and areas of the world. No color or ethnic group is free of cancer. However, there are different rates and susceptibilities to various forms of cancer throughout the world.

HOW CANCER IS DETECTED

31. *Can a person recognize cancer in himself without seeing a physician?*
No. Only a physician is trained to diagnose and distinguish cancer from other diseases.

32. *Can a thorough examination to detect cancer be performed in a physician's office?*

Yes, most cancers can be detected in the physician's office. The physician knows when and how to arrange for further special examinations, if needed, and how to interpret the results of such examinations.

33. *Is a cancer specialist the only physician able to detect cancer in a health checkup?*

No. Every practicing physician has basic training in cancer detection and is supplied with latest information in medical journals and materials provided through medical societies and the American Cancer Society.

34. *What is a health checkup?*

It consists of a health interview followed by a thorough physical examination. Usually, the body surface is inspected, followed by examination of various organs or areas such as the heart, blood vessels, lungs, mouth, nose, ears, eyes, throat, abdomen, rectum, sex organs and breasts. The blood, urine, uterine cells, or other body fluids may be examined or tested as necessary. Other examinations deemed necessary by the physician, such as proctosigmoidoscopic examination or x-rays of parts of the body, may also be performed.

35. *What is a proctosigmoidoscopic examination?*

It is a visual inspection of the lining of the rectum and lower bowel with a lighted tube.

36. *Why is a proctosigmoidoscopic examination important?*

Because 70 per cent of cancers of the colon and rectum can be discovered in this way. X-ray is not usually helpful in discovering early cancer in this area.

37. *How long is it safe to wait after signs of possible cancer have appeared before consulting a physician?*

Waiting is unsafe. Any delay may be dangerous.

38. *How can a physician tell if a growth is cancer?*

Through a complete case history and physical examination, in conjunction with a biopsy.

39. *What is a biopsy?*

A biopsy is the taking of a tiny sample of tissue which is then examined under the microscope by a pathologist—a physician who specializes in such examinations. The biopsy provides reliable proof of a diagnosis.

40. *Does blood in bowel movements indicate cancer?*

Not necessarily. There are other possible causes for blood to appear in bowel movements, but cancer is the most important one. This is a significant Danger Signal and a physician should be consulted promptly.

41. *Does blood in the urine indicate cancer?*

Not necessarily, but only a physician can diagnose the cause of blood in the urine.

42. *Does a lump under the arm or elsewhere mean cancer?*

Not necessarily, but such lumps should be promptly examined by a physician.

43. *Is pain an early warning signal?*

No. It is usually a *late* symptom. If any danger signal is present one should not wait for pain before seeing a physician.

44. *If a person has been cured of cancer, can he develop another cancer? In the same place? In some other part of the body?*

Yes, to all three questions. Therefore, regardless of the past medical history, including the cure of a previous cancer, such a person should be examined at regular intervals for the rest of his life, just as should those who have never had cancer.

HOW CANCER IS TREATED

45. *Are many cancers being cured?*

Cancer can be cured and is being cured every day by surgery and/or radiation. More than 1,200,000 Americans are alive today who once had cancer and are cured, providing living proof of the effectiveness of early detection and proper medical treatment.

46. *How should cancer be treated?*

It should be treated by competent physicians. Surgery and/or radiation are necessary to obtain cures. Radiation is produced by x-ray machines, radium, radioactive materials, the cobalt^{60} unit, the betatron and others. Hormones and chemical agents may also be used in treating some types of cancer. Hormones and drugs themselves do not cure cancer, but they are often effective aids to surgery and radiation in relieving pain and prolonging life, sometimes for very long periods. Cancer should never be treated with so-called "home remedies" or "secret cures."

47. *Can cancer be diagnosed and treated effectively in every hospital?*

No, not in every hospital. For the proper management of cancer, the hospital must have an operating room, access to a laboratory for microscopic diagnosis of tissue, and x-ray equipment suitable for diagnosis and treatment. It must be staffed by physicians adequately trained to make effective use of these facilities. Physicians know which hospitals qualify in these respects.

48. *Are x-ray treatments effective against all kinds of cancer?*

No. Treatment results depend on the type and location of a growth. Some cancers are treated with x-rays or radium and some by surgery, and others with both x-ray and surgery.

49. *What is a radioactive isotope?*

An isotope is a chemical "brother" of any particular element, such as cobalt, iron, iodine, carbon, gold, etc. A radioactive isotope is one that gives off rays of energy like x-rays, some of which are able to destroy cancer cells.

50. *Can radioactive isotopes cure cancer?*

Yes, but only when used locally like x-rays, as in the cobalt[60] unit.

51. *Can hormones cure cancer?*

No, but treatment with certain hormones may prolong life and lessen pain in some patients, such as those with advanced breast cancer or prostate cancer.

52. *What is a hormone?*

A chemical substance produced by glands which affects activities of other organs. Some hormones can also be manufactured artificially.

53. *Is progress being made in controlling pain caused by some advanced cancers?*

Yes. Powerful radiation techniques, radioactive isotopes, certain surgical procedures, new sedatives and pain-killing drugs, and selected hormones can keep pain under control in many patients.

54. *Is cancer curable only in the early stages?*

No, but the chances of cure are best by far in the early stages. Some cures have been effected in cancer of long duration and advanced stage. The chances of a cure depend on the kind of treatment, and the type and duration of the cancer.

55. *Is there any chemical that destroys cancerous tissue without harming normal tissues?*

Many chemicals will destroy cancerous tissue but, unfortunately, most of these also destroy normal cells. Numbers of chemicals have been found that are sufficiently more destructive of cancer than of healthy tissues to be of therapeutic value in treating cancer. These chemicals lessen suffering and prolong life, sometimes for years. They are not secret drugs and are available to all physicians and hospitals. There is as yet no chemical which, administered internally, will regularly cure human cancer.

56. *How long will an untreated cancer patient live?*

This will differ with each individual and with the location and type of cancer. Some persons die of untreated cancer after only a few months, others have been known to live for years.

57. *If cure is not possible, can the spread of a cancer be stopped or slowed down for a time?*

Yes. Many cancers which are in an incurable stage may be controlled for months or years by radiation, surgery, hormones, or chemical agents.

58. *What progress is being made in cancer research?*

Important advances are being made in all fields of cancer research. Experimental work in chemical treatment is especially promising. Certain drugs discovered in recent years have already proved useful in slowing down cancer growths for long periods. Drugs are being sought which will destroy cancer and also prevent it from starting. Important research is being done in immunology in an attempt to make vaccination against cancer possible, and to find better methods of cancer detection.

59. *Is there hope of finding cures for all cancers?*

Yes. This and prevention are the big goals of cancer research. Scientists are more hopeful now than ever before that they will eventually reach their goal.

CANCER IN MEN

60. *Do more men than women die of cancer?*

Yes. Since 1949 more men than women have died of cancer.

61. *Why is the cancer death rate increasing among men and not among women?*

Mainly because of the rapidly rising death toll from lung cancer in men. Also, more women are now being saved by early detection and effective treatment for two reasons: 1) they consult physicians more regularly and they pay more attention to Danger Signals, and 2) cancer strikes women in sites such as the womb and breast where the disease is more accessible for diagnosis and treatment.

62. *Is lung cancer a special danger for men?*

It is for men who smoke or who have been steady smokers of cigarettes. Lung cancer is increasing faster than all other forms of cancer. It is more prevalent in men than in women but the rate is increasing in women who smoke cigarettes or who have smoked them over a period of several years.

63. *What are the more common cancers in men?*

Cancer of the digestive organs and cancer of the lung account for more than half of all cancers in men. Cancer of the prostate is one of the most common forms of cancer in men over 60 years of age.

CANCER IN WOMEN

64. *What are the more common forms of cancer in women?*

Cancer of the reproductive organs and cancer of the breast account for almost half of all cancers in women. Other cancers which occur frequently in women are: cancer of the intestines, stomach, rectum, and skin.

65. *What can every woman do about breast cancer?*

Every woman should have her breasts examined by a physician as part of her annual health checkup. She should learn from him the proper technique for examining her own breasts once a month and should continue this practice for life. How to do this is explained in a film, "Breast Self-Examination," and a folder, both of which may be obtained from your local Unit or Division of the American Cancer Society.

66. *Are most breast lumps cancerous?*

Fortunately, most breast lumps are not cancer, but only a physician can tell and should be consulted immediately for all lumps. If a biopsy is performed, microscopic tests will show whether the lump is malignant or benign.

67. *Is there danger in a patient's watching a lump in the breast "to see what happens"?*

Yes. Time is an important factor in the control of cancer. Cancer of the breast is the commonest cancer in women and any delay in treatment may be dangerous. Waiting "to see what happens" may result in curable cancer becoming incurable. Only a physician can decide how and when a lump should be treated.

68. *Is there any evidence that a tight-fitting brassiere causes cancer?*
No.

69. *Can cancer result from a baby's suckling or by bruising the breasts?*
There is no evidence that suckling or bruising of the breasts will cause cancer.

70. *What precautions should be taken against cancer of the uterus (womb)?*
All injuries from childbirth should be corrected. All adult women should have a pelvic examination at least once each year. A simple, painless cell examination which many physicians include in the pelvic examination is one of the best aids in the early detection of uterine cancer. All unusual vaginal discharge should be treated. Irregular vaginal bleeding before the change of life, and vaginal bleeding thereafter, call for an immediate examination by a physician.

71. *What is the cell examination for uterine cancer?*
Fluid is removed from the vagina painlessly by the physician. This can readily be done in his office. Examination of this fluid under the microscope will reveal whether cancer cells are present even before there are symptoms of cancer. This is often called the "Pap" smear test, after its originator, Dr. George N. Papanicolaou. The cell examination should be included in the woman's annual health examination. Proof of cancer, suspected from a cell examination, requires a biopsy.

72. *Is a woman who has had a hysterectomy free from the risk of cancer of the uterus?*
If the woman has had a total hysterectomy, the procedure in which the entire uterus (womb) and cervix (neck of the womb) are removed, she is, of course, free of the possibility of cancer in these sites. If she has had a partial hysterectomy, the procedure in which the cervix is not removed, there is still a real risk of cancer of the cervix. Similarly, the remaining ovaries may become the site of cancer in any woman.

CANCER IN CHILDREN

73. *Does cancer occur in children?*
Yes. No age group is free of cancer and certain forms, notably leuke-

mia, are found in young children. Cancer takes the lives of more children between the ages of one and fourteen than any other disease.

74. *Once started, does cancer develop more rapidly in children than in adults?*

Probably not. The rate of cancer growth at any age depends upon the type of cancer and the patient's natural resistance.

75. *How do the chances of cure of cancer in children compare with that in adults?*

The cure rate of cancer has little relation to age. It depends upon the type of cancer, the extent of its growth at the time it is detected, the effectiveness of the treatment and the patient's natural resistance.

CANCER'S VITAL STATISTICS

76. *Where does cancer stand compared with other diseases as a cause of death?*

Cancer is second only to heart disease as a cause of death. One of every six deaths in the United States is caused by cancer.

77. *Is cancer increasing?*

The number of recorded cancer deaths each year has increased from 41,000 in 1900 to about 284,000 in 1963. This bears a direct relationship to the increase in the total population and the increase in the number of people over the age of 45—the age when the cancer death rate rises sharply. Lung cancer, which was a rare disease in 1900, has shown the most notable increase of all types of cancer.

78. *Does cancer attack young people as often as it does older people?*

No. The incidence of cancer increases with age. However, cancer is a serious problem at all ages. For example, in the U.S., about 22,500 persons between the ages of 15 and 44 died of cancer in 1963.

79. *Has the cure rate of cancer been improved in the past ten years?*

Yes. One of every three patients with cancer is being cured today. This is a great improvement over the record of ten years ago when only one in four cases was being cured.

80. *How many Americans could be saved from cancer with present medical knowledge and techniques?*

Today American Cancer Society figures indicate that at least 90,000 more Americans could be saved each year if they would go to their doctors in time for early diagnosis and effective treatment. With present knowledge the cure rate could be raised from one-in-three to one-in-two.

81. *Are people one skin color or ethnic group more prone to certain types of cancer?*

Statistics are not entirely conclusive on this point. Present figures show that white persons do have a larger percentage of skin cancers and cancer of the breast than Negroes. Cancer of the prostate, stomach and uterus are reported more frequently among Negroes than among white-skinned people. Jewish women seldom have cancer of the cervix and Jewish men rarely have cancer of the penis. Among the Bantus of South Africa, cancer of the liver is more common than among white people. Cancer of the nasopharynx is more common among Chinese men than among white men. Whether all these differences are inborn or due to the way of living is not known.

82. *Do certain types of cancer occur more frequently in certain geographical areas?*

Yes. In parts of India, Malaya and the Dutch East Indies, cancer of the inner surface of the cheek is very common, whereas it is comparatively rare elsewhere. Cancer of the bladder is more prevalent in Europe than it is in the U.S. In Texas and Arizona, skin cancer is about three times more frequent than in Maine and Vermont. Breast cancer is the most common form of cancer among white women in England and the United States whereas is it comparatively rare in Japan. Men in Denmark are more than twice as likely to get cancer of the stomach as are men in New York State.

23

Your Heart

The healthy heart is a very strong organ. It is only about the size of a large fist, but most of its bulk is muscle. Its one job is to pump into the arteries the blood returned to it by the veins. All the cells in the body de-

From *Your Heart* (revised October, 1965). Courtesy of the Metropolitan Life Insurance Company.

pend upon the rapidly circulating blood stream for oxygen and nourishment and for removal of wastes.

Your blood makes up only about 8 per cent of your body weight. But to keep that blood in circulation through miles of blood vessels during an ordinary day of work, play, and rest, the healthy heart pumps many, many hundreds of gallons of blood at an average daily rate of 70 to 80 strokes a minute. Its normal pumping action is a continuous series of regular contractions and relaxations—beat-rest, beat-rest, beat-rest.

Your heart normally rests twice as much as it works. But during periods of strenuous physical activity or emotional strain, it may beat twice as fast as usual and pump out twice as much blood. The faster the heart beats, the harder it works, and the less time it has to rest. However, most hearts can endure great physical exertion without difficulty. Strenuous physical exercise and work do not primarily cause heart disease, although they may aggravate difficulties already present.

It's a fact that heart disease is widespread in this country. More than 10 million Americans of all ages have some form of cardiovascular (heart and blood vessel) ailment. More than half of all deaths each year are due to heart and circulatory diseases. About 35 per cent of these occur among people 45 to 64 years of age.

But while it is true that heart disease affects many people in middle and later life, it is also true that more people are living longer than ever before. Fewer lives are cut short by infectious diseases of childhood and youth which medical science now prevents and controls. Thanks to modern knowledge and more accurate methods of diagnosing heart and circulatory disturbances, some ailments once incorrectly attributed to other causes are now properly classified as heart disease. This accounts, in part, for the statistics.

Great strides have been made in research, diagnosis, treatment and control of heart disease. Progress has made it possible for thousands of people to survive and recover from heart and blood vessel ailments. Brilliant surgical techniques for correcting heart defects have been developed in recent years. Scientists foresee even greater advances in the near future. Right now:

—Most people who have heart attacks recover.

—High blood pressure (hypertension) can be controlled.

—Recurrent attacks of rheumatic fever, which damage the heart, can be prevented.

—Many heart defects can be repaired.

—Medical science can do a great deal for people with circulatory disorders.

Today's scientific knowledge is being applied to help people with heart disease live and work happily and productively. In addition, research has brought to light knowledge which can help people reduce the risk of acquiring heart ailments. So, although heart disease has by no means been conquered, there is every reason for optimism.

Sometimes the term "heart disease" is confused with "heart attack." But they are not the same. Heart disease includes many different conditions and disorders affecting the heart and the circulatory system. The word *cardiovascular,* which means heart and blood vessel, is therefore more apt and more descriptive. Here, we describe several common cardiovascular ailments:

ATHEROSCLEROSIS

This is the most important form of "hardening of the arteries." It is a complex process which is believed to begin when the body's mechanism for handling certain fatty particles such as cholesterol—either eaten or developed within the body—breaks down. These fatty substances start to collect in the inner lining of the walls of the arteries. As more and more particles are deposited in the arterial wall, the channel through which the blood flows gradually narrows.

Atherosclerosis may begin to develop at a relatively early age. People may have the condition in a mild form without noticeable difficulty, throughout a long life. When symptoms do occur, they usually show up at middle age or later.

Intensive scientific studies go on all the time to find ways to prevent and cure atherosclerosis. Among the factors being explored are diet, smoking, exercise, stress, hormones and heredity. There is growing evidence that diet is an important factor contributing to heart attack risk. The substitution, whenever possible, of vegetable and fish oils for animal fats is now encouraged by many authorities as a precautionary measure. This substitution tends to lower the level of cholesterol in the blood. It is known that populations with lower levels of cholesterol and other fatty substances in the blood have a lower incidence of coronary heart disease than those with higher levels. Any special, fat-controlled diet however should be prescribed by a physician.

CORONARY ARTERY DISEASE

When you hear that someone has "heart trouble," it often means coronary artery disease. Today this condition is being seen more frequently than it once was among young and middle-aged adults. However, it occurs most often among people between the ages of 40 and 60, and affects more men than women.

The coronary arteries supply the heart muscle itself with blood. The chief cause of coronary artery disease is thickening of the coronary arteries (coronary atherosclerosis). When these arteries become narrowed, due to the process of atherosclerosis, the heart muscle receives a smaller amount of blood. This sometimes results in what is known as coronary insufficiency —which means that the heart muscle itself is less efficient due to the lack of proper nourishment.

Many people are able to live quite comfortably with coronary artery disease if they are careful not to place too great a strain on their hearts.

HIGH BLOOD PRESSURE

In medical language, this is hypertension—a condition which affects about 5 million Americans. The popular notion that high blood pressure is caused by aging is not based on fact. There is no reason for anyone to feel that because he is getting along in years, he must be developing high blood pressure.

To understand high blood pressure, it is first necessary to know the meaning of "blood pressure." Everyone has "blood pressure," and everyone's pressure normally goes up and down. Blood pressure is simply the pressure of the blood against the walls of the arteries. It is highest during systole—the period when the heart pumps a fresh supply of blood into the elastic-walled arteries which stretch to accommodate it. It is lowest during diastole—the period when the heart pauses between beats to fill with blood. *Diastolic* pressure is more significant than *systolic* pressure. That is because diastolic pressure represents the basic pressure exerted on the arterial walls without the additional pressure due to the contraction of the heart.

The nervous system influences blood pressure. For example, it is natural for pressure to go up when a person is excited. The smallest branches of the arteries (arterioles) are controlled by nerves which cause them to constrict when you are keyed up with strong feelings such as joy, fear, or anger. When the arterioles tighten up in this way; the resistance to the flow of blood is greater, and this increases pressure in the arteries. When excitement subsides, the arterioles dilate, opening wider, and the pressure goes down.

When a person has high blood pressure, the arterioles remain in a more or less constantly constricted state. Other influences, besides the functioning of the nervous system, cause this constriction. It is generally accepted by physicians that certain chemical substances set free into the blood stream from various glands and organs also cause the arterioles to constrict. Why this happens in some people and not in others, what the relationship is between these substances and the influence of the nervous system, are still questions which scientists are exploring.

Sometimes high blood pressure occurs with other diseases, such as kidney trouble or disturbances of the endocrine glands. In these cases, when the disease is cured, usually the hypertension is, too. When the cause is unknown, as it is in the majority of cases, the condition is called essential hypertension. It seems to run in families and occur more often among people who are overweight. Nervous tension apparently aggravates the condition in some people.

HYPERTENSION AND THE HEART

How does hypertension affect the heart? First of all, the heart must work harder, although not necessarily more rapidly, to pump blood through the arteries. Pressure in the arteries must increase to keep the blood flowing through the constricted arterioles at nearly the normal rate. As a result of this continual, excessive work over a long period of time, the heart muscle enlarges. This is an important step in the development of hypertensive heart disease. Often, but not always, the walls of the arteries become scarred, thickened, and lose their elasticity—that is, they become atherosclerotic.

What are the symptoms of hypertension? In some cases, there are none. In others, there may be headaches, dizziness, fatigue. Any or all of these symptoms do not definitely indicate high blood pressure, but they do mean that something is wrong and a medical checkup is in order.

Sometimes high blood pressure clears up by itself. Even if it does not, modern medicine can do a great deal to keep it under control. Very often high blood pressure can be lowered to a safe level by new and effective drugs, by changes in diet and living habits. Occasionally, surgery corrects the condition. The important thing in managing hypertension is to follow the physician's advice faithfully.

LOW BLOOD PRESSURE

Many healthy people have this condition. "Low-normal" blood pressure, as it is sometimes called, actually involves less work for the heart and blood vessels to keep the blood in normal circulation. Although rarely associated with serious illness, low blood pressure is sometimes a symptom of disease. A physician can tell if it is significant.

HEART ATTACK

This term usually means the sudden closing (occlusion) of a coronary artery by a blood clot (thrombus). Although it happens suddenly, this is often the result of a gradual process of atherosclerosis in the coronary arteries (see page 158). When the narrowed artery becomes clogged, a portion of the heart is deprived of its blood supply. This condition usually causes a severely painful feeling of pressure in the chest, often accompanied by sweating, weakness, shortness of breath, and possibly loss of consciousness. Sometimes there is nausea and vomiting. This, plus the pain, may be mistaken for acute indigestion. Only a physician can tell the difference, and he should be called at once when these symptoms occur.

The doctor may prescribe various treatments, but most of the healing is done by the body itself. When a coronary artery closes, other arteries nearby increase in size and new branches develop to deliver blood to the part of the heart that needs it. This is called collateral circulation. At the same time, scar tissue begins to form in the damaged part of the heart.

Time required for recovery depends on the extent of the damage, rate of healing, and whether or not there are complications. Treatment is aimed at giving the heart a chance to heal. In some cases, the physician prescribes anticoagulant drugs to prevent formation of new blood clots.

Heart attacks are more common among men than women. Most patients recover from a first attack. In fact, healing is usually so successful that most people can return to work and resume usual activities after recovery. Of course, there may have to be some changes made in living habits. If so, the physician, taking into consideration the patient's particular problems and circumstances, will determine what changes are indicated.

Medical terms for heart attack are: coronary thrombosis, coronary occlusion, myocardial infarction.

ANGINA PECTORIS

This means cardiac pain. Even when there has been no thrombosis, pain may be experienced if the coronary arteries are diseased. It may be a sensation of pressure in the chest or it can be a severe pressing or strangling pain under the breast bone and radiating down the arm. Such discomfort is usually a brief warning that the blood supply to a part of the heart muscle is insufficient at the moment. Exertion, excitement, or digesting of a heavy meal may produce the pain in a susceptible person. Anyone who experiences it should see a doctor, who will give medication that will ordinarily relieve the pain almost at once. The physician will also instruct the patient in how to regulate his life and use medication to prevent or lessen the severity of such attacks.

STROKE

This circulatory disorder affects many people, but not only the aged, as is commonly believed. What is a stroke? If the blood supply to part of the brain is reduced or completely blocked, a stroke occurs. Nerve cells, in that part of the brain deprived of blood, cannot function. As a result, part of the body which these nerve cells control also cannot function normally. When this happens, a person may become partially paralyzed, and may have difficulty speaking.

Stroke is commonly caused by a blood clot (thrombus) which forms in an artery narrowed by atherosclerosis. Sometimes it is caused by a clot which is formed elsewhere in the body and is carried to the brain by the blood stream. This is called an *embolus*. Another cause of stroke is hemorrhage, or bleeding from an artery in the brain.

Some people recover completely. Others may require a long time to make even a partial recovery. It depends upon the extent and type of damage. Immediate physiotherapy is highly important in helping a patient to regain lost or impaired muscular control—and prompt attention should be given to the prescribed exercises and massages, as well as positioning in bed. The sooner rehabilitation can begin, the more effective it is. Surgery has been successful in treating some types of stroke—for example, those caused by blockage of the arteries in the neck. To prevent a possible recurrence, physicians can prescribe anticoagulant drugs for some patients, depending on the type of stroke.

RHEUMATIC HEART TROUBLE

Heart trouble can result from repeated attacks of rheumatic fever, although, today, this can usually be prevented. Rheumatic fever is not so prevalent as it once was, but it still occurs among some children and young adults. It strikes most often between the ages of 5 and 15. Grownups may have heart disease which stems from childhood attacks of rheumatic fever.

Rheumatic fever can be precipitated by a streptococcus infection such as "strep" sore throat (sore throat accompanied by fever), "strep" ear infection, or scarlet fever. It attacks the connective tissues of the body, and may injure the covering and lining of the heart, the heart muscle, and the valves. Signs and symptoms which may indicate rheumatic fever are persistent, slight fever; pain in the joints and muscles; poor appetite; failure to gain weight; unexplained fatigue; repeated nosebleeds.

Remember that rheumatic fever itself is not contagious. Nobody can contract it by being near a person who has it. But "strep" infections *are* contagious. Today, if a youngster contracts a streptococcal infection, adequate treatment usually prevents subsequent development of rheumatic fever. Prompt medical treatment of sore throats and other infections protects against rheumatic fever.

A first bout with the disease may not harm the heart. Many patients recover without any damage whatsoever. But once a person has had rheumatic fever, he is susceptible to recurrent attacks. To prevent this, the physician prescribes regular doses of sulfa drugs or antibiotics over a long period of time. This preventive medication is usually successful.

CONGENITAL DEFECTS

Every year, about 30- to 40-thousand babies are born with defective hearts. An inborn or congenital heart defect means that the heart, or a blood vessel near the heart, failed to develop normally during the prenatal period of growth. What causes most of these malformations is not yet known, although researchers are delving into the question.

Inborn heart defects are sometimes mild and sometimes serious. If the trouble is mild, surgery may never be necessary, and the person may lead a normal life. More serious defects can often be helped by surgery, and each year research paves the way for more defective hearts to be helped by surgery. Even when this is not possible, good medical care is beneficial.

When surgery is used, it may correct the defect completely or partially so that circulation becomes normal or at least nearly normal. Youngsters with congenital heart defects need close medical supervision during their growing years so as to avoid any infections which might cause difficulties. Standard immunizations are a "must."

BACTERIAL ENDOCARDITIS

This is an infection of the heart lining (endocardium) usually caused by bacteria of the streptococcus family. People with congenital heart defects or rheumatic heart disease are the most susceptible. Today this disease can usually be treated successfully. Modern medicine, using antibiotics, is able to cure most cases. To prevent the possibility of bacterial endocarditis, doctors prescribe antibiotics before performing certain surgical procedures—even tooth extractions—which might allow the infection to gain a foothold in a susceptible person.

24

Walter Reed and the Conquest of Yellow Fever

Grace T. Hallock
Claire E. Turner
John J. Lenz, assistant

The story you are about to read is one of the great adventure stories of medical science. Before the mystery of yellow fever was finally solved, courageous American soldiers had braved hardships and danger; a gallant young scientist had given his life; and his comrades in the great adventure had gone on to complete without him one of the most brilliant scientific achievements in the annals of medical history. The leader of the little band of scientists and volunteers who solved the mystery of yellow fever was Walter Reed, and with him the story begins.

In 1898 the Spanish-American war broke out. Sanitary conditions in the army camps were deplorable, and it was not long before epidemics of typhoid fever appeared among the volunteer troops. Major Reed and two distinguished civilian physicians were appointed to a commission to study the origin of these epidemics and how to stop them. The year-long painstaking investigation made by this commission, of which Major Reed was chairman, added greatly to the store of scientific knowledge needed to fight this dangerous disease.

Grace T. Hallock and Clair E. Turner, assisted by John J. Lenz, *Walter Reed and the Conquest of Yellow Fever* (1958). Courtesy of Metropolitan Life Insurance Company.

The work of the typhoid-fever commission was no sooner completed than another menace to the health of American soldiers appeared in Cuba where the war was being fought. This menace was yellow fever—long a challenge to medical research. Before telling the story of how Walter Reed and his co-workers met this challenge, let's pause to review its history so that we shall have a better understanding of what their work has meant both to our country and to the world.

YELLOW FEVER ON THE MARCH

Yellow fever is an acute infectious disease of the tropics and sub-tropics, where its nickname is yellow jack. It took its name from the lemon-yellow skin tint seen in victims with severe cases. In the worst epidemics of yellow fever as many as 80 out of every 100 persons who caught it died. Those who survived were usually immune for life.

The earliest known occurrence of yellow fever in the Western hemisphere was in Central America in 1596. The disease spread rapidly and made large areas of the tropical Americas almost uninhabitable for the white man. It invaded New York for the first time in 1668, Boston in 1691, and Philadelphia in 1695. In the 200 years from 1705 to 1905 more than 160 epidemics of yellow fever occurred in the United States. In New Orleans, Philadelphia, Memphis, Charleston, Norfolk, Galveston, New York, Baltimore, and many other cities, it took a heavy toll of life while doctors looked on, helpless.

But mere dates and statistics do not tell the full story of the terror of yellow fever. That can be made clear by looking at the experience of just one city during a yellow-fever invasion.

In 1793, six years after the adoption of the Constitution of the United States, yellow fever appeared on a street near the busy wharves of Philadelphia. As it spread, fear gripped the people and all the streets and roads leading from Philadelphia were crowded with families fleeing to the country for safety. So many doctors were sick or had died of yellow fever that "at one time there were only three physicians who were able to visit patients, and at this time there were probably not less than 6,000 persons ill with the fever." Dr. Benjamin Rush, famous in yellow-fever history and then a physician in Philadelphia, relates that a cheerful contenance was scarcely to be seen in the city for six weeks. About to enter a patient's house he met a 2-year-old child on the street who looked up at him and smiled. "I was strangely affected by this sight," Dr. Rush tells us. "Few persons were met in the streets except those who were in quest of a physician, a nurse, or the men who buried the dead. The hearse alone kept up the remembrance of the noise of carriages or carts in the street."

EARLY CLUES

What causes yellow fever? How is it spread? For more than 200 years learned men had searched for the answers to these questions. Probably most of you know these answers. The cause of yellow fever is a specific virus, that is, a germ so small that it can pass through the finest filters. This virus is carried from one person to another by the bites of female *Aëdes aegypti* mosquitoes. From what you know now, it is easy to see how closely the mosquito's habits tally with the spread of yellow fever. See if you can tell why the following clues taken from old accounts of yellow fever might have put early investigators on the right track if they had even dreamed that a greatly feared and often deadly disease might be carried by so lowly a creature as a mosquito.

1. Epidemics of yellow fever commonly started in the low wet regions or around the docks of cities near the sea coast.

2. In the high and dry parts of a city the disease was not contagious. In many epidemics people from low-lying sections fled to the higher part of the city or to the country districts. Although many of these people came down with yellow fever after they had left their homes, the disease did not spread to other people in the new neighborhood. This observation made many intelligent investigators think that the disease must be present in the air of certain districts and not in others.

3. Some observers noticed, also, that whenever the wind blew strongly in a certain direction, yellow fever broke out in its path. When the air was still, the infection was limited to the houses of an already infected neighborhood.

4. Yellow fever flourished when the weather was hot, but it was stamped out by frost. This observation made many investigators believe that "heat was a very common exciting cause of the disorder."

If you have interpreted these clues correctly, you know why they point to the mosquito as the guilty party in the spread of yellow fever. Mosquitoes breed in still water. Mosquitoes travel through the air. Mosquitoes are blown in the direction of the prevailing wind. Mosquitoes are active in hot weather and are killed by frost.

THE MOSQUITO ACCUSED

The first suggestion that both yellow fever and malaria are carried by insects came from Dr. Josiah C. Nott, of Mobile, Ala., in 1848. But to Dr. Carlos J. Finlay, of Havana, Cuba, belongs the full credit for first advancing the theory that *mosquitoes* are the carriers of yellow fever. He outlined this theory in a paper read before the Royal Academy of Havana on August 11, 1881.

Dr. Finlay did more than suggest that mosquitoes in general were the logical suspects. He accused the exact species of mosquito—now known as *Aëdes aegypti*. For 19 years—from 1881 to 1900—Dr. Finlay labored diligently to gather evidence in support of his theory.

Unfortunately he failed to plan and carry out convincing experiments and made some understandable mistakes in interpreting his findings. As a result, not a single doctor or research scientist, except his assistant, believed Dr. Finlay. Up to 1900 his theory was treated with ridicule and neglect.

In the year 1900 the Spanish-American war had ended, but Cuba was still under American military control, with General Leonard Wood as Military Governor. Yellow fever had become epidemic in Havana and in the town of Quemados, 6 miles away. Near Quemados was Columbia Barracks where American troops were stationed. Already a number of American soldiers in the Cuban army of occupation had caught yellow fever and some had died. No wonder that Dr. George Miller Sternberg, Surgeon General of the Army, and his medical officers were worried!

For many years, Dr. Sternberg had been one of the world's leading authorities on yellow fever. In Havana, in Brazil, in Mexico he had searched laboriously and unsuccessfully for its cause in the bodies of yellow-fever patients. He alone was not to solve the mystery of yellow fever, but this accomplishment was to be the crowning event of his long and brilliant administration.

In May 1900 General Sternberg appointed a Board of four medical officers to investigate acute infectious diseases, and especially yellow fever on the island of Cuba. The four doctors were Major Walter Reed, the leader, and acting assistant surgeons James Carroll, Jesse W. Lazear, and Aristides Agramonte. All four were highly skilled bacteriologists, thoroughly familiar with the mysterious disease which they were about to challenge with the courage, self-sacrifice, and scientific accuracy that characterized their work.

Dr. Lazear and Dr. Agramonte were already in Cuba making studies related to yellow fever at the time they were appointed to the Board. Major Reed and Dr. Carroll joined them at Columbia Barracks, Quemados, Cuba, on June 25. And so the great adventure began.

THE EARLY STEPS

At first the Board gave its entire time to a thorough search for the causative agent—the germ—of yellow fever. Several investigators, including Sternberg and Finlay, had found bacteria of one kind or another in the bodies of yellow-fever patients. Then in 1897 an Italian scientist, Dr. Giuseppe Sanarelli, claimed that he had found the specific cause of yellow fever in the form of a certain bacillus.

As a yellow-fever epidemic was raging in Quemados, the Board was able to obtain plenty of material for study. After examining cultures made from the blood of 18 living patients and from the tissues of 11 patients who had died, the Board stated that in not a single one had they found Sanarelli's bacillus or any other bacteria whatever that might be the cause of yellow fever.

As no germ could be found, Walter Reed and his co-workers decided to abandon their search for the cause of yellow fever for the time being and to go on to the next big question—how is yellow fever spread?

At that time almost everyone thought that yellow fever was carried by fomites—that is, by the articles of clothing, bedding, and other materials that had been contaminated by the excretions of yellow-fever patients. Careful reading of the reports of yellow-fever epidemics and his own personal observations had convinced Walter Reed that fomites had little, if anything, to do with the spread of yellow fever. On the other hand, he was greatly impressed by the peculiar way in which the infection jumped from one house to another in Quemados even when no contact existed between any persons or with any contaminated articles (fomites).

Another thing that especially impressed him and Dr. Lazear was the length of time it took to change a noninfected house into an infected one. In the report of a yellow-fever epidemic made in 1898, Surgeon Henry R. Carter of the Marine Hospital Service had shown that the first case of yellow fever in each one of 16 widely separated houses was not followed by new cases for about two weeks or more. Where were the germs responsible for the first case before they got around to claiming new victims?

Dr. Ronald Ross, an English army surgeon, had recently found the parasites of malaria in the stomach wall of *Anopheles* mosquitoes which had fed upon the blood of malaria patients. Was it possible that mosquitoes which had bitten yellow-fever patients had the germs in their bodies and could later pass on the germs to others by their bites?

The time had come to call on Dr. Finlay. Major Reed reported that the doctor received his visitors with great courtesy and gave them reprints of everything he had published relating to yellow fever. What is more, he presented them with eggs of the species of mosquito—*Aëdes aegypti*—which he had been using in his experiments. This precious gift consisted of a small basin of water to the edge of which, above the water line, a number of jet-black cigar-shaped eggs were clinging. Back at the laboratory the investigators raised the level of the water in the basin, and after a short period the eggs hatched into larvae, or wrigglers. Six or seven days later the wrigglers changed into pupae, or tumblers. After another

26 hours the adult mosquitoes took to the air. With these mosquitoes, hatched from the eggs furnished by Dr. Finlay, the first series of experiments to test the mosquito-transmission theory were made.

But before undertaking the experiments it was necessary to make a grave decision. As it was then believed that yellow fever could not be given to animals, the only way of investigating it was to experiment on human beings. It was a tremendous responsibility to expose men deliberately to a dangerous disease for which there was no specific cure. After careful thought, however, the Board decided that a solution of the yellow-fever mystery, and all that it would mean in the saving of life, justified experimenting on human beings. Of course, those who volunteered for the experiments must give their free consent and be told of the risks they ran. Moreover, the members of the Board agreed that it was their duty to experiment on themselves as well as on the volunteers.

Before the first series of experiments began, Dr. Reed was called back to Washington to work on the report of the typhoid-fever commission. Dr. Carroll was put in charge during his absence, but it was Dr. Lazear who made the mosquito-biting experiments.

THE FIRST EXPERIMENTS

In this first series of experiments 11 volunteers were bitten by female *aegypti* mosquitoes after these mosquitoes had already bitten patients with well-marked cases of yellow fever. Of these 11 persons, only two developed the disease. The first positive case was that of Dr. Carroll. He had a severe attack of yellow fever from which he recovered. The second positive case was that of an Army private, William Dean, who had been bitten by the same mosquito that had bitten Dr. Carroll and also by three other contaminated mosquitoes. He came down with a mild, but well-marked, case of yellow fever six days later.

The case of William Dean had special importance because his was the first experimental case in which it could be proved that there had been no other source of infection except the bites of contaminated mosquitoes. Dr. Carroll's case was defective because he had gone places where he might have been infected in some other way between the time he was bitten and the time the disease developed.

Dr. Lazear had been the sixth person to be bitten in the early experiments. The results were negative. Later, on September 13, while collecting blood for study from yellow-fever patients in Las Animas Hospital, a mosquito settled on the back of his hand. He allowed it to stay there until it had drunk its fill. Five days after the bite, on September 18, he came down with yellow fever. On the evening of September 25,

1900, he died at the age of 34 and "in dying," in Major Reed's own words, "added one more name to that imperishable roll of honor to which none others belong than martyrs to the cause of humanity."

Major Reed returned to Cuba early in October and Dr. Carroll handed Dr. Lazear's notes over to him. A careful study of these notes convinced Major Reed that "the mosquito serves as the intermediate host for the parasite of yellow fever." He said so in these words at the end of the famous preliminary note on the etiology (cause) of yellow fever which he read at the annual meeting of the American Public Health Association in Indianapolis late in October. But what of the uncertainty about Dr. Carroll's case? What about those nine negative cases? It is not difficult to imagine that there was more headshaking than handclapping at that meeting. And rightly so, because it is the duty of medical men to withhold acceptance of any new theory until its truth has been proved beyond shadow of doubt. Major Reed's brilliant scientific achievement—what entitles him to be called "the conqueror of yellow fever"—is that he produced that proof.

THE EXPERIMENTS AT CAMP LAZEAR

To demonstrate that the mosquito is the only carrier of yellow fever, it was necessary to conduct experiments in such a way as to make it impossible for the men experimented on to get yellow fever accidentally.

Major Reed and his associates took a piece of ground about 6 miles from Havana and built a camp there, which they named Camp Lazear after their dead comrade. The camp site was well drained and freely exposed to sunlight and winds. In this camp were quartered men who had never had yellow fever and who were therefore called nonimmunes. These men were the American soldiers and the Spanish immigrants who had volunteered for the experiments.

When it became known that soldiers were wanted for yellow-fever experiments, the first volunteers were John R. Kissinger, a private in the Hospital Corps, and John J. Moran, a headquarters clerk. Major Reed talked the matter over with them, explaining the risk of suffering and even of death. They held to their purpose. Kissinger volunteered, to use his own words, "solely in the interest of humanity and the cause of science." Major Reed's comment on this young man was: "In my opinion this exhibition of moral courage has never been surpassed in the annals of the Army of the United States."

The Board proposed to attempt the infection of nonimmunes with yellow fever in three ways: (1) by the bites of mosquitoes that had previously bitten yellow-fever patients; (2) by the injection of blood taken from yellow-fever patients; and (3) by exposure to the most intimate contact with fomites. All three sets of experiments were carried on at approximately the same time.

Experience had shown that if a person is going to contract yellow fever, he develops it within six days after exposure. Therefore, if the men were kept in quarantine for two weeks without developing the disease, this fact would show they had not become infected before they entered camp. Things were now so arranged that if any man developed yellow fever, the Board would know that the disease was the result of the experiment in which he had taken part, and nothing else.

FOMITES PROVED INNOCENT

To test the fomites theory a small frame house called "the infected-clothing building" consisting of one room, 14 by 20 feet in size, was erected at Camp Lazear. It was tightly built, and the doors and windows were so placed as to admit as little sunlight and air as possible. The room was kept like the hold of a ship in the tropics—warm, dark, and moist.

The building was now ready for the experiment. Three large boxes filled with sheets, pillow slips, blankets, and clothing contaminated with the excretions of yellow-fever patients were placed inside; and on November 30, 1900, Dr. Robert P. Cooke, acting Assistant Surgeon, United States Army, and two privates of the Hospital Corps, all nonimmune young Americans, entered the building. They unpacked the boxes, giving each article a thorough shaking in order to fill the air with the specific agent of yellow fever if it was contained in these fomites. They then made the beds with the soiled bed clothing and slept in them. Various contaminated articles were hung about the bed in which Dr. Cooke slept. For 20 nights this room was occupied by these nonimmunes. They packed up the soiled articles every morning and unpacked them at night, but not one of the men developed yellow fever.

From December 21, 1900, to January 10, 1901, the room was again occupied by two nonimmune young Americans. These men slept every night in the soiled garments and on the bedding used by yellow-fever patients throughout their illness. They also remained perfectly well. The experiment was repeated a third time with the same results. This series of experiments blasted the fomites theory.

Remember that the young men who took part in them shared the universal belief that contact with fomites was practically the same as catching yellow fever. Their bravery was as great as that of the volunteers who caught yellow fever as the result of mosquito bites.

THE MOSQUITO PROVED GUILTY

The mosquito-biting experiments began on November 20. At first the results were discouraging. But on December 5, Kissinger was bitten by mosquitoes which had bitten yellow-fever patients from 15 to 20 days before. Four days later he had a well-marked case of yellow fever, from which he recovered. Four more positive cases developed in one week (December 9 through 15). In all, 13 men at Camp Lazear were infected by means of the bites of contaminated mosquitoes, and the disease developed in 10. Fortunately, they recovered. No one else in the camp became ill.

As a result of these experiments it was found that yellow fever could be carried from one person to another by the bite of a female *Aëdes aegypti* mosquito that had bitten a yellow-fever patient in the first three days of his illness, and had then been kept for at least 12 days before it was allowed to bite a human being who had never had yellow fever. If that plan were followed, the person bitten would generally come down with the disease within six days. It now became clear as to why it took so long for a case of yellow fever to infect a house. Mosquitoes had to bite the patient during the first three days of his illness. Then 12 days had to go by before they could pass on the disease by biting another person in the household. But after that interval of 12 days they were a menace to every nonimmune who entered the house or its immediate neighborhood.

HOW A HOUSE IS INFECTED WITH YELLOW FEVER

Since it was proved that a house could not be infected with yellow fever by fomites, the next question to be settled once and for all was: "How *does* a house become infected?" The experiment designed to answer this question was made in the "infected-mosquito building." It was similar to the infected-clothing building except that it was well ventilated. It was divided into two parts by a wire screen that extended from top to bottom and allowed air but not mosquitoes to pass freely from one side to the other. "Now," said Major Reed, "I am going to infect one side of this building with yellow fever and not the other side."

On December 21 he set free in the larger room 15 mosquitoes that had previously bitten yellow-fever patients. Five minutes later John J.

Moran entered the room containing the mosquitoes. In the room on the opposite side of the screen were two nonimmunes who acted as controls. Moran paid three short visits to the mosquito room within two days and all 15 mosquitoes bit him. On Christmas morning this "plucky Ohio boy," as Major Reed called him, came down with yellow fever and had a sharp attack which he bore without a murmur. The two controls who had slept each night in the mosquito-free room and continued to sleep there for 13 additional nights remained in perfect health. Therefore Reed concluded that as the air on both sides of the wire screen partition was exactly the same, it must have been the presence of contaminated mosquitoes that infected the side in which Moran contracted yellow fever, and the absence of mosquitoes that made the other side noninfectious.

By the end of the year 1900 the experiments at Camp Lazear had left no grounds for doubting that one of the greatest medical mysteries of all time had been solved. Mosquitoes—and mosquitoes only—were the carriers of yellow fever.

THE VIRUS OF YELLOW FEVER

You will remember that the third way in which the Board proposed to produce experimental yellow fever was by inoculating nonimmunes with blood drawn from yellow-fever patients. They succeeded in doing this in three out of four cases. This served to show that the specific agent, or germ, of yellow fever is present in the blood of its victims. After the completion of the work at Camp Lazear, Dr. Carroll remained in Cuba to continue further blood-inoculation experiments planned by the Board. In October 1901 he was able to produce unmistakable yellow fever in two American soldiers by inoculating them with filtered blood serum derived from a yellow-fever patient.

Major Reed and Dr. Carroll recognized that the production of yellow fever by the injection of blood serum that had previously been passed through a laboratory filter capable of removing all bacteria was a matter of extreme importance. It seemed logical to them to conclude that "the specific agent of yellow fever is of such minute size that it passes readily through the pores of a Berkefeld filter." They had, in other words, discovered that the cause of yellow fever is a filterable virus.

THE FRUITS OF VICTORY

Walter Reed passed sentence on the mosquito carriers of yellow fever in these words: "The spread of yellow fever can be most effectually controlled by measures directed to the destruction of mosquitoes and the protection of the sick against these insects."

The task of executing this sentence in Havana fell upon William C. Gorgas, then a Major in the Medical Corps, United States Army, and Chief Sanitary Officer of that city. Practically no one thought that it could be done! For the guilty mosquitoes were legion—and they were everywhere—at times in such numbers as to cloud the sky. To tell Gorgas that a thing was impossible was not the right way to keep him from trying it. The experiments at Camp Lazear had not convinced him that the mosquito is the only way, or even the ordinary way, of spreading yellow fever. But "*if* it is the mosquito," he said, "I am going to get rid of the mosquito."

He was aided in his gigantic undertaking by the yellow-fever mosquitoes themselves. These mosquitoes never stray far from the human habitations where the females can get the meals of human blood which they must have in order to lay their eggs. Moreover, they prefer to lay their eggs in clean standing water in artificial containers—rain barrels, pails, pitchers, tin cans, broken bottles, flower vases, pans, and other household utensils. Gorgas had a record made of every habitation and every family in Havana—then a city of 300,000 population—with a list of every possible water receptacle in and near each house and a note as to its location. He ordered his inspectors on their monthly visits to check each one to make sure that it was kept free of standing water and that rain barrels and other water-storage receptacles were kept screened.

The end of yellow fever in Havana was as dramatic as old "yellow jack" itself had always been. For 140 years this disease had not been absent from Havana for a single day. On September 28, 1901, Gorgas recorded the last case to occur there for several years. This spectacular achievement awed the scientific world and converted Gorgas himself from a doubter to an enthusiastic disciple of "that great man Walter Reed." Later Gorgas freed the Isthmus of Panama of yellow-fever mosquitoes, with the result that the United States was able to build the Panama Canal.

THE END OF THE ADVENTURE FOR WALTER REED

After the Yellow Fever Board broke ranks at Camp Lazear in February 1901, Major Reed was called back to Washington. During the brief remainder of his life he devoted most of his time to teaching at the Army Medical School and at Columbian (now George Washington) University. On November 23, 1902, he died following an operation for appendicitis. It is good to know that before he died he saw the great city of Havana delivered from her ancient foe, and the way made clear for the saving of his own beloved country from a great plague.

As leader of the heroic undertaking in which the mystery of yellow fever was solved, Major Reed received many honors during his lifetime. But it was not until after his death that his country began to appreciate the greatness of what he had done. The one tribute that he would perhaps have valued most came in 1909 when his comrades of the Army Medical Corps named the great Army hospital in Washington after him. Today, Walter Reed General Hospital symbolizes military medicine at its best in treatment, research, and teaching. In 1945 he was elected to the Hall of Fame at New York University, the first physician to be so honored, and in 1951 the Walter Reed Society was founded to perpetuate his memory.

YELLOW FEVER TODAY

The heroism of Walter Reed's little band of scientists and volunteers has run like a golden thread through all the later work done in connection with this disease. Later investigators proved that Reed and Carroll had been right in thinking that the specific cause is an agent so minute that it can pass through a laboratory filter. This agent is now called the virus of yellow fever. You will get some idea of its smallness from the fact that the head of a pin could accommodate 25 million particles of the virus with room to spare.

In 1927 it was found that certain kinds of monkeys are susceptible to the virus, and so it became unnecessary for experimenters to use human beings as subjects. In 1937 a vaccine against yellow fever was perfected and has since been used to immunize millions of people living in, or traveling to, parts of the world where yellow fever is still a threat.

Vigorous campaigns against *Aëdes aegypti* mosquitoes have banished yellow fever from the centers where it had once been a major cause of death. In the two Americas as a whole, the last case of yellow fever known to have been transmitted by these house-dwelling mosquitoes was in Trinidad in 1954. Before that, however, it was discovered that certain forest-dwelling mosquitoes transmit yellow-fever virus to men and susceptible animals—particularly monkeys—living in the tropical and subtropical forests of Africa and Central and South America. Vaccination is the only way of controlling jungle yellow fever, as it is called, because it is impossible to get rid of its forest mosquito carriers by any known anti-mosquito measures.

There is as yet no cure for yellow fever. But this ancient foe is surely on the way out, thanks to the gallant men who solved its mystery and to all those who have added to, and applied, the knowledge they won. Let's hope that the bugles blown on New Year's eve 2000 will sound "Taps" for old "yellow jack!"

25

Plant Pathology and Human Welfare

A. J. Riker

Diseased plants have always been with us and influenced our well-being. The history of mankind through the ages has been the story of hungry men in search of food. Tribes that tended sheep or cattle for their own food needed forage for their animals as well. The desire for food and forage has brought on many conflicts, small and large, from the beginning of time.

Diseases of plants have causes similar to those among animals and man. In early times, physicians using medical terms wrote about plant diseases—even though plants do not feel ease or disease as men do. But plants with disease may be so impaired that their usefulness to themselves or to mankind is seriously reduced. With the dawn of history we find reports of famine resulting from mildew and rust, induced by fungi. Certainly, plant diseases were troublesome even in the earliest historic times. Doubtless they were present in evolutionary times, as fossils show. Many of the extinct plants probably had diseases that hastened their disappearance.

How plant diseases developed is not definitely known. Probably when weakened plants died, various microorganisms assisted in decomposing them and in returning the materials to the soil to enrich it. Presumably most of these microorganisms worked only on dead plants and animals, clearing away debris and building humus. However, some microorganisms apparently were able to cause decay while the plants were still alive. This was a parasitic mode of life. By further adaptation, other microorganisms, such as certain rust and mildew fungi, were able to attack and grow on living tissue only.

Certain common names for plant diseases came easily enough. The rust fungi often had the color of iron rust. Terms like soft rot, dry rot, wilt, and leaf spot are descriptive.

A. J. Riker, "Plant Pathology and Human Welfare," *Science*, Vol. 152, No. 3725 (May 20, 1966), pp. 1027-1032. Copyright 1966 by the American Association for the Advancement of Science.

CAUSE OF DISEASE

Diseases are not always caused by microorganisms. Injuries that occur because of accidents, poisons, or defects in the environment often result in diseased tissue. Fire, flood, frost, higher animals, insects, and machinery, as well as poor agricultural techniques, may also produce damage. Many chemicals are beneficial, but when improperly used they too can cause losses.

Important environmental factors may be damaging; for example, the weather can be too hot or too cold, too wet or too dry. The light can be too intense or too weak; or the length of daylight may be too short or too long. There can be too little or too much fertilizer. In addition to the common mineral elements, such as potassium, phosphorus, and nitrogen, many plants require traces of boron, zinc, copper, manganese, or other nutrients.

Between the nonparasitic diseases and those caused by pathogens (literally, disease-causers) is a large additional group caused by viruses. There is no agreement about whether or not viruses are living. But this depends on what we regard as life, rather than on our ignorance about these viruses. Much of our basic information about the viruses that cause serious diseases of animals and men has come from the study of plant viruses, especially tobacco mosaic virus.

Most groups of living microorganisms include some that may be pathogenic. The concept of pathogenicity was established by Prevost in 1807 but went unrecognized until the middle of the last century. The research was done with covered smut, a disease in which the grains of wheat were replaced by fungus growth, looking mostly like black dust but being in reality a black powdery mass of spores. The disease was always present, but was not epidemic. Sometimes it caused heavy loss in one field and little in another. When Prevost put some of the black dust in water and watched it under a microscope, the black dustlike bodies grew. He also observed that traces (about 1 part per million) of soluble copper from a dirty copper kettle would prevent growth. These two keys were basically important. However, they were not turned in the lock to open the way for the control of bunt until later in the century.

The idea that specific living microorganisms could cause disease was accepted quite slowly. Many received such ideas only with chuckles of amusement—whether disease of plant, animal, or man made no difference. Many preferred to generalize about disease as a principle. It was to be overcome by another principle, health and natural good. Comparable ideas persist today.

But the means of securing adequate evidence was soon at hand. For plants we use the rules of proof for pathogenicity, known as Koch's postulates, adopted from medicine. Briefly, the pathogen must be consistently associated with the diseased tissue, it must repeatedly be isolated and characterized in culture, it must reproduce the disease symptoms when inoculated onto or into the host plant, and it must again be isolated and proved to be identical with the first isolate. Most of the pathogens causing plant diseases are bacteria or fungi. One has only to mention a few examples, such as those causing blight of potatoes (fungus), fire blight of apples and pears (bacterium), chestnut blight (fungus), and Dutch elm disease (fungus). Such major crops as wheat, corn, rice, potato, apple, and tomato are subject to 50 or more diseases. In addition, certain flowering plants prey on other plants and cause disease. Examples are mistletoe, dodder, and witchweed. By common consent, the eelworms (nematodes) appear among the plant pathogens. Only in recent years have we recognized their great importance.

On the other hand, some microorganisms are beneficial. Certain bacteria induce the root nodules of legumes, such as alfalfa, clover, and peas, and thus make possible the fixation of atmospheric nitrogen. Various fungi aid germination of seed and normal growth of plants such as orchids, heaths, and trees by association with the roots.

Fortunately, the pathogens of plants rarely produce diseases in animals or man. However, some of the fungi are poisonous when eaten. Ergot of rye has been notorious. This fungus grows as long, hard, purple masses replacing some of the grains in a maturing head of rye. It was often included in low-cost bread until its poisonous nature was discovered. A toxic alkaloid in the fungus induced abortion and gangrene. Epidemics of ergot poisoning swept over France nine times in the 17th century and eight times in the 18th century, and thousands died. Various other fungi, including certain mushrooms, are poisonous when eaten.

SOME HISTORIC LOSSES

Enormous losses of food, history-making losses, have been frequent in the story of mankind. Before epidemics were understood, they were considered as special kinds of plagues. Many factors have combined for the final result—the plant pathogens often need suitable weather, especially warm temperature and high moisture. Sometimes insect vectors, in addition to the damage they themselves do, add further injury by spreading or injecting disease-inducing microorganisms or viruses. But the importance of microorganisms was slow to be recognized. All could see the devastations of swarms of locusts—they descended on fields, ate every green leaf or twig, and left fields bare—but the stealthy work of fungi seemed obscure to the farmers.

Various famines, and even the outcomes of wars, have been influenced by the shortage of food caused by plant disease microorganisms. Speculation about the supernatural was common. After the Irish Famine, or potato murrain, which began in 1845–46, the real cause was worked out. Potatoes had originated in the Andes in America and, no doubt, the blight fungus did too. However, blight in Europe corresponds in time to the advent of steamships. Men have argued the possibility that diseased potatoes, which decayed on slow sailing vessels, could have landed from fast steamships and started the potato murrain. In any case, this is doubtless an early example of a way in which growers have moved dangerous microorganisms from one country to another.

The potato famine continued for several years. Starvation occurred in Ireland and in western Europe. Rebellions, looting of landowners' property, even murders, took place. During this time, America benefited by the immigration of many of the western European people. They were a select group. A few were criminals, but usually only those with initiative and an adventurous spirit would say "good-by" to relatives and tradition for a try in the New World.

The proof that the potato famine was caused by a fungus helped explain the riddle of the common barberry bushes and rust. Stem rust on wheat was proved to be caused by a fungus that appeared first red, then black, and had the barberry as an alternate host. The rust was worse near barberries, and laws had been passed against growing them.

Rusts on stems or leaves of wheat had been a plague since the dawn of history. The Romans had a god called Robigus whom they tried to appease for a good harvest. During the 1st century, annually on 25 April, they held a procession to his sacred grove, poured red wine over the altar, and sacrificed a red dog. This was also the time that rust first appeared generally, and that the dog star was thought to be malign. Robigus was thus cajoled into accepting a cheap red substitute for the red on the wheat, into calling off the dog star, into saving the wheat, and thus into letting his mortal followers have their bread.

Rusts of stems and leaves probably prevented wheat from becoming a major food crop in the southeast of the United States—hence the wide use of corn products there. Rust was serious during World War I in both Europe and North America; in the single year 1916, it was estimated that 300 million bushels of wheat were lost in the United States and Canada. Such slogans as "Food will win the war" were common. The food losses from potato blight and other diseases in Germany doubtless helped to shorten World War I.

Wheat rusts, wheat smut, and potato blight have been carried all over the world, but they are only several examples of the many diseases on all our crops. The world's important food crops include bananas, beans, cassava, corn, peanuts, potatoes, rice, soybeans, sugar beets, sugar cane, wheat, and many others. Plants yielding fiber, lumber, drugs, and so on, are valuable in our daily lives. We must not forget rubber and tobacco. Each has many diseases. Merely to list the plants and diseases by name occupies a large book. Ignorance about them often causes hardship in developing countries. Let us consider two examples.

Coffee rust put an end to a thriving coffee industry in Ceylon. In 1879 the Ceylon government sent an appeal for help to the botanical institution at Kew in England. It was a decade too late. The rust took the leaves off the trees, and after several defoliations the trees died. After much economic hardship, Englishmen planted tea and the English became confirmed tea drinkers. Coffee rust has spread widely; it occurs in Malaya, India, Java, Sumatra, the Philippines, and the east and west coast of Africa. Big growers doubtless can handle it, but the small growers cannot afford control measures. With planes going so fast and frequently, how long will it take the rust to reach South and Central America, where over 99 percent of the coffee trees are susceptible? And how much more in aid money will be needed to help coffee-growing countries? A seldom-considered Damocles' sword is hanging over American coffee growers.

But American fungi also present some threats to the Far East. Rubber trees growing there were native to South America. But in America, a fungus causes a defoliating leaf spot, making rubber-growing expensive. By lucky circumstances, the fungus was left behind when Englishmen took the rubber trees to Malaya, and rubber plantations have spread in the Far East. Here again, how long will it be before the leaf spot moves to and attacks the eastern rubber trees?

These are only two diseases. Many more could be discussed. Their control or prevention is in the hands of a relatively few scientists throughout the world. Their chief means of operating is mentioned very briefly.

CONTROL

The control of plant pathogens is ordinarily based upon an understanding of the pathogens' points of vulnerability. Since, with occasional exceptions, individual plants are of relatively small value, the plant pathologist is concerned with the control of epidemics. An epidemic occurs when there is a rapid repetition of the cycle whereby the pathogen enters the plant, becomes established and reproduces, comes to the surface again, produces spores and so forth, and is carried somehow to another host. Under favorable conditions a new generation can occur in from 8 to 14 days.

Each infection produces hundreds, sometimes many thousands, of spores. These phenomenal "population explosions" can cause devastation of a crop. Plant pathologists secured the ideas of cycles from medical workers. Control measures can be applied at various points in this cycle where weak links occur in the chain of events. For example, the use of quarantines, inhibiting agents, special cultural practices, repulsion of disseminating insects, and the development of disease-resistant plant varieties, all have successful applications.

Most of the other control measures, in the minds of some people, are merely stopgap procedures to be employed until disease-resistant varieties can be developed. However, the development of new varieties must be more or less continuous. For as smart men breed a variety that resists disease, the microorganisms may have or evolve a different race or strain of the pathogen or even a different pathogen to attack it. So the plant breeder has a problem to keep one jump ahead.

For breeding, undisturbed or natural areas are most important. Here the breeder searches for native plants having desirable characteristics. When natural areas are destroyed, his problem becomes serious. Every effort must be made to preserve a suitable number of natural areas over the world. Every year of delay means that potentially important plants, bearing genes for resistance or other valuable characteristics, become extinct.

In Europe and North America, research has made possible the reduction of plant diseases so that in some cases we have an abundance or a surplus in storage of products such as wheat, corn, or cotton. (Fungi also may attack food in storage.) This supply is possible only as a result of continued research of the pathologists, along with their colleagues in agronomy, horticulture, entomology, soils, genetics, engineering, and so forth. After the War Between the States, research stations and substations were established frequently in the areas to be served, because what was suitable for one place might not be right for another. The large supply of crops was produced by the applications of many years of research.

Although this supply in North America may cause problems, one should not overlook the enormous asset it provides in case of armed conflict. Better still, it serves as a strong deterrent for men in any nation who might try to overcome any country in North America. At the same time, it may provide food for developing countries while they work on their own problems.

DEVELOPING COUNTRIES

Many people in Euorpe and North America do not realize that much of the world's population goes to bed hungry every night. Also, it has often been erroneously thought that if some of the South American, African, and Asian countries would use our seed and our methods, there would be plenty of food to go around. Unfortunately, the procedures that work in Europe and North America are quite apt to fail in other places. For that matter, procedures that are suitable for southern Wisconsin may not be suitable for northern Wisconsin. Research has been necessary in order to learn the application of basic knowledge for particular localities. Consequently, these questions are raised: Without research by plant scientists, including pathologists and their colleagues, can the developing countries be wholly or partly self-sustaining? Likewise, can they be encouraged to produce much of their own food rather than depend upon purchases or gifts? Do they need a philosophy of responsibility and activity along lines that would make them largely or entirely self-sustaining? The 2-year assignments of experts to developing countries too often have proved inadequate. What is needed mostly is long-term research, comparable to that sustaining North America and western Europe. This cannot be emphasized too strongly.

Among the primary problems are these: What can we do with the arid lands? They occupy about one-third of the world's land area. What can we do with fertilizers? This is important almost everywhere, including the apparently fertile wet tropics, because many such areas are badly leached. What can we do about weeds? Can chemicals wisely replace cultivation?

Some have argued that an increase in food production is self-defeating, especially when the products of arable land are consumed by the exploding populations. However, populations must be fed until the explosion can be controlled. Meantime, the prevention of plant diseases holds great promise. But, the measurement of losses points up the magnitude of the problem.

DISEASE LOSSES IN MODERN TIMES

Plant disease losses in developing countries are difficult to determine at present. Vallega and Chiarappa have given a few examples. In 1947–48 in New South Wales, Australia, stem rust caused a loss of wheat estimated at 270,000 tons. This represented food for about 3 million people for 1 year. In South Africa, disease losses in sorghum have recently averaged about 1 million tons. This is enough food for 5.5 million people for 1 year. A small "Irish Famine" occurred during 1951 in Chiloe, southern Chile. The mean loss there of potatoes from the late blight area was 40 percent, with 23 percent for the entire country. Ghana and Nigeria have suffered severe losses in cocoa. Coffee has never come back as a crop after the coffee-rust epidemic in Ceylon in 1880–90. In South India, the loss from coffee rust sometimes may run to 70 percent; in East Africa, 30-percent loss from coffee rust is frequent. In the Philippines, of an original population of 250,000 coconut trees on San Miguel Island prior to the appearance of cadang-cadang in 1961, only 80 trees were still bearing fruit in 1965. In the state of São Paulo, Brazil, 75 percent of the 6 million citrus trees were infected and killed by tristesa in 1949. And so goes the story of disease. Many times, in a single-crop area, great economic disturbances occur that result in much suffering because of crop losses.

In the United States, the figures on losses are much more accurate. LeClerg has given many details, some of which are summarized in Table 1. Here the average annual loss from pathogens for 1951–60 was $3,251,114,000. To this total must be added the average annual loss from nematodes of $372,335,000, and the average annual expenditures of $2,255,000 for suppression of plant diseases and nematodes. In round figures, this is an annual loss caused by plant disease in the United States, held down from an unknown very large sum, to just over $3½ billion.

There is an excellent report by Ogawa of losses in California, and this serves as an example of the situation in a leading agricultural state. A summary appears as Table 2, which shows losses in landscape plantings, apparently omitted by LeClerg.

After total destruction no loss appears on the record. The foregoing discussions and tables of losses do not take into account the losses from crops that have already been wiped out. For example, nothing is noted about the loss from fire blight on commercial Bartlett pears in central or eastern United States. Fire blight killed the trees. Nothing is said about losses from chestnut blight. The chestnut trees were killed by the blight fungus. So it goes with Vicland oats, stone fruits in the Salt River Valley, Arizona, hops for beer near Milwaukee, certain varieties of corn, citrus, cotton, flax, and many other crops. This is a continuing process. In some places the Dutch elm disease alone, or together with phloem necrosis, is now destroying the American elms.

Without the use of control measures, the crop losses from plant diseases would be really serious. Doubtless harvests would often be reduced greatly and some crops would be completely destroyed. Prices would be enormously increased, and for some things we would go hungry, even in the United States. And our souls would miss much of nature's beauty.

PATTERN FOR CONTROL

To control plant diseases, the time-honored means is as follows. Basic research is done on the host, on the pathogen, and on their interaction, as well as on the environment. The most promising control measures are tried in fields that represent the extremes of environment likely to be encountered by the plant in question. After successful control measures are found, they are imparted to the agricultural workers via the extension procedures. They are also given to students. The success achieved in the United States has often followed this pattern.

This is a procedure that is promising for developing countries as well. But it takes years of trial and error in each new location to insure success. Although the basic principles may be known, their application must be modified in most cases for a new location and usually for a new environment.

To make such environmental studies, crude facilities were built years ago. Now, some institutions provide batteries of growth chambers with excellent control of temperature, moisture, light, and nutrition, suitable for growing small plants. For larger plants, many possibilities are provided by mountains having warm bases and a cool top, wet and dry sides, ridges and valleys for variations in light, and so on. But suitable precautions are necessary to prevent dangerous pathogens from spreading.

The introduction of foreign disease organisms is one of the major problems for all countries, but especially for developing countries. Few of them have adequate quarantine laws and services. Still fewer have enough competent men and facilities for the operation of such services. Thus, when men import promising crops, at the same time they too often import disease organisms and injurious insects that make their plant growth difficult or impossible. Quarantine officials complain particularly against diplomats and their wives, who claim diplomatic immunity against examination of their luggage as they move about.

THE OUTLOOK

No gift of prophecy is needed to say we shall always need food. We eat plants and certain animals, but these animals also eat plants. Wherever crop plants can grow there are diseases that need control.

Dedicated men will take the basic work already done, will try it on the land, and will pass on to the growers the results of successful trials. Likewise, these or other men will educate the students.

This is particularly important for developing countries. But here the basic information developed elsewhere must be tried under local conditions. Since planting, growing, and harvesting usually occur only once a year, a competent man usually needs a year in an area new to him to learn what problems are important. Then the second year he can make experiments. Many times, his first experiments fail because of some unanticipated circumstance. So several years of undisturbed continuity are necessary— as any Agricultural Experiment Station can testify. Then taking the results of successful experiments to growers requires much skill. In developing countries, this is often best done by dedicated natives. For best results, they should devote their lifetimes to plant pathology.

One can hardly overemphasize the importance of taking tried and true successful local results to the growers. Neither can one overemphasize the importance of educating the native students who face the challenges of the future.

Further progress depends on many factors. They are similar oftentimes to the needs in sister sciences. For example, we need a better means of classifying knowledge so that we can go to the libraries and find what is known about a given subject. Also, in the United States and, to a lesser extent, in Europe, the subjects plant pathology, entomology, soils, genetics, and so on are separated for convenience in administration and teaching. But in nature, they are seldom separated—all work together. Correspondingly, men who are trained in these subjects often have a better chance of success if they work together as a team. A team should be able to continue its function, however, with or without a substitute, if for some reason a member drops out.

Additional basic information also will foster progress. An indication of some of the numerous fundamental problems is given in various recent publications. Among the subjects needing further research are: improved control with chemicals (including chemotherapy); effect of temperature, moisture, and other environmental factors on the host and the pathogen (and their interaction); genetics of the pathogens; genetic development of the host plant to increase resistance; chemicals in the host or parasite that influence either resistance or pathogenicity, and chemicals (phytoalexins) produced by the interaction of host and parasite that affect resistance; ecology, especially concerning the effects of crop rotations on soil-borne diseases; biological control; hidden disease agents and inhibiting agents that reduce crop yields; nematodes and their direct damage, as

Table 1. Average annual loss in crop groups due to disease.

Commodity	Average annual loss 1951–60 inclusive ($1000)
Field crops	1,890,836
Forage crops and pastures and ranges	808,701
Fruit and nut crops	223,505
Ornamental plants and shade trees	14,099
Forage seed crops	23,584
Vegetable crops	290,389
Total	3,251,114

well as their introduction of other pathogens; tissue culture, the comparison of the metabolism of host and of pathogen; microscopic observation of the responses of host cells to parasitic attack under various conditions; mycorrhiza and pathogens near the roots; and so on and on. These are merely a dozen among many possible examples. The order in which they appear and the omission of others have no significance. The field is so broad that a plant pathologist must be able to work with other colleagues who understand related subjects from agronomy through to zoology.

No doubt future crops will be protected by future dedicated plant pathologists, who will find great personal satisfaction in recognizing and accepting the great challenge and opportunity for service. They, along with other colleagues, will be helping provide mankind with some of the basic needs—including food, clothing, and shelter which we, in the United States, too often take for granted.

Table 2. Summary of crop group losses and disease-control costs for 1963 in California.

Commodity	Losses and control costs for 1963 ($1000)
Citrus and subtropicals	23,088
Field crops	79,749
Forest crops and products	18,015
Fruit and nut crops*	105,467
Ornamental crops†	136,339
Small fruit crops	9,564
Vegetable crops	290,389
Total	440,646

*Mostly grapes, peaches, plums, and prunes.
†Mostly landscape plantings.

SUMMARY

Diseases have always been present in plants and have caused many changes in the lives of men. They have influenced what men ate, what they wore, the shelter they used, and so on. Industries have flourished and have disappeared. Famines have occurred; populations have moved; even the outcomes of wars have been influenced. Important plants are frequently attacked. Losses each year in the United States are held down from unknown enormous sums by various control measures. The control of disease is one of the promising means by which developing countries can maintain and advance themselves. Dedicated scientific men, no doubt, will continue serving mankind by their research, extension, and teaching about plant diseases, if given the opportunity. They will need to cooperate with colleagues in related fields.

26

Medical Utopias

René Dubos

In medicine, even more than in other fields of science, theories and practices have always been under the sway of *a priori* philosophical attitudes and rationalized beliefs. The social forces that have influenced medical history range from the primitive fear of demons to the current wave of faith healing, from Rousseau's assertion that "hygiene is less a science than a virtue" to the modern illusion that diseases can be conquered by drugs. Among all the medical utopias that have flourished in the course of time, none has blossomed so constantly and in so many forms as the belief that disease can be entirely eliminated from the earth. At the present time this illusion is based on an uncritical faith in the magic power of experimental science. But fundamentally it arises from the mystical belief in the existence of what Thomas De Quincey, in "Confessions of an English Opium-Eater," called "that sort of vital warmth . . . which would probably always accompany a bodily constitution of primeval and antediluvian health."

Many thinkers of classical Greece certainly believed that reasonable men could achieve the millennium of health by the exercise of wisdom. Witness the cult of Hygeia, which was an expression of the faith that men could enjoy *mens sana in corpore sano* if they lived according to reason. Carrying this doctrine to its logical conclusion, Plato wrote that the need for many hospitals and doctors was the mark of a bad city; there would be little use for them in his ideal Republic. In Imperial Rome, Tiberius asserted in a similar vein that anyone who consulted a doctor after the age of thirty was a fool for not having yet learned to regulate his life properly without outside help.

From René Dubos, *The Dreams of Reason* (New York: Columbia University Press, 1961), pp. 63-98. Reprinted by permission.

The widespread conviction that health is purchasable, not only in limited areas but also on a world-wide scale, seems to be justified by the advances made during the past half-century in the fields of nutrition and infection. In reality, however, it has not yet been shown that these achievements justify the wide extrapolations made from them. There is overwhelming historical evidence that the evolution of diseases is influenced by many determining factors which are not as yet amenable to social or medical control, and may never be. The changes that have occurred without benefit of conscious human intervention in the prevalence of various diseases during the past few centuries should serve as a warning that it is unwise to predict the future from the short perspective of the past decades.

Granted the lack of precise information, it is clear that there have been spontaneous ebbs and flows in the prevalence and severity of many diseases. Plague invaded the Roman world during the Justinian era; leprosy was prevalent in western Europe until the sixteen century; plague again reached catastrophic proportions during the Renaissance; several outbreaks of the sweating sickness terrorized England during Tudor times; syphilis spread like wildfire shortly after 1500; smallpox was the scourge of the seventeenth and eighteenth centuries; tuberculosis, scarlet fever, diphtheria, and measles took over when smallpox began to recede; today virus infections occupy the focus of attention in our medical communities; and long before viruses had become scientifically fashionable, pandemics of influenza at times added a note of still greater unpredictability to the pattern of infection.

Coming now to our times, who could have dreamed a generation ago that hypervitaminoses would become a common form of nutritional disease in the Western World; that the cigarette industry, air pollutants, and the use of radiations would be held responsible for the increase in certain types of cancer; that the introduction of detergents and various synthetics would increase the incidence of allergies; that advances in chemotherapy and other therapeutic procedures would create a new staphylococcus pathology; that alcoholics and patients with various forms of iatrogenic diseases would occupy such a large number of beds in the modern hospital?

Despite the dark spots on the health picture of the modern world, many facts seem to provide support for those who claim that we are approaching medical utopia.

Largely because of the control of microbial diseases and the improvements in general nutrition, the immense majority of children survive. Moreover, even those suffering from diabetes, congenital heart abnormalities, and many other formerly fatal diseases can now have an almost normal span of life. True enough, progress has been much less dramatic with regard to the diseases which affect adulthood. Yet even in this age group several types of ailments and accidents which once were uniformly fatal can now be treated so effectively that they have been all but eliminated as causes of death. As a result, more and more persons in our communities exceed the life span of threescore and ten to which so few could aspire in the past.

The achievements of modern medical science are, indeed, almost miraculous. Surgery restores to function broken limbs and damaged hearts with amazing safety and little suffering; sanitation removes from our environment many of the germs of disease; new drugs are constantly being developed to relieve physical pain, to help us sleep if we are restless, to keep us awake if we feel sleepy, and to make us oblivious of worries.

Within limits it is true that we can control many of the diseases that "our grandparents and parents took for granted." But this does not prove that we know how to control the disease problems that will be encountered in the future, or even, for that matter, those of the present. It is seldom recognized that each type of society has diseases peculiar to itself—indeed, that each civilization creates its own diseases. Furthermore, there is no evidence that the techniques developed for dealing with the disease problems of one generation can cope with the problems of another.

Progressively mankind managed to cope with this problem by developing certain kinds of natural immunity and by introducing sanitary practices. Today the situation is different. Horses have been displaced by automobiles, and the diseases they brought about have therefore disappeared. But unsought results of this advance have been the pollution of the atmosphere by automobile exhausts, and forty thousand fatalities each year on our highways. We are beginning to think constructively about these new problems and may learn to do something about them, but we may expect that new difficulties will soon arise from further improvements in methods of transportation.

Among the new problems arising from the partial control of man's ancient plagues, some have an economic basis and are apparent chiefly among the underprivileged peoples of the world. In the past, microbial diseases acted as one of the checks in population size by killing large numbers of children and keeping down the number of persons who reached old age. To put it crudely, nature balanced the books for us. Today, public health measures, supplemented by the use of insecticides and antimicrobial drugs, greatly reduce the number of early deaths. As the birth rates show as yet no sign of decreasing, the world population is growing in an unprecedented manner. In Ceylon, for example, the partial control of malaria resulting from the use of DDT has resulted in a sudden increase of the population during the past few years.

Unfortunately, the results of infection control are not an unmixed blessing, especially as some national economies are not capable of making orderly adjustments to the new state of affairs. It is of particular importance in this regard that food production and especially the supply of well-balanced proteins cannot keep pace with the increase in world population. Advances in agriculture and industrial technology will, of course, improve food supplies, but not fast enough for the needs. While the world population increased by eight per cent during the past ten years, food production increased by only five per cent, and in consequence more people go hungry today than did a decade ago. It is to be feared that food deficiencies will in the long run cause more physiological misery and suffering than have been prevented by the partial control of infection.

Less apparent as yet, but also constituting a threat for the future, are the economic and biological consequences of the survival of persons suffering from various types of physical and mental deficiency. The availability of techniques capable of postponing death in every age group and arresting almost any type of disease will increasingly present to the medical conscience difficult alternatives. For example, to save the life of a child suffering from some hereditary defect is a humane act and the source of professional gratification, but the long-range consequences of this achievement mean magnified medical problems for the following generations. Likewise, prolonging the life of an aged and ailing person must be weighed against the consequences for the individual himself and also for the community of which he is a part. These ethical difficulties are not new, of course, but in the past they rarely presented issues to the medical conscience because the physician's power of action was so limited. Soon, however, ethical difficulties are bound to become larger as the physician becomes better able to prolong biological life in individuals who cannot derive either profit or pleasure from existence, and whose survival creates painful burdens for the community. Increasing numbers of these persons cannot pull their full weight in society and require constant medical supervision and economic assistance. They constitute a social burden which is likely to grow heavier with time, precisely as a result of medical advances.

Even more important than these economic considerations, however, is the fact that many of the biologically defective individuals who are saved from death transfer to their progeny the genetic basis of their deficiences. Speaking of our "load of mutations," Professor H. J. Muller has repeatedly emphasized that, as medical science becomes more effective in prolonging survival, there will be an increase in the frequency of detrimental genes allowed to accumulate in our communities.

Whatever the theories of physicians, laboratory scientists, and sociologists, it is of course society that must decide on the types of threats it is most anxious to avoid and on the kind of health it wants—whether it prizes security more than adventure, whether it is willing to jeopardize the future for the sake of present-day comfort. But the decision might be and should be influenced by knowledge derived from a study of the manner in which different ways of life can affect the future of the individual and of society.

V
Ecology

27

The Ecology of Man, the Animal

S. Charles Kendeigh

The fundamental and basic concepts of animal ecology are also the fundamental and basic concepts of human ecology. Primitive man had few, if any, characteristics not also found in animals. Modern man is certainly more highly developed and specialized psychologically than any animal, but specialization of one sort or another is found in every animal species. Specialization is a product of evolution, and those characteristics or traits of man often considered to be unique can all be traced back to primitive characteristics, traits, or potentialities found also in animals. Many analogous traits not in direct line of descent to man have been evolved in other organisms. Let us enumerate a few.

Erect bipedal locomotion occurs in birds. A squirrel will use its hands to manipulate a nut, or a monkey a banana, as expertly as man. Laughter in man appears as an exaggeration of facial expressions and specific behavior indicating pleasure found among mammals at play. Sticks are used as a tool by a Galapagos finch to pry insect larvae out of holes in dead wood; spiders set a web net to capture food from the air as a fisherman does from the water; and hermit crabs use empty shells as homes and shields against predation by enemies. Many tropical species maintain sexual and reproductive activities throughout the year as does man who comes from tropical ancestors. Parental care of young is perhaps more complex and highly developed in birds than in any other animal, including man. Intercommunication between individuals is well evolved within animal species, not by use of a vocabulary or the written word it is true but by a great variety of scent stimuli, color displays, sounds, call-notes, and songs, each conveying a special meaning. It may not be entirely co-

S. Charles Kendeigh, "The Ecology of Man, the Animal," *BioScience*, Vol. 15 (1965), pp. 521-523. Reprinted by permission of S. Charles Kendeigh, Professor of Zoology, University of Illinois.

incidental that the songs of birds have an esthetic appeal to man; perhaps they have also to birds themselves who have evolved specific song patterns, melodies, and qualities of tone through a long period of natural and sexual selection. Social hierarchies exist among many gregarious species of animals and territorial behavior is evidenced among solitary nesting ones, equivalent to similar behavior in the human species. The leaf-cutting ants of the tropics practice agriculture when they bring leaves into their nest-mounds on which they cultivate a mold used as food. They likewise practice sanitation by systematically removing and depositing feces and wastes at some distance from their nests. The organized industry of ants, termites, and some birds is well shown in the construction of colonial nests. Division of labor is expressed at various levels in the animal kingdom, beginning with separation of reproductive and somatic cells in the colonial proto-zoans and the differentiation of tissues and organs in the lower inverte-brates and attaining complex dimensions among the social insects where different individuals are adapted for special functions. Division of labor is also evident in the biotic community where various species play special roles in the cycling of nutrients, the capture and transmission of energy, the regulation of population balances, the creation of microclimates, etc., analogous to the role of different trades or vocations in the human community. Animals may even have a primitive type of culture and ethics, if we mean a mores or behavior that is beneficial and traditional for the species and which is handed down to succeeding generations in large part by learning of the young.

Man's chief claim to uniqueness lies in the highly specialized development and functioning of his brain. His morphological and physiological capacities to do things are very limited, likewise his innate tolerance of even moderately rugged climatic conditions. However, his highly evolved intelligence has enabled him to circumvent many of his limitations: he has invented complex tools to do his tasks, he uses fire and air-conditioning to keep his shelter comfortable, his manufactured clothing allows him to invade microclimates for which otherwise he is not physiologically adapted, and his industrial skill has enabled him more completely to ex-ploit natural resources. Conceptual thought, capacity for abstraction and synthesis, the use of symbols in speech and writing, ability to reason and anticipate events, self-consciousness, and the spiritual and esthetic values seen in religion and art were doubtless latent in primitive man and had to be developed through effort and practice to reach the fruition seen in modern man. This cultural evolution has gone on mostly independently of biological evolution, and the mind of modern civilized man is the latest step in an evolutionary process that began only about 40,000 to 50,000 years ago and reached explosive proportions only within the last

5000 years. This specialization, although unique to man, is actually no more unique in evolution than specializations of other sorts found in many other animals. Man still requires food, water, and space; a favorable microclimate; protection from enemies; and reproduction. To obtain these requirements for life he must fit into an ecosystem as do other animal species, even though the ecosystem is a highly modified one of his own creation.

If one looks at the geological time table, one sees that during the last billion or so years life has evolved from single celled plants and animals living in the sea to more complex invertebrates and primitive fish, invasion of freshwater and land habitats, and evolution of insects, amphibians, reptiles, birds, and mammals. Man did not come physically into this succession until a million or so years ago. There can be no prediction nor certainty but that in the next million years—or billion years —many new types of animal life will appear; and man, as we know him today, will either be exterminated or greatly altered in appearance, form, and function.

Man probably originated, as did most groups of vertebrate animals, in the Old World tropics and dispersed as shifting climates, vegetation, and land bridges permitted, into Europe, northern Asia, North and South America, Australia, and southern Africa. In these different areas, populations of man became isolated for many thousands of years and were prevented from interbreeding with other populations by physiographic, climatic, or biotic barriers. As is common with animals, this geographic isolation allowed genetic variations to occur and become established, involving color of skin, texture of hair and other characteristics. Variations in tribal customs evolved. Occupancy of new environments and contacts with different biota exposed populations in different areas to different selection pressures and they came to occupy somewhat different ecological niches. If this geographic isolation had persisted a few more thousand years, doubtlessly reproductive isolating mechanisms, already partially formed, would have become fully established, and *Homo sapiens* would have differentiated into a number of new species. The evolution of civilization, however, interrupted this process of speciation. Artificial means of transportation encouraged world-wide travel, and this brought the by-passing of geographical barriers, the breaking down of ecological and ethological evolving reproductive isolating mechanisms, and the fusing of the races and their cultures again into one, so that the species was preserved in its biological unity.

The population density and distribution of primitive man varied in relation to natural conditions according to the normal or Gaussian curve, reaching a peak under optimum conditions and tailing off toward both maximum and minimum limits of physiological tolerance for environmental extremes. Shelford's law of tolerance is a generalization of these relations between abundance, physiological comfort, and environmental factors applicable to all organisms. Modern man has skewed the curve somewhat by this fabrication of artificial home and working environments but the law still applies.

Liebig's law of the minimum and Blackman's limiting factors state that growth, activity, or even existence of an organism is determined or regulated by that essential factor or condition in shortest supply. Modern man has developed methods of distributing essential elements or products to alleviate local deficiencies, but when his transport system breaks down or in areas where it has not been perfected, the working of this law is apparent.

Primitive man was certainly a constituent member of the biotic community. He was dependent upon the vegetation for shelter from the weather, as protection against enemies, as a source of food, and for use in other ways. His niche in the community has been compared with that of one of the larger carnivores. He had to compete with other carnivores and the larger herbivores for the essentials of life, and his role in the community was determined by his successes and failures in establishing favorable interrelations. When primitive man changed into modern man with the perfection of his intelligence and his invention of new tools, he changed from an ordinary member of the community to an ecological dominant. By building a home of his own that gave shelter from both weather and enemy and the development of agriculture, he was no longer dependent on the community as it was originally constituted. He modified the community to suit his own needs, determined to a large extent what other species he would permit to associate with him, and established the rules and conditions for their doing so. During geological time there have been a long series of organisms that have assumed dominance for periods of time, and often by no less drastic changes in the habitat and community. Man, in fact, has not yet obtained complete dominance in the arctic tundra, the desert, the tropical rain forest, or the ocean. Even in temperate regions, whenever man relaxes his dominance or mismanages the habitat, there is reversion of the region to dominance by other native species.

Civilized man, as primitive man, is still dependent on plants for nutrition and energy. Civilized man, however, has created an ecosystem where the kinds of nutrients that he likes and the energy that he needs can be obtained more efficiently than in ecosystems which he does not dominate. Crops have been developed through selective breeding and have been cultivated by special methods to give high yields. Competition for food from other species has been greatly reduced by use of fences, guns, pesticides, and the hoe. Plant crops are either consumed directly or fed to domesticated animals in a higher trophic level, so that meat as well as vegetables are eaten. In removing this harvest from his ecosystem he removes nutrient elements that in natural ecosystems circulate continuously, first through plants, then animals, then to the transformers in the soil that render them available for reabsorption by plants. Man acknowledges the important role of nutrient cycles in the ecosystem when he returns the nutrients that he has taken for food in the form of fertilizers unsuitable for his direct assimilation.

In natural ecosystems, food chains start with green plants because of their unique ability to capture solar energy and to synthesize nutrients from raw materials. With each additional link in the food chain through which energy and nutrients are transmitted there is a loss of some 80 or 90%. Each trophic level uses energy for maintaining its own existence and activities and there is wastage through prey not eaten, nonpredatory deaths, excreta, and heat. Consequently, with addition of links in the food chain, there is decrease in number of individuals or biomass that can be supported and in variety of species. The biomass of herbivores is always greater than the biomass of carnivores. In densely populated parts of the human world, man has largely given up the luxury of eating beef, pork, fowl, and lamb and depends instead on wheat, rice, or corn, thereby eliminating one trophic level and taking fuller advantage of the productivity of the land. If man could reduce the length of the food chain still further through bypassing plants and using solar radiation directly for the manufacture of food and for other uses, he would have a supply of energy several hundred times greater than is now captured by plants.

The sigmoid growth curve represents approximately the manner and rate by which cells, organs, individuals, populations, and communities increase in size and complexity. In the lower part of the curve, conditions for growth are very favorable and growth proceeds at an ever accelerating pace. However, inhibiting factors come to exert an increasingly important role and beyond the point of inflection they gradually bring the growth curve to an asymptote. With animals, the size of the asymptotic population is determined by available space, suitable food, and favorable climate. Factors that may ultimately stabilize the population at the asymptote are density-dependent, that is, they vary in intensity of their action with the density of the population. These factors consist of predation, disease, emigration, competition, and fecundity. Some species, certain insects and perhaps Arctic rodents and grouse among others, never attain stabilized populations. Their populations continue to increase to the limit of space or food supply or until unfavorable weather occurs. Then there is a crash and the few scattered survivors start the growth process over again.

Modern man has largely eliminated predation as a mortality factor, he has conquered many diseases and may conceivably subdue the rest, and he has emigrated to all favorable parts of the world even though he has not settled in large numbers as yet in some parts of it. With the harnessing of solar energy and intelligent use of minerals, man may be able to produce a super-abundance of food through a sort of artificial photosynthesis as well as apply this energy industrially. Likewise, he may obtain control over the weather. Space is limited, however, at least on earth, and it is difficult to see what he can do about it aside from building megalopoli, skyscrapers, underground burrows, sea platforms, or vast air chambers underwater. Space may be the limiting factor ultimately setting the limit to the size of the human population on earth. The amount of space reduction that the human animal will tolerate may not be just space to stand on but space in which he can carry on a comfortable existence. Competition will continue to be a potent factor, as it is in regulating all animal populations. War may someday be eliminated and the world someday may function as a single economic unit, but it is difficult to conceive how competition between individuals can be significantly reduced as the limits of space are approached; more likely it will become accentuated in the final struggles for existence.

With the advent of civilization and modern industrialization, all efforts to date have been to reduce mortality rates and expand available resources. This has thrown the stabilized populations of primitive man out of balance and brought on a new accelerating phase in the growth curve. Populations will not again be brought into stabilization until birth rate and mortality rates again balance. This means that the birth rate must be reduced in proportion to the reduction of mortality rate. This occurs in populations of wild animals more or less automatically through changes in physiology and behavior. Man's biggest challenge in the present age is whether his great intellect will give him the self-discipline and skill to regulate his own population growth to the level best suited for the perpetuation of the culture that has evolved as well as for his physical existence.

The laws of Nature apply to man as they do to animals. There are no exceptions. If he can come to understand what they are and how they work, he will know better what to anticipate concerning their effects on himself. He cannot ignore the dynamic forces of the environment with impunity, but being blessed with an intelligence far above that of other animals, he can guard against them or alleviate their effects to his own advantage.

28

Biology, Society,
and Culture in Human Ecology

Frederick Sargent II
Demitri B. Shimkin

Human ecology seeks to understand man and his problems by study-ing individuals and populations as biological entities profoundly modified by human society and culture and by studying the effects of physical, bi-ological, and cultural environments upon man and those of man upon his environments. The viewpoint of ecology is at once statistical and typo-logical. The observational reality is always a set of tolerances pertinent to the physics and chemistry of an individual's metabolism and behavior and to those of his behavioral products. Yet this reality persists only through genetic and social mechanisms that transcend individual life se-quences to provide the continuities, feedback stabilities, and progressive adaptations of biological and cultural evolution.

GENERAL CONCEPTS

Biologically, man has both generic and unique characteristics as an organism. Among the former, the phenomena of distinctiveness and of persistence over time, through physiological and morphological changes, are central.

Frederick Sargent II and Demitri B. Shimkin, "Biology, Society, and Culture in Human Ecology," *BioScience*, Vol. 15(8) (1965), pp. 512-516. Reprinted by permis-sion of Frederick Sargent II, Professor of Physiology, Director of Center for Human Ecology, and Demitri B. Shimkin, Professor of Anthropology and of Geography.

By what processes is this constancy maintained? To answer this question we must have some concept of a free-living organism in its natural life-situations. Many biologists prefer to view organisms as systems of self-regulatory processes. By this view alone one cannot really understand organisms. Equilibrium and constancy are important, but a more fundamental organismic characteristic among free-living animals is direction. Direction arises both from the organism and the environment, for the survival of the organism depends upon its finding an environment which is adequate for it. To succeed in this search the organism must select, from all sorts of environmental stimuli that act upon it, only those events that are pertinent to it. This milieu is certainly not "definite and static"; rather it forms continuously as the active organism grows, matures, and ages. Thus organism and environment are in essence inseparable. It is this bond that gives rise to direction in organismic behavior and to selection in evolution.

In finding this adequate environment, the free-living animal organism exhibits preferred behavior. To determine whether a particular phenomenon which seems to be preferred behavior is essential and genuine, one must consider the entire organism. As Goldstein states it, "We are dealing with genuine attributes or constants if we find, by examining as many fields as possible, order and 'adequate performance' in the rest of the organism. . . . In this way we apprehend certain characteristics of the organism with which we are dealing, certain norms and constants of its nature."

Among these "constants" of the nature of the organism are ways of behaving; sensory and motor thresholds; intellectual characteristics; affectivity; psychic or mental and physical traits; physiological attributes such as temperature, respiration, pulse, blood pressure; chemical qualities of the blood; blood types; and reactivity to noxious and stressful circumstances. The living organism tends to approach these relative constants or the "average mean." Thus, Goldstein remarks, "We are only in position to speak of one and the same organism, if, in spite of temporary changes, these constants become manifest."

There are two groups of "constants": those which express "the essential nature of the species" and the "individual constants." Goldstein emphasizes the fundamental significance of the "individual constants": "On the basis of the constants of the species, the life of the normal and especially of the defective individual cannot be sufficiently comprehended, notwithstanding certain congruencies between the individuals of the same species. For that objective, an acquaintance with the nature of the individual, that is with the *individual's normal constants*, is prerequisite."

Merely enumerating innumerable constants, however, does not define the essential nature of the organism. The constants themselves are equivocal because they are measured under isolating conditions. To determine which phenomena are biologically relevant and which are not, we need "a conception of the organism in its qualitative organization and holistic function." This conception is *"the capacity of the organism to become adequate to its environmental conditions. . . .* Whenever we speak of . . . the organism, we have in mind these essentials for the realization of adequacy between the organism and its environment. And these are the principles. of composition of that picture which biology has to grasp. . . ."

SPECIES CONSTANTS

Man is a species that has proved unique in its fitness to survive and multiply under extremely varying selective pressures. In the Pliocene, the protohominids appear to have been brachiating dwellers in tropical forests, a habitat which favored depth perception, color vision, sound production and hearing, and truly prehensile hands. Increasing drought in the late Pliocene and early Pleistocene forced adaption to a forest-edge and grasslands environment, in which both escape from predation and increasingly successful predation were basic elements of survival. During this period, the precursors of man (Australopithecenes) become effective runners, in consequence of mutations and selection leading to the human heel, the reduced jaw, and the S-shaped spine. In general, less robust and more juvenile body builds sacrificing strength for endurance were evidently favored. These factors, jointly with the direct advantages of better perception, memory, symbolization, cerebral inhibition, learning and communication, fostered the absolute and relative growth of the brain.

Over the past half-million years, man has adapted to a wide range of nontropical climates, as a consequence both of migrations and climatic fluctuations during the ice ages. These events must have been associated with periods of population growth and dispersal alternating with others of decline and concentration. Mechanisms such as these account, in fact, for the extraordinary combination of long-persistent geographical variability and full reproductive unity characterizing man. Even more important have been the selective advantages of variability, role specialization, and cooperation in human society. These and other expressions of polygenesis even in small populations of man are undoubtedly related to the propensities toward out-breeding and mating stability ubiquitous in man. The prolonged mobility and self-sufficiency, in primitive conditions, of pre-adolescent children, in combination with taboos on parent-child and sibling intercourse and the continuous sexual receptivity of the human female, seem to have been the behaviors crucial to expressing these propensities.

The increasing range and effectiveness of taught behavior—culture—have vastly altered selective pressures during the past half-million years. It limited the restrictions of cold through fire, shelter, and clothing. Effective cooking ended the limitations of unaided human digestion. Thus, with seed-gathering and, later, agriculture, hunger became less of a control on human numbers. But sedentary life, land clearance, the elimination of other potential pathogenic hosts, and symbiosis with domestic animals made disease immunity and behavioral safeguards against infection basic selection mechanisms. The significance of this later selection has been insufficiently stressed. Larger populations made more mutations possible, while group survival became far less random than earlier. On one hand, new technology in some areas radically increased population-bearing capacities. On the other, endemic diseases (parasitism, malaria, tuberculosis) systematically induced child-birth and infant mortality, while epidemics carried off entire susceptible populations (e.g., smallpox and measles in North America and Oceania). Thus, intense growth in favored areas—the Near East, India, China, Middle America—and stagnation or decline elsewhere, have predominated since the rise of agriculture.

Associated with the control of food and the increasing size of human populations has been the increasing importance of management: the determination of goals, the discovery of means, the organization of efforts, and the distribution of gains—in human societies. An allied process has been the increasingly high evaluation of play and symbolic expression as ever more structured societies have repressed wider areas of biological desire. At the same time, the change from simple face-to-face communities to stratified states brought with it lessened capacity to identify and harness individual variation. Social criteria, such as the accidents of conquest or defeat, urban or rural residence, white skin or black, have dominated role choices. The significance of complex individual variations in human adaptation has thus been diminished through feedbacks from history. This diminution has also lowered man's evolutionary adaptability.

At his present stage of evolution, man as a species has many distinctive characteristics. He matures slowly; some 25% of his life span is occupied with maturing. This long period of maturing is, however, merely an exaggeration of a primate phenomenon. Bolk has called the slowing "foetalization." Another term is neoteny.

Neoteny has had several important consequences. First, it is advantageous for learning and social cooperation to be taught while the organism is docile and sexually nonaggressive. Second, neoteny may be the cause of nakedness in man. According to Huxley, "The distribution of hair on man is extremely similar to that on a late foetus of a chimpanzee, and there can be little doubt that it represents an extension of this temporary anthropoid phase into permanence." Hairlessness is, except for desert inhabitants, unique among terrestrial animals. The hairless state, Huxley speculates must have encouraged humans to protect themselves against their enemies and the elements and thus have been a spur to intelligence.

Perhaps this hairless state has played a role in man's dependence upon evaporative cooling as a method of heat economy. This physiological regulation, of course, is not exclusively human, for many terrestrial animals employ evaporative cooling as a defense against overheating. What is unique about man in this respect is that he is an "eccrine animal." He is probably the only animal utilizing active sweat secreted by the eccrine sweat gland as a process of evaporative cooling. Other animals sweat but their sweat derives from apocrine glands.

One might speculate that the long period of maturing of the young has been genetically related to the post-mature longevity characteristic of man. The survival of animals beyond the reproductive period is unusually brief. In man, long survival allows the species to utilize social benefits accruing from speech and tradition. The menopause of the human female is unusually complete and sudden, and her long postreproductive period is exceptional among mammals. Williams suggests that these features may have developed in man because of the selective advantages offered to the slowly maturing offspring.

Man exhibits great reproductive variability. The differential fertility among men is enormous, ranging from infertility to families of 1 to 12 and even 20. This differential fertility is of greater selective advantage than differential mortality; it provides a basis for rapid changes in human gene pools.

The rapid and profound evolution of man's brain (primarily encephalization) allowed for plasticity and potential variety. This plasticity has had several different consequences. With encephalization and growing cortical dominance, man's power of attention has shifted to self-stimulative phenomena. As a result he experienced not only tensions, e.g., memory tensions of inhibition, but also symbolic satisfactions. These satisfactions have allowed survival and adaptation to stresses, e.g., through ascetism and celibacy, not withstood by animals. Because of the tensions, however, ". . . man is the only organism normally and inevitably subject to psychological conflict." While experimental neurosis can be produced, under natural conditions avoidance of conflict is the general rule. "Only the peculiarities of the human mind," according to Huxley, "have forced its partial abandonment upon man." Association mechanisms bring into relation knowing, feeling, and willing. Both unified mental life and mental illness result. Repression is a device for resolving conflicting impulses, but this repressed input may become harmful and lead to mental disturbance.

Taraxis or disorder has come to dominate the lives of men. Events appear to be overwhelming and incomprehensible; everything appears to be in disorder. We suffer confusion, defeat, frustration, failure, remorse, humiliation, grief, and so on. Richards writes:

If one looks . . . at biology and the biological species, it is curious that the human being should be so sensitive and subject to external events and tormented by things that do not physically hurt; that it cannot accept adversity with the same philosophy that rabbits, rats, and guinea pigs can. To be sure, experiments can be set to torture the rat, the dog, possibly even the rabbit in taraxic patterns, but they have to be most deviously contrived. With man these things happen daily by themselves.

Thus creativity and disorder, distress and sublimation, are complementary properties of man in society and culture.

CONSEQUENCES AND IMPLICATIONS

Man's unique endosomatic and particularly his exosomatic, evolution have brought him to a position as the dominant animal. In almost all environments, he dominates the ecosystem and holds much of his own evolution in his own hands. Cultural evolution—so inexorably interwoven with man's unique psychoneurological traits—has brought him to this position of power. He not only dominates but also consciously manipulates ecosystems. By virtue of this power he has created a biological revolution directed primarily toward the immediate enhancement of human welfare at the expense of competing species and often with reckless disregard for long-range consequences. Only in recent decades has there developed a broad awareness of the need for a continuing strategy of resource management.

A few examples will illustrate the problems man now faces. He has created what Rostlund appropriately terms "the domesticated landscape," that panorama of domesticated plants and animals, cultivated fields and pastures, and monosystem reforestations. This domesticated landscape (*anthroposere* may be suggested as a technical term) comprises a series of artificial ecosystems designed to assure man of plentiful food and raw materials to meet his domestic and industrial requirements. The domesticated plants and animals selectively bred to inhabit these ecosystems depend upon the continuing intervention of man for their survival. Because of competition with other organisms which continually invade these ecosystems man has been forced to institute control measures. These measures nave been chemical more often than biological. The use and misuse of the biocides, moreover, have often complicated the problems of management, for not only do these chemicals have their intended effects but also unintended ones, ofttimes remote. Through his actions man tends to create a negative balance in the nutrient cycles of ecosystems. He extracts more than he returns. For example, he has caused a definite species reduction. Furthermore, since his artificial ecosystems are most susceptible to erosion through the agencies of water, wind, and fire, he must treat his fields and pastures with concentrated chemicals—the fertilizers. These fertilizers must be applied with care else more undesirable reactions accrue. There has resulted what in essence is a continuing managerial struggle to maintain the artificiality of the domesticated landscape.

The capture of energy is another problem for resource management strategy. It can be argued, for instance, that cultural advance is directly dependent upon an increased ability to capture energy. In the United States today, man's consumption of energy outside of the food chain exceeds that used directly and indirectly in food by some 25 times. While this energy has been vital in the support of man's technological establishment, there have resulted two profound consequences. In the first place, the disposal of technological wastes has become an increasing problem. Water and air have provided ready vehicles for discharge. The exponential increase in man's domestic and industrial use of energy has now demonstrated that the vital natural resources are not unlimited in their capacity to dilute and degrade his wastes. Water pollution and air pollution have become central problems of our times and there is ample evidence accumulating that these pollutants exert diverse and profound disturbances throughout ecosystems.

In the second place, this capture of energy has brought to him enormous power, power with which man can destroy himself as well as all other forms of life. This power will necessitate a drastic revision of his mode of thinking. He must turn from traditional views of ingroup survival to concern for the survival of mankind. Chisholm states the matter precisely:

The whole method of survival by groups in competition to the death with other groups has broken down. The survival group, for the first time in human experience, has become the human race itself. From now on we will survive as members of the human race or not at all, but we have no previous experience of this situation and no traditional concern or education for survival of the human race. The occasion for such concern had not arisen until about fifteen years ago and was not foreseen or provided for by our parents or ancestors. Now we are all threatened with extinction by our own traditional survival patterns, a position which most of us still find impossible to accept as real, because we have been taught from infancy to depend upon our "conscious" values, and even to consider changes in them is commonly felt to be immoral and disloyal.

This same view was eloquently expressed by Lord Brain in a recent article entitled "Science and Antiscience":

The evolution of the human race is now threatened by a failure of integration. [By "integration" Lord Brain means bringing man into *adequate* relation with the ecosystem.] That integration is a social function, necessary both within individual national societies and, in the interest of our common humanity, between those societies.

The magnitude, speed, and imbalance of cultural advances over the past century have created other problems. New levels of anticipation have spread more rapidly than productive skill and technology. The control of epidemic diseases has had insufficient returns, too often in work opportunities for a growing, healthier labor force. More unemployment and more pressure on resources have been the tragic results. In addition, the world's population is already so large and the rates of growth are seemingly so rapid that the prospect of Malthusian limits has become real. Vast increases in productivity, better systems of international exchange, and drastic increases in birth control are essential. These problems involve complex moral as well as technical issues. In a world of prejudice, the problems of eugenics, except for overwhelming diseases, can scarcely be broached. This is especially true since traits of selective value in some environments, such as the sickle-cell gene and perhaps diabetes, are very deleterious in others.

INDIVIDUAL CONSTANTS

A basic question in human ecology is thus a clarification of relationships and values. What is "health?" How does one measure health? No one really knows the answer to either question. Why must we understand health so that we can measure it? As man more and more rapidly disturbs his ecosystem, he makes it increasingly difficult for each individual to find an adequate environment. The rapidity of environmental changes may soon exceed the norm of reaction, the adaptability, of the human organism. Thus it becomes urgent that we gain some insight into the limits of the adaptability of individual organisms.

The disturbances which man has created in the ecosystem are manifold. He has polluted the water and the air and has contaminated his food. His gregariousness has led him to live in congested urban agglomerations where, if he is well off, his private quarters and place of work are air-conditioned. His physician administers to him an increasing array of chemicals designed fundamentally to assist him in coping with illness but which take their toll in iatrogenic diseases.

Problems such as these have led to an increasing concern about "environmental health." Attention is now turning to controlling the environment so that it will not become inadequate. Questions that now confront those working on problems of environmental health include: (1) What are the long-term effects on human health of low levels of toxic chemicals such as biocides and water and air pollutants? (2) What are the long-term effects of living in atmospheres with closely regulated temperatures and humidities? (3) What effects accrue from such labor-saving devices as the automobile which eliminate the necessity of walking? (4) What impact do these man-made changes have on the ecosystem and how do these impacts affect the health of man?

To provide answers to these questions we must be able to measure health with sufficient precision to detect deviations from the healthy state before there is morbidity and mortality. To do this means a radical reorientation of our thinking, for health has heretofore been defined in terms of lack of evident morbidity and mortality. To arrive at a productive model of health we must begin with the individual's normal constants, needs, and requirements.

Several features of individuality must be integrated in this model. One particularly characteristic constant of individuality is "the constant in the temporal course of processes." Goldstein writes:

> Every human being has a rhythm of his own, which manifests itself in various performances. . . . A performance is normal when an individual can accomplish it in a rhythm which is his adequate rhythm for this performance. Just as for physiological processes, like heartbeating and respiration, this is valid for physico-chemical processes. The time constant indicates a particular characteristic of the personality.

In addition, there is a relation between biochemical and physiological individuality and sensitivity to noxious environmental influences and susceptibility to illness. Individuality is largely quantitative rather than qualitative; each individual mobilizes different configurations or patterns of component homeostatic processes in making adjustments to environmental change. This diversity is probably polymorphic. Through systematic study of the diversity will emerge knowledge of the individual's adaptive capacity, which is required to deal constructively with the problems of environmental health.

Some examples may be given to illustrate these general points. Without a doubt, air pollution is a serious problem. The acute disasters serve to emphasize the grim prospects. Low levels of air pollution are now present in many urban centers. How do these low levels affect the health of the population? The individuals we should be most concerned about are those most sensitive to air pollution. If attention is devoted only to the "individual at the mean," many persons will be severely incapacitated or dead before the group within the "normal range" are affected. The most susceptible persons must be identified, for their individuality is a matter of fundamental importance in establishing criteria for air quality and other environmental standards.

The human being has a propensity to store excess energy as fat. This propensity creates significant health problems for a segment of the population identified as obese. Obesity predisposes to a variety of illnesses—for instance, diabetes mellitus, hypertension, and coronary artery disease. There is an individuality in the matter of fat storage. The ectomorph stores fat more readily than the endomorph. This fact suggests that the configuration of the component physiological regulations of the ectomorph differs from that of the endomorph. The needs and requirements of these types are not the same. That these types exist suggest that there are probably polymorphisms of physiological regulations in the population. These polymorphisms can only be elucidated through systematic studies of individuality. Such studies should contribute to an explanation of why some people have a high frequency of illness and others have a low frequency, why some persons are successful in finding an adequate environment and others are not.

EPILOGUE

Human ecology is, above all, a way of asking questions that may be productive in understanding man's evolution, nature, and problems of adaptation. It recognizes that, in man, biology, society, and culture are deeply interrelated. Culture and society have transformed man's environment but, in doing so, have changed rather than eliminated the selective pressures to which he must adapt effectively if he is to survive.

The problems posed by human ecology are very difficult. In fact, until the theoretical structure of operations research and the modern armament of instrument and data processing had become available, few of these problems could be effectively attacked. Today, both the necessity for, and possibility of, effective human ecological research present great challenges for the biological and behavioral sciences. . . .

29

The Ecology of Disease

Marston Bates

The study of the incidence and transmission of disease is the province of the special science of epidemiology, although this study could equally well be called the ecology or the natural history of disease. Epidemiology stems from *epidemic,* an unusual or severe outbreak of a disease. Epidemics have played an important role in all through human history, and many minds have been devoted to analyzing and fighting them. The epidemic, the unusual situation, however, cannot be understood without a study of the endemic, or the more usual condition, in which the disease is scarcely

Marston Bates, MAN IN NATURE, SECOND EDITION, © 1961. Reprinted by permission of Prentice-Hall, Inc., Englewood Cliffs, N. J.

noticed because it is a steady and continuing part of the community environment.

The word epidemiology can be applied very broadly, to cover such subjects as the causes and incidence of mental disorders, of accidents, or indeed of any sort of disease situation, but in the context of this book, we are concerned chiefly with the epidemiology of infectious disease, since this is basically a biological problem that is dependent on the interactions of hosts, pathogens, and environment. Incidence means numbers of cases, and epidemiology is in large part a statistical science, although the statistics are meaningless except in terms of the biology of the situation.

We are only beginning to understand the complicated host-parasite interactions in infectious disease. Some parasites are highly host-specific, that is, they attack only one species of animal, or perhaps only a single kind of tissue within the animal. Parasites which require two or more different hosts to complete their life cycle may be highly specific for both of the alternating hosts, though one might be an insect and one a mammal. Other parasites are less specific in their host relations. In general, related animals are apt to have related parasites, and particular parasites often seem to have a long evolutionary history of association with their hosts. But there are many exceptions; the only way we have of predicting the specificity of a parasite is to test it in the laboratory on numerous possible hosts. Many human pathogens are highly host-specific for man. This is true, for instance, of the viruses associated with the common cold, and it has greatly handicapped their study, since they cannot be tested on experimental animals.

Pathogens vary greatly in virulence, in the extent of damage they cause to the host. The same strain of pathogen may be highly virulent in one host and not in another. A given strain of yellow fever, for instance, may infect and multiply in a species of opossum with no apparent injury to the opossum, and at the same time be highly fatal for certain monkey species. Indeed, it may be fatal for one kind of monkey and harmless for another kind. Individuals of a given host species also may vary greatly in their reaction to a particular strain of pathogen, ranging from relatively resistant to susceptible. Differences in virulence of human pathogens at different times, or in different populations, are a commonplace in the history of disease.

There is always some sort of a serological (biochemical) reaction on the part of a host in which a parasite has become successfully established. These reactions are investigated by the sciences of serology and immunology. In many cases the parasite acts as an *antigen* which provokes the development of neutralizing *antibodies*. This is particularly clear with the viruses, and the course of the disease can be visualized as a race between virus multiplication and antibody production. With a pathogen such as the yellow fever virus, the host may be killed before the virus is controlled by antibody production, or the antibodies may win and the virus be eliminated. Some pathogens, especially many viruses like those causing yellow fever, smallpox, and measles, produce in the host, after one infection, the ability to continue manufacturing antibodies as long as it lives, and it thus remains *immune* to a second invasion of the same virus. We do not really understand this process: one theory holds that traces of the virus remain established in some part of the body and continue to stimulate antibody production. The principle of vaccination, with smallpox and yellow fever, is to infect the host with an innocuous strain of virus, making it immune to subsequent infection with virulent strains. With other viruses, like those of influenza, antibody production may be only temporary, so that the host presently is again susceptible to infection.

The self-limiting infections—smallpox and measles, for instance—must obviously have a continuing fresh supply of new hosts if they are to continue; such pathogens, then, are normally endemic in dense host populations and, they reach scattered populations only as occasional epidemics.

A great many pathogens show an alternation of hosts, and are not normally directly contagious from one individual to another of a given host species. Four human diseases—schistosomaisis, malaria, yellow fever, and plague—will serve as examples of different kinds of transmission mechanisms.

SCHISTOSOMAISIS

The species of blood flukes of the genus *Schistosoma* are pathogenic for man and are important agents of disease in some parts of the world. The life histories vary in detail, but the cycle generally starts with the eggs being passed out in human excreta; the miracidial larvae that hatch from the eggs must find certain species of aquatic snails to serve as intermediate hosts. After a period of development in the snail, forms called *cercariae* escape from the snails into the water in large numbers. If they encounter a mammal host in the two or three days that they are able to live, they bore into the skin (infection may also occur from drinking), develop into the adult phase, and start producing eggs again. The schistosomes that infect man may also infect other mammals with habits that bring them into snail-infested water.

MALARIA

Four species of the protozoan genus *Plasmodium* cause various forms of malaria in man. In the human host, the parasites live within the red blood cells; the parasites normally multiply asexually, but from time to time sexual forms, *gametocytes*, are developed. If these are picked up from the blood by an appropriate mosquito (of the genus *Anopheles*), the male forms (*microgametes*) burst from the host blood cell in the mosquito stomach and fuse there with the female *macrogametes*. The resulting zygote penetrates the stomach wall and forms a cyst of multiplying cells that eventually burst out (in the form of *sporozoites*) and make their way through the mosquito body to the salivary glands. When the mosquito next bites, they are injected into a new vertebrate host.

The human *Plasmodia* are all host-specific for man; other species attack primates besides man, as well as birds, lizards, and a few other vertebrates. All, as far as is known, have mosquito intermediate hosts, but different *Plasmodia* infect different kinds of mosquitoes.

YELLOW FEVER

Yellow fever is unusual because it shows two epidemiological patterns, one urban and one sylvatic. The pathogen is a virus which causes a self-limited infection in man (the human host either dies within around 12 days after infection or recovers with a lifetime immunity to re-infection). In the urban form, the intermediate host is a mosquito, *Aëdes aegypti*, which in tropical America, at least, is always closely associated with man, breeding in rain barrels, tin cans, vases, and so forth. When the mosquito bites a host with virus circulating in the blood stream, it becomes infective for new hosts after a period of about 12 days (the incubation period depends on the temperature) and remains infective for life (which, in the case of a mosquito, is usually short, at most 30 days or so). The virus was long thought to be host-specific for man, and since there is no other known host in urban areas, the virus requires a large human population for survival.

Under these circumstances, it seemed possible to eliminate yellow fever from the Western hemisphere by eliminating it from the large cities (like Rio de Janeiro) that served as foci of infection. When a campaign with this purpose was started, however, it was discovered that the disease also exists in remote parts of the upper Amazon and Orinoco river systems, where the *Aëdes* mosquito does not live, and where the human population is small and scattered. It turned out that in these inland regions various species of monkeys served as the mammal host of the virus, and that forest mosquitoes (*Haemagogus*) are the intermediate hosts; man enters the cycle only accidentally, though a man, infected in the forest, could return to a town or city and set off an urban epidemic.

PLAGUE

The Black Death, which caused such devastating epidemics in Europe in the Middle Ages, is still an important disease in some parts of the world, especially in India. It is now endemic in the western United States in wild rodents and causes occasional human deaths, providing a constant worry for public health officials. The pathogen is a bacterium, *Pasteurella pestis*. Plague shows several epidemiological patterns. Normally it is a disease of rodents, and the great epidemics of history involved both rat and human populations. The bacillus is ordinarily transmitted from rat to rat by fleas, and fleas may also carry it from rat to man and from man to man. In a severe human epidemic, a "pneumonic" form of the disease develops, which is directly contagious from man to man.

In the course of a plague outbreak in San Francisco in 1900, ground squirrels outside the city became infected, and a sylvatic form of the disease has persisted in the western United States despite all efforts to exterminate it. Some 18 species of wild rodents have been found to serve as hosts, and at least 30 species of fleas associated with these rodents are able to transmit the disease under laboratory conditions.

30

Wastebasket of the Earth

William A. Albrecht

Contamination in the food we eat, the water we drink, and the air we breathe suggests close connection with the soil. Usage such as "your hands

"Wastebasket of the Earth" by William A. Albrecht is reprinted with permission from the October 1961 issue of the *Bulletin of the Atomic Scientists*. Copyright 1961 by the Educational Foundation for Nuclear Science. One of a group of eight papers dealing with MAN AND HIS HABITAT.

are dirty," serves as a reminder that the thin surface layer of the soil is the wastebasket of the earth, the collector for the disposal of all matter that has once lived and moved.

ROLE OF THE SOIL

The thin layer of the earth's surface is an intensive transformer of all the waste it collects. In that shallow stratum elements are separated out of combinations and reunited into other compounds, effecting vast changes in every kind of matter. These activities include transformations of energy by such processes as oxidation, reduction, hydration, hydrolysis, and molecular rearrangement. Oxidation, like combustion, dissipates energy in the form of heat, which escapes from the earth. Reduction concentrates it in compounds of high heat and fuel values. This is illustrated most significantly by the plant's reduction of carbon dioxide by water, storing the sun's energy in the resulting carbohydrates.

These transformations of matter and energy create, nourish, protect, and maintain all living creatures. These creatures vary in physiological complexity from the simplest microbial cell to man, whose high state of evolution has equipped him with a mind to comprehend—and to modify— his environment, even as far as unwittingly contaminating it.

The term *contamination* has many meanings. The wastes of one population may be either the poison or the life-support of another. We consider populations of different forms of life to see whether their coexistence is cooperative or competitive, and whether their respective wastes may be of benefit or harm to each other.

A high degree of cooperation through evolution and adaptation characterizes nature's management of environment. But when man manages environment, competition stands out—with frequent examples of contamination. As managers, we are biased toward aims and benefits for man alone. We have concerned ourselves little with how, in modifying the environment for ourselves, we may be disrupting it for all the other populations of the biotic pyramid—microbes, plants, animals, and man—all supported by the one creative foundation—the soil.

Instead of speaking of the soil as "dirt" to emphasize its contamination of ourselves, the converse might be more appropriate. Man is upsetting much of the natural environment by his contamination of the air, the water, and particularly the soil, reducing its ability to dispose of wastes safely, and to nourish healthy populations of men and all other living things. It is a dangerous boldness to believe that we can manage environments completely by technologies designed for our economic advantage.

THE TRUE AGRARIAN

Given to a belief in the homocentric purpose of the earth, we have come to take our soil for granted. This view is quite the opposite of that of the pioneer—living mainly by agriculture—who respected and studied his environment and struggled to be naturally fit for his evolutionary survival there. He considered the seasons, the annual amount and distribution of the rainfall, the degrees of heat and cold, the winds and storms. He did not consider land as a commodity. The pioneer appreciated the fact that the soil had been built by nature during the ages pre-dating him, brought about by the climatic forces breaking down the rocks, growing the microbes, the plants, the many other kinds of life. For him, those were the natural forces of soil construction, and he knew he must maintain soil productivity if he were to survive. The pioneers were truly agrarian people. For them the soil was holy ground. Too, it was living soil.

Because of the scientific organization of our recently increased knowledge about the soil, we forget that the decomposition of rocks, the growth of vegetation, and the complete return of that organic matter in place—all under nature's management—are what brought about productive soils. At first, these soils were not contaminated against the healthy coexistence of a specific, but limited, set of species. The early balance represented an evolutionary set, each form unique in relation to the others, to the soil's particular geologic-climatic setting, and its degree of development in a given area. Examples of this limited balance would include the particular plant and wildlife forms of virgin forests, or the American plains or prairies. All of these conditions were major determinants of the coexistent species; the survival of each was dependent on the survival of the others.

Man's management of agricultural crops and livestock has not been directed by knowledge of the limitations of soil fertility, nor by knowledge of the required climatic-geologic setting for crops and livestock with each in its natural ecological climax. Instead, we have been given to transplanting any species from anywhere to everywhere for economic gain, ignoring biological benefits or dangers to the species involved. We have brought in higher (or lower) species while depleting the very soil fertility support required to grow them in health.

We have thrown natural evolution into reverse. We struggle to nurture species we have made unfit for the environment because creative forces there cannot offer the required quality of food and energy support. We now need to view the pampered species as contamination against all other lower species which would otherwise arrive at their natural climax. We must accept the fact that the soil, with its dynamics of producing and accumulating organic substances through plants with the support of climatic forces, is still the only energy supply on which all kinds of life depend. Transformation is the major role played by the soil.

Granting that the entire biosphere is dependent on the inflow of that bit of the sun's energy fixed in organic substances by photosynthesis, it is helpful to note that as Nelson G. Harston, Frederick E. Smith, and Lawrence B. Slobodkin said in their article, *Community Structure, Population Control and Composition,* in *The American Naturalist* in 1960, populations divide themselves appropriately into three trophic levels: the decomposers, the producers, and the predators.

THE DECOMPOSERS

The decomposers are represented by the varied kinds of microbial life which live by degrading organic debris through processes giving the microbes their energy and growth substances. The slow accumulation (at great depths below the earth's surface) of these remnants as fossil fuels of organic origin and a high degree of oxygen removal indicates that this heterotrophic group did not have much in the way of energy-giving "leftovers." Nor can these remains be considered contamination when they are far beneath the soil surface. But when they are brought into the atmosphere, and into the highly aerobic surface soils, after laboratory work has turned them into products such as antiseptics, pesticides, and herbicides, they are the most extensive and powerful biochemical contaminations we have yet known. Their range of disturbances covers the entire biotic pyramid.

Hydrocarbons, which can disrupt the transformations in the soil's surface zone, were buried by nature at great soil depths. These high concentrations of energy are now our industrial fuels. But even such deep burial of the wastes resulting from the use of atomic fuels will not serve as safe removal. Atomic fuels, with their lingering rays for a lingering death of all living cells, are not respecters of the beneficial portions of the soil's microbial flora.

Nutritional requirements of microbial decomposers are met by the contents of the debris and the soil. The essential elements remain very much in the cycle of use and reuse, since sulfur, phosphorus, nitrogen, and carbon occur as major elements in the leftovers. Oxygen is almost absent there, but carbon, linked to hydrogen, occurs in high concentration.

Ever since the work of Pasteur, our fear of microbes has singled them out as our environment's major contamination. We have made them the victims of vengeance and we boil them under steam pressure at every opportunity. Their disrepute has been shared recently by dusts, fungus spores, pollen grains of trees, grasses, weeds, and other particles. Today the professional allergist devotes his attention to atmosphere contaminants and to other substances disturbing the mucous membranes and similar tissues of the human body. But when microbes are viewed as disposers and transformers they become major benefactors for other populations. Microbes in surface soil serve as wrecking crews and salvage agencies. Simplifying the residue of past populations for energy release and reuse, these decomposers make the upper stratum of soil the real living foundation of the entire biotic pyramid. They keep open the sewage disposal systems of all the population levels.

Microbes are uniquely equipped to maintain their own populations. They reproduce at the rate of one generation per hour or even faster. They synthesize their own extra- and intra-cellular compounds—some of which we term antibiotics—for protection against competitors for their environment. The antibiotic quality may be merely an evolutionary accident that served to bring death to competitor cells. Nature's conservation practices use wastes from some life forms to make the environment serve its own survival more completely.

Benzene rings characterize the chemical structure of the antibiotic terramycin, for example. Modified ring structures with substitutions of nitrogen and sulfur for some of the carbon are found in penicillin, aureothrycin and other microbial products developed for their bacteriocidal effects on the human body. That ring structure represents highly reduced organic compounds such as those found in crude oil and coal. The chemical structures and biochemical energy potential represent the opposite of that of natural organic wastes dumped on the surface soil. While natural organic wastes offer much as energy through microbial oxidations, crude oil and coal are too stable for biochemical transformation and energy release, even though they rank high as industrial fuels. They are seldom broken down by digestion. They overload the liver, the chemical censor of the human body. They are leftovers from anaerobic microbial populations, and are well removed as serious contaminants by their natural placement far below the surface soil and by disposal well beyond the entire biotic pyramid.

The benzene ring, in a simpler compound distilled from coal tar—carbolic acid—was an early antiseptic. But now, long-chain compounds and ring structures of carbon, sulfur, or nitrogen substitutions, or in chlorinated, nitrated, and sulfonated forms as synthetics from the industrial chemistry laboratory, are being distributed extensively, acting as deadly poisons against the populations in the biotic pyramid. They come into the atmosphere in "smog" and carbon monoxide, and in herbicides, pesticides, and the like. Those microbial wastes welling upward from the depths of the earth, in their natural forms and in our more poisonous alterations of them, must be considered contamination by man of his own environment and of the environments of all populations that support him. His efforts to so completely destroy microbes are contributing to his gradual destruction by his own hand. Decomposers are not respecters of man when they release their own wastes as contaminants.

THE PRODUCERS

The second group among the populations, or trophic levels, of the earth are the plants, which produce organic compounds carrying the chemical and other energy transferred from the sun. They are the only means of storing and distributing that supply. Energy is collected by photosynthesis, the unique process whereby the chlorophyll of the leaves binds it into compounds of carbon, hydrogen, and oxygen in the molecular arrangement of carbohydrates. Plants are the source of energy for all biochemical processes, and of their own starter compounds into which they synthesize nitrogen, sulfur, and phosphorus to yield the different amino acids of proteins and living tissues which grow, protect, and reproduce. Plants are the only producers since they are the sources of food energy and growth potential synthesized directly from the chemical elements and flowing through all the other trophic levels.

Plants root themselves first into the soil and then extend their tops into the atmosphere. They may be vulnerable to contaminants from both directions. Their unique position and special processes bring both inorganic and organic decompositions from the soil into biochemical union with water, and carbon dioxide, and nitrogen. Plants, representing that limited zone where earth and atmosphere meet, act as a kind of interface for concentrations of different kinds of matter, becoming the significant stratum for the creation of all that lives. All life is possible because the synthetic power of sunlight operates through the plant fluid, chlorophyll. It is a mobilizer, or chelator, of the chemical elements, unique because the plant itself creates it. Its chemical structure consists of the inorganic element magnesium as the core, combined with nitrogen, linked with carbon, and all three connected with hydrogen. Even this chelator's composition represents a chemical union between the soil, which furnishes the magnesium, and the atmosphere, which yields the nitrogen, carbons, and hydrogen.

Because plants support themselves by their own capacity for combining elements and using solar energy to create compounds, they surpass all other populations in the struggle for survival. Microbes can use the elements in synthesis but must decompose the organic compounds synthesized by plants to provide the necessary energy. Plants, in turn, profit in their extended survival because the microbes simplify the accumulated organic matter to keep the soil's inorganic elements and the atmosphere's organic elements—carbon and nitrogen—in cycles of reuse. Otherwise the accumulated products of plants would contaminate their own environment.

Plants and microbes may be considered in a symbiosis for survival independent of more complex populations. But even that symbiosis may be disrupted by one or the other symbiont acting as a competitor, a parasite, or a predator. Either may even produce contamination by its waste products: plant compounds may be poisons for microbes and microbes may be poisons for plants. By competing for essential inorganic elements—calcium, magnesium, phosphorus, potassium, nitrogen, sulfur—and the several "trace" elements, one may limit the other via the soil.

All trophic levels above the plants must live by the compounds of the latter's synthesis—carbohydrates for energy; proteins for growth of tissue, protection, and reproduction; and inorgano-organic combinations associated with the proteins. Proteins in plants result, not from photosynthesis, but from the plant's biochemical processes, which require expenditures of stored energy and assembly of inorganic and organic requirements by the roots. The roots penetrate only a limited volume of soil, living there largely through activities of the decomposers. Plants, like microbes, use carbon dioxide waste—from the roots—to produce active hydrogen in the resulting carbonic acid to mobilize the soil fertility elements for plant survival. These two populations, the producers and the decomposers, as contaminants or as transformers, determine the environmental support of all other populations.

THE PREDATORS

All the heterotrophic populations crowd each other to get to the food delivered to them by that mundane team of autotrophs—the symbiotic team of microbes and plants. That crowding, under the deficiencies provoking it, makes the wastes of each a contamination for the other whenever the natural processes of the producers and decomposers are disrupted. All populations above plants and microbes are included in the third category: the predators. They prey upon the plant population, and upon each other to an increasing degree, since the plants are not nourished by the living soil completely enough to be ample prey for man and all the other predators and parasites.

Predators—other than man—do not destroy their prey completely before the numbers of predators drop down so far that the numbers of prey mount to domination again. Increase in prey favors an increase in predators, and then, in turn, a decrease in prey, to yield naturally alternating dominations but not the extinction of either. But man is not merely the predator of one trophic level; he also aims his technology at complete extinction of many populations. Thus he breaks the law of predator-prey relations and of survival. When he causes extinction, he reduces the number of basic segments by which the biotic pyramid supports man.

Interpopulation predations increase as the soil becomes less able to grow the vegetation of nutrition in required quality and quantity. When the soil's inorganic elements have been depleted, then the exploited soils must eventually register their damage on all trophic levels. The most serious effects fall first on man, raising the question of whether the baffling degeneration of our bodily health, now increasing our concern about what was once commonly called "disease," may not suggest patterns of hidden causes connected in some way with the climatic-fertility pattern of the soil. Thus, human ecology may develop into the most important science.

HUMAN LIFE CAME LATE AND MUST GO EARLY

When the numbers in any population are charted as a graph against a base of time, they give a sigmoid curve. Its shape suggests the top of the letter S pulled to the right while the bottom remains attached. The introduction of a single living microbe into a given volume of medium results in a slow increase in numbers with the curve moving along the near-horizontal. But soon the move turns toward the vertical, suggesting a population explosion. Then the increase lessens, ceases, and, finally, there is a population decrease followed by eventual extinction. Contamination by its accumulated non-transformed wastes, coupled with exhaustion of nutritional and other environmental supports, eliminates the population from its limited setting.

Populations of older countries, similarly charted, suggest the final third of the biotic curve. France, Scandinavia, Italy, and Spain, starting as far back as 1900, are illustrations. The United States illustrates the lower two thirds, or the beginning of the chart. Predictions from 1920 onward pointed to the falling percentages of increase, if immigrations were limited.

Since the multiplication of man still conforms to the natural laws of biological phenomena, and since human multiplication is by no means managed to give biological advantages for improved survival, we must characterize man, at this stage, as the main biological liability, not only to himself, but to the other populations supporting him. *He is the contamination in the environment.*

Man's disregard of his ecological limitation to the temperate zone—by the required supply of proteins alone—should be cited as only one powerful factor. As one moves from the temperate to the torrid and humid tropical zone, the desperate struggle for proteins at any trophic level is evident in the carnivorousness and cannibalism that are common. Here, life forms are mainly predators. The same is true as one moves from the temperate to the frigid zone.

The migrations into the frigid zone, into climatic-soil-fertility settings of little or no soil construction, are badly handicapped by the paucity of producers and decomposers. The predators win support by their carnivorousness or through lifelines reaching back into the temperate zone. In the tropics, high rainfall and temperatures have caused excessive decomposition of the rocks to the point of destruction of soils which then fail to fully nourish plant life. Even proteins are there replaced by poisonous compounds of many producers. Carnivorousness and cannibalism characterize the survival of decidedly limited populations. The dry tropics are in the same category. Populations at climatic extremes are limited because the producers, operating in combination with the decomposers, are not providing the necessary proteins in complete array, nor with their natural accompaniments.

CAN MAN MANAGE HIS OWN SPECIES?

The epoch of man is but a minute segment in the paleontological column of the earth's populations as they have come, gone, or remained. Man has shifted away from the rugged individualism of open country and its diversity of agriculture according to the laws of nature. He has collected himself into congested cities which have been said to require monocultures and chemicalized agricultures; he has controlled the environment of those cities according to the dictates of technology and economics, disregarding nature's laws and even his own biochemistry.

During the latest part of the brief epoch of man's existence, his technologies and their political complications have served to harvest the natural living resources, to exploit soil fertility and to compel the human march from east to west. The march has rolled on until the resources of most recent possession—those of the western hemisphere—are dwindling rapidly under the political demand for coexistence of the Western world with those bringing up the rear in the march—a total world population approaching three billion predators.

Because they must behave according to the natural laws controlling biological bodies, each population below man has—through evolution—exhibited itself as a climax crop for a limited time in its limited ecological setting. But man, with mental capacity transcending that of the others, has used most of the other levels to his advantage and their disadvantage so that, in general, he does not conform to the pattern of evolution. His technological powers disrupt the pattern and destroy the very conformers that support him. Unwittingly, his development and management of environmental control over materials and energy have increased the contamination of the soil and the atmosphere. He has destroyed the decomposer populations to the extent that the natural basic support of the producers is weakening; the entire biotic pyramid is tumbling because of man's dominance at the top.

In managing her contaminations, nature either transforms them through biotic disposers in the surface soil, or buries them safely at greater depths. Man, managing his contaminations as a helpless novice, seems to be on his way to his own destruction by and amongst them. In all probability, nature, not he, will determine the final outcome.

31

Space Tracks

Dwain W. Warner

In the few years that have passed since the mid-Twentieth Century, we have come to the realization that technology has developed both the power and the tools to enable us to explore more completely earth, space, our moon, and even nearby planets. These explorations, which at present fall almost entirely in the realm of the physical sciences and engineering, are proceeding at a rate few can grasp.

Meanwhile, biologists, and especially those concerned with the studies of the natural environment and its faunal and floral elements, have noted the marvelous accomplishments with mixed feelings. Particularly they have envied the new tools for making numerous measurements,

Dwain W. Warner, "Space Tracks," *Natural History*, Vol. 72 (1965), pp. 8-15. Courtesy of NATURAL HISTORY.

which in turn, have led to the accumulation of vast amounts of information. The field biologist, unfortunately, still depends largely on sight and hearing for his information and, as a result, often obtains data too discontinuous and incomplete for reliable statistical analyses and interpretation. Yet the same biologist also recognizes that the information and measurements that have been collected by the physical scientist, who have always been considered to be in a discipline apart, have been but little concerned with life of the earth on which we live. Interdisciplinary research between biologists, physical scientists, and engineers in studies of our natural environment has been slow and pursued with reluctance.

More than thirty years ago the conflict was expressed by the pioneer ecologist Dr. Royal Chapman who, in 1929, wrote: "Ecology is bound to become quantitative. Many of us are observing this inevitable tendency with regret. There is a feeling that the wonders of observational natural history are to be brushed aside by the cold, dry calculations of a mechanistic mathematics. . . ." But he added: "The urgent needs are, first, more accurate measurements of environmental factors and the populations which make up the natural associations, and, in the second place, better methods of evaluating the measurements of the factors."

A brief review of one aspect of man's efforts in these directions may help to put into better perspective the need for expanding interdisciplinary research and the real potential of modern instrumentation as applied to the biological sciences.

Watching and listening to the passage of animals in their seasonal migrations has been a necessary and traditional behavior pattern of man since he began to evolve as a flesh eater. Increasing curiosity about bird migrations led to the first markings of individual birds several hundred years ago, and the usefulness of this technique was well recognized by the early 1900's. As a result, several million birds and many other animals have been tagged with numbered metal bands or with various color markers. But this method has told us only a little of an animal's movements, for band recoveries represent a relatively small percentage of the marked animals. Usually, all we have available as an end result are two points on a map—the banding and recovery sites—with a known time interval, but an unknown distance of travel, between. This information has served many purposes, but has contributed little or nothing to understanding the animal's orientation, navigation, or relationship and responses to its environment.

Now, observations of an animal's motility are of utmost significance. Since the environment apparently furnishes or modifies the stimuli that trigger basic responses, the ability to follow an animal's movements continuously and to attempt to correlate these movements with environmental factors seems essential to advances in ecology. Nearly all animals are at some time motile, and since the causal factors of this motivation are not adequately understood, major emphasis must be given to a continuous recording of animal movements correlated with other environmental events.

For instance, various researchers have gathered data indicating a relationship between the distribution and abundance of animal populations and the biotic and physical forces of their natural environments. However, only a few quantitative studies on an individual animal's motile responses to environmental factors have been attempted *under natural conditions.* In addition, relatively few studies have been concerned with accurate measurements of the effects animals have on their immediate microclimates and the relation of these alterations to the animal itself and to its habitat.

In order to describe a total energy balance of an environment, the following physical properties must be measured: absorbed and reflected solar and infrared radiations, air and soil temperatures, relative and absolute humidities, precipitation, and barometric pressures. Current advances in instrumentation give hope for truly accurate measurements of these and many other variables. Movement studies have previously been based almost entirely on visual observation, recapture of previously trapped and marked individuals, and on the appearance in study areas of species intermittently captured by various sampling methods. From these studies have come current interpretations of an animal's response to environmental change, the area of its "home range," its migration and dispersal, population structure, and even conclusions on systematics, evolution, and biogeography. Under conditions of adversity, an animal adjusts physiologically (for example, by changing heart, respiratory, and metabolic rates). It may shift its position in its normal home area; it may migrate; it may die. If we use the problem of animal movements and environmental stimuli as a basis for interdisciplinary research among engineers, physical scientists, and biologists, what can we present as a feasible technique to give us results of an importance equal to those being obtained by researchers in the physical sciences?

Of course, the development of radar during World War II enabled us to "see" movements of birds both day and night on the radarscope and on film, and also to see weather and the responses of the birds to it. It now allows us to measure, within the radar's range, the magnitude and speed of the migration, altitudes of flight, and direction. But we cannot very accurately identify the birds as species nor can we distinguish between individuals and flocks. The use of radar by biologists evolved slowly—partly as a result of wartime security measures and partly because of the reluctance of many scientists to recognize that nearly all "angels" seen on radar were really birds. (See NATURAL HISTORY, October, 1961.)

Within the last three or four years, the availability of transistors and other miniature and now microminiature electronic components has given us another major breakthrough in the study of animal movements in their natural environment. Tiny radio transmitters, which, together with batteries, weigh less than an ounce and which can transmit a signal for weeks, have been placed on or in animals. To date, ruffed grouse, cottontail rabbits, woodchucks, porcupines, skunks, and other animals have been located intermittently by portable receivers carried in the field. Some of the results obtained have been both surprising and dramatic. The transmitted signal was sometimes altered by the behavior of the animal and by one or more body functions. Changes in the signal have distinguished between a resting and a flying bird, and analyses of signals recorded on paper have given accurate measurements of rates of respiration and wingbeats of a mallard duck.

Information on relatively sedentary animals and their environments may become known by telemetering data to ground stations over short distances. But radio signals do not curve, as does the earth's surface, so signals traveling along the ground are largely lost over any considerable distance. Thus, tracking long migratory movements would require either numerous receiving antennas on ground towers or planes equipped with receivers—a tremendous expenditure in equipment and manpower.

Is there any way we could obtain line-of-sight radio signals from numerous animals that may be moving over vast distances in all three of the earth's mediums? How can we find out where the penguins of Antarctica go after mating season; the routes of the wandering albatross or the Caribbean turtle; the forces governing caribou movements; the track of the Canada goose? One tool in common current use by physical scientists and engineers could answer all these and many more. That is the artificial satellite.

Satellites carrying various intruments have already relayed back to earth vast amounts of data in the fields of geophysics, radiation, and other aspects of space studies. Most instruments for making these measurements and the radio transmitters for sending the data back to earth are very small in size and light in weight. What equipment would be needed to locate animals on various parts of the globe and to transmit the information back to earth? To obtain the necessary calculations, I went to my colleague, William W. Cochran, Director of the Bioelectronics Laboratory in the Minnesota Museum of Natural History. His experience in designing and building both satellite- and animal-borne radio transmitters and receivers places the following instrumentation plan beyond the realm of mere speculation.

A satellite could be instrumented to receive and relay to ground stations the signals obtained from many transmitter-carrying animals in various parts of the world. Initially, we might seek only the migration track of each animal. Cloud patterns and perhaps other meteorological and geophysical data that might affect animal movements might be available from measurements made by other projects (such as the Tiros satellites) for areas of the earth over which birds would fly or swim. These data could provide information on such phenomena as disorientation of birds under conditions of overcast. Successes in tracking animals on a world-wide basis by the use of a satellite would, it is hoped, provide guides for further instrumentation to telemeter one or two physiological or environmental factors concurrently with migratory movements.

Species that could be tracked by this method, and for which prototype transmitters have already been designed and tested, are larger birds such as geese, swans, cranes, penguins, and albatrosses. Among mammals the caribou could be tracked in its migrations. Species in these groups are large enough to carry currently available transmitters and power supply. Their modes and regions of travel and their physical environments are so different that numerous tests of the instrumentation could be provided effectively. For example, Canada, blue, and snow geese, which could be tagged with radio transmitters, pass over much of continental North America, moving mostly in long, direct flights. The longest nonstop flight is probably from James Bay, the southern extension of Hudson Bay, to the Gulf Coast of Louisiana and east Texas.

Instrumentation to track these and other animals on a global basis could be relatively simple. Each animal could carry a transmitter and power supply weighing approximately 20 to 60 grams. The satellite, traveling 18,000 miles an hour (approximately 5 miles per second), at an altitude of 200 miles above the earth in a polar orbit, would cross over both North and South Poles once about every 103 minutes. In the satellite would be a receiver and transmitter weighing a few pounds—or possibly even less—and occupying perhaps half of one cubic foot of space. Power supply, of course, would require additional weight and space, but might be supplied by solar cells, which would extend the period of tracking and would weigh less than batteries.

In order to receive the signals from the satellite at all times in its flight, twenty-four optimum-located receiving stations would cover the earth. A tape recorder at each of the ground stations would record the signal that had been received in the satellite from an animal-borne transmitter and then retransmitted to earth. This tape would then be run through an audiospectrometer. The spectrograph would be displayed and used—together with the known positions of the satellite in its passes within the line-of-sight range of each animal—to locate the animals at various times of day and night.

Some of the details of this tracking method might be of interest. The tiny radio transmitters, each with its battery pack, would be no larger than the first joint of a thumb. It would be attached to a simple harness with the antenna forming one of the harness loops around the body of the animal. It has already been found that animals adjust relatively easily to harnesses that do not inconvenience their habits. The entire unit would weigh some two ounces or less, depending on the number of batteries. The transmitter signals would be intermittent pulses, each at a slightly different frequency and, therefore, distinguishable from others in the same part of the earth.

To help determine just how far a signal from these small instruments could be received, we attached half-ounce transmitters to high-altitude balloons used for research by the University of Minnesota Department of Physics. With radiated power of much less than one microwatt—far less than that anticipated for satellite tracking—we received the signal from 270 miles away when the balloon was 25 miles above the earth. And this was in a region of considerable radio interference. The test adequately demonstrated the feasibility of long-range line-of-sight transmission.

The proposed satellite would contain a receiver and an antenna tuned to that band of frequencies occupied by the transmitters. Satellite transmitter power should be at 500 microwatts to assure a satisfactory signal (distinguishable from all types of interference) at the ground receiving sites. A lower power could be used at the expense of adding or utilizing more ground receiving sites.

Signals from the satellite could be received by a ground station at a distance of about 1,200 miles. The satellite could receive signals from the animals up to about 800 miles. Thus, the effective coverage area for one receiving station for tracking animals is about 4,000 miles across. Therefore, one station near the center of North America could conceivably cover most of the United States and Canada. A few stations in the Pacific islands could cover the whole Pacific area.

Each orbit of the satellite "scans" a swath about 1,600 miles across. The overlap in successive orbits depends upon the latitude. No overlap would occur at the Equator and a 100 per cent overlap would occur at the Poles. Thus, in equatorial zones, two locations, or fixes, a day are possible. In temperate latitudes, four fixes daily are possible, and in arctic latitudes about 14 (the number of orbits per day). Of course, to get a fix the satellite must be in range of both the receiver and the tag on the animal, so the maximum number of fixes is obtained only if ideal receiver distribution is used—that is, at least one receiver must be so located as to cover any point in the area concerned. This means that receivers can be spaced somewhat less than 1,200 miles apart, depending on the area covered, whereas for computing coverage, a radius of about 2,000 miles from the ground station can be used. For example, on Pass No. 1 of the satelllite both ground station receiver and tag transmitter are in range of the satellite; but on Pass No. 2 only the tag is in its range. Thus, if we consider the number of fixes as the number of times the satellite is in tag range, we must provide receiver coverage to insure satellite contact. This means an overlap of receiver circles, each 1,200 miles across. But if we are only interested in complete coverage and not in the maximum number of fixes possible each day, we can use overlapping 2,000-mile circles. This is of importance at low latitudes, where tagged animals could be missed.

We have said that if a satellite is 200 miles high it will cross over both the North and South Poles once every 103 minutes, or every one hour and 43 minutes. (Its orbit can be thought of as fixed in space, for although precession occurs, it is very gradual.) If the satellite passes northward over point A on the Equator at noon, it will pass southward over the Equator 51½ minutes later, approximately on the opposite side of the earth. About 103 minutes later it will return, but this time it will pass over the Equator about 1,600 miles *east* of point A, which is the distance earth (and point A) has rotated during the satellite's orbit. The next orbit will be about 3,200 miles east of point A, and seven orbits after crossing A the first time, the satellite will pass over the Equator about 11,500 miles east of A, going north. Since 11,500 miles is about one half the circumference of the earth, point A will see the satellite coming south on its seventh orbit.

In each ground receiving system would be one FM receiver and associated antenna tuned to the frequency of the satellite transmitter, one two-channel tape recorder, and one highly accurate clock to emit sound signals that could be recorded as time intervals. Equipment of this type is available and relatively simple to operate.

Each time the satellite passed within the 1,200-mile maximum range, a recording would be made of the modulation of the satellite transmitter and, on the tape's other recorder channel, of time tones accurate to one second (the satellite travels at five miles per second). These recordings are preserved for analysis. The signals from the transmitters may or may not be heard through the interference, depending on the distance between the satellite and the tagged animals. Much of the time they will be inaudible. The tapes will be run through an audiospectrometer with a resolution of 10 cycles per second, or less; the narrow band width of the spectrometer will reduce the interference to a point at which the signals are discernible.

When these signals are plotted on paper as radio frequency versus time, they form an S-shaped curve. This curve is a result of the Doppler effect between the satellite receiver and the signals coming to it from the transmitter on the animal. This curve, plus accurate time, plus the satellite's path would enable us to locate the animal in a circle 50 miles or less across.

Paradoxically, extracting these data from a single tape may take some

1,500 times as long (about four continuous days) as the four minutes or so required to record it initially, although the time could be reduced by using audiospectrometers with higher capacity.

The complexity of analyzing the tapes suggests the creation and use of analysis centers. And here still another field is introduced into this cooperative scientific venture—the adequate utilization of computers whose programing could be jointly undertaken by physical and biological scientists. The information that could conceivably be transmitted by, say, a goose equipped with a transmitter, is almost limitless, at least theoretically. The speed, altitude, and direction of flight are only a few examples. Wing-beat and respiration rates could be sent to the satellite, as could temperatures of the individual animals. These factors could be examined by one of the new biological computers, which have been specially designed to extract desired information from tapes that might be cluttered with various kinds of interference. Latitude and longitude calculations to locate the animals could also be determined to accuracies of about 20 miles, depending on the particular electronic system utilized.

With knowledge of long-distance movements of only a few kinds of animals in various parts of the world, we could begin to obtain data on environmental and physiological factors, and with these to work with, answers could be found to such questions as: does the wandering albatross really wander, or does it follow routes prescribed by environmental factors?

To plan ways in which to use natural resources properly and to expand basic knowledge of the earth's ecologies, more extensive information on the biological and physical factors of the natural environment is obviously essential. It is also essential that such information be acquired at a rapid enough pace to bridge the gap that now exists in data acquisition between the physical and the biological sciences. If biologists are ever to participate in the application, to their own disciplines, of measurement programs such as those demonstrated during the I.G.Y., they must be ready to understand and to use advanced instrumentation whenever it is expedient.

On the last day of October, 1962, seven Canada geese, each wearing one of our transmitters, were monitored at their mid-continent stopover before the last leg of their fall migration flight from the Arctic to Texas. For twelve days previously they had done little flying—they ate, preened, walked, or swam. At that time we could determine the location of each goose and what each was doing by the signals from their transmitters. During those twelve days we learned much about goose behavior at a stopover area. When they left on that last long flight, and disappeared over the horizon, their signals were lost to us on the ground. But those signals were still being sent out into space where, if a satellite had been "listening," it might have been able to tell us infinitely more than we know now about the mysteries of migration.

32

Bird Migration

There is little to attract visitors to the sparsely-settled Baraba steppe of western Siberia; the landscape is uninspiring, the summers are dry, and winter comes early and is harsh. Yet this otherwise uninviting land is the site of Lake Chany, which covers 1300 square miles, and creates one of the finest wildfowl nesting areas in the world. Much of the marsh land near the lake has been reclaimed and is farmed by the Ural-Yenisei Agricultural Collective; but the men and machines who work the rich, black soil disturb the tranquility of the lake region only twice each year, first to sow and then to harvest. By early August, the harvesting crews have already come and gone, taking with them the crop of early ripening wheat. Thus there is seldom a witness, unless by a naturalist come for that purpose, to the yearly gathering of the Graylag Geese on the marshy south shore of Lake Chany.

The geese have mated during the spring, and have passed the summer incubating the eggs and rearing the six or so goslings born to each couple (life-long monogamy and familial togetherness is the rule among geese). One evening in early autumn—August is early autumn in Siberia—the geese cease feeding and splashing among the heavy growth of reeds that mask much of the lake. A day or so of general restlessness follows, and then the birds begin to gravitate to one particular point on the lake shore. As if drawn by a magnet, they waddle and swim from points all around Chany. Gathering by tens of thousands, they wait briefly until all the families have arrived, and silently set off on one of the least understood events in the natural history of birds, the yearly migration.

AN ARMY ON THE MARCH

Many types of birds nest along the shore of Lake Chany, and in the fall migrate to various destinations. In the case of the Graylags, the goal is the great Ganges Valley about 2000 miles away. In making the passage,

"Bird Migration," *The Sciences,* Vol. 5(1) (1965), pp. 1-5. Reprinted by permission of The New York Academy of Sciences.

some of the most forbidding terrain in the world will be crossed. Often flying at altitudes in excess of 16,000 feet, the birds will clear range after range of mountains, skim above desolate high plateaus, and battle fierce Himalayan gales. They will complete the trip in about three weeks.

Offhand, three weeks does not seem like a particularly speedy journey for these wildfowl, who can cruise at 45 miles per hour all night long, and who are capable of speeds up to 70 m.p.h. But allowances must be made, because when they begin their journey, the Graylags cannot fly. The geese start southward almost as one, a silent army some five miles wide; in the next ten days they will cover somewhat over 100 miles—on foot.

In *The Great Migrations* (Macmillan, 1960) Georges Blond describes this marching exodus of the Graylags. The birds must walk at first, he points out, because the overpowering urge to migrate comes upon them while they are still molting. The old wing feathers have been shed and the new growth is not complete. Yet if the geese would only wait another 10 or 12 days at Lake Chany, they would be able to fly over their walking route in less than three hours. Why then do they strike south at such an unpropitious time? Or, to raise the larger question that ornithologists have yet to fully answer, how does any migratory species know when the time has arrived to be moving on?

THE PUZZLING URGE TO MIGRATE

Broadly speaking, of course, migratory birds travel for self-preservation. Unlike the sedentary species which are able to cope with changing conditions of weather, food, shelter and the like, the migrants must either seek more favorable locales or perish. It appears unlikely, however, that changes in temperature, food supply, or cover vegetation are, as biologists once thought, solely responsible for launching the birds on their way. There are many known cases when a premature change in the weather has wiped out entire flocks, because the time to migrate had not yet arrived. The birds simply sat and froze to death. Another theory has had it that sex hormones, which are produced in greater and lesser quantities at certain times of the year, were chiefly responsible for initiating migration. Injection with male sex hormones, for example, causes an increase in fatty tissue in many migratory species. It is from fat deposits that birds derive the energy needed for their arduous flights. But as with changes in the environment, the level of sex hormones cannot be the sole determining factor of when to migrate. It is known that castrated birds will also migrate at the appropriate time.

Currently, one of the most favorably received theories is that a change in the activity of the hypophysis gland, which stimulates the gonads and performs other physiological functions, is the triggering mechanism. This glandular change is thought by some ornithologists to be influenced by the seasonal increase or decrease of daylight hours. Yet like all previous theories, there are exceptions to this one also. Birds in the tropics begin to migrate although changes in the photoperiod are so slight as to be nearly imperceptible. Thus, it is likely that different species respond to different clues, and many biologists are of the opinion that some of these clues are so subtle that, to date, only the birds are aware of them.

Many of the Graylags are lost during the walking phase of their migration. Villagers, and their dogs, waylay and slaughter thousands of the birds for food. But the loss is proportionately small, and the tenth night's march brings the survivors to Lake Kulunda, southeast of their summer home. Here the birds rest for three days.

On the fourth day, there is considerable pre-dawn activity. The wing feathers are now grown in, and every family makes short test flights. Then, with the first light of dawn, the entire army of geese takes to the air. For as long as their route keeps them over the steppes, the geese fly in broad waves, one parallel line after another, each line stretching over several miles. But at the edge of the steppes lie the mountains, and to fly over this terrain a more flexible formation is needed. Thus, an observer on the ground hears a sudden increase in gabbling, or "talk"; the long lines break into fragments, and each fragment smoothly adjusts itself into the familiar "V" formation of migrating wild geese.

Once the geese take wing, they complete their trip in good time. Flying only while it is dark, they cover from 160 to 220 miles each night, with one night's flight extended to 300 miles so as to avoid landing on a spur of the Gobi Desert. Storms, treacherous down drafts, and birds of prey will take a heavy toll before the geese reach the Ganges Valley. In the early spring, the Graylags will retrace their route and return to the breeding grounds at Lake Chany.

NAVIGATING BY DAYLIGHT

Whether the migratory route is 9300 miles long, as that travelled by the American Golden Plover which flies from north of Newfoundland to the Argentine pampas, or the more modest 2000-mile trip of the Graylags, perhaps the most puzzling aspects of these yearly flights is the navigation involved. When the birds are near their breeding grounds or wintering

area, it is probable that they orient themselves by sighting familiar landmarks. It is known that migratory birds possess a remarkable visual memory. But what about the vast stretches between summer and winter homes?
It is most unlikely that any bird could remember enough landmarks, and
their relationship to other landmarks, to navigate thousands of miles. In
any case, landmarks are of little value to night-flying birds. Moreover, it is
known that some, and perhaps most, migratory species can orient themselves and head for home even when released in distant and completely
alien lands.

Considerable experimental evidence suggests that some birds may
look upward, rather than to the ground, for orientation. German researchers detained birds whose restlessness indicated they were ready to migrate.
The birds were kept in a closed room; periodically sunlight was allowed to
enter from one or another opening in the walls and ceiling. The birds always maintained the same general orientation to the sun, just as they
would have had in flight. Diffusing the light, as if the day were overcast,
tended to confuse the birds. Since the position of the sun shifts during each
day, it appears that migrants must have some means, perhaps a "metabolic
clock," to correct for this shift so as to remain flying on target.

STEERING BY THE STARS

It seems that many night-flying species guide themselves by the stars.
European warblers used in one series of tests were exposed to the night
"sky" of a planetarium. The flight pattern of these birds in the wild was
known, and as their apparent location was changed (by altering the position of the stars on the planetarium dome) the birds oriented themselves
in their cages to correct for these changes, just as they would do in flight.

These and other experiments into bird navigation are explained further by Dr. Wesley E. Lanyon (American Museum of Natural History) in
his book *Biology of Birds* (The Natural History Press, 1964). As Dr. Lanyon made clear, although naturalists now have some idea about the nature
of the signposts used by migratory birds, the actual mechanism of navigation still remains obscure. But, however they manage it, it is certain that
the Graylags will cease feeding one evening this August, and leaving behind the plants, grubs and seeds so prodigally provided at Lake Chany,
will unhesitantly begin to shuffle across the Siberian steppes, right on
course for the distant Ganges.

33

The Flower and the Bee

Mary S. Percival

'The might of Britain depends on its old maids.' Old maids keep cats. Cats kill mice. Empty mouse holes form good nesting places for bumble bees. Bumble bees pollinate red clover, clover feeds beef—beef gives Britons their drive and energy!

Even if this chain reaction appears somewhat fanciful, we have abundant evidence that our crop economy is geared to this amazing strong, yet delicate, link between the plant and insect kingdoms—between *the Flower and the Bee.*

I want to discuss some facets of this remarkable relationship and to indicate current lines of research in this field, which are biased, as you might expect, towards man's attempt to exploit it and profit by it.

POLLINATION

All flowering plants are highly specialised organisms, and one result of this is that there is a separation in space between the male and female organs in the flower (stamens and ovaries), so it becomes necessary for the pollen to be carried in some way or other over this spatial barrier. This transference and placing of pollen grains on the receptive stigma of the ovary is what we term *pollination*—whether or not *fertilisation* and seed set follows is entirely due to whether the right kind of pollen has been placed on the stigma.

Reproduced by permission of the Editor from *The Advancement of Science,* Vol. 18 (1961), pp. 148-152. We acknowledge with thanks the author's permission to publish.

Wind, water, birds and insects may all act as pollinating agencies and bridge the gap, not only in individual flowers, but between one flower and another or between one plant and another effecting cross-pollination.

Many floral forms make self-pollination virtually impossible and establish an *outbreeding* mechanism for the species.

This appears to be a present-day evolutionary platform in many Angiosperm species. But will it remain so? The dandelions and hawkweeds have already evolved to another method of reproduction, *not using pollen at all*. They are *apomictic*, i.e., their seeds develop without fertilisation. Although their flowers still exhibit a beautiful mechanism for cross-pollination by insects backed up by a liquid inducement of concentrated nectar, it is obsolete. Try it yourselves by cutting off the stamens and styles of a dandelion head: it will still set good seed.

Entomophilous flowers, i.e. those pollinated by insects, exhibit many features which we find pleasing—colour, scent, form—but bees only visit flowers for food, pollen and nectar for rearing their grubs, for their daily needs, and, in the case of the *honey bee* for winter store as honey or packed pollen. An inhibitory substance in the pharyngeal glands of the bee prevents *germination* of pollen in cells which would possibly ferment the honey and ruin the winter store. But we now know, as a result of many fine researches on the senses of the bees, that these other attributes (colour, scent, form) have a meaning for the bees and therefore assist in attracting them as pollinators.

The delicacy and precision of the bees' senses can be judged from the following facts:

SENSE OF SMELL

Bees can distinguish, recognise and remember flower scents. They can pick out one flower perfume from amidst thirty others. They are also very sensitive to the scent they themselves extrude from their abdominal scent organ.

COLOUR SENSE

They can distinguish, recognise and remember three regions of the visible spectrum and ultra violet. This latter is a very real 'colour' for the bees and some flowers which appear self-coloured to us, may be exhibiting a colour contrast for the bees' eyes. For example, in *Mimulus* and the *Yel-*

low Flag Iris the opening to the flower tube is shown by strong ultra-violet radiation from the petals at this point. The bee will perceive this as a guide to the nectar of ultra violet on a yellow ground.

SENSE OF TASTE

Bees can appreciate degrees of sweetness and even show preference for certain mixtures of sugars. Dr. Raw of Rothamsted reported that consistent preferences were shown for single sugars in the following descending order:

(*a*) sucrose;
(*b*) glucose;
(*c*) maltose;
(*d*) fructose;

but when a mixture was offered, an anomalous high preference for sucrose–glucose–fructose solution, which was quite different from predicted preference on the basis of an additive effect of the constituent sugars.

Recently it has been shown that the families which contain so many 'bee' flowers actually have this mixture of sugars in their nectar.

Also in several 'climax' groups of plants such as the Crucifers (cabbages), the nectar is composed of simple digestible monosaccharides—fructose and glucose—in virtually the same proportions as are found in honey. So, many of these highly evolved 'modern' plants are producing a nectar which is technically a 'honey' already. The digestive invertase of the Hymenopteran (bee) visitors is not required! The nectar can be assimilated immediately by the insect. Has this any biological significance?

To return to the bee senses. Von Frisch has proved that the bees can communicate their sensual experiences to their hive mates by dancing and hence recruit workers to forage a particular crop.

But this emphasises a difference between the hive and bumble bee. Honey bees do not connect the flowers with food instinctively and have to learn that their food is in the flower. Whereas a novice bumble bee worker on her first foraging flight will fly straight to a flower.

TIME SENSE

This is highly developed in the honey bee. There is some evidence that this may be employed in pollen collecting. It has been found that different species 'present' their pollen at different times of day, e.g.:

Poppy	early morning (peak 6 a.m. (5–10 a.m.)
Dandelion	morning (peak 10–11 a.m.)
Raspberries and blackberries	all day
Broad beans	afternoon (12 noon–3 p.m.)
Vegetable marrow	night (10 p.m.–3 a.m.)

In a number of species the rhythm of pollen presentation shows a positive correlation with the rhythm of pollen collection by the bees. For example, in the Water Plantain pollen is presented from 11 a.m. to noon. Just before 11 a.m. bees will arrive and scout among the plants to see if any flowers are open (flower opening and anther dehiscence is simultaneous). It is not only bees which have this time sense. In the early morning, hover flies have been seen clinging, head downwards, on the undehisced anthers of maize, lipping around the terminal pore of the anther and waiting for opening time. So this time sense can be employed for the mutual benefit of both plant and insect for in all cases of bees collecting pollen it was seen that pollination was also effected.

RAPIDITY OF LEARNING

This is a striking feature of honey-bee psychology. To quote one, e.g., a 'Novice' bee on maize searched in between the glumes of the male flowers for 'something', then by chance passed under a group of stamens and dislodged some pollen on to herself and immediately turned on to her back and began to collect pollen.

INDIVIDUAL TRAITS

Bees exhibit quite individual traits in collecting nectar and pollen. The pollen collectors are like women shopping, some neat and expeditious in their pollen packing, others much slower. One working the broom by shouldering between the standard and keel of the young flower, was able to remove all the pollen without springing the flower.

Then there are those bees which the American orchardists call 'stinkers', which take the nectar from apple-blossom while clinging to the outside of the flower, thus failing to pollinate them.

And here is a link between bee physiology and flower physiology. In early spring, fresh pollen is urgently required by the bee colonies for brood rearing. Flowers blooming in February, March and April require a temperature from 8·8–10° C. (50° F.) for free anthesis (free production of pollen). 10° C. has been stated to be the limiting temperature for (hive) bee flight; inaction of the wing muscles is said to occur below this. It is seen that the February–April flowers have pollen available at a slightly lower temperature than this. So there is a pretty balance here, the bee food being available in the flowers at just about the same temperature level that the pollinating insect can fly. There is yet another parallel. Crocus and snowdrop flowers open at 4° and 5° C. respectively if in sunlight, and the bees were seen working these crops at 4° and 5·7° C. respectively if it was sunny. So direct sunlight compensates for the lower air temperature at a comparable level for both insect flight and flower opening.

There are other attributes of bee psychology which facilitate pollination. *Constancy* is one of the foremost of these. Coupled with the honey bee's sense of location it is immensely valuable to agriculturalist and orchardist. As long as the food—be it nectar or pollen—is plentiful, the bees will continue to visit a crop exclusively. But there is a danger in this very constancy, for, other things being equal, bees will be attracted to crops with the strongest nectar. They may even select individuals in *one crop*.

Take the case of the orchardist. Cross-pollination is essential for fruit set in certain 'self-sterile' varieties of apple (or plum), so orchardists frequently plant a mixture of varieties in the expectation that the bees will effect this.

But see what happened in an American plum orchard. Three varieties were planted, the sugar concentrations of whose nectar differed considerably:

Maynard	10·1 per cent sugar in nectar
Eldorado	14·9 ” ” ” ” ”
Milton	28·4 ” ” ” ” ”

Milton attracted most bees and was well pollinated, and note that it would receive pollen from its own race. Now, if the variety is self-fertile, this is satisfactory, its 'pollination potential' is high if honey bees are the pollinators. If however, taking a hypothetical case, the variety was self-sterile its pollination potential would be very low.

This would also be so if it was self-sterile (or fertile) and had very weak nectar. It would only succeed in being cross-pollinated if it could compete on even terms, as regards nectar concentration with neighbouring varieties for the bees' services.

So a plant may miss the biological bus in this way. Another example of this is recorded by Vansell in Oregon.

Some plants have nectaries outside the flowers, e.g. on leaves, petioles, stipules, the so called extrafloral nectaries:

Plant	Nectar	Percentage sugar
Common Vetch	blossom	22·6
" "	stipular	56·5
Hungarian Vetch	blossom	25·2
" "	stipular	47·7

The bees work stipular nectars assiduously and neglect the flowers—these species have also missed the bus!

Another example of biological misfortune occurs in the loco weed (*Astragalus lentiginosus*), Nevada, and the buck eye (*Aesculus californica*). Both produce poisonous nectar, containing selenium and alkaloid, respectively. These are deadly to bees and *Aesculus* is particularly dangerous because the nectar is very concentrated (almost supersaturated). Even the movement of a flower may prejudice its pollination potential. For example, when a bee alights on a legume flower, she 'trips' it. The wings and keel are pressed down and the stamens spring up and shower her with pollen. This latter action in Alfalfa (*Medicago sativa*), is so violent and deals the honey bee such a shrewd blow, that some workers say she is disconcerted and deterred from further foraging. Dr. Nielsen in Denmark has found a strain where the staminal column is nearly straight and does not strike the bee. It may have an economic future.

INTERDEPENDENCE OF FLOWERS AND BEES

Bees will exploit any flower in which they find 'good' nectar (probably that containing over 18·0 per cent sugar) but some flowers with deep-seated nectar in long-tubed flowers are dependent on bees for pollination. This link may be very close, e.g. in certain *Aconitum* spp. (Monkshood), where the geographical range of the species in Europe and the range of certain long-tongued *Bombi* is said to coincide. There are other close links.

There is sometimes a coincidence of the 'imago' stage of some wild bees and the flowering of certain plants, a classic example being the Pickerel Weed (*Pontederia cordata*) and the Pickerel Weed bee (*Halictoides novae-angliae*). The flowering of the former coincides with appearance of bee, and it is believed that the bee does not visit any other plant for nectar or pollen. It is a *monotropic* bee.

Others are 'oligotropic', the Vernal Andrenas visiting only species of Willow and the Autumnal Andrenas visiting only species of Golden Rod.

Dr. Gorton Linsley reports that perhaps the most exquisitely precise bee-flower associations occur in the Californian desert between a species of *Oenothera* (Evening Primrose genus) and a black solitary bee (Anthophorid). Before dawn it is cold, dark and silent. As the first light comes, the flowers of the *Oenothera* open their petals and face the place where the sun will rise. As the sun strikes them, the stamens, which stick out in front, release their pollen. At this very moment, the black bees arrive, land on the stiff stamens, and whip off the pollen (and pollinate the flowers). The desert is bright with flowers and humming with bees. In an hour, the flowers have collapsed limp and dying in the hot sun, the bees have disappeared into cool crannies and all is still and dead once more.

BEE BEHAVIOUR AND THE EVOLUTION OF PLANT SPECIES

The behaviour of bees may vitally affect the evolution of plant species. Related species growing wild may occupy the same range without apparently hybridising but when brought into breeding plots will hybridise freely! So the barriers to interbreeding cannot involve incompatability or hybrid sterility.

But it may be that interspecific pollination is not occurring in the wild because the pollinating systems of the plants are acting as isolating mechanisms. Verne Grant (U.S.A.) says this could be because (1) the floral mechanisms of the two species may differ, so that a bee pollinating one, cannot pollinate the second—he calls this *mechanical isolation*—or (2) the bees are 'specific', or constant to a species. Here cross-pollination is mechanically possible but does not occur because of bees' flower constancy. He calls this 'ethological' isolation.

This latter type does exist among three subspecies of *Gilia*. Two of these have lavender flowers and sweet scent and the third smells of creosote, and is deep violet.

Subspecies	Colour	Scent
Gilia capitata capitata	lavender	sweet
G. capitata tomentosa	lavender	sweet
G. capitata chamissonis	deep violet	creosote

Eighty plants of these three were randomised in a plot. If a bee visited the 'creosote' plant she remained constant to it (although investigating flowers of the other two). Others worked the two 'sweet' subspecies with free interchange. This isolation held during spring, later in summer some bees on 'sweet' subspecies occasionally visited the 'creosote' flowers and vice versa but this was not customary. These field observations were reinforced by sowing the seed of all the plants and classifying the progeny as subspecies or hybrids.

The two 'sweet' subspecies produced 58·7 per cent hybrids, but there was no contamination of these two by pollen from the 'creosote' subspecies. So here one subspecies was, by the bees' action, kept genetically pure, while heterozygosity was impressed on the other two. This kind of bee behaviour might possibly be a useful tool in the hands of the geneticists.

Two of the most important fodder crops in the world today are alfalfa and red clover. The demand for red clover seed exceeds the supply, and red clover is dependent on long-tongued bumble bees for its pollination. Realisation of this important fact has been slow, resulting in such mistakes as the introduction of red clover into New Zealand, where there were no indigenous *Bombi*.

The New Zealand story is particularly interesting. The error was remedied by the importation of four species of British bumble bees (1884–5) with phenomenal success. (But even this was faulty, because one of these was *Bombus terrestris* which has a short tongue and robs the flowers of their nectar by biting through the base of the corolla tube without effecting pollination.) Yields of 400 lb. of seed per acre was averaged on the plains and, in the valleys in the hills, a prize field reached 1100 lb. per acre. Then in the plains the yields gradually dropped to 170 lb. per acre. What had happened? The bees were still there, but they had become adapted to the New Zealand climate. When first exported, they produced colonies with plenty of workers at the time when the clover was in flower. Then, gradually, their habits changed. The queens ceased to hibernate and remained active all the year, so that, to quote Mr. Anderson of the New Zealand Grassland Division of the D.S.I.R., 'the colonial maxima are now much more widely spread over the year'. So the problem had to be tackled again. Dr. Elwood Montgomery (U.S.A.) suggested that the American species *B. impatiens,* which is specially adapted to life on the plains might be introduced. The Department of Agriculture endorsed this policy but the beekeepers opposed it, because they thought it would reduce the honey crop, and they also feared the introduction of acarine disease.

Now, the tube of the flower is too long for the honey bee to exploit red clover for nectar, although they may visit it for pollen. Nevertheless, the introduction was stopped, but an educative campaign initiated by Dr. Montgomery bore fruit, and reconciled the beekeepers to the government policy. But Mr. Anderson says the scheme has not yet been implemented. . . .

What of the position in other countries? Today, in parts of America and in Scandinavia the natural population of bumble bees has been so diminished that the position is becoming critical.

Intensive methods of agriculture are responsible for this, involving, as they do, the destruction of nesting sites by the cutting down of wood-lands, elimination of 'rough' ground and the use of fencing posts as boun-daries instead of hedges. Other contributory causes are, the spraying of crops with insecticides when they are in bloom—particularly orchard trees, and the diminution of the natural flora by use of selective weed killers especially along roadsides and grass verges.

The majority of papers at the 'Symposium on Pollination' held in Copenhagen last August dealt with the problem of establishing adequate numbers of the right species of bumble bees to pollinate alfalfa and red clover. Indeed, in the States they are experimenting in the domestication of bumble bees. As the 'fall' approaches, wooden boxes, filled with sphag-num or dried grass and baited with corn, are placed along fences and edges of woods. The mice are attracted to hiberate therein and they 'work up' the moss into 'desirable residences' for the queen bees next spring! Both Danish and American workers report a substantial increase in work-er bees in the domesticated colonies. . . .

34

The Rain Forest

Marston Bates

My two favorite kinds of places in this world are coral reefs and rain forests. I don't know how I would vote if I had to choose between them, had to decide that I could go only to reefs and never to forests again, or vice versa. My idea has long been to live by a broad, sandy beach with a rain forest behind me and a coral reef offshore before me, with either open to exploration or contemplation. Maybe someday I'll achieve the ideal. There are places where it is possible—some of the islands of the South Seas, or Trinidad and Tobago in the West Indies, for instance.

Certainly they are different enough, the rain forest and the coral reef.

They have no inhabitants in common, nor even any general kinds of inhabitants in common. There is no way of comparing their appearance, either. The reef world is bright with color and movement. The forest is all green and brown, dim and still. The reef is Baroque, the forest, Gothic.

They have this in common: one is the product of the most favorable possible conditions for life in the sea, the other for life on land. Sunlight, warmth, moisture, are always abundantly present, stable, and favorable throughout the year. Moreover, they have remained about the same over long stretches of geological time. As a result, there is a tremendous variety of different kinds of organisms in both environments—and these organisms, among themselves, have developed a tremendous variety of different kinds of relationships.

"Rain forests" and "jungle" are frequently taken to mean the same thing. But I have never liked the word jungle. It has all the wrong connotations. You hack your way painfully through the lush vegetation of the jungle, dripping sweat in the steam-bath atmosphere; snakes hang from trees and lurk under foot; leopards crouch on almost every branch and there is always a tiger just beyond the impenetrable screen of foliage. There are hordes of biting, stinging and burning things. The jungle is green hell.

I doubt that there is any place, outside of books and movies, where all these conditions are combined, though certainly there is plenty of nasty and difficult country, both in the tropics and out. The thickest tangle of vegetation is the second growth that springs up after rain forest has been cleared. Everywhere in the tropics, people follow a slash-and-burn type of agriculture. Trees are felled, allowed to dry, burned, and crops planted among the charred logs. Sometimes crops are harvested for two or three years or more, but presently the land is abandoned and a new area cut. The abandoned clearing is taken over by a thick tangle of vegetation that for several years may be almost impossible to penetrate except by slow and painful cutting with a bush knife. Small mammals and rodents multiply in this vegetation, providing abundant food for the snakes that move in. Such places sometimes harbor swarms of mites, ticks, flies, mosquitoes and a wide variety of stinging things. It's about as close to a green hell as you can get.

The true rain forest, untouched, almost untrodden by man, is a very different sort of place. The forest floor is open, carpeted with the richly variegated browns of many different kinds of fallen leaves, sometimes brightly spotted with blue or red or yellow from flowers that have fallen from unseen heights above. The carpeting is thin, easily scuffed away to show the red lateritic clay soil so characteristic of the equatorial regions. There is no thick accumulation of leaf mold like that of northern forests, no rich accumulation of humus. The processes of decay are too fast to permit much organic accumulation in the soil.

There is little vegetation on the forest floor since the light is too dim for plants. There is a thin growth of tree seedlings (which have no chance to grow unless some catastrophe to a forest giant should open space), ferns, sometimes dwarf palms, or scattered thickets of huge-leaved aroids, the sort of plants that also grow well in the dim light of hotel lobbies. But basically, the forest floor is open, with vistas of a hundred feet or more, vistas framed and closed by the straight trunks of the trees that disappear into the vaulted green canopy that they support above.

The cliche often used for the forest is "cathedral-like." The comparison is inevitable: the cool, dim light, the utter stillness, the massive grandeur of the trunks of forest giants, often supported by great buttresses and interspersed with the straight, clean columns of palms and smaller trees; the gothic detail of the thick, richly carved, woody lianas plastered against the trunks or looping down from the canopy above. Awe and wonder come easily in the forest, sometimes exultation—sometimes, for a man alone there, fear. Man is out of scale: the forest is too vast, too impersonal, too variegated, too deeply shadowed. Here man needs his fellow man for reassurance. Alone, he has lost all significance.

The rain forest is perhaps more truly a silent world than the sea. The wind scarcely penetrates; it is not only silent, it is still. All sound then gains a curiously enhanced mystery. A sudden crack—what could have made it? An inexplicable gurgle. A single clear peal—that was a bird, probably a trogon. A whistle, impossible to identify. But mostly silence. The silence sometimes becomes infectious; I remember sometimes trying to blend into this world by moving along a trail without rustling a leaf with my feet or popping a twig. But more often I purposely scuffled, broke noisily through this forest where I didn't belong, tried to advertise my presence both to reassure myself and to warn the creatures of the forest that a stranger was there—I had no desire to surprise a fer-de-lance.

In contrast with the reef, it is a monotonously-colored world. Everything is some shade of brown or gray or green. I have lugged cameras loaded with color film all day without finding anything that seemed to warrant color photography, and in despiration, got my companions to wear red kerchiefs and blue jeans so that they could provide color contrast as well as "human interest." But I always found color photography difficult in the forest where the dim light requires long exposures, and the light itself is greatly altered by being filtered through the thick, green canopy. Only by taking advantage of the margins of clearings, or by using a flash, can you be sure of results.

Perhaps I am making the forest sound too easy, too open, too cathedral-like, overdoing my rebellion against the idea of jungle. It is difficult to give an objective description, to convey an accurate impression of a landscape like the rain forest which may, in one person, arouse awe and wonder, and in another, fear and hatred. P. W. Richards, in his book, *The*

Tropical Rain Forest, has justly remarked that "tropical vegetation has a fatal tendency to produce rhetorical exuberance in those who describe it." The exuberance mostly tends toward the green hell side, but perhaps I have overdone the cathedral analogy.

I doubt whether the rain forest is anywhere easy to penetrate for any great distance. There are always obstructions: occasional fallen trunks, sudden tangled thickets, and above all, stretches of swamps and countless streams. Sometimes the streams are small, clear, shallow sandy brooks, looking no different from the forest brooks of New England, and easily negotiated. But sometimes they are broad rivers, sometimes they move sluggishly over bottomless mud, sometimes they are choked with impenetrable masses of fantastic vegetation. The green hell analogy becomes vivid enough in these forest swamps. They are the reason that man has had so little success in making trails or roads through the forests; why he clings to the major rivers either for exploration or trade.

The world I have been describing bears no obvious resemblance to the world of the coral reef. This is partly, of course, because we have been looking at the forest from the bottom, from the point of view of walking on the forest floor, while we see the reef from above, floating over it. I loved the rain forest from my first encounter with it when I had just left college and was working at a research station of the United Fruit Company in Honduras, but I think I never really appreciated the forest until the years of yellow-fever study in Colombia, when I worked comfortably from platforms high in the trees—which gave a quite different perspective. But in any event, the similarities only become apparent when we examine the two habitats as biological systems, and for this we need a biological description of the forest.

Rain forest is the type of vegetation that occupies the lowland tropics in regions of high rainfall, where the rain is fairly evenly distributed throughout the year. The minimum rainfall to support such a forest is generally considered to be about eighty inches a year, though usually the rainfall is much higher, well over a hundred inches. The seasonal distribution is as important as the total amount: where there is a pronounced dry season of several months with little or no rain, the forest changes considerably in character and is generally called a monsoon forest. In such a forest the trees are not so tall, there is more undergrowth, and many plants drop their leaves during the dry season. The forest also changes with mountain altitude and various kinds of montane forests can be recognized. Heavy forests occur in some high rainfall areas outside of the tropics, in southern Chile, in New Zealand, and along the coast of the state of Washington in North America; but these again have a different character from the tropical forest and are best considered as a separate vegetation type.

There are three major areas of tropical rain forest: the American, the African and the Indo-Malayan. They cover all of the land masses crossed by the equator except the east coast of Africa. The American forest is by far the largest and most continuous, covering most of the Amazon drainage in central South America and extending south on the inner side of the Andes in Bolivia into the drainage of the Plata, and north in Colombia into the drainage of the Orinoco. This is hardly separated by the northernmost ranges of the Andes from a Pacific strip that follows the coast from Ecuador to Panama and continues, in Central America, along the Caribbean coast almost to the line of the Tropic of Cancer in Mexico. There is an isolated stretch of rain forest along the southern coast of Brazil, and rain forest once covered much of the West Indies, though now there are only scattered remnants.

The African rain forest is the smallest of the three, and there is considerable debate both about its present limits and its former extension. It covers, essentially, the central drainage of the Congo, with a north and west extension along the gulf of Guinea to Liberia.

The Indo-Malayan rain forest is the most fragmented. It covers most of the large islands of the East Indies—Sumatra, Borneo, Celebes, New Guinea, the Philippines—and the Malay Peninsula, with outlying areas on the west coast of India, in Burma, on the coast of Indochina, and along the coast of northern Queensland in Australia.

In structure and appearance, the forests of the three areas are very much alike. The taller trees reach a height averaging about 150 feet, though individual trees more than 200 feet in height are not uncommon. The tallest reported rain forest trees are somewhat less than 300 feet. Rain forest trees are thus in general taller than trees in the temperate forests of Europe or North America, where the average for taller trees in the least disturbed forests is around 100 feet, with 150 feet an exceptional height. But trees in the tropical forest do not reach the gigantic proportions of the California redwoods or the Australian eucalyptuses. The tallest measured sequoias reach 364 feet, the tallest eucalyptuses, 350 feet.

The rain forest everywhere has a multi-storied canopy. The layers of the canopy, like the depth zones of the sea, are hard to define since they are not sharply separated, but it is customary to refer to the upper, the middle and the lower zones of the canopy. This multiplicity of tree layers reflects the great variety of different kinds of trees that go to make up the rain forest. Most temperate zone forests are made up of one or two or a very few kinds of trees, with a maximum, in the Appalachian forests of the eastern United States, of perhaps 25 species of trees. Probably fifty species of trees is about the minimum for any rain forest, and in most places there are many hundreds of species.

Alfred Russel Wallace, who spent many years exploring both the Amazonian and Malayan regions wrote, in his book *Tropical Nature:* "If the traveller notices a particular species and wishes to find more like it, he may often turn his eyes in vain in every direction. Trees of varied forms,

dimensions and colors are around him, but he rarely sees any of them repeated. Time after time he goes towards a tree which looks like the one he
seeks, but a closer examination proves it to be distinct. He may at length,
perhaps, meet with a second specimen a half a mile off, or he may fail
altogether, till on another occasion he stumbles on one by accident."

Because of this immense variety, the catalog of rain forest trees is still
far from complete, and anyone collecting botanical material in remote
areas is liable to turn up species of trees unknown to science. And the trees
belong to almost the whole range of plant families. Families that in the
north are known only as herbs—the *Compositae*, or daisy family, for instance—are represented by trees in the rain forest. Even grass takes on a
tree form in bamboo; and ferns, in the tree ferns.

There is a great development of woody vines—lianas. A considerable
proportion of the foliage in the canopy, sometimes nearly half of it, is from
the great vines that are supported by the trees, and these woody vines, like
the trees themselves, belong to a great variety of species and to many
different plant families.

Trees, woody vines and epiphytes are the characteristic life forms of
plants in the tropical forest; and of these the epiphytes, the plants that
perch on the branches and trunks of trees, are probably the strangest to the
observer from the north. Lichens and mosses grow as epiphytes in northern
forests, but in the rain forest the branches and trunks of the trees are
covered with a bewildering variety of other plants: ferns, orchids, peppers,
cactuses, bromeliads. In all, something like 33 families of seed plants and
ferns are represented by epiphytes in the rain forest flora.

Epiphytes grow in the rain forest, but without access to the soil they
are faced with a water problem. Their niche on dry branches high in trees
is in a way a sort of micro-desert. Many of them, the cactuses, for instance,
are relatives of typically desert plants and have the fleshy look of desert
plants. There is a good reason for this, since in both situations it is important
for the plant to be able to conserve water, hence the frequency of succulent bulbs and leaves, as in the orchids. The bromeliads, as I mentioned in
the last chapter, have solved the water problem by forming watertight
tanks where they can collect their own supply, and where also they can get
food from the rotting organic matter. The bromeliads are often very numerous, forming, as someone has remarked, a "marsh in the treetops."

The epiphytes are also faced with mineral problems. They must get
the salts they need from the extremely dilute solutions in the rain that
washes them, or from the humus and debris that collects in the cracks of
the bark of the host trees or in the tangle of their own roots. Somehow
they get sufficient minerals from these sources. Frequently the epiphytes
live in a close symbiotic association with fungi, and the thin mycelial webs
of the fungi help both partners in food collection. Fungi live in close rela-

tionships with the roots of many kinds of seed plants, forming associations that are called *mycorhizae*.

The roots of epiphytes also, with surprising frequency, are used as nesting sites by the ants that abound in the forest; and it has been suggested that the epiphytes have an additional source of food in the material that the ants are constantly hauling into their nests. This too would be a symbiotic relationship: the ants get a fine, well-protected home, built by the plant, and provide food by way of rent. Perhaps they also provide defense since many of these ants sting fiercely. They certainly defend the epiphytes valiantly against stray humans trying to make collections.

The rain forest crawls with ants of many different kinds, occupied with many sorts of business. Close associations between particular kinds of plants and particular species of ants are quite frequent. Sometimes the ants clearly serve to protect the plants that provide them with nesting sites in hollow stems. One learns to avoid brushing against the trunks or foliage of certain trees, like Cecropia, with the same care that one learns to avoid poison ivy or poison oak in more northern situations. With the ant-protected trees the fiery consequences of transgression are immediate as well as painful.

The ants are one example of the incredible abundance of insects in the rain forest. It is an abundance of kinds, rather than of individuals. Within a range of about ten miles of our laboratory in Colombia, we found 150 different species of mosquitoes (there are only 121 species known from all of the United States and Canada). But you may get more mosquito bites in northern woods than in tropical forests. In northern woods, the mosquitoes biting you are apt to be all the same kind; while in the rain forest, almost every bite will be from a different species of mosquito—if that is any comfort.

The task of collecting, naming and describing all of these insects is endless. Every collector brings back new things and no one really has any idea how many different kinds there are, which leads people, in guessing about how many species of insects there are in the world, to give figures that vary from one million to ten million. Whatever the figure, it is a big one, with a respectable proportion inhabiting the rain forest.

The biggest known insects are found there: for wingspread, butterflies and moths; for bulk, rhinocerous beetles; for length, walking sticks. But there are relative giants among almost all insect groups: cockroaches that look like small turtles, big flies, big wasps, monstrous grasshoppers. There are also big mammals, elephants in the old world, tapirs in the new, and there is a gigantic frog in the Congo forest with a body approximately a foot long. But the woolly mammoths that roamed Europe, Siberia and North America until almost recent times were bigger than elephants, and in general with mammals, and birds, the forest representatives do not strike one as particularly big. As a matter of fact, forest species—forest deer, for instance—tend to be somewhat smaller than their cousins in the savanna or outside the tropics. Perhaps it is only the cold-blooded animals —anacondas and boas and pythons, for example—that find a special opportunity for bigness in the rain-forest environment.

The color is mostly high in the canopy: the flowers of the trees, lianas, epiphytes; birds and butterflies. There is, it seems to me, a special tendency for animals, especially birds and butterflies, to be colored in metallic blues and greens. The wings of a great morpho butterfly, flashing in the sun, are especially famous, but many kinds of day-flying insects have metallic colors, even mosquitoes! Species that fly at night and species of the forest floor zone are, however, apt to be dull or at least softly colored. With the butterflies, as the with the birds, the brilliance tends to be a male characteristic.

The structure of the rain forest and the appearance of its inhabitants is much the same in America, Africa and Indonesia, but the three areas have had independent evolutionary histories, and are made up of quite different kinds of plants and animals. The only animal I can think of (besides man) common to all three regions is the leopard, which is hardly distinguishable from the jaguar of the New World. But though these big cats are at home in the rain forest, they are far from restricted to it, or to the tropics either for that matter. The leopard, in prehistoric times, ranged far into Europe, and the jaguar ranged all over both American continents until man managed to exterminate it in the settled regions.

The African and Indo-Malayan forests are more similar to each other in composition than either is to the American forest. They are separated now by the Indian Ocean within the tropics, and by the barriers of the Sahara and the Himalayas to the north. But the Himalayas are the youngest of mountains and the Sahara was once wooded, so that a few million years ago communication between Africa and Malaya was easier than now. But the Amazonian forest, all this while, was completely isolated by a sea barrier, only recently bridged by the isthmus of Panama.

Thus we find great apes in both the African and Indo-Malayan forests, gorillas and chimpanzees in the former and orangs and gibbons in the latter, but no great apes in tropical America. There are monkeys in all three regions, but the American monkeys belong to quite different families from the Old World monkeys, and have had a separate evolutionary history for a very long time.

Visitors to the tropics who expect to see monkeys everywhere are generally disappointed. In the rain forest, particularly, what one will see is very uncertain. The animals are there, all right, but they are not exhibitionists. They have learned, particularly, to be shy of possibly harmful human intruders. That this is learning, in part at least, is shown by animal

behavior in places where the fauna has been long protected—in the park
reservations and on the lands of Buddhist monasteries in the East.

One of the very few fully protected rain forest areas in the American
tropics is a small island in Gatun Lake in Panama called Barro Colorado
which was set aside in 1922 as a reserve to be used only for biological
study. I only lived there for six months, and I probably saw more forest
mammals in that period than in all my years of residence in other parts of
the tropics. Mostly you get only a fleeting glimpse of a band of monkeys as
they take off rapidly through the treetops—they have spotted you first, and
are having none of it. On Barro Colorado, the monkeys did not really become pals with the visiting scientists, but at least they didn't panic at the
sight of a man. As a result, any time you went out on a trail, you were sure
presently to come across a band of monkeys and could watch them for a
while.

I think, however, that I got more pleasure out of the coatis than out
of the monkeys during this period on Barro Colorado. Coatis are long-
nosed tropical relatives of the raccoons—and they are even more charm-
ing, inquisitive and intelligent than their northern relatives. They are hated
by hunters because, ganging up, they can kill the hunters' dogs, and they
are not notably careful about poultry or gardens. Men and coatis are thus
usually at odds, but on Barro Colorado they achieved a considerable mutual tolerance. If you stood quietly, the coatis would pay little attention to
you while they went on about their business of rummaging among the leaf
litter or scampering up the trees after insects and nuts.

Frank Chapman was there while I was, carrying on his life-long study
of bird habits. He tried to devise a feeding station for birds that the coatis
couldn't get at by hanging a cigar box from a wire trolley strung between
a tree and the verandah of his little house, so that bananas, for birds only,
could be suspended in midair. It didn't take a neighboring coati long to
figure that out. The coati, sniffing the banana from the ground, rapidly
made for the tree, climbed it, did a tightrope act on the wire out to the
cigar box, and got the banana. Chapman gave up and spent the rest of the
time trying to fool the coati, with little success. He has told the story in his
book, *My Tropical Air Castle*. As far as I know, coatis have not been investigated by psychologists, which seems a pity because they must have one
of the highest I.Q.s in the animal kingdom.

Among the rain-forest animals, there are many survivors from the
geological past. We tend to think of marsupials as primitive mammals that
have survived and proliferated in the isolation of the Australian continent,
except for the common and tough opossum of North America. But in the
tropical American rain forest, there are dozens of kinds of marsupials. They
are not as spectacular as the kangaroos and their relatives of Australia, but
they are interesting enough. There is a sleek water opossum (*Chironectes*)

living on the margins of the forest streams; a bright-eyed woolly opossum (*Caluromys*) with lovely, thick fur; and many different species of tiny, mouse-like opossums (*Marmosa*) as well as several other genera. The sloths are another archaic group (and they look it) now confined to the trees of the American rain forest, though in the recent geological past there were also many kinds of ground sloths.

The catalog of ancient animal types surviving only in the rain forest is a long one, though most of the items on the list can be appreciated only by the zoological specialist. Because of this, the rain forest has sometimes been regarded as a sort of backwash, a refuge from the more strenuous and progressive parts of the biosphere. But the whole complex and wonderful system of adaptations within the forest is clearly a consequence of evolutionary forces operating within this environment. Thus, by another chain of reasoning one can come to the conclusion not that the rain forest is a backwash, but that it is the place where evolutionary change is most active.

It is in the rain forest that "jungle law" reigns supreme: the struggle for existence, nature red in tooth and claw. Here we find the most fantastic contrivances for catching food or for avoiding becoming food, the most perfect examples of animal camouflage. The struggle for existence is symbolized by the strangling fig which starts out as an epiphyte, a seedling growing high on some tree, sending down roots which reach the ground and grow until finally the host tree is smothered by the encircling fig, which then stands alone. And I can think of nothing more devastatingly fierce, more irresistible, than a horde of army ants on the move, killing and dismembering every animal they encounter that cannot fly away or run fast enough. We had a snake pit in the laboratory where I worked in Honduras, where we kept many kinds of vipers for their venom, which was used for making antivenin. Once, I remember, we were invaded by army ants. We tried everything we could think of to stop them or at least to make them change their course, but to no avail. The ants poured on in their tens of thousands, swept through our snake pit, and left us with a collection of bare skeletons.

Life, then, can be grim enough for the forest inhabitants. Only the clever, the carefully protected, the extremely prolific, the most modern, seem to have any chance of survival. Yet, scuttling through the leaves of the forest floor, and nestling in the debris collected around the roots of epiphytes high in the trees, are scores of kinds of cockroaches hardly different in any way that we can see from the fossils of their ancestors that lived three hundred million years ago in the forests of the Carboniferous period. Push over a rotting log and you may very well find a Peripatus: a soft, brown, delicate, multilegged, caterpillar-like thing that, on examination, turns out to be a very queer creature indeed. The ancestors of all the land arthropods, of the millipedes, centipedes, spiders, insects, the first animals to learn to live on land, must have been something like this. But this anachronism is still getting on very well in the warm, damp world of the forest, meeting (as far as we can see) unchanged the shifting hazards in hundreds of millions of years of forest life.

Of course, neither the rain forest nor the coral reef has any monopoly on anachronisms. The horseshoe crabs of the Atlantic coast of the United States might have crawled out of the most ancient seas; the tiny collembola that jump through the leaf mold of northern woods are hardly different from the earliest of insect fossils. Every pond and every tidepool teems with survivors from the ancient past. I don't think we have any clear answer as to why some kinds of things have survived and other kinds perished as, with the onward flow of time, new kinds of organisms have come on the scene. Our explanations are mostly circular: horeshoe crabs have survived because they were adapted or adaptable, that is, able to survive; trilobites became extinct because they weren't able to survive. One of the remarkable things is that very few of the major plant or animal types—phyla or classes—have become extinct. Proportions change—ferns and mosses give way to seed plants as trees, giving structure to the forests—but the ferns and mosses are still with us. Reptiles give way to mammals and birds as dominant animals in the forest scene, but reptiles are still with us. Change seems to be not so much a matter of absolute replacement as of diversification.

But with all these reservations and qualifications, the rain forest still seems to have more than its fair share of survivors from the past. One can visualize the struggle for survival, the competition, the strenuousness of life in the rain forest. But then in the next instant, looking at this multitudinous accumulation of organisms one gets the feeling that there is so much warmth, so much light, so much moisture, so much food, that almost anything can survive and that almost everything does.

This is the paradox shared by the rain forest and the coral reef. Shallow, tropical seas and low, rain-drenched tropical lands with their associated swamps, lakes and rivers represent the most favorable conditions for the processes of life on the surface of our planet. The physical environment is not a problem except in special situations like that of the epiphytes of the forest where the collection of water or minerals may have particular difficulty. The problems of living things involve not so much the physical environment as other living things. When one moves away from the optimum of these two environments, the physical condition starts to become limiting. The open sea has a less diversified biota than the reef because it has no solid substrate, no place where fixed organisms can grow; everything has to drift or swim. Descending from the surface of the sea, light and temperature become less favorable; going toward the poles in surface waters, temperature becomes less favorable. Similarly, on land, as one moves from the rain forest to other types of habitat, various factors of the physical environment become limiting, present special problems which require special adaptations on the part of the organisms living in the habitat. Organisms must always cope with other organisms, but outside of the rain forest and the coral reef they must increasingly cope with climate too.

VI

Conservation and Economic Biology

35

The Vandals

Angelo Patri

It was Sunday evening and the cars were filled with returning holiday makers. Every seat held its quota of weary, sleep-beset children, and from their relaxed hands drooped thousands of dead and dying wild flowers. When the car stopped at their corner their guardians pulled them up and dragged them out and the flowers strewed the passageway.

One sleepy towhead clutched a little tin pail, and as she was dragged along the pail caught somehow and overturned. A foot kicked it along and its contents were scattered about. I looked at them and saw that the child had gathered a score or more of white violet plants. Now they lay smashed beyond recognition on the floor of a dirty trolley car.

I knew the spot where those violets had grown. There is a little dark brown wood pool in which tall trees stand, each rising from a throne of velvet green moss. Out of the moss grow the tiny white violets and the "wind lily of the valley." It is a fairy place, a place that catches one's breath by its exquisite solemn beauty. And the child had tried to gather the beauty and carry it home in the little pail.

Why didn't the grown person with her tell her that she could never do that? Why didn't she tell her that the beauty was a thing of sky and sunshine and color and fragrance and water and wood and could be carried away only in her heart?

Why didn't she tell her that she was carrying death to something that the Creator had instilled with life that it might make glad the spaces of a spirit? Didn't the mother know? I'm afraid she didn't, because she left a bundle of dogwood in the seat behind her!

People with gardens, gardeners who cherish beautiful grounds in great estates, park superintendents who fight to preserve a little of the beauty of the earth that its people may see and know it, cry out against the vandalism of the children.

Reprinted from the first edition.

Better cry out against the vandalism of their elders, who teach them that flowers are to be gathered regardless. The children only follow their parents' example.

There are some people who cannot bear to see anything lovely without longing to possess it. Flowers cannot defend themselves and fall victims to the greed of possession. Women who could not bear to kill a noxious fly will slaughter a bank of wild flowers and go carelessly on their way.

There must be a sad spiritual lack about such people, and the saddest part of it is their passing it along to the children.

Teach the children to look at the beauty of the flowers and keep their hands off. Show them the difference between the beautiful little flower growing in its mossy bed and the dead and dreary thing they hold in their hands. Teach them to love and preserve the beauty that gladdens their eyes and rests their souls in the fields and woods about them.

36

The Useful and Beautiful Forest

Erhard Rostlund

On the tenth birthday of this magazine I wish to remember Nicholas Collin, who one hundred and seventy years ago expressed ideas that are part of LANDSCAPE's heritage. On April 3, 1789, he read a paper before the American Philosophical Society, an essay that Gilbert Chinard of Princeton has called the first American document which "frankly and unequivocally" deals with forest conservation. The essay is much more than a discourse on the woods, but I want to confine this memorandum to Collin's remarks on forestry, and particularly to his belief that a forest utilized by man can be both useful and beautiful.

"Our stately forests are a national treasure," he said, "deserving the solicitous care of the patriotic philosopher and politician. Hitherto they have been too much abandoned to the axes and thoughtless wood-choppers. What person of sense and feeling can without indignation behold millions of young oaks and hickories destroyed? . . . Some parts of Europe

From LANDSCAPE, Vol. 10, No. 1 (Fall, 1960). Reprinted by permission.

were thus laid waste in former centuries; and the present generations must with great labor and expense repair the ravages of their forefathers."

He was not a mere alarmist but made practical proposals: "In many parts of this country a preservation and increase of the timber for fuel and other domestic uses renders these queries important. What trees are of the quickest growth? At what ages do they increase most? What is the proper distance between them? What is the best method of pruning, for promoting this growth, and taking off superfluous branches? What kinds are suitable to different soils? What species thrive best together? The judicious lopping of the branches, thinning close the clumps of trees and clearing the ground of underwood, will make many woodlands good pastures and form then into beautiful parks. This management would also improve the quality of timber by procuring the benefits of sun and air."

The statement has an astonishingly modern ring, for the questions asked and the proposals made are precisely those that engross the forester of today.

Nicholas Collin talked not only like a forester but like a landscape architect: "We may sincerely wish that the owners of venerable woodlands might regard them as principal ornaments of their country; and while they clear cut for the purposes of agriculture, leave those hills crowned with towering pines and stately oaks, suffering likewise the groves of tulip trees and magnolias to wave among yellow harvests and blooming meadows. In some of the old countries many gentlemen would purchase such rural charm at any expense. . . . Is it not then deplorable that so many American farmers daily destroy what their offspring of better taste will deeply regret! This evil might in great measure be lessened by a treatise on ornamental planting adapted to the present circumstances of this country." In this plea for preservation and enhancement of the beauty of the woodlands Collin anticipated some of the foresters of our time, for example Josef Köstler who reminded his colleagues that "forestry is also landscape care."

The idea of a forest both useful and beautiful has broken apart, so that in the common opinion of today, a forest may be useful or beautiful but seldom both.

The action of "rude and thoughtless wood-choppers" continued after Collin's time in such a manner that seriously wounded forest landscapes became common throughout the land, and the language acquired terms like "cutover," "logged over," "logged out," none of which connotes beauty. How seriously wounded the forest is can be learned from *Timber Resources for America's Future* (1958). Headlines have been made of the finding that in the country as a whole the annual growth of wood is now about equal to the annual cut and in some regions considerably greater; but not much has been said about the alarming report that the quality of land and timber is deteriorating, for example the fact that less than half of the nation's 489 million acres of commercial forest land is well stocked or not stocked at all, or the evaluation showing that 54% of the volume of the eastern hardwood forest consists of low grade timber and 20% of diseased and deformed cull trees. It is shocking to find that nearly three-quarters of this forest, which once was the finest stand of hardwoods in the mid-latitudes of the world, is now rated as of low grade. What these data mean is that much of the forest is very ugly and it is not strange if the common opinion is that a utilized forest is not a beautiful forest.

Two different attitudes toward the forest are observed; the one identified with the beautiful, the other with the useful. The first attitude is held by people who might be represented by Henry David Thoreau or John Muir. Another attitude is found among those who think of the forest as primarily an economic resource. This group might be represented by Gifford Pinchot, the first chief of the Forest Service. That the forests are in this camp is no surprise; but it is astonishing how overwhelmingly the sense of the practical dominates all the most influential works in the history of American forestry. More than one-third of George Perkins Marsh's *Men and Nature,* is given to a discussion of forests, most of it dealing with practical matters. In Lowenthal's words, "Thoreau appealed chiefly to esthetic sensibility, Marsh to practicality." The same emphasis on the practical runs through other early contributions that have significantly influenced American thought and practice in the forest, for example the writings of Frederick Starr, Jr., Franklin B. Hough, Bernard E. Fernow, Gifford Pinchot. The Conference of Governors in the White House in 1908, the "beginning" of the conservation movement, was almost completely overshadowed by the utilitarian interest in resources, as was the report of the National Conservation Commission, which met after the conference. That report contains eighteen hundred and forty pages, only two of which are devoted to the virtue of preserving scenic beauty.

To speak of two attitudes toward the forest is not to say that only two exist. There are many. According to the *Conservation Yearbook,* the United States now has well over three hundred private organizations and numerous government agencies, each with a program of developing, promoting, protecting, conserving, studying, using wisely, or otherwise doing something to something in nature, including the forests, and as often as not the attitudes, aims, and ambitions of the various groups are in conflict. The outstanding example at the moment is no doubt the "feud," "battle" or "war," as it has been called, between the National Park Service and the Forest Service over the proposal to make more parks from national forest land, which is administered by the Forest Service. Impressive data are cited by each side, showing why the one must have more land and why the other cannot give up any; the Park Service reported over 60 million visitors in 1959 and expects 80 million in 1966, while the national forests—

which comprise an area about ten times as large as that of the parks—had some 68 million visitors in 1958, over 80 million in 1959, and what the number will be in 1966 nobody knows, maybe 100 million. It is interesting to note that "esthetic enjoyment of the forest" is reported as the most common purpose of the visits. The national forests must also help to provide timber for a population which is expected by the Forest Service, basing its forecast on data of the Census Bureau, to number about one-third of a billion people in A.D. 2000, and to meet the projected demand of wood at that time it is estimated that the annual growth of sawtimber in the country must be doubled. Whether it *can* be doubled is another question, but in any event, the Forest Service cannot spare an acre. And thus, as *American Forests* says, "the battle is joined."

The ammunition is words and phrases packed with explosives, such as "multiple use," "sustained yield," "greatest good for the greatest number," and other words not so nice, and much of the shooting impresses me as more doctrinaire than pragmatic, for often the question seems to be not whether a proposal is good or bad but whether it is good multiple use. How the battle will end is hard to say, but I suspect that the juggernaut of population growth will roll over these feuds and dispose of them. A day is coming when there will be so many people in the country that we shall have to use all of the forest to accommodate everybody who wants to go to it for esthetic enjoyment and when, at the same time, we shall have to use all of the forest to grow the timber needed to meet the demand for wood; that is, the *same* forest will have to do for both. At stake in the feuds and in all our dealing with the forest are two things: part of the American economy and part of the American landscape, or, if you wish, the useful and the beautiful. Both are indispensable to human life, and the only road to survival for either is the road of compromise. On that road we shall have to adjust not only our action in the forest but our thought. Since the useful and beautiful must travel together, a unified concept of the forest will be needed, a new attitude or an old one, rather, that of Nicholas Collin. We must believe with him that a forest utilized by man *can* be both useful and beautiful.

We must try to save some of the wilderness always, but the rest of the forest will come more and more under the influence of man. Such a forest need not be ugly, but it will be unless we give as high priority to the preservation of beauty as to the preservation of profit. However, we must also recognize the truth of the reverse, for there can be no forestry nor any of Köstler's "landscape care" unless it is economically feasible. It is my hope, as I think it is that of everyone who cares for the landscape, and for LANDSCAPE, that we will be able to make the wish of Nicholas Collin come true and keep our woodlands so that they will always be principal ornaments of the country.

37

Turning Insects Against Themselves

From that time in the distant past when a mosquito first dined on human blood, mankind has been engaged in a guerrilla war against insect pests. In recent years, the conflict has been escalated into all-out and total warfare. Famines caused by insect depredation of crops, and diseases transmitted by arthropod vectors, presently take millions of lives annually. Obviously, we dare not let up in our attack—but dare we continue? According to many conservationists and public health officials, we may win a Pyrrhic victory if we continue poisoning our wildlife and ourselves with the deadly insecticides now employed.

OUTWITTING THE FOE

Clearly, new weapons are needed, and additions to the arsenal are being promised by scientists in many disciplines. Reports of synthetic hormones, aromatic chemicals and a variety of other agents, devices and techniques presently under investigation or being tested, indicate that the design for victory, as in conventional warfare, is based largely on outwitting the foe. For example, the old military maxim "Divide and conquer" has been given a new interpretation by the development of synthetic sex attractants. The strategy here is to divide the males from the females.

As is the case with many higher animals, at least some species of insects employ scent to attract mates. As is true of any good perfume, the fragrance is most effective when used sparingly. Male cockroaches, for example, are excited by as little as 30 molecules of the aromatic chemical produced by the female. A perfumed female silkworm moth can seduce males from as far away as two and a half miles. It is interesting that in concentrated doses, the potent chemicals tend to confuse the males, or even to repel them—suggesting an obvious way that these attractants can be used as weapons. Indeed, a synthetic attractant has already been em-

"Turning Insects Against Themselves," *The Sciences*, Vol. 4(8) (1965), pp. 25-28. Reprinted by permission of The New York Academy of Sciences.

ployed successfullly against the gypsy moth by spraying it over an area in such quantities that the males became confused, and many were unable to find the waiting females. Synthetic attractants also show promise as lures, drawing males to poisoned traps.

Not surprisingly, nearly every species uses a different scent as a sexual attractant, so the time-consuming process of extraction, isolation and analysis must be carried out for each attractant chemists want to synthesize. The "brute force" approach was taken by chemists determined to break the cockroach code. Clean dry air was blown through a container of female cockroaches, the air was collected as it emerged, and its volatile contents were condensed in a chilled container. After nine months of collecting, and with the unwitting aid of 10,000 virgin females, the experimenters were able to isolate only 12.2 milligrams of the pure attractant—enough, however, to identify the chemical constituents.

INFILTRATING THE RANKS

An alternative approach to the strategy of destruction by sexual disruption is to release sterile males into a wild population. The sterility may be achieved by selective cross breeding, by the use of radiation, or by treating the insects with chemical sterilants. However the insects are made sterile, the tactic is to release enough of the males so that many of the fertile males will be deprived of mates. Obviously, total eradication is not likely with this technique, but the release of sterile males might be employed as a holding action, keeping an insect population in check until the newer lethal weapons could be trained on the problem area. Of perhaps greater promise as a total control measure would be the release of males which carry a "daughterless gene." Such a gene would spread through a population and might eventually wipe it out.

TURNING APPETITE TO ADVANTAGE

Just as an insect cannot help but respond to a sexual attractant, so too is it drawn unfailingly to food lures. These are chemicals which arouse the feeding response. One such chemical, combined with an insecticide, has already been used against the oriental fruit fly population on a Pacific island. The island was heavily infested with the flies until many small boards, coated with the lure and the poison, were dropped from the air. Within a short time, the flies were eradicated, and at a cost of only 50 cents per acre.

In the war against insects no holds are barred, and other control measures under investigation include the release of diseases lethal to these pests but harmless to higher animals, and the application of hormones which promote grotesque growth patterns and ultimate death. Several viruses, for example, are known which kill cabbage loopers, sawflies and other pests. In application, diseased larvae of these pests are ground up, the mash mixed in a solution, and the solution sprayed over the crop. With this technique it takes only about ten infected caterpillars to protect an acre, and only one application is needed per season.

At one point in their life cycle, larvae respond to hormonal changes and pupate, to emerge later in the mature, winged form of the insect. A hormone has been synthesized which indefinitely delays pupating in many destructive forest insects. As a result of being sprayed with the hormone solution, the caterpillars simply continue feeding and growing larger. Eventually, they may grow so enormous that they pop, actually succumbing from a surfeit of tasty leaves.

ALLIES IN THE INSECT RANKS

In his book *The Insects* (Columbia University Press, 1964) Url Lanham notes that "Insects' worst enemies are themselves." This fact has already been used to advantage as a means of controlling undesirable species. Some years ago, the cottony cushion scale, an insect which attacks orchard trees, was brought under control by ladybird beetles imported in great numbers (they can be purchased by the quart) from Australia. Just recently, a species of parasitic beetles has been released in New Jersey to prey on gypsy moth eggs and larvae. Gypsy moths have also been under attack in Pennsylvania, where their eggs are eaten by the larvae of tiny parasitic black flies, imported from Japan. Unfortunately, parasitic insects will seldom wipe out an undesirable species. Another approach to biological control, however, can be used to entirely rid an area of a pest. The ploy here is to import a species related to the pest which, because of competitive superiority, will drive the undesirable insects out. Such a program was successfully carried out in Sardinia, where the malaria-carrying *Anopheles labranchiae* mosquito was deliberately replaced by the hardier, and harmless *Anopheles hispaniola*.

It is apparent that many of the new weapons mentioned—and the listing is far from complete—are essentially tools and techniques for manipulating the unthinking responses "programmed" into insects. It is not likely that insects could evolve a resistance to a sexual attractant or a food lure without perishing in the wild state. Blind instinct may yet be the death of them.

38

Science Attacks the Screwworm

Norris Randolph

Today, more than ever before in its infant history, atomic energy is being utilized to advance the frontiers of science in the interests of peace and productivity. This is particularly true in the world of agriculture.

Currently under way in this field is a revolutionary program—the use of nuclear power as a means of eradicating the screwworm, one of the worst menaces to livestock growers in the southern United States.

The deadly work of this pest represents a yearly loss of 20 million dollars to livestock raisers, particularly hard hit in the Southeast. To the cattleman especially, the fly is no longer simply an unpleasant menace—it has become a dangerous, uncompromising foe that threatens the industry.

This insect, technically known as *Cochliomyia hominovorax*, and identified as early as 1842 in Texas, has been a serious killer of herds since 1933. Severe screwworm outbreaks have been reported frequently in Florida, Georgia, Alabama, South Carolina, Mississippi and Tennessee. Surveys also have determined that from time to time infections were present in Kentucky and Virginia and as far north as New Jersey.

The screwworm's looks belie its destructive instincts. In appearance it resembles the common "blow fly," is bluish-green in color and has three dark stripes on its back.

Although mating only once, the female is capable of laying from 100 to 400 eggs at a time on the edges of wounds in warm-blooded mammals. Depositing eggs at four-day intervals, she is able to lay as many as 3000 whitish eggs. Within six to twelve hours the eggs hatch, the mature larvae leave the wound or lesion in about five days, and burrow in the soil. In approximately two weeks, the outer skin of the larva having hardened and formed a pupal case, the adult fly emerges. In two to five days the fly is ready to mate and continue the cycle. The average egg-to-egg cycle is twenty-one days, although cool weather may prolong it.

Norris Randolph, "Science Attacks the Screwworm," *Nature Magazine*, Vol. 52 (1959), pp. 460-463. Reprinted by permission of *Nature*.

Predatory beetles and ants destroy some of the larvae and pupae, but not in sufficient numbers to effect any appreciable control. Nature's most efficient population regulator is temperature. If the daily average temperature is less than 55 degrees Fahrenheit for more than two months, screwworm pupae die in the soil. In winter, therefore, the "survival line" is considerably restricted, and the pest can usually over-winter only in Florida, south Texas and Mexico.

During the spring and summer, the screwworm fly is on the wing and at its most active. It can migrate thirty-five miles weekly, infesting all of Florida, the southern two-thirds of Georgia and the southeast corner of Alabama in the Southeast; most of Louisiana, Arkansas, Texas, southern New Mexico, southern Arizona and California in the Southwest; and Oklahoma, Kansas and Missouri in the mid-West. However, the days of the screwworm seem to be numbered—at least in the Southeast.

In 1951, new techniques were undertaken to eradicate the insect in preliminary experiments. Using X-ray equipment, scientists and entomologists revealed that female screwworms, when sterilized by radiation, were infertile. Similarly, normal female flies, after mating with males made sterile by radiation, produced eggs that did not hatch. Could this be a means of control?

After achieving notable success in mass-rearing sterile flies under laboratory conditions, a small-scale field test was begun on Sanibel Island, off the coast of Florida.

The results of this exploratory study were not conclusive, since screwworm flies from the nearby mainland infiltrated the island and reinfested it. Yet researchers nevertheless gained first-hand experience in propagating, mass irradiation and liberation of treated screwworms. An important step forward had been taken. The battle lines were being drawn.

Backed by further experimentation in rearing techniques, sterilization by exposure to cobalt 60, and the behavior habits of the fly in the laboratory, the United States Department of Agriculture entomologists were ready for the first major offensive.

On March 26, 1954, seventeen thousand sterile male screwworm flies, the first batch to be exposed to the gamma rays of radioactive cobalt, were released by airplane over Curacao Island, in Netherlands West Indies. Systematic releases of flies were continued weekly.

Five months later, a ground survey showed that the screwworm population was decreasing, but not disappearing. The number of sterile flies was increased from 100 to 400 per week on each of the island's 170 squares miles. Eradication occurred rapidly. Since December, 1954, Curacao, fifty miles from the nearest land and therefore safe from migratory flies, has been safe from the screwworm. Reviewing its findings, United States Department of Agriculture officials determined that the vexing problem in the Southeastern States could probably be handled as it had been during the Curacao test.

In Texas and the Southwest, however, the diagnosis was not as encouraging. The area's geographical location posed a knottier question, since normal flies can immigrate from Mexico with impunity.

Deciding on an all-out campaign in Florida, the Department was aware that many scientific problems had to be solved before such an important launching could be undertaken. It was necessary to know how to blanket an area of 50,000 square miles rather than Curacao's 170. The weekly rearing and distribution of 50,000,000 sterile male and female flies presented its own problem. Many additional scientists had to be gathered. The Florida eradication scheme had to have more than the half-dozen men who had worked on the Caribbean project.

The job of raising and sterilizing a million flies a week was begun on a pilot plan basis. In the spring of 1957, fortified by more experimentation and study, entomologists decided to put their experiences and knowledge to use in the major operation.

Between April and August, in a zone forty by fifty miles southeast of Orlando, 2,000,000 sterile male screwworm flies were released from low-flying airplanes at a rate of 500 per square mile, each week for four months.

At first it was doubtful that the egg count would be reduced because of the infiltration of normal screwworms, as well as emigration of sterile flies, in the 2000 square mile area. But even with reinfestation from three sides, seventy percent sterility was obtained in twelve weeks. Valuable data also was compiled on the percentage reduction of fertile eggs at the center, as opposed to that beyond the area's boundaries.

At last, after years of testing, research and planning, a screwworm eradication program for the Southeastern States switched into "high gear." Last summer, with the completion of fly-rearing facilities on a gigantic scale at Sebring, Florida, extermination tactics were begun.

From first to last, the process requires intricate, exacting performance. When the screwworm pupae are five and a half days old, they are packed in canisters in lots of 18,000 and lowered into a cask of cobalt 60. They are exposed to this radioactive substance for about twelve minutes, or long enough to become saturated with 8000 roentgens of gamma rays. On removal, the screwworm pupae are placed in cartons resembling small egg boxes, and stored in an air-conditioned room at a constant temperature of 80 degrees F. until the flies emerge.

Then they are ready for distribution by twenty light planes that fly six hours a day, six days a week, from such central locations as Orlando, Gainesville, Miami, Sebring and Tallahassee, Florida, and Troy, Alabama. Besides the pilot, each plane carries a U.S.D.A. crewman who handles the systematic dispersal of 1000 boxes of flies a day.

Various kinds of release mechanisms had been tried before a Department scientist designed the most satisfactory one to date. It is an automatic dispersing apparatus that may be timed for various dispersal rates, and which opens and counts the cartons as they are dropped. This method is a far cry from the one used at Curacao, where dispersal was a matter of tearing open fly-filled paper bags and throwing them out of the plane!

Every safety precaution is taken to safeguard all workers and scientists from overdoses of radioactivity. Technicians who work with the cobalt 60 casks are equipped with film badges and pocket chambers. In the event a cask malfunctions, it can be hoisted through the roof of the building and immersed in water before repairs begin. Workers receive special attention so that they may not inadvertently carry any fertile female flies from the plant. Showers and fresh change of clothes are mandatory at the end of each shift.

By the middle of the past summer, approximately two and one-half billion flies had been reared for the 50,000 square-mile region encompassing the Florida Peninsula and the southeast corner of Georgia. As an added precaution during the two to three years it may take to eradicate the pest there, the average overwintering line has been extended 100 miles to the north. Livestock inspectors, manning more than 100 fly traps, gather information weekly on the incidence and relative abundance of both wild and sterile flies throughout the treated area.

Although the project is far from completed, "Operation Screwworm" furnishes a fine example of how the power of the atom can be used to benefit man rather than to destroy him.

39
Bristlecone Pine, Oldest Living Thing

Edmund Schulman

Only recently have we learned that certain stunted pines of arid highlands, not the mammoth trees of rain forests, may now be called the oldest living things on earth.

Microscopic study of growth rings reveals that a bristlecone pine tree

From Edmund Schulman, "Bristlecone Pine, Oldest Living Thing" *National Geographic Magazine*, Vol. 113 (1958), pp. 355-371. Reprinted by permission.

found at nearly 10,000 feet began growing more than 4,600 years ago and thus surpasses the oldest known giant sequoia by many centuries.

California continues to hold the championship, for the newly discovered tree also grows in the Golden State. It stands in the Inyo National Forest, in the White Mountains of east-central California.

These oldest pines are now but living ruins. Their trunks, 10 to 30 feet high, are little more than eroded stumps. Yet each possesses its life line, a few inches wide, of bark-covered tissue leading from partly bare roots to a thin crown of branches. And each is still able to produce cones occasionally, as it has for well over 4,000 years.

After studying a photograph of one of these trees, a friend of mine remarked enthusiastically, "Don't you wish we could all live to be that old?"

To this his wife replied, "Who wants to be 4,000 years old, if she looks like that!"

In *potential* life span the giant sequoia seems to come back into first place, for the General Sherman Tree and many other mammoth sequoias appear to have little or no decay. Barring accidents, mature sequoias living now could well be living still, in their protected parks, in A.D. 5000. By that time the oldest living bristlecone pines will surely have long since gone.

VII
Exobiology

40

Significance and Status of Exobiology

Gilbert V. Levin

The title of this paper, "Significance and Status of Exobiology," has been carefully selected. The *significance* of the term "exobiology" is in dispute and there are those who declare that the subject has no *status*. The term is of recent origin and is intended to denote the study of extraterrestrial life. The argument arises not only from those normally protesting the adulteration of the English language with newly-coined words but from those who literally interpret the prefix "exo" as meaning "out of, outside, or outer layer." Some contend that a better term would be "xenobiology" in that the prefix "xeno" connotes "strange or foreign." Others feel that "biology" is sufficient, for it would encompass extraterrestrial creatures. These arguments may have semantic merit, but "exobiology" has been adopted by the National Aeronautics and Space Administration and is now a part of the literature. A dispute over nomenclature should not discourage biologists from pursuing the subject.

The more serious objection to the "science" of exobiology is that it has no status. Since there are no data on extraterrestrial life, how, some contend, can there be such a science?

The subject matter is too important to permit such "sea-lawyer" rationalization to impede its investigation. I hope to demonstrate this.

The true significance of exobiology is best revealed by the questions it can help answer. The key question is "Is life limited to this planet?" Although we have no direct data, there is indirect evidence of two kinds. The first type consists of Earth-based physical observations of Mars which suggest the existence of life on that planet. Salisbury has summarized these. Perhaps the strongest evidence of this nature was the infrared spectroscopic analysis of Mars by Sinton which indicated the presence of aldehydes. Recently this interpretation has been questioned by Rea and Cal-

Gilbert V. Levin, "Significance and Status of Exobiology," *BioScience,* Vol. 15(1) (1965), pp. 17-19. Reprinted by permission of Gilbert V. Levin, Director Life Systems Division, Hazleton Laboratories, Inc., Falls Church, Va.

vin, but they offer no better single fit for the data obtained. The presence of water vapor on Mars has now been established, but in amounts which are considered too small by some to support life. Nonetheless, when all such data are considered, many scientists believe that the most likely explanation which generally accommodates them is that there is life on Mars.

The second type of data bearing on the question, "Is life limited to this planet?" is statistical. Although the size of the sample (one planet) is small, the statistical argument for life elsewhere is believed by many to be very strong. While Mars is generally considered to be the only other likely habitat of life in the solar system, Shapley has calculated that there are more than one hundred million stars which have planets sufficiently similar in composition and environment to Earth to support life. Our sample of one tells us that life does exist and, statistically, one would have to conclude that the probability of life on other planets is very high. Of course, yet unknown factors may operate to reduce significantly or even eliminate this probability. Nonetheless, the presently available facts require that biologists become seriously concerned with exobiology even though those facts do not include direct data on extraterrestrial life.

Let us, for the sake of argument, assume that somehow the search for life elsewhere in the universe had been completed and found to be negative. The chemical and environmental information gained from the search would, nonetheless, be invaluable in resolving the *biological* question of why life arose only on Earth.

On the other hand, if alien life is found, a parade of significant questions follows. "Is the life found biochemically similar to our own?" "Are 'they' and 'we' of common origin?" The most exciting prospect would be if the two types of life were different. On the other hand, if they were similar, the old question of panspermia would come to the fore. "Does life travel the void between planets or does it arise independently?"

The search for extraterrestrial life will certainly help resolve one of the most fundamental questions in biology: "Is life a distinct, discrete entity, or is it an inevitable manifestation of matter as chemical combinations become increasingly complex?" After Darwin elucidated biological evolution, biologists appropriated the word for their exclusive use. However, the term "chemical evolution" is now used to describe the abiogenic production of life precursor compounds from inorganic chemicals under appropriate conditions. Only a few years have seen this area progress from the abiogenic production of simple organic compounds and amino acids to the abiogenic synthesis of fairly complex intermediates and the production of "proteinoids." The theory of continuous generation of matter in the universe has gained considerable acceptance as has the evolution of the elements from neutrons or hydrogen gas. Is it possible, then, that life is just one segment of a vast continuum of evolution on a universal scale? To speculate, did the following developmental sequence take place as part of this continuum: Space (as far back as we dare imagine), energy, elemental particles, hydrogen, the other elements, increasingly complex compounds, structured matter exhibiting the characteristics of life, consciousness, social evolution? Although there are many gaps in this theory of an evolutionary continuum, there is also much evidence for it. In the portion of the spectrum of interest to biologists, we may not be too far away from achieving abiogenic synthesis of macromolecules which are identical to those functioning in living material. The largest gap facing the biologists in attempting to explain the development of a living cell from inorganic compounds is that of structure. Even if we could synthesize all of the chemicals of a cell, how can we assemble these materials into specialized components such as membranes, walls, ribosomes, mitochondria, and the like? Here, too, however, there are now indications that at least part of the explanation lies in the natural geometric accommodation of very complex molecules. The finding of life elsewhere might shed light on the theory that the geometrically possible combinations of elements, as modified by chemical and physical constraints operating under a range of environmental conditions, inevitably produce self-replicating material subject to genetic mutation.

The interest in exobiology extends beyond possible simple alien forms of life. A question of utmost significance and fascination is "Is there *intelligent* life elsewhere?" The finding of even unicellular life on Mars would add greatly to the probability that the answer is "yes." Life on a second planet would double the size of our sample and would strongly indicate that life exists on many planets in the universe. While prospects for intelligent life do not seem favorable in our solar system, it would then be exceedingly likely that other stellar systems contain planets favorably situated and endowed to permit the evolution of intelligent organisms. The consequences of such an assumption are awesome. If the Earth is but one of a great many planets supporting life, it becomes highly improbable that the Earth possesses the most advanced form of life.

The ramifications of a positive answer to the last question posed jar the imagination. The significance includes but transcends the realm of biology. Morrison has represented the growth of technology as a vertical line at some point on the galactic time scale. It would seem, thus, that, once having begun, the elucidation of all science occurs almost immediately. Therefore, those planets possessing beings of greater intelligence than ours would be beyond this infinitesimally short blip on the time scale. Contact with such beings could provide us with an almost instantaneous scientific denouement of the universe! While the time saved would be minute on the galactic scale, it would be very large compared to the life span of a man.

Such, then, is the scope of significance of exobiology. Now, what about its *status?* No one can deny that the significance greatly over-shadows the status. While it is true that there are no generally accepted data, concerted research on the subject is in its infancy. We have not yet had the opportunity to deliver instruments to other planets. It now appears the possibility to do this is at hand, and it is hoped that the instrumented exploration of Mars will begin shortly. However, there are other avenues of exobiological research including highly important experiments which can be conducted in Earth-based laboratories. Origin of life experiments, the abiogenic synthesis of macromolecules, and other empirical and theoretical investigations of life are potentially important to exobiology. If we could learn how life on Earth evolved from inorganic chemicals, we could probably answer the first question posed, "Is life limited to this planet?"

Pasteur was probably the first empirical exobiologist. He attempted to culture a piece of the Orgueil meteorite and found no growth. Today there is considerable dispute over the possible biological origin of some materials found in meteorites. Evidence was recently presented for the identification of exobiological material in the same Orgueil meteorite. This evidence consists of a characteristic carbon chain length distribution of alkanes similar to that found in living material on Earth and isotopic ratios significantly different from those in terrestrial alkanes. On the other hand, the ease with which terrestrial microorganisms can contaminate meteorites has been demonstrated. The subject remains open, as does the possibility that the examination of meteorites can supply the first positive evidence of extraterrestrial life. However, the source of the meteorite would remain unknown.

Ground and rocket-based visual and infrared observations of Mars will be intensified during the 1965 and 1967 planetary oppositions. While information derived from these studies will not directly answer the question of life, the hospitality of the Martian environment to life, as we know it, will be better revealed.

Instruments are now under development for the biological exploration of Mars. These instruments look for metabolism, growth, or chemical and physical properties peculiar to living matter. NASA is now considering the possibility of sending a package containing a number of such instruments to Mars in 1969. Plans are also being studied for landing much heavier instrument capsules in 1973.

The recent extraordinary photographs obtained from Ranger 7 indicate that the moon may contain a wealth of exobiological information. The entire surface of the moon seems to be composed of in-fall. It seems likely that, since its formation, the moon has been sweeping space, actively collecting vast quantities of materials, including planetary fragments from a great variety of near and distant sources. The galactic beachcombing that can be achieved through an examination of moon samples may produce fossils or other evidence of once living organisms. Such samples should become available within the next few years.

There are engineers who believe that manned exploration of Mars will be possible in the 1980's. This would permit a detailed exploration of Mars and, perhaps more important, the return of a sample to Earth laboratories for extensive studies. While we cannot say that planning for such a mission has yet begun, at least the subject is under discussion by the space agency.

There is one other facet to the current status of exobiology. It concerns the means by which we will probe for life beyond the solar system.

Purcell presents what seems to be an irrefutable case against the possibility of manned space travel far beyond the solar system. He does this solely on the basis of the propellent mass required for a round trip journey in which the ship approaches the speed of light. Assuming the development of perfect nuclear fusion propulsion, he demonstrates that the ratio of the initial mass of the rocket to the final mass is 1.6×10^9. Thus, for every pound that made the round trip, a starting weight of 1.6 billion pounds would be required. Even assuming that the ultimate is attained, the perfection of matter-antimatter propellant, the ratio of the initial mass to the final mass is 40,000. The tremendous energies thus shown to be required for manned interstellar space travel make such travel extraordinarily unlikely. It might also be pointed out that, at travel at or near the speed of light, tremendous radiation problems would result from collisions of the ship and occupants with atomic nuclei in space. In these difficulties, perhaps, lies the answer to the question raised by skeptics of intelligent extraterrestrial life, "Since they are smarter than we, why haven't they come here?"

Nonetheless, the solar system is not the limit of our exobiological exploration and indeed a brief, preliminary experiment probing beyond it has already been made. In contrast to the tremendous energies required for space travel, the electromagnetic energy required to traverse vast regions of space is quite manageable. Cocconi and Morrison show that our present capabilities are sufficient to permit radiocommunication over a distance of 10 light years. Cameron, on the basis of the statistical frequency of environments similar to Earth, estimates that there are 2×10^6 advanced civilizations within our galaxy. He believes it highly probable that many of these contain inhabitants whose scientific achievements have surpassed our own. If so, they, too, are faced with the inefficiency of interstellar space travel. Accordingly, it seems possible that many distant societies have already contacted each other by electromagnetic communication systems. During their existences, such societies would probably continually search for new civilizations which attain the technology required to join in this communication. Hence, we may now be the target of intelligent electromagnetic signals—signals that started their journey many years ago. The preliminary search for the signals which has been made, entitled "Project Ozma," was conducted with the 85-foot radio-telescope of the National Radio Astronomy Observatory. Two target stars, of the type thought likely to harbor Earth-type planets, were searched during May, June, and July, 1960. No signals of extraterrestrial intelligent origin were detected, but the prosecution of such a program will take many years of painstaking work. It will undoubtedly be undertaken at a serious level.

I have attempted to show that exobiology has considerable signifi-cance and that it is rapidly improving in status. In doing so, I fear that some of the possibilities discussed may not only have taxed your imagina-tion, but may have exceeded your credulity. Perhaps some of these of-fenses may have done disservice to my goal of stimulating your interest and active participation in exobiology. However, the severest test I wish to impose on your imagination has been saved until last. It is that, in a universe containing on the order of one trillion galaxies, each consisting of hundreds of millions of stars, there is, nestling in an arm of one galaxy, one star which swings about it a planet completely covered with the only life to be found in all that infinite cosmic desert.

41

The Biology of Space

WHAT MAN FACES IN SPACE

To survive and to fulfill the missions assigned to him in space, man must learn to live there with a reasonable degree of comfort, efficiency, and freedom of movement. The greatest problem posed for man in this regard is the necessity of creating for himself in space an environment which will reasonably duplicate the one he is accustomed to on earth.

Man is a complex mechanism. He has developed through thousands of years of living under one set of general conditions. Although he can be trained and acclimatized, he cannot be reengineered. He must take his

From Space, the New Frontier (EP-6), an educational publication of the National Aeronautics and Space Administration, Washington, D.C. 20546.

manner of living with him wherever he goes. This involves not only the air
he breathes and the temperature and humidity he feels, but also his protection from heat, cold, weightlessness, and radiation. In addition to these,
there are the related problems of food and water and the disposal of human wastes—plus the factors of fatigue and boredom.

Man uses in the neighborhood of 2 pounds of oxygen each day. This
he gets, of course, from the atmosphere. In space there is no atmosphere.
For human breathing purposes the atmosphere ends well below 50,000
feet. An aircraft pressurizes its cabin from surrounding atmosphere even at
40,000 feet, but because a spacecraft has no surrounding atmosphere, it
must be pressurized from one of three sources carried along: compressed
gaseous oxygen, liquid oxygen or chemical compounds which liberate
oxygen.

Cosmic rays lose their original power and intensity when they enter
the atmosphere. But, in space outside the atmosphere, any object is exposed to a powerful bombardment of cosmic ray particles.

Sunburn is caused by the ultraviolet rays of solar radiation. On earth
the atmosphere gives lifesaving protection from solar radiation. But out in
space its intensity is lethal.

Thousands of tiny meteoroids cross the regions of space. As they enter
the atmosphere they normally are set afire by friction, become meteors, and
burn up. But they constitute a possible hazard to any craft in space.

There are many psychological problems. Man is accustomed to a certain day-and-night cycle and performs best when he works, eats, and sleeps
in his usual manner. He must be able to walk about and shift positions, to
flex his arms, legs, and neck. He must have some sort of visual orientation
within the spacecraft and he must be able to make minor adjustments in
his environment (like raising or lowering the lights) just to relieve the
monotony. In space, man faces the problem of fatigue—the kind that comes
from long commitment to one task and confinement within a relatively
small compartment. This fatigue results in impaired judgment, decline in
alertness, irritability, and indecision. His power of perception suffers.

FOOD IS A MORALE FACTOR

Food is highly important to the space explorer both for nutrition and
sustaining his morale. The cook, the engineer, the flight surgeon, and the
nutrition expert have all combined in creating a menu the astronaut will
look forward to, and of giving him a way to eat it. Three general feeding
plans have been worked out for space flights. The first covers a short trip
of 2 or 3 days. The second covers from 3 days to several months. The third
or long-range covers a flight extending over months or years.

The first or short-range plan includes food bars, each of 250 calories, cut into bite-size pieces; water in plastic bags with plastic drinking tubes; both liquid and semisolid foods packaged in squeeze tubes (soup, meat, fruit, chocolate, milk, ham, turkey, and cheese); dehydrated foods and fruit juices to be reconstituted with water.

For longer range missions, ranging from 3 days to several months, the food experts assume that space scientists will have perfected a means of producing artificial gravity within the spacecraft. They also assume that water will be recovered from the atmosphere within the spacecraft and from body waste, purified and reused.

Where weight and space are crucial, the meals will consist of pre-cooked, dehydrated food, plus ordinary beverages.

Where weight is less of a problem, food would include canned, dehydrated, and instant types, none of which would require refrigeration. Spices, herbs, condiments, pickles, jellies, raisins, nuts, and candy would also be available.

Where weight and space are of no concern, the meals would be very much like those served today on the most modern commercial airliner.

For the long flights in the relatively distant future, those flights which may last for months or years, it is not feasible to carry expendable supplies. Such flights will require a completely regenerative, closed and balanced ecological system capable of producing food and oxygen (and absorbing carbon dioxide), and of recycling wastes to supply materials essential to the human body.

Since earth, itself, is a successful closed ecological system, man will probably take earth as his model in creating such a system for space. The regenerative cycle is well established by Nature. Man and other animals eat the plants of earth, the products of the sea (and each other), return their wastes and even their bones to the earth in the recycling process.

ENABLING MAN TO LIVE AND WORK IN SPACE

Steps have already been taken toward development of an artificial closed-cycle ecological system for space flight. Among those under development are prototype systems that can sustain five men in shirtsleeve comfort for 30 to 60 days; four men for 3 to 6 months; and eight men for a year. The systems will be designed to purify water and air for reuse and provide for waste disposal and for food.

Tests are being conducted to learn how man will perform and how he will react in the relative isolation of long space flights. One volunteer remained for about 5 months in a compartment approximately the size of an efficiency apartment. During the experiment, he performed directed tasks in sequence as if he were piloting a spacecraft but he saw no one else and had only voice contact with the outside. Tests with two or more volunteers are scheduled.

NASA is observing the effects of strong magnetic fields on organisms to determine any adverse effects from surrounding manned spacecraft with magnetic fields as a radiation shield. The artificial magnetic fields would function just like earth's magnetic field which diverts much lethal radiation hurtling to earth from outer space.

Biologists are considering induced hibernation for long space trips. An additional attribute of hibernation is that it appears to increase resistance to radiation.

NASA is studying algae and other plants as possible sources for a continued food supply. Moreover, studies are being carried out on development of compact, lightweight, nutritious, palatable, and morale-supporting meals that require neither refrigeration nor heating.

Some of these are in puree form to be taken from tubes; others are in solid form and must be chewed. (Foods that can be chewed are most desirable.) Some of the solid foods are dehydrated or freeze dried and must be reconstituted with water. In many cases, however, the moisture required can be supplied by the astronaut's salivary glands.

Space suits are being fabricated that will protect man from high vacuum temperature extremes, small meteoroids, and radiation in space or on the airless moon, yet permit reasonable freedom of movement.

A series of recoverable bioscience satellites will provide information about the effects of weightlessness for as long as a year on animals and plants. Scientists generally agree that lengthy periods of weightlessness can reduce muscle tone; i.e., weaken muscles. However, other biological effects are still to be determined.

Crewless instrumented spacecraft, such as Ranger, Surveyor, and Mariner, will precede man to the moon and planets. They will transmit vital information about the celestial body that he is to explore and about what he will face on the voyage through black uncharted space.

Orbiting Solar Observatories, Pioneer spacecraft, and interplanetary monitoring platforms (IMP) will furnish data on radiation and other space phenomena and contribute to development of reliable methods for forecasting large solar flares. Such flares flood space with lethal intensities of radiation.

THE SEARCH FOR EXTRATERRESTRIAL LIFE

In a related program, NASA is investigating the possibility of life elsewhere than on earth. Life normally results where the conditions for it are appropriate. However, most scientists agree that the appropriate conditions need not necessarily resemble those on earth nor must all life be comparable to earth forms.

The conditions of space are simulated in earth-based laboratories. Micro-organisms are inserted in simulators to determine whether and how long organisms can survive the temperature extremes, high vacuum, and radiation of space. The results of these studies may have important implications relative to life on other planets.

Life scientists have simulated in the laboratory the kind of environment believed to exist on Mars. They have discovered that certain terrestrial lichens, mosses, and bacteria can survive for a limited time in this kind of environment. This does not necessarily mean that such organisms live on Mars but that organisms such as these could live on Mars. In the opinion of scientists, Mars is the best candidate in the solar system for some sort of life like that on earth.

Balloon-borne instruments have made infrared studies of Mars. These and other studies detected minute quantities of water vapor and considerable carbon dioxide in the atmosphere. Their existence suggests the possibility that specially adapted lower forms of life may exist on the Red Planet.

During its exploration of the moon, NASA plans to analyze lunar materials for signs of life. Such analysis may disclose remnants of extinct life or organic substances that might signify the presence of life. On the other hand, the study may bring to light prelife chemicals (chemicals identified with life) that have accumulated through natural processes over millions of years but have not been organized into living things. Such a find would be invaluable to the study of how life originated or evolved.

As part of this program, NASA is also supporting the examination of meteorites for organic compounds and studying the origin of compounds of living organisms under primeval geochemical conditions.

Several life detection devices are being readied for landing on other planets. These miniature laboratories are primarily designed to report on microbial life. They are quite small, and some weigh as little as 1½ pounds.

One is named *Gulliver* for Jonathan Swift's fictional discoverer of the tiny Lilliputians. After landing, Gulliver will fire adhesive cords outward and then reel them in. It is expected that dust and other surface substances will adhere to the cords. The cords will be immersed into or drenched by a nutrient solution containing radioactive carbon. If earthlike organisms are present, they will ingest and ferment the solution, creating radioactive carbon dioxide gas. This would be registered by a Geiger counter and the exciting results transmitted to earth.

Another device, which operates on a similar principle, is the *Wolf Trap*, named for its designer Dr. Wolf Vishniac. The Wolf Trap will suck in samples of soil and air and immerse them in nutrient solutions. If the samples contain organisms, the solutions will undergo changes in acidity and turbidity which would be reported to earth.

Among the other life detection devices are the *Multivator* which is in effect a miniature laboratory that can make 24 biochemical tests for organisms, a microscope which can radio images back to earth, and a TV telescope that can survey the landscape for such possible signs of life as moving or waving objects.

Newer approaches include devices for determining the characteristic absorption of polypeptides and DNA in the *UV range;* for determining *optical rotation* (typical of complex molecules of living or once living systems); *gas chromotography* for the detection and analysis of various life related materials; and *mass spectroscopy* for the identification of relatively large submolecular groups by means of density. Another device may consist of a simple colorimeter which will measure the visible light absorption reaction ("*J*" bands) between certain dyes and proteins. Recent experiments have shown that by varying the pH and temperature, it may be possible to render this device "analytical" not only with respect to proteins but also with respect to other biologically significant molecules.

42

Travelers in Space

Samuel Moffat
Elie A. Shneour

During the conquest of Mexico in 1520 the Spanish invaders brought with them not only weapons and baggage, but also disease. The famous historian W. H. Prescott has told of "that terrible epidemic, the small-pox, which was now sweeping over the land like fire over the prairies . . . leaving its path strewn with the dead bodies of the natives. . . ."

History is full of such incidents. Travelers to new countries have often

Samuel Moffat and Elie A. Shneour, "Travelers in Space," *Life Beyond the Earth,* Vistas in Science No. 2 (Washington, D.C.: National Teachers Association, 1965), pp. 99-104.

spread infection. And just as often they have succumbed to unfamiliar ailments themselves or carried diseases back to their homes. A vital function of the U.S. Public Health Service is the quarantine at every port of entry to prevent travelers from spreading disease. The U.S. Department of Agriculture maintains even stricter controls against the entry of plants and animals that might harbor infections.

The past has an important lesson to teach us in the space age. We face the possibility of finding unfamiliar forms of life elsewhere in the solar system or, perhaps, in the universe. Scientists recognize that organisms from the earth could pose a serious threat to life on other worlds, and extraterrestrial forms of life could represent an equally serious threat if brought back to our planet. According to one estimate, common bacteria could completely occupy a planet the size of the earth in a few days or weeks if conditions were suitable for growth and spread. Who knows how fast an unfamiliar microbe could do the same here?

These problems may seem a long way off, since we will probably not make manned landings anywhere other than on the moon for many years. But they are really of immediate concern. Spacecraft have already crashed on the moon. These craft were not completely sterilized before takeoff, and we can no longer be sure that any bacteria that may be found on the moon originated there. The scientific implications are very serious, for we would have liked to examine the moon's surface to find out what lifelike or prelife forms might have collected there. Some, but not all, scientists have seriously questioned whether organisms could survive under lunar conditions. Were we to detect one bacterial spore, it could have important meaning—if we knew for certain a spacecraft had not brought it there. The same questions will hold for the planets when we reach them.

With this in mind, researchers have conducted many laboratory tests to see whether earthly organisms could survive in an environment much harsher than ours.

HOW ADAPTABLE IS LIFE?

Several groups of scientists have tried to simulate certain characteristics of the environment of Mars to test some of the speculation about that planet. They wanted to find out what happens to living things when they are subjected to temperatures below freezing for long periods of time, to nearly waterless conditions, to alternate freezing and thawing, and to very low-oxygen atmospheres.

Many of the organisms die, of course. But what is remarkable is that some of them manage to survive, and a few even thrive under these difficult conditions. One investigation involved certain bacteria that grow without oxygen. The microbes were mixed with sterilized crushed volcanic lava to simulate soil conditions we might expect on Mars. They were dried and kept under a vacuum for eight months. Every eight hours the temperature was alternated between —23° and +25° C. (—10° and +77° F.) to parallel the changes due to the Martian day and night. In one strain 10 per cent of the bacteria survived. The results were similar for other species.

Other bacteria can survive and grow well under conditions that approximate a typical summer day at the Martian equator: 24° C. (+75° F.) at mid-day, —74° C. (—101° F.) at night, with only 4½ hours a day above the freezing temperature of water.

Single-celled organisms are not the only ones that can withstand extreme conditions. More than 30 species of multicellular plants have been tested in a low-oxygen atmosphere and have survived. The "air" in the test chamber had between .2 and .002 the amount of oxygen in the earth's air and was at a tenth the atmospheric pressure. The plants included the cucumber, which is very delicate, as well as peanut, barley, and turnip. These plants did not merely survive; they did much better than they do in the earth's atmosphere. Their seedlings grew more rapidly and became taller. The plants ripened better and lived longer. This unusual atmosphere has also been shown to speed up biological processes in certain birds, amphibians, shellfish, and other marine animals. Seeds of winter rye will sprout in a nearly waterless atmosphere at less than a tenth the normal air pressure.

We should understand that such simulation experiments have definite limitations, ones the researchers are well aware of. The chambers in which the microbes and plants grow are designed to regulate temperature, pressure, patterns of light and dark, and other conditions in order to approximate as closely as possible the environment on Mars. But we do not have very precise information about the Martian environment. We do not know the nature of the soil on the planet, or the exact air pressure at the surface, or what radiation reaches the surface—to mention just a few of the many gaps in our knowledge. Actually all we know are a few "gaps." So the results of these experiments may prove only as useful as our guesses about Mars prove accurate.

Nevertheless, the experiments do teach us a couple of lessons. First, they indicate that living things are remarkably adaptable, far more so than biologists have thought. It appears that organisms can show tremendous flexibility in adapting to available atmosphere, water and warmth. The experiments also remind us that we are still not very well informed about many life processes. It would be exceedingly risky to suggest that parallels might exist between life here and any other life that we might later learn exists. Perhaps we should not expect parallels, but we should not be surprised if we find them.

Second, the results re-emphasize the importance of sterilizing all space vehicles on lunar or planetary missions. If one organism is aboard and later colonizes the moon or a planet, we will have destroyed forever the original conditions there. We will have lost an invaluable scientific resource. This will be true even if, as some researchers believe, there is no life there beforehand.

43

What Do We Seek in Space?

Joshua Lederberg

What do we seek in space?

Clearly, the journey will give us two unique rewards: a perspective on our own planet and a prospect on other worlds.

The first pioneering steps in space have already proved their value. Today orbiting satellites analyze the earth's atmosphere, reveal weather patterns, speed communications, and improve navigation. Tomorrow, more powerful craft will be developed, extending our reach and giving us new objectives.

Among these objectives, exobiology—the study of life beyond the earth—is the most subtle and demanding, for it insists "Know thyself." When we have learned as much about life as earthbound science can teach us, then we will be ready to lift our gaze to the planets and the stars.

In the past century, biology has experienced a remarkable development as a scientific discipline, particularly in our understanding of the biochemical mechanisms of life. Once Darwin had set forth the concept of evolution, this understanding could come about. For it is this magnificent concept that helps to explain how structures as diverse as the microscopic amoeba and the giant Sequoia could have developed.

Our understanding of life on earth has now progressed to the level of cells and molecules. Evolution, we now know, has a chemical basis.

Joshua Lederberg, "What Do We Seek in Space?", from *Life Beyond the Earth* by Samuel Moffat and Elie A. Shneour, Vistas in Science No. 2 (Washington, D.C.: National Science Teachers Association, 1965), pp. 153-156.

Despite the outward differences of living organisms, their chemistry is the same. In all organisms the genetic material consists of nucleic acids. And in all organisms the cell structures are composed mainly of proteins. Indeed, on chemical inspection we find the composition of living cells so similar that it is difficult to tell the nucleus of a human nerve cell from the virus that might attack it.

In the world we know, nucleic acids and proteins come about only as copies of what has evolved before them. Their blueprints are handed down from parent to offspring. But how did these complex substances come about originally—without pre-existing cells or brains to guide their production?

Thirty years ago many people thought the answer to this question was beyond the reach of science. Today the question leads us to fundamental problems of exobiology:

Are nucleic acids the only substances that can link the generations of living things that might exist anywhere in the universe? Or are they merely the only links that earthly life has encountered?

Are proteins the only means of building up cell structures? Or are they the accidental result of early chemical events on earth?

It is the purpose of exobiology to probe for the answers—and for a larger one as well.

In the past, biology's domain has been limited to the thin shell of the earth, to the way in which one spark of life has illuminated one speck in the cosmos. By contrast, the basic laws of physics are derived from the motions of the stars; and we know the scope of chemistry from studies of the light emitted by stars at the boundaries of the observable universe.

As yet, biology has no such grand universal system. But there is a principle which we confidently expect will prove to be universal—the principle of evolution. Until we have evidence from the planets themselves, however, we can only speculate about evolution elsewhere.

The ultimate goal of the exobiologist, then, is to answer questions about *all* life, about *all* evolution.

It would be difficult to point to any practical fruits of this research. Expeditions beyond the earth may be among the most costly experiments ever undertaken, but surely they count as one of the very aims of the human adventure. Is not the search for life beyond the earth the next stage of the great journey that has always led men into the unknown?

VIII
Heredity

44

Gregor Mendel and His Work

Hugo Iltis

It is 145 years since, in a small village on the northern border of what was called Austria at that time, a boy was born in a farmer's house who was destined to influence human thoughts and science. Germans, Czechs and Poles had settled side by side in this part of the country, quarreling sometimes, but mixing their blood continually. During the Middle Ages the Mongolic Tatars invaded Europe just there. Thus, the place had been a melting pot of nations and races, and, like America, had brought up finally a splendid alloy. The father's name was Anton Mendel; the boy was christened Johann. He grew up like other farmers' boys; he liked to help his father with his fruit trees and bees and retained from these early experiences his fondness for gardening and bee-keeping until his last years. Since his parents, although not poor compared with the neighbors, had no liquid resources, the young and gifted boy had to fight his way through high school and junior college (Gymnasium). Finally he came to the conclusion, as he wrote in his autobiography, "That it has become impossible for him to continue such strenuous exertions. It was incumbent on him to enter a profession in which he would be spared perpetual anxiety about a means of livelihood. His private circumstances determined his choice of profession." So he entered as a novice the rich and beautiful monastery of the Augustinians of Bruenn in 1843 and assumed the monastic name of Gregor. Here he found the necessary means, leisure and good company. Here during the period from 1843 to 1865 he grew to become the great investigator whose name is known to every schoolboy to-day.

On a clear cold evening in February, 1865, several men were walking through the streets of Bruenn towards the modern school, a big building still new. One of these men, stocky and rather corpulent, friendly of countenance, with a high forehead and piercing blue eyes, wearing a tall hat, a long black coat and trousers tucked in top boots, was carrying a manu-

Hugo Iltis, "Gregor Mendel and His Work," *Scientific Monthly*, Vol. 56 (May, 1943), pp. 414-423. Reprinted by permission.

script under his arm. This was Pater Gregor Mendel, a professor at the modern school, and with his friends he was going to a meeting of the Society of Natural Science where he was to read a paper on "Experiments in Plant Hybridization." In the schoolroom, where the meeting was to be held, about forty persons had gathered, many of them able or even outstanding scientists. For about one hour Mendel read from his manuscript an account of the results of his experiments in hybridization of the edible pea, which had occupied him during the preceding eight years.

Mendel's predecessors failed in their experiments on heredity because they directed their attention to the behavior of the type of the species or races as a whole, instead of contenting themselves with one or two clear-cut characters. The new thing about Mendel's method was that he had confined himself to studying the effects of hybridization upon single particular characters, and that he didn't take, as his predecessors had done, only a summary view upon a whole generation of hybrids, but examined each individual plant separately.

The experiments, the laws derived from these experiments, and the splendid explanation given to them by Mendel are to-day not only the base of the modern science of genetics, but belong to the fundamentals of biology taught to millions of students in all parts of the world.

Mendel had been since 1843 one of the brethren of the beautiful and wealthy monastery of the Augustinians of Bruenn, at that time in Austria, later in Czechoslovakia. His profession left him sufficient time, and the large garden of the monastery provided space enough, for his plant hybridizations. During the eight years from 1856 to 1864, he observed with a rare patience and perserverance more than 10,000 specimens.

In hybridization the pollen from the male plant is dusted on the pistils of the female plant through which it fertilizes the ovules.* Both the pollen and the ovules in the pistils carry hereditary characters which may be alike in the two parents or partly or entirely different. The peas used by Mendel for hybridization differed in the simplest case only by one character or, better still, by a pair of characters; for instance, by the color of the flowers, which was red on one parental plant and white on the other; or by the shape of the seeds, which were smooth in one case and wrinkled in the other; or by the color of the cotyledons, which were yellow in one pea and green in the other, etc. Mendel's experiments show in all cases the result that all individuals of the first generation of hybrids, the F_1 generation as it is called to-day, are uniform in appearance, and that moreover only one of the two parental characters, the stronger or the dominant one, is shown. That means, for instance, that the red color of the flowers, the smooth shape of the seeds or the yellow color of the cotyledons is in evidence while the other, or recessive, character seems to have disappeared. From the behavior of the hybrids of the F_1 generation, Mendel derived the first

*What is meant here is that the eggs in the ovules are fertilized by the sperms in the pollen grains. (Ed.)

of the experimental laws, the so-called "Law of Uniformity," which is
that all individuals of the first hybrid generation are equal or uniform.
The special kind of inheritance shown by the prevalence of the dominant
characters in the first hybrid generation is called alternative inheritance
or the pea type of inheritance. In other instances, however, the hybrids
show a mixture of the parental characteristics. Thus, crossing between a
red-flowered and a white-flowered four o'clock (*Mirabilis*) gives a pink-
flowered F_1 generation. This type of inheritance is called the intermediate,
or *Mirabilis*, type of inheritance.

Now, Mendel self-pollinated the hybrids of the first generation, dust-
ing the pistils of the flowers with their own pollen and obtained thus the
second, or F_2 generation of hybrids. In this generation the recessive characters, which had seemingly disappeared, but, which were really only
covered in the F_1 generation, reappeared again and in a characteristic and
constant proportion. Among the F_2 hybrids he found three red-flowered
plants and one white-flowered plant, or three smooth-seeded and one-
wrinkled-seeded plant, or three plants with yellow cotyledons and one
with green ones. In general, the hybrids of the F_2 generation showed a
ratio of three dominant to one recessive plants. Mendel derived from the
behavior of the F_2 generation his second experimental law, the so-called
"Law of Segregation." Of course, the characteristic ratio of three dominant
to one recessive may be expected only if the numbers of individuals are
large, the Mendelian laws being so-called statistical laws or laws valid
for large numbers only.

The third important experimental law Mendel discovered by crossing
two plants which distinguished themselves not only by one but by two or
more pairs of hereditary characters. He crossed, for instance, a pea plant
with smooth and yellow seeds with another having green and wrinkled
seeds. The first, or F_1, generation of hybrids was of course uniform, showing both smooth and yellow seeds, the dominant characters. F_1 hybrids
were then self-pollinated and the second hybrid, or F_2, generation was
yielded in large numbers, showing all possible combinations of the parental characters in characteristic ratios and that there were nine smooth
yellow to three smooth green to three wrinkled yellow to one wrinkled
green. From these so-called polyhybrid crossings, Mendel derived the
third and last of his exprimental laws, the "Law of Independent Assortment."

These experiments and observations Mendel reviewed in his lecture.
Mendel's hearers, who were personally attached to the lecturer as well as
appreciating him for his original observations in various fields of natural
science, listened with respect but also with astonishment to his account of
the invariable numerical ratios among the hybrids, unheard of in those
days. Mendel concluded his first lecture and announced a second one at
the next month's meeting and promised he would give them the theory he
had elaborated in order to explain the behavior of the hybrids.

There was a goodly audience, once more, at the next month's meeting. It must be admitted, however, that the attention of most of the hearers was inclined to wander when the lecturer became engaged in a rather difficult algebraical deduction. And probably not a soul among the audience really understood what Mendel was driving at. His main idea was that the living individual might be regarded as composed of distinct hereditary characters, which are transmitted by distinct invisible heredity factors—to-day we call them genes. In the hybrid the different parental genes are combined. But when the sex cells of the hybrids are formed the two parental genes separate again, remaining quite unchanged and pure, each sex cell containing only one of the two genes of one pair. We call this fundamental theoretical law the "Law of the Purity of the Gametes." Through combination of the different kinds of sex cells, which are produced by the hybrid, the law of segregation and the law of independent assortment can be easily explained.

Just as the chemist thinks of the most complicated compound as being built from a relatively small number of invariable atoms, so Mendel regarded the species as a mosaic of genes, the atoms of living organisms. It was no more nor less than an atomistic theory of the organic world which was developed before the astonished audience. The minutes of the meeting inform us that there were neither questions nor discussions. The audience dispersed and ceased to think about the matter—Mendel was disappointed but not discouraged. In all his modesty he knew that by his discoveries a new way into the unknown realm of science had been opened. "My time will come," he said to his friend Niessl.

Mendel's paper was published in the proceedings of the society for 1866. Mendel sent the separate prints to Carl Naegeli in Munich, one of the outstanding biologists of those days, who occupied himself with experiments on plant hybridization. A correspondence developed and letters and views were exchanged between the two men. But even Naegeli didn't appreciate the importance of Mendel's discovery. In not one of his books or papers dealing with heredity did he even mention Mendel's name. So, the man and the work were forgotten.

When Mendel died in 1884, hundreds of mourners, his pupils, who remembered their beloved teacher, and the poor, to whom he had been always kind, attended the funeral. But although hundreds realized that they had lost a good friend, and other hundreds attended the funeral of a high dignitary, not a single one of those present recognized that a great scientist and investigator had passed away.

The story of the rediscovery and the sudden resurrection of Mendel's work is a thrilling one. By a peculiar, but by no means an accidental, coincidence three investigators in three different places in Europe, DeVries in Amsterdam, Correns in Germany, Tschermak in Vienna, came almost at the same time across Mendel's paper and recognized at once its great importance.

Now the time has arrived for understanding, now "his time had come" and to an extent far beyond anything of which Mendel had dreamed. The little essay, published in the great volume of the Bruenn Society, has given stimulus to all branches of biology. The progress of research since the beginning of the century has built for Mendel a monument more durable and more imposing than any monument of marble, because not only has "Mendelism" become the name of a whole vast province of investigation, but all living creatures which follow "Mendelian" laws in the heredity transmission of their characters are said to "Mendelize."

As illustrations, I will explain the practical consequences of Mendelian research by two examples only. The Swede, Nilsson-Ehle, was one of the first investigators who tried to use Mendelistic methods to improve agricultural plants. In the cold climate of Sweden some wheat varieties, like the English square-hood wheat, were yielding well but were frozen easily. Other varieties, like the Swedish country wheat, were winter-hard but brought only a poor harvest. Nilsson-Ehle knew that in accordance with the Mendelian law of independent assortment, the breeder is able to combine the desired characters of two different parents, like the chemist who combines the atoms to form various molecules or compounds. He crossed the late-ripening, well-yielding, square-hood wheat with the early-ripening, winter-hard, but poor-yielding Swedish country wheat. The resulting F_1 generation, however, was very discouraging. It was uniform, in accordance with Mendel's first law, all individuals being late-ripe and poor-yielding, thus combining the two undesirable dominant characters. In pre-Mendelian times the breeder would have been discouraged and probably would have discontinued his efforts. Not so Nilsson-Ehle, who knew that the F_1 generation is hybrid, showing only the dominant traits, and that the independent assortment of all characters will appear only in the F_2 generation. Self-pollinating the F_1 plants he obtained an F_2 generation showing the ratio of nine late-ripe poor-yielding to three late-ripe well-yielding, to three early-ripe poor yielding, to one early-ripe, well-yielding wheat plants. The desired combination of the two recessive characters, early-ripe, well-yielding, appeared only in the smallest ratio, one in sixteen—but because recessives are always true-breeding, or as it is called "homozygous," Nilsson-Ehle had only to isolate these plants and to destroy all others in order to obtain a new true breeding early-ripe and well-yielding variety which after a few years gave a crop large enough to be sold. Thus, by the work of the Mendelist, Nilsson-Ehle, culture of wheat was made possible even in the northern parts of Sweden and large amounts heretofore spent for imported wheat could be saved.

Another instance shows the importance of Mendelism for the understanding of human inheritance. Very soon after the rediscovery of Mendel's paper it became evident that the laws found by Mendel with his peas are valid also for animals and for human beings. Of course, the study of the laws of human heredity is limited and rendered more difficult by several obstacles. We can't make experiments with human beings. The laws of Mendel are statistical laws based upon large numbers of offspring, while the number of children in human families is generally small. But in spite of these difficulties it was found very soon that human characters are inherited in the same manner as the characters of the pea. We know, for instance, that the dark color of the iris of the eye is dominant, the light blue color recessive. I remember a tragi-comic accident connected with this fact. At one of my lecture tours in a small town in Czechoslovakia, I spoke about the heredity of eye color in men and concluded that, while two dark-eyed parents may be hybrids in regard to eye color and thus may have children both with dark and blue eyes, the character blue-eyed, being recessive, is always pure. Hence two blue-eyed parents will have only blue-eyed children. A few months later I learned that a divorce had taken place in the small town. I was surprised and resolved to be very careful even with scientifically proved statements in the future.

Even more important is the Mendelian analysis of hereditary diseases. If we learn that the predisposition to a certain disease is inherited through a dominant gene, as diabetes, for instance, then we know that all persons carrying the gene will be sick. In this case all carriers can be easily recognized. In the case of recessive diseases, feeblemindedness,* for instance, we know that the recessive gene may be covered by the dominant gene for health and that the person, seemingly healthy, may carry the disease and transmit it to his children.

With every year the influence of Mendel's modest work became more widespread. The theoretical explanation given by Mendel was based upon the hypothesis of a mechanism for the distribution and combination of the genes. To-day we know that exactly such a mechanism, as was seen by the prophetic eye of Mendel, exists in the chromosome apparatus of the nucleus of the cells. The development of research on chromosomes, from the observations of the chromosomes and their distribution by mitosis to the discovery of the reduction of the number of chromosomes in building the sex cells and finally to the audacious attempt to locate the single genes within the chromosomes, is all a story, exciting as a novel and at the same time one of the most grandiose chapters in the history of science. A tiny animal, the fruit fly, *Drosophila*, was found to be the best object for genetical research. The parallelism between the behavior of the chromosomes and the mechanism of Mendelian inheritance was studied by hundreds of scientists, who were trying to determine even the location of the different genes within the different chromosomes and who started to devise so-called chromosome maps.

Correns, Baur and Goldschmidt in Germany; Bateson and his school in England; Devries in Holland; Nilsson-Ehle in Sweden, are the out-

---

*Not all feeblemindedness is inherited. Some cases are due to accidents or falls, some to disease. (Ed.)

standing geneticists of the first decade after 1900. But soon the picture changed. The Carnegie Institution for Genetic Research in Long Island, under the leadership of Davenport and later under Blakeslee, became one of the world's centers of genetic research. In 1910, T. H. Morgan, then at Columbia University, later at the California Institute of Technology, started his investigations with the fruit fly, *Drosophila*, and founded the largest and most active school of geneticists. The U.S. Department of Agriculture with its network of experimental stations connected with more than a hundred agricultural colleges became the most admirable organization for breeding of better crops and farm animals based upon the principles of Mendelism. The ideas developed by Mendel have found a new home here in the new world.

From 1905 to 1910, I tried by lectures and by articles to renew the memory of Mendel in my home country and to explain the importance of Mendelism to the people. This was not always an easy task. Once I happened to be standing beside two old citizens of Bruenn, who were chatting before a picture of Mendel in a book-seller's window. "Who is that chap, Mendel, they are always talking about now?" asked one of them. "Don't you know?" replied the second, "it's the fellow who left the town of Bruenn an inheritance!" In the brain of the worthy man the term "heredity" had no meaning, but he understood well enough the sense of an inheritance or bequest.

45

The Language of the Genes

George W. Beadle

Our methods of communication with our fellow men take many forms. We share with other animals the ability to transmit information by such diverse means as the posture of our bodies; by the movements of our eyes, head, arms and hands; and by our utterances of non-specific sounds. But we go far beyond any other species on earth in that we have evolved

Reproduced by permission of the Editor from *The Advancement of Science*, Vol. 17 (1961), pp. 511-521.

sophisticated forms of pictorial representation, elaborate spoken and written languages, ingenious methods of recording music and language on discs, on magnetic tape and in a variety of other kinds of code.

Our remarkable skills in communication depend of course on our highly developed nervous systems with their provisions for transmitting information from various receptors to the central brain where it can be stored, integrated and reproduced. In this way it has been possible for us as a species to acquire knowledge and understanding in a cumulative way. Present-day cultures, including religion, art, music, language, literature, technology and science are the result. All these we pass on from one generation to the next, adding to the sum with each such passage.

In this lecture I am going to talk about the transmission of biological directions for development and function from generation to generation in organisms as varied as submicroscopic viruses and man.

THE EGG CELL

Let me begin by reminding you that each of us begins development as a small almost microscopic single cell, the fertilised egg. It is about 1/300 of an inch in diameter—about one-tenth the diameter of the head of a pin. A human egg does not look very different from the egg of a rabbit, a guinea pig, or a chimpanzee. In fact it is not too unlike the egg cell from which spinach plant develops. Yet each of these cells obviously "knows" what its potential future is, for gross mistakes do not occur. The egg of a rabbit never gives rise to a guinea pig. Clearly the egg cell must contain information that says what it is going to do. A human egg carries specifications for growing into a person—not just any person but a very specific and truly unique one.

It is these specifications about which I wish to speak. I'll begin by posing five questions: First, how are these specifications or directions transmitted from one generation to the next? Second, how are they "written," that is, what is the "language" of heredity? Third, how are they replicated or "reprinted" as they must be with each of the many cell divisions that intervene between the egg of one generation and the egg and sperm cells of the next? Fourth, how are these directions "translated" during development? How are they used in the transformation of a tiny spherical egg into one of us? Finally, do errors or changes in the directions ever occur and, if so, what are the results?

Although it is by no means possible to give complete answers to these questions, we can come much closer to doing so than we could a few years ago. But before I go ahead, let me narrow my task considerably. The egg cell of an animal is, of course, complex, despite its small size. It consists of cell membranes enclosing cytoplasm, which constitutes the bulk of the cell, and a centrally located nucleus. I am going to confine my remarks largely to the nucleus. In doing this I do not wish to leave the impression that I believe the cytoplasm to be unimportant. The fact is in all cellular forms it is indispensable. It is endowed with highly specific properties and in a real sense carries essential hereditary information. This is clear from the experiments of the kind Dr. Fischberg of Oxford University, Prof. John Moore of Columbia University and several other embryologists have made in which the nucleus of the egg of one species of animal is replaced with that of another. Thus, in the two species of frogs, *Rana pipiens* and *R. sylvatica,* the nucleus of the fertilised egg of one species can be removed and replaced by that of the other (Moore, 1958). Whichever way the switch is made, the egg fails to develop, although the comparable transfer in which donor and recipient are of the same species leads to normal development. *Rana pipiens* cytoplasm is not compatible with a *R. sylvatica* nucleus and vice versa. This is only one of several lines of evidence indicating that the egg cytoplasm has specific properties that cannot be easily modified by the nucleus.

In confining my attention largely to the nucleus, I likewise do not wish to belittle the role of environmental factors. They, too, are absolutely necessary. For a human egg cell to develop into a person, for example, a highly specific physical and chemical environment must be maintained, especially in the early stages of foetal development. Raw material of the proper kind must be available in the right amounts and at the right times. Before and after birth the nervous system is being indelibly impressed with information. Especially after birth the information that is fed into the nervous system in massive amounts plays a large and important role in determining what we are. It includes a large input of cultural inheritance.

THE NUCLEUS AND GENES

Getting back to the nucleus, there is an impressive body of evidence showing that in it is contained a very large part of the primary biological information that directs development and function. Mendel demonstrated in his garden peas that this information is particulate. Unfortunately, he was far ahead of his time and was quite unable to convince such persons as the German botanist Nägeli that what he found should be taken seriously. Had Darwin known of his work, the history of science might have been profoundly changed.

Mendel postulated the units of heredity that we now call genes. He did not know they were in the nucleus of the cell or that they were carried in chromosomes. But he did know that they determine whether pea seeds will be round or wrinkled, whether green or yellow, whether the flowers will be purple or white, whether the pea plant will be tall or short, and so on. He had a remarkable understanding about how genes are transmitted from one generation to the next. Although modified in important ways, his laws of inheritance still hold as first approximations to the ways of nature in communicating specifications from parent to offspring.

We now know that the most basic features of the process of transmission of biological directions for development are common to viruses, bacteria, algae, protozoa, higher plants, multicellular animals and man. Let me give you an example in man. About seven out of every ten persons find the chemical substance phenylthiourea most unpleasantly bitter. The remaining three find it essentially tasteless. The two classes of people differ in the hereditary specifications. Individuals who taste it carry specifications in their cells that somehow say, "I can now taste phenylthiourea," whereas those who do not taste this substance carry the alternative form of this message, "I cannot taste phenylthiourea." This message, in its two forms, is one unit of inheritance—a gene. Each fertilised egg, and all the cells descended from it contains two representatives of this message, one from the mother, via the egg, and one from the father, via the sperm. There are, therefore, four possible types of persons with respect to this particular bit of specification, viz.:

From the mother	*From the father*
1. Taste	Taste
2. Taste	Not taste
3. Not taste	Taste
4. Not taste	Not taste

The first is a pure taster. The next two are alike in having one message of each kind. They are "hybrid" for this message. They taste, which is a way of saying the positive taster form of the message is *dominant* to the non-taster form, or, vice versa, that the negative form is recessive.

When sperms or eggs are produced by individuals of these types, each carries one or the other of the two messages, either the maternal *or* the paternal one. Thus from any pair of parents it is easy to predict statistically the types of offspring, just as Mendel did with his peas.

How many such units or genes are contained in the nucleus of a human egg cell? We do not know with any degree of certainty. But we estimate that it is probably more than 10,000 kinds and less than 1,000,000, each present in duplicate except for sex-linked genes which are for the most part present singly in the male. What do these genes specify? Many characteristics: eye colour, hair colour, hair form, skin colour, and hundreds of other characters by which the species may differ.

You may remark, as many biologists did in the early part of the century just after Mendel's work was rediscovered and while the young science of genetics was struggling for recognition, that these are all trivial characters. So they are, as are most of the characteristics responsible for the uniqueness of normal individuals. But we now have abundant evidence that most genes carry information of vital importance. Thus two genes in man carry the instructions for making the haemoglobin molecules that play such an essential role in carrying oxygen and carbon dioxide. Haemoglobin is *not* trivial.

Soon after the rediscovery of Mendel's classical paper, it was suspected that genes were carried in chromosomes. The clinching proof came in 1915 from the laboratory of the late Thomas Hunt Morgan. His student, Calvin Bridges, showed that errors in transmission of genes are exactly paralleled by errors in chromosome behaviour.

DNA *AS GENETIC MATERIAL*

Chromosomes were known to be made up largely of protein and nucleic acid, the latter of the deoxyribose type. Deoxyribonucleic acid has now become widely known as DNA. Are the genes protein of DNA—or possibly both? At first their specifications were thought to reside in protein, for chemists knew that proteins are long polymer molecules consisting of linear sequences of amino-acid building blocks of some twenty kinds. Since there are obviously almost unlimited possibilities in proportions and sequences of amino acids, it was easy to believe that the gene was a kind of coded message in protein. DNA, on the other hand, was believed by many to be a rather monotonous polymer built of four kinds of nucleotide units arranged in segments of four that were repeated many fold. If this were its structure, there would clearly be little opportunity for specificity; therefore it was not considered a serious candidate for the role of primary genetic material.

A series of investigations on pneumococcal bacteria, beginning in 1928 and leading up to the classical paper of Avery, MacLeod and McCarty (1944), severely shook the faith in protein as the basic stuff of heredity. It became clear that the type of polysaccharide capsule produced by a pneumococcal strain could be altered experimentally by treating it with pure DNA from another strain. Thus DNA from a type III pneumococcus could cause a type II recipient cell to be transformed permanently into type III, and henceforth to produce DNA specifying type III polysaccharide. The experimental procedure by which this is accomplished is not quite as simple as the above account implies. Nevertheless it appeared that polysaccharide-specifying DNA from the donor strain might be entering the recipient and somehow replacing its homologous DNA. There were, however, alternative interpretations, which, though less straightforward, continued to be preferred by many geneticists and biochemists.

By 1953 more direct evidence had come from another source. By then the life-cycles of certain bacterial viruses—bacteriophage—had been worked out and sufficient genetic work done on them to make it clear that like higher organisms they exhibited particulate inheritance. In other words, these viruses, too, have genes.

Bacterial viruses consist largely of protein coats containing cores of DNA. Electron microscopy suggested that when a bacterial cell is infected by a virus particle, its coat does not enter the host cell. The matter was most elegantly settled by the use of radioactive tracers. Hershey and Chase (1952) infected bacteria with viruses whose protein coats were labelled with sulphur-35, a radioactive isotope. The labelling was done by growing a crop of viruses on bacteria that in turn had been grown on a medium containing radioactive sulphur in the form of sulphate. After infection, the protein coats were removed from the bacterial hosts by shearing them off in a high speed blender. Separated by centrifugation, the virus coats and infected host cells could be separately examined for presence of radioactive sulphur. Almost all of it was found in the virus coats that did not enter host cells. Since proteins contain sulphur while DNA does not, this result suggests that only DNA enters the host on infection. Experiments in which DNA was labelled with radioactive phosphorus-32 led to the same conclusion. Now the coats were largely unlabelled after infection had occurred, while the host cells contained most of the radioactivity. Since DNA contains phosphorus—one atom per nucleotide—and protein does not, it is clear that DNA and not much else enters the host cell. Since viruses have genes and only DNA enters the host cell, the viral genes must be DNA. Actually a small amount of protein does enter with the DNA, but labelling experiments in which the radioactivity entering a host cell in protein or DNA is followed to the next viral generation show that it is the DNA, not the small amount of protein, that is responsible for the transfer of genetic information from one generation of viruses to the next.

What about higher organisms—spinach plants and man? Are there primary genetic specifications likewise written in DNA? The evidence is not conclusive but since the most conservative hypothesis assumes they are, we proceed on that assumption until evidence to the contrary comes forth.

STRUCTURE OF DNA

What is the structure of DNA that enables it to carry hereditary information? A tremendous step was taken toward answering this question in 1953 by a young American biologist, James D. Watson, and the English chemist, Francis H. C. Crick, working together at Cambridge University.

Making use of the information then available about DNA—nucleotide composition of DNA of various sources, X-ray diffraction observations of M. H. F. Wilkins and associates at King's College, London, general knowledge of the structural arrangements of atoms in nucleotide components, etc.—they succeeded in constructing a molecular model of DNA that seemed to satisfy essentially all requirements (Watson and Crick, 1953). Now, some seven years later, it is generally agreed that the Watson-Crick structure is essentially correct for the native DNAs of a number of organisms. It is now clear that their achievement is outstanding in modern-day biology. This is so because their model goes so far in suggesting plausible answers to the questions posed at the beginning of this lecture.

According to this model, DNA consists of a pair of antiparallel polynucleotide chains wound helically around a common axis and cross-linked through specific hydrogen bonding between purine and pyrimidine bases. Letting A, T, C, and G represent the four nucleotides characterised by adenine, thymine, cytosine and guanine, a four-unit segment of DNA can be represented in two dimensions as follows:

$$A–T–C–G$$
$$\cdots \cdots \cdots \cdots$$
$$T–A–G–C$$

Paired dots represent hydrogen bonds. The two chains of the DNA molecule run in opposite directions. This is determined by the orientations of nucleotides in the two chains.

INFORMATION IN DNA

Genetic information must somehow be determined by sequence of nucleotides. Since only A:T and C:G nucleotide pairs are possible in the normal structure, the two chains obviously carry complementary information. As we shall see this is of special significance in hypotheses of DNA replication.

One can think of information being carried either as a sequence of nucleotide pairs in the double molecule or as nucleotide sequences in the two single chain components.

How much DNA is in a single human cell? It is estimated that the total DNA of the 46 chromosomes of a fertilised human egg contains something like 5,000,000,000 nucleotide pairs. Since the genetic material is carried in duplicate in such a cell, one complete set of information is written in sequence of some 2,500,000,000 such pairs.

Prof. Crick has estimated that this amount of DNA is sufficient to encode the contents of some 500 large library volumes. This is another way of saying that the genetic specifications for producing a person from an egg cell, given a proper environment, adequate food of the right kind, etc., might be written in English in this number of volumes.

What about the physical size of DNA molecules? The diameter of the double helix is 20 Ångström units. The base pairs are spaced at $3\cdot4$ Å intervals. Thus a continuous linear double helix of the 5,000,000,000 base pairs of a single human egg would be somewhat more than 5 ft. in length —only slightly less than the height of an average person. This is a convenient way to remember the amount of DNA in a single human cell. If the strands were packed side by side in a monolayer on the head of a pin 1 mm. in diameter, this amount of DNA would cover less than $\frac{1}{200}$ of the surface.

REPLICATION OF DNA

The Watson-Crick structure immediately suggested how DNA molecules might reproduce by separation of the double structure into single chains followed by sythesis of new partners against each of the old chains. Since the two originals are complementary, each carries the information necessary to direct the synthesis of its partner. It is presumed that single chains serve as templates against which free nucleotides are properly ordered by specific hydrogen pairing. Just how the problems of separation of paired chains helically coiled around a common axis is solved is not known. The forces required to "untwist" the double helix would not be great if it were to rotate around its axis in the manner of an automobile speedometer cable.

Is there any evidence that DNA replication in fact occurs in this way? Yes, two kinds of evidence indicate that it does.

One of these depends on labelling old and new chains so that they can be distinguished. This can and has been done with radioactive phosphorus-32, but there are difficulties in this method that have not been overcome in an entirely satisfactory manner. A second method of labelling involves the use of the stable heavy isotope of nitrogen, N^{15}. Bacteria grown on a culture medium containing only N^{15} eventually become fully labelled with this isotope. Since there are seven or eight nitrogen atoms per pair of nucleotides of molecular weight approximately 700, replacing all N^{14} with N^{15} increases the weight a bit over one per cent. Since the size does not change, the density increases by a corresponding amount. "Heavy" DNA molecules can be separated from the light variety in an analytical ultracentrifuge.

The method for doing this was first developed by Meselson, Stahl and Vinograd (1957) and consists in centrifuging DNA in a cesium chloride solution of proper density. The cesium chloride molecules are thrown down in a high centrifugal field, but, being small, they diffuse sufficiently to establish an equilibrium density gradient in the centrifuge cell. If the range of density so established includes that of DNA, the DNA molecules in solution will form a band at a level exactly corresponding to their bouyant density. Being large they diffuse only slowly and hence form a narrow band, the position of which is easily established by means of an ultraviolet optical system. A mixture of N^{15} and N^{14} DNA molecules form two cleanly separated bands.

This method makes possible the following elegant experiment first carried out by Meselson and Stahl (1958). Bacteria are grown on N^{15} medium until equilibrated, that is, until they become uniformly heavy. The bacteria are then transferred to a medium containing only nitrogen of atomic weight 14. After one cell generation, as determined by doubling of the total population, all DNA molecules should have one heavy old chain and one light new complement. That is, they should be "hybrid" and hence intermediate in density between heavy and light DNA. They are. In a second round of replication—which doubles the population again—heavy and light chains should separate and each then directs synthesis of a light complement. Hence, half the DNA molecules after exactly two cell divisions should be hybrid and half light. Again they are.

If a population of hybrid DNA molecules—present after one replication of heavy molecules in an N^{14} medium—are heated under the right conditions, molecules about half the molecular weight are found and they are light and heavy in equal numbers. The evidence is fairly convincing that these are single chains of DNA.

This experiment does not prove that the Watson-Crick hypothesis of DNA replication is correct but it strongly suggests it. A perverse nature might have devised another way of giving the observed result.

THE KORNBERG SYSTEM

An even more dramatic way of investigating the mechanism of DNA replication is that devised by Arthur Kornberg and his co-workers (1959). In a suitable buffer solution containing magnesium ions, the four nucleotides of DNA as triphosphates, and a DNA polymerising enzyme, DNA is rapidly synthesised if primer DNA molecules are added. Single stranded DNA, obtained by heating native DNA, is much more effective as a primer than is carefully prepared native material. Something like a twentyfold increase in DNA over that added as primer has been obtained.

That the primer is copied is indicated by the fact that the base composition of the product is like that of primer. DNAs from different sources may have quite different rations of A:T to C:G base pairs, and it is therefore possible to determine whether the ratio of the primer is reproduced in the product.

Without primer, DNA is spontaneously synthesised in the Kornberg system after a lag of two to four hours. But unlike natural DNA, this spontaneously synthesised material contains only A:T base pairs. The As and Ts alternating in sequence in each of the two chains as follows:

If this A:T copolymer is now used as a primer in a fresh system, more A:T polymer is formed without a lag period. C and G nucleotides are excluded although present in abundance in the system. Here too it appears that the primer is copied as postulated.

Again, the agreement between hypothesis and the facts observed in the Kornberg *in vivo* synthesis of DNA does not prove the hypothesis. But it enormously strengthens the case.

USE OF DNA INFORMATION

How is information in the form of DNA made use of in the development of an organism like man? This is clearly a question of the most fundamental importance to biology. At the same time it is an enormously difficult one and we are a long way from knowing the complete answer.

All living systems contain DNA (or in some viruses a related form of nucleic acid, ribonucleic acid, called RNA) and protein. In cellular forms the proteins are of many kinds. We know that many genes, perhaps all, are somehow concerned with synthesis of specific proteins. Many of these serve as organic catalysts—enzymes—or as components of these catalysts. Enzymes accelerate vital reactions that would otherwise proceed at rates too low to sustain life. In cellular organisms there are thousands of kinds of enzymes, each owing its specificity to a particular protein. We can therefore narrow the problem of gene action, at least in some cases, to that of protein synthesis.

An hypothesis at present widely used as a working basis visualises the process of protein synthesis in the following way: for each protein potentially capable of being formed, there is in the nucleus a specific segment of DNA that carries the information by which the twenty kinds of amino acid sub-units in that protein are properly ordered during its synthesis. Take human haemoglobin as an example. Each molecule of this vital oxygen-carrying red protein consists of four protein chains and an equal number of heme groups each containing an atom of iron. The protein chains are of two kinds, called alpha and beta chains. There are two of each, the members of a pair being identical and each made up of about 150 amino-acid units arranged in a precisely determined sequence. For each of the two kinds of protein chains, there is presumed—with some evidence—to be a gene consisting of a segment of DNA. This segment is, by the definition I shall use, a gene. It may be something of the order of 1000 nucleotide pairs in length.

How is the information in the gene for the alpha haemoglobin chain made use of? The hypothesis assumes the following sequence of events: from the gene in the nucleus, information is transferred to RNA, presumably by the DNA somehow acting as a template in the ordering of the four kinds of ribose nucleotides in RNA. This informational RNA then moves from the nucleus to the cytoplasm of the young red blood cell—before it loses its nucleus. There it is incorporated into microsomes, which are sub-microscopic bodies made of structural protein and structural RNA. Once in microsomes, informational RNA molecules serve as templates against which amino-acids are arranged in proper order to make alpha haemoglobin protein chains.

Prior to this the amino-acids are activated and attached to small carrier segments of RNA, each specific for its own amino-acid. Thus for each of the twenty amino-acids there is a corresponding carrier RNA segment. Carrier RNA molecules are somehow coded to specific sites on the informational RNA in the microsome. In this way each amino-acid is carried to its proper position on the template. They are then joined through peptide linkages to form alpha chains and are released from the template and microsome. Whether association of alpha and beta chains with their hemes, and with each other, occurs in the microsome or outside is not known.

Not all proteins for which genetic directions are available in the nucleus are synthesised in any one cell. There are ingenious control mechanisms in operation which determine whether the information in a given gene will be used and, if so, when and for how long. In some cases it is clear that the presence or absence of substrate determines whether a given enzyme will be synthesised. In this way it is assumed that enzymes are not made in quantity when there are no substrates on which they can work. Through studies on such control mechanisms we are beginning to understand how it is that cells with identical genetic information in their nuclei may do quite different things, depending on their environmental context or on their previous history.

There are now known many instances in a variety of organisms in which specific protein variation is known to be related to particular genes.

I have already referred to haemoglobin protein in man. Similar situations are known in viruses, bacteria, algae, fungi, insects, higher plants, mammals, etc. (Beadle, 1960). The haemoglobin case in man is interesting in that it is known that gene changes may result in substitution of a single amino-acid in a chain of 150 units. Thus sickle cell haemoglobin, synthesised under the direction of a modified form of the gene in control of the beta protein chain, differs from normal haemoglobin in that a single glutamic acid unit in the chain is replaced by a valine. In the presence of a third form of this same gene the same glutamic acid unit is replaced by the amino-acid lysine. In all, about a dozen modifications of human haemoglobin are known, many of them investigated genetically.

Another example in man is found in the genetic disease galactosaemia. Here is a specific enzyme, galactose-1-phosphate uridyl transferase, essential for the conversion of galactose into a usable form, which is partially or wholly inactive. The enzyme defect is referable to a gene change.

In bacteria, fungi and other micro-organisms correlations between gene change and specific protein modification are much easier to detect than they are in man with his several obvious disadvantages for biochemical and genetic investigations. As a result there are dozens of examples known in such forms as *Escherichia*, *Salmonella* and *Neurospora*.

MUTATION

In terms of DNA structure gene mutation is believed to be the result of alterations in nucleotide sequence. Many mutations are thought to be the result of errors in DNA replication. In their original paper on DNA structure, Watson and Crick pointed out that if at the precise moment of partner selection a purine or pyrimidine were to exist in an improbable tautomeric form, it might form hydrogen bonds with a "wrong" nucleotide. At the next round of replication such a "wrong" nucleotide would direct that its own complementary nucleotide be inserted in the paired chain. Thus one of the two daughter DNA molecules would differ from its sister in one nucleotide pair. Its informational content would be modified accordingly.

Experimentally mutations can be increased in frequency in a number of ways. High-energy radiations—ultraviolet, X-rays, etc.—are effective in doing this. Transmutation of artificially incorporated radioactive isotopes such as phosphorus-32 is known to produce mutations. Since radioactive isotopes occur naturally in low frequencies, they are no doubt responsible for a small fraction of spontaneously produced mutations.

Many chemical substances are known to be mutagenic. Perhaps the one best known from the standpoint of mechanism of action is nitrous acid. This specifically oxidises amino groups. In this way it may chemically change a natural DNA pyrimidine or purine in such a way that its hydrogen bonding specificity is modified. The mutagenic properties have been especially well studied in a tobacco mosaic virus, an RNA virus. Here the natural pyrimidine, cytosine is converted to uracil, which is also a natural occurring pyrimidine in RNA. Adenine is oxidised to hypoxanthine, the latter not a normal constituent of RNA. In a similar way guanine is changed to xanthine. It appears that the oxidation of any one of 3000 of the 6000 nucleotides in a tobacco mosaic virus particle results in an inactivating mutation.

The purine and pyrimidine analogues, 2-aminopurine and 5-bromouracil, produce mutations, presumably by being incorporated in replicating DNA in place of their natural counterparts and thereby leading to errors in complement selection. Since these analogues presumably replace their natural counterparts, purine for purine and pyrimidine for pyrimidine, it might be expected that they would be effective in reversing the mutations they induce. In a special class of bacterial virus mutants, investigated by Ernst Freese, this seems to be the case, whereas other classes of mutants, for example those induced by proflavine, are not so reversed by base analogues. It is presumed that the latter brings about replacement of purine by pyrimidine and vice versa. Investigations of this kind offer the hope of giving us a deeper understanding of the mutation process than we now have.

FINE STRUCTURE OF GENES

If, as I have suggested, genes as functional genetic units of DNA are hundreds or thousands of base pairs long, it ought to be possible experimentally to demonstrate multiple mutational sites within a single such unit. Furthermore these should be arranged linearly within a unit. So called fine-structure studies on genes of bacterial viruses, bacteria, fungi and other organisms show that this is indeed the case (Beadle, 1960). Clearly the unit of mutation is much smaller than the unit of function, for such sites within a functional unit undergo recombination in much the same way as do separate genes within a chromosome. On the basis of frequencies of such recombination it is possible to construct intragenic maps of mutational sites and thus to show that they are linearly arranged. The shortest distances that can be measured by such recombination are not far from those that are calculated to exist between adjacent nucleotides in DNA.

THE CODING PROBLEM

How are sequences of nucleotides in DNA related to amino-acid sequences in proteins? DNA and protein can be thought of as four- and twenty-symbol systems. If they are both equivalent to simple linear codes, it is clear that it requires at least three nucleotides to specify an amino-acid, for the maximum number of two-letter words is only sixteen. Several possible coding systems have been investigated but so far the problem has not been solved (Levinthal, 1959). Perhaps it will not be until nucleotide sequences in a gene can be compared with amino-acid sequences in the protein specified by that gene. As you know, complete amino-acid sequences have been worked out for only a very few proteins and unfortunately these are from organisms that are far from ideal for genetic study. There are now investigations under way in many laboratories designed to correlate genetic fine structure with protein fine structure. Virus proteins and bacterial enzymes such as alkaline phosphatase and tryptophane synthetase are among the systems that look especially favourable for such combined genetic and chemical studies.

EVOLUTION

Presumably DNA replication bears no immediate relation to its informational content. Biologically useless DNA is replicated just as faithfully as that playing a vital role. Presumably, too, the mutation process is a random affair. If so, meaningful DNA sequences are much more likely to be made less useful through random mutation than they are to be converted into sequences more useful to the organism of which they are a part. In this sense they may be likened to random typographical errors in a useful message. Direct experiment verifies this expectation; most mutations are unfavourable in the context in which they occur.

If mutations are mostly unfavourable but are as faithfully reproduced as are their normal counterparts, why do they not accumulate with successive rounds of replication just as a typist would accumulate errors in the Lord's Prayer if she were to type copies in succession, each from the previous typing, in a purely mechanical way without proofreading or correcting errors! The answer is that biologically unfavourable mutations specify organisms with reduced reproductive fitness. The errors in their DNA are not corrected but the lines of descent carrying such errors are statistically bred out of existence over a shorter or longer number of generations depending on the degree of reduction in reproductive fitness. We call this natural selection.

Positive evolutionary progress depends on rare favourable mutations that increase reproductive fitness. They gradually replace the ancestral types from which they arose.

Modern concepts of organic evolution hold that all living systems have evolved gradually, mutation by mutation, from pre-existing organisms. Sometimes, as in parasites, it is advantageous to become simpler and to count increasingly on the host for raw materials, a proper environment and protection against enemies. But from the beginning, the overall trend in many lines such as our own has evidently been toward greater complexity.

Speculation as to how organic evolution began in the first place leads to the conclusion that there is no clear qualitative break in the sequence of events that spans the advent of life on earth. This is only another way of saying that we cannot clearly distinguish between living and non-living systems. No matter what system one contemplates, it is possible to imagine a closely related one, only slightly simpler, that could have given rise to the former by a single mutation-like step.

The simplest living systems we know today are viruses. Tobacco mosaic virus particles are submicroscopic rods about 800 Å units in length. They consist of a cylindrical protein coat and an RNA core, the latter being made up of about 6000 nucleotides. In a living tobacco cell infected with a particle of this virus more viruses are synthesised. The bacterial virus øX174 contains about the same amount of nucleic acid. Its units are almost spherical. They, too, have a protein coat and a nucleic acid core, but their nucleic acid is DNA, not RNA.

Some people say such viruses are not living—that they cannot carry on metabolism, synthesise their component parts, or do any of several other things that living organisms do. But they do reproduce their kind, given a proper environment. And they are mutable, and hence capable of organic evolution. Whether one calls them living or not depends on one's definition of life and that in the end must be purely arbitrary.

Let us imagine that virus-like systems were among the earliest "organisms" to evolve on earth. They were not like present day viruses, for there were no living cells from which they could derive their parts— nucleotides, amino-acids, perhaps a few enzymes, etc. We can reasonably believe that at that stage of the earth's history there were myriads of spontaneously formed organic molecules around, including nucleotides, amino-acids, proteins, etc., and that these were the building blocks of the postulated virus-like creatures. After all we now have abundant experimental evidence that a variety of organic molecules are formed spontaneously under conditions assumed to have been characteristic of parts of the earth's crust a few thousand billion years ago (Miller, 1957).

If the building blocks of the postulated virus-like systems were around, would they not have interacted, again spontaneously, to form nucleic acids, proteins, etc.? Nucleotides interact in the Kornberg system to form DNA capable of replication. Since the role of man in this experiment is merely that of making the conditions more favourable for this particular re-action—that is, increasing its probability—would it not have occurred in his absence when the conditions became right?

As every organic chemist knows, organic molecules are formed through the interaction of inorganic molecules—again when the conditions are right. And as every inorganic chemist knows elements interact to produce inorganic molecules. Nuclear physicists tell us that elements themselves evolve from simpler elements as a result of processes that are both natural and inevitable, given the appropriate circumstances.

Thus it is clear that the sequence:hydrogen—helium—beryllium-8—carbon—oxygen—other elements—water—other inorganic molecules—simple organic molecules—more complex organic molecules like nucleotides, amino-acids, and small proteins—nucleic acids capable of replication—nucleic acids protected by protein coats—virus-like systems with protein coats serving catalytic functions—multigenic but subcellular organisms—simple cellular systems like bacteria—autonomous cellular forms like algae—protozoa—multicellular plants and animals and, in our line of descent, man himself—is a natural one that could have arisen by steps no one of which need have been larger than the individual mutational steps we know in today's living systems.

In the beginning there was a universe of hydrogen. How and when it was created—or whether it is and always has been in a steady state of continuous creation—science knows very little. In whatever way the universe began, there must have been built into it from the very beginning the potentiality of essentially unlimited orderly evolution.

REFERENCES

Avery, O. T., MacLeod, C. M., & McCarty, M. (1944): *J. exp. Med.* **79**, 137-58.

Beadle, G. W. (1960): *Annu. Rev. Physiol.* **22**, 45–74.

Hershey, A. O. & Chase, M. (1952): *J. gen. Physiol.* **36**, 39–56.

Kornberg, A. (1959): *Rev. mod. Physics,* **31**, 200–9.

Levinthal, C. (1959): *Rev. mod. Physics,* **31**, 249–55.

Meselson, M., Stahl, F. W. & Vinograd, J. (1957): *Proc. nat. Acad. Sci., Wash.,* **43**, 581–8.

Meselson, M., & Stahl, F. W. (1958): *Proc. nat. Acad. Sci., Wash.,* **44**, 671–82.

Miller, S. (1957): *Biochim. biophys. Acta,* **23**, 480–9.

Moore, J. A. (1958): *Exp. Cell Res.,* **14**, 532–40.

Watson, J. D. & Crick, F. H. C. (1953): *Nature,* **171**, 737–8.

46

DNA and the Chemistry of Inheritance

Barry Commoner

Living organisms are unique, among the known forms of matter, because they are capable of creating their own specific, highly organized structure of substances taken from far more disorganized surroundings, and can transmit this capability to their offspring. Perhaps the oldest and most profound theoretical problem in biology is the effort to explain the curious paradox that, despite its unique capability for self-duplication and inheritance, a living organism is nevertheless a mixture of substances which are separately no more possessed of these properties than are the more prosaic molecules that never occur in living cells. This question has been at the root of a long train of experiments, debates, and speculations that begins in classical times and continues unbroken through the development of present-day "molecular biology."

The basic issues are simply stated. If the component parts of a cell are not themselves alive, whence come the life-properties exhibited by the whole? Apart from the untenable notion of a mystic non-material "vital force" which supposedly animates the otherwise dead substance of the cell, the debate has elicited two main positions: (*a*) There is, in fact, some special cellular component which possesses the fundamental attribute of self-duplication, and which is therefore a "living molecule" and the basic source of the life-properties of the cell. (*b*) The unique properties of life are inherently connected with the very considerable complexity of living substance and arise from interactions among its separable constituents which are not exhibited unless these components occur together in the complex whole. In this view, only the entire living cell is capable of self-duplication.

There is at this time a widespread impression that this issue has now been resolved and that the cell does indeed contain a component—DNA—

This article originally appeared in *American Scientist*, Vol. 52 (1964), pp. 365-388. Reprinted by permission.

which, according to the theory of the "DNA code," possesses the basic attribute of life, self-duplication, and which guides the activities of all the inheritable processes of the cell.

The importance of this conclusion is self-evident, for it would answer, at last, the basic question of the origin of the unique properties of life, and, if correct, should lead to unprecedented technological control over these properties. It is appropriate, therefore, to ask what criteria are required to establish that a molecule, such as DNA, is capable of self-duplication, to examine the degree to which the available evidence meets such criteria, and to determine whether the undoubted importance of DNA in the biology of inheritance may be due to some properties other than those attributed to it by current theory. . . .*

SOME IMPLICATIONS

The chief conclusion to be derived from the foregoing considerations is that the unique capability of living organisms for self-duplication and inheritance arises from complex multi-molecular interactions among at least several classes of cellular components. Neither DNA nor any other cellular component is a "self-duplicating molecule" or the "master chemical of the cell"—terms which sometimes appear in current generalizations. There is no evidence from recent investigations of the bio-chemical aspects of genetics which requires abandonment of the conclusion, long established by biological data, that the least complex agent capable of self-duplication is the intact living cell.

The point of view developed here also suggests alternatives to a number of current views of phenomena related to inheritance. (a) Various hypothetical schemes for regulating the "activity" of template genes are invoked in order to explain how the DNA code might operate in cellular differentiation and development. Alternatively, it may be suggested that differentiation is associated with the nucleotide sequestration system, tissue-specific changes in DNA snythesis (e.g., at chromosome "puffs") regulating nucleotide levels and thereby governing the size and metabolic character of the cell. (b) The relationship between DNA and a species' characteristic sensitivity to ionizing radiation is often interpreted in terms of radiation-induced mutations in genetic templates. Alternatively, radiation-induced inhibition of DNA synthesis, which results in the accumulation of toxic concentrations of free nucleotides, may be regarded as the mediating process. This view is compatible with Sparrow's observation

*Dr. Commoner now develops his reasoning on DNA and those with the proper background are urged to read the full account.

that in certain non-polyploid plants, radiation sensitivity is proportional to cellular DNA content, and is particularly affected by the relative proportions of heterochromatin. (c) Sahasrabudhe has suggested that tumor cells may be characterized by marked changes in free nucleotide level resulting from nucleotide sequestration due to DNA synthesis. In this connection, it is also of interest that tumor and other rapidly growing cells exhibit distinctive pathways of oxidative metabolism, which are in turn regulated by free nucleotide levels. (d) The theory of the DNA code suggests a seemingly simple explanation for the emergence of the first forms of life from the prebiotic organic environment: that life began with the fortuitous appearance of a "self-duplicating nucleic acid molecule" which then organized the complex chemistry of life around itself. In contrast, the viewpoint developed here suggests that the primitive function of nucleic acid was to sequester free nucleotides, and thereby regulate over-all metabolic activity. Thus, the nucleic acid template is to be regarded as a late development which improved the precision of the earlier modes of regulation of cellular activity, and which is, in any case, incapable of self-duplication.

The theory of the DNA code, if correct, also leads to important expectations regarding the feasibility of technological control over inheritance. If the nucleotide sequence of DNA were indeed a self-sufficient source of the inherited specificity of living things, then it might be possible, in the not too distant future, to synthesize artificial DNA molecules, which, on being introduced into living organisms, would artificially establish new inheritable characteristics quite outside the range of those normally observed. However, if, as we have concluded, biological specificity is only partly due to DNA, then it is likely that the specificity represented by proteins may impose severe limits on the acceptability, to the cell, of abnormal DNA nucleotide sequences. This view suggests that technological control over biological inheritance may be far less plausible than indicated by inferences drawn from the code theory.

Finally, the viewpoint developed here bears on some fundamental questions regarding the relationship between physical theory and biology. The theory of the DNA code is often regarded as an example of the success with which "modern physics" can solve basic problems about living systems which have eluded the supposedly less critical analyses of classical biologists. This view leads to the generalization that, despite its obvious complexity, the living cell must be governed by the "laws of physics"—as revealed by analysis of non-living systems—and that the most effective strategy for elucidating its unique properties is to study isolated parts which are sufficiently simple to permit their analyses in physico-chemical terms. However, several developments in theoretical physics suggest that the fundamental properties of matter are in better harmony with the view that the unique properties of the cell are derived from interactions of its molecular parts and are inherently incapable of being elucidated by a simple summation of the observed properties of the isolated parts. This viewpoint is a direct outgrowth of Bohr's theory of complementarity. It may also be closely related to the more recent theory of the "Bootstrap Universe." This theory suggests that the unique properties of the atomic nucleus are inherently associated with its complexity, and are not accountable by the observed properties of fragments isolated from disrupted nuclei.

It may be suggested then, that, if biology is to be guided by the insights into the properties of matter that are afforded by modern physical theory, the role of DNA in the living cell must be viewed as subsumed under the complex properties of the system—the living cell—of which functional DNA is a part. The theory of the DNA code is sometimes epitomized by the statement "DNA is the secret of life," an aphorism which appears increasingly to guide the course of current biological investigations. The viewpoint developed here suggests that biology might be more wisely guided by the aphorism, "Life is the secret of DNA."

47

Heredity and Hiroshima

David M. Bonner
Stanley E. Mills

In the course of the past sixty years, we have learned much about heredity and its underlying chemical basis. In turn, genetic knowledge has contributed to man's welfare on many levels. The material rewards to society derived from such knowledge have already been large, and will undoubtedly prove larger in the future. An exciting chapter in genetic history has been written in the production of high-yield strains of hybrid corn, of high-yield wheat strains resistant to attack by the fungal parasites, rust and smut, which formerly caused nationwide crop failure, and in the more recent, slightly incredible, use of X-ray sterilized male blow flies to help eradicate the pestilent screw worm in the South. These all attest to the value of genetic knowledge in eliminating pestilence and in breeding animals, plants, and microorganisms to give hardier, more productive strains and to increase the world's available resources of raw materials, antibiotics, and food.

Today a glance at the newspapers, with articles on population explosions, the drive of newly emerging nations for economic self-sufficiency, and live polio vaccines obtained from mutant virus strains, will again remind you of some of the consequences of man's curiosity about the so-called ivory-tower concepts of the gene, DNA, and messenger RNA.

However, let us turn our attention to still another topic of contemporary importance, caught up in recurrent ominous headlines, to a topic that now engages the attention of people throughout the world—the global genetic problem arising from the harnessing and exploitation of atomic energy. We know that a portion of the stupendous energy released from nuclear fission and fusion is released in the form of high-energy ionizing radiations, and in the form of radioactive isotopes of elements such as strontium and carbon. Ionizing radiations are highly mutagenic. Before the advent of atomic energy, the known mutagenic agents with which the human population had to contend were not of alarming concern. For example, ultraviolet light has low tissue-penetrating properties and though it causes burning of skin and may even induce skin cancer, it has no marked mutagenic effect on other human cells. Chemical agents such as mustard gas are deleterious only when fools deliberately set them loose to be inhaled, and base analogues are ordinarily not present in the diet, although they may be used to treat or control various cancers. In general, these are mutagenic agents under our control. They can be used or forgotten at will.

Ionizing radiation, however, is a different kettle of fish. High-energy radiation is capable of deep tissue penetration and is massively destructive and mutagenic. Since our environment is bombarded by a certain amount of background radiation from naturally occurring radioactive elements and from outer space, ionizing radiation is a mutagen we cannot entirely control and against which we are never completely protected. Our present concern is with the increasing amounts spewn into our environment from nuclear explosions. Each of us now receives more radiation than did our forefathers, and our children may receive more. Since the background radiation has shot upward in the past twenty years and since ionizing radiation is mutagenic, we must give thoughtful consideration to the possible genetic effects of this increase and of how great an exposure the human population can withstand.

Our concern with ionizing radiation is of two kinds, its effects on germinal tissue and succeeding generations, and its effect on somatic tissue, on us. Let us first consider somatic effects. Is there an association between somatic abnormalities, such as cancer, and radiation? The frequency of leukemia, a cancer characterized by an excess formation of white blood cells, can be increased by radiation. In the population of Hiroshima and Nagasaki that survived the atom bombs, there was a marked increase in leukemia during the subsequent five years. The association between leukemia and radiation is exhibited in other groups that have somehow been exposed to increased radiation. There is therefore a clear relationship between increasing amounts of radiation and increasing incidence of cancer.

We know that radiation results in somatic mutation. In view of the correlation found between leukemia and radiation, does this mean that cancer is mutational in origin? We do not know. We have experimental evidence that some animal leukemias can be induced by a virus; further, we know that interactions between bacteria and bacterial viruses are modified by radiation. We cannot, therefore, conclude that the increase in leukemia associated with an increase in radiation arises as a consequence of mutation, for it could result from the interaction of irradiation, virus, and host. This is, perhaps, a fair assessment of the relation of radiation to cancer in general. Radiation could induce cancers for a number of different reasons. Since cancers have diverse origins, they may be caused by a virus, a mutation, or other factors. Regardless of the details, however, there is an association between an increasing amount of radiation and an increasing incidence of cancer. Radiation is clearly a potential somatic hazard.

We know of still other somatic effects of radiation, for a relationship between irradiation and aging has been observed. With increasing amounts of radiation, longevity is shortened. In fact, from animal experiments it appears that the shortening of human life may well be measured in days per unit dose. Again, increasing radiation must be viewed as a somatic hazard.

Uncontrolled release of nuclear energy also imperils the human population because it increases the abundance of certain radioactive elements. For instance, radioactive strontium 90 formed as a consequence of hydrogen-bomb explosions is extremely dangerous, since it has a long half life and can replace calcium in bone. It is carried into the ionosphere and is ultimately washed down and widely deposited over the earth's surface by rain and snow. From the soil, strontium 90 is absorbed by growing plants, the plants are ingested by cattle, and strontium 90 appears in milk and milk products. When taken into the body, this radioactive isotope can take the place of calcium in the bone tissue, particularly in growing children. Strontium 90 in bone constitutes small centers of radioactivity and, if present in sufficient amounts, can give rise to bone cancer and a variety of other abnormalities. This is truly a new cycle of nature, a "twentieth-century cycle." The amount of strontium 90 has already been markedly increased by nuclear explosions, and we have no clear-cut answers as to how much strontium 90 can be safely tolerated in the human diet or how big an increase in the total amount of strontium 90 can be absorbed without adverse effect on the population as a whole.

Safety levels in man are difficult to determine. They require long-term study, but our restless world denies us time. Decisions affecting the use of nuclear energy must be made, but, unfortunately, our information about the deleterious effect in man per unit increase of radiation is inadequate to permit us to offer unequivocal biological advice. The thoughtful person must agree that an increase in radiation is attendant with hazard, and that any political decision leading to an increase in radiation must be made on the basis of the gravest, most soul-searching considerations.

A second problem posed by bomb testing is the effect of ionizing radiation on germinal tissue. There is no question that mutation rates are enhanced by radiation. This was shown years ago by H. J. Muller with X-rays and Drosophila. By far the great majority of such mutations are lethal or deleterious. As background radiation increases, the average dose received by each of us increases, and presumably the total number of mutations present in our gametic cells also increases. If the total number of transmissible mutant genes is on the increase, the number of genes having a deleterious developmental effect obviously must also rise. For the sake of future generations, we desperately need information on how big an increase in the genetic burden a human population can withstand and survive!

In the populations of the cities of Hiroshima and Nagasaki that survived the atom bomb, despite the observed increase in frequency of leukemia, no substantial rise in the frequency of spontaneous abortions or in the number of stillborn infants has been noted. These findings, though fragmentary, are of interest, since the rate of spontaneous abortions and stillbirths perhaps should provide some clue about the increase in dominant mutant lethal genes in the irradiated population, and the increase in dominant lethals in turn might give at least a rough estimate of the increase in recessive lethal genes. But no increase was found. Perhaps dominant lethals in humans are rare compared to recessive lethals, or perhaps dominant lethals are quickly filtered out by cell death. Inbreeding experiments are necessary to answer this point, but such experiments are denied us.

Many indirect methods have been used to estimate the so-called "genetic load" (number of recessive lethal and deleterious genes carried in the human population). Analysis of the vital statistics of various small populations in which consanguineous marriages have occurred for many generations permits a rough estimate of genetic load. The estimates have varied, but in general they have indicated a smaller load than would have been anticipated from studies of other organisms. For example, relatively large numbers of recessive lethals can accumulate and be maintained in laboratory populations of Drosophila, with a consequent reduction in the vitality of the population when inbred.

In human populations, the number of recessive lethals appears to be relatively small. It must be emphasized that the data on human populations are few and the analysis is uncertain. However, it is possible that lethals do not accumulate in man, but are eliminated within the first few divisions of the fertilized egg. If this is true and if the data obtained from the Nagasaki and Hiroshima populations illustrate what we can expect in human populations, then the evidence suggests that an increase in radiation may constitute a greater somatic than a germinal hazard; but irradiation and its effect on the genetic load of the human population remain virtual unknowns.

One fact does remain crystal clear. Increased radiation represents a serious human hazard, a hazard of recent origin and one that must be studied in detail. In the absence of overriding political considerations, background radiation obviously should not be increased without a sounder knowledge of the biological consequences of such an increase. How can more detailed information on human populations be obtained? The answer, in part, must come from population studies of other organisms, and it also hinges on how successful we are in securing detailed information about the genetics of man. Techniques are now being developed that in time may enable us to grow differentiated cells in tissue culture, and we may soon be able to study differential human cells much as we now grow and study bacterial cells.—The problems are immediate and urgent and require the thoughtful attention of all of us.

IX
Origin of Life

48

Chemical Origin of Life

Cyril Ponnamperuma

The problem of the origin of the universe is the greatest challenge the human intellect has ever faced. Indeed the origin of the universe, along with the origin of life and of intelligence, may be regarded as the fundamental question of our time. It is the purpose of this article to outline how modern science is searching for the secrets of life's beginnings.

While the very concept of the birth of the universe is staggering to the human mind, the unravelling of the riddle may come from a surprisingly simple observation or experiment. Abbé Lemaître's theory of an evolutionary universe arising from a primeval atom will stand or fall when an astronomer's penetrating gaze has compared the spatial density of galaxies 50 million light years away with those of 10,000 million light years away. The rival cosmology of continuous creation demands the appearance of hydrogen at several billion trillion tons per second in the observable universe. This idea will be satisfactorily proved if nuclear physicists demonstrate the formation of hydrogen at the rate of one atom per year in a volume about the size of a New York skyscraper.

In our attempt to understand the origin of life, the enormity of the enigma is paralleled only by the complexity of the possible hypotheses. It is this difficulty which prompted the physicist J. D. Bernal to write in 1949: "It is probable that even a formulation of this problem is beyond the reach of any one scientist, for such a scientist would have to be at the same time a competent mathematician, physicist, and experienced organic chemist, he should have a very extensive knowledge of geology, geophysics and geochemistry and, besides all this, be absolutely at home in all biological disciplines. Sooner or later this task will have to be given to

Cyril Ponnamperuma, "Chemical Origin of Life," *Science Journal* (May 1965). Reprinted by permission.

groups representing all these faculties and working closely together theoretically as well as experimentally."

Our ancestors thought that they had found a ready solution to the
problem in the belief that life arose continually from the non-living. One
had only to accept the evidence of the senses: worms from mud, maggots
from decaying meat, mice from old linen and fireflies from the morning
dew. Aristotle had propounded the doctrine of spontaneous generation in
his "Metaphysics," and this teaching was accepted by the long line of European thinkers who had turned to him as the final authority in matters
metaphysical and physical. The ancient Hindu scriptures described life
as having evolved from non-living matter. The Rig Veda, for example,
pointed to the beginning of life from the primary elements while the
Atharva Veda postulated the oceans of the Earth as the cradle of all life.

The world's literature is full of allusions to the popular belief in spontaneous generation. Virgil, in his "Georgics," tells us how a swarm of bees
arose from the carcass of a calf. Lucretius in "De Natura Rerum" refers to
the Earth as the mother of all living things.

The Belgian chemist and physician, Van Helmont, even had a recipe
for the making of mice. "If a dirty undergarment is squeezed into the
mouth of a vessel containing wheat, within a few days, (say 21), a ferment drained from the garments and transformed by the smell of the
grain, encrust the wheat itself with its own skin and turns it into mice. . . .
And, what is more remarkable, the mice from corn and undergarments
are neither weanlings nor sucklings nor premature but they jump out fully
formed."

Beliefs such as these could not long withstand the rigours of advancing scientific method. Francesco Redi, a celebrated member of the Acca-
demia del Cimento, demonstrated that the worms in putrefying flesh were
larvae from the eggs of flies. His proofs were as simple as they were decisive. He showed that meat placed under a screen so that flies cannot lay
their eggs on it never develops maggots.

But soon, with the [use of the microscope by Antoni van Leeuwenhoek to study natural sciences] in the second part of the 17th century, the
doctrine of spontaneous generation began to reappear. Some investigators
were unable to explain the origin of the varied organisms which the microscope showed in infusions from animal and vegetable matter. Among
these organisms they discerned nothing that resembled the process of
sexual generation. Thus they were led to assume that matter, once alive,
keeps after death a special vitality.

About this time the English Jesuit, John Turberville Needham, published a work in which he described experiments to support the theory of
spontaneous generation. The Italian Abbé Lazaro Spallanzani counter-
acted by showing that nutritive broths, sealed off from the air while boil-

ing, never develop micro-organisms and hence never rot. Needham objected that by too much boiling Spallanzani had rendered the broth and the air above it incompatible with life.

In the middle of the last century Louis Pasteur demonstrated by a series of brilliant experiments that living organisms could not arise out of non-living material. Pasteur dealt the death blow to the theory of spontaneous generation which was based on incompetent observation and the willingness to accept the evidence of the senses. Unfortunately, his work also gave rise to the misconception that the problem of the origin of life could not be approached by scientific methods. The question of life's beginning was therefore considered to be unworthy of the attention of any serious scientific investigator. But it is transparently clear that what Pasteur proved was that micro-organisms could not be grown from sterile starting material; his experiments had no bearing on the gradual formation of organic compounds leading to the emergence of biologically significant polymers.

With the growth of organic chemistry a new approach to the problem appeared to be possible. J. J. Berzelius thought that organic compounds were produced from their elements by laws different from those governing the formation of inorganic compounds. This led him to believe that organic compounds were produced under the influence of a vital force and that they could not be prepared artificially. In 1828 Friedrich Wöhler converted ammonium cyanate into urea, a substance hitherto obtained only from animal sources. This synthesis weakened the distinction between organic and inorganic compounds. The distinction was completely ended with the synthesis of acetic acid from its elements by A. W. H. Kolbe in 1845, and the synthesis of methane from a mixture of carbon disulphide and hydrogen sulphide by M. P. E. Berthelot in 1856.

The vitalists objected that Wöhler had obtained his ammonium cyanate from ammonia and cyanic acid, both of which were of animal origin. But already in 1781 Joseph Priestley had prepared ammonia by the reduction of nitric acid which was synthesized from its elements by Henry Cavendish in 1785. Potassium cyanide had also been obtained by K. W. Scheele by heating a mixture of potassium carbonate and carbon in the presence of nitrogen. Since potassium cyanide is readily converted into potassium cyanate, Wöhler's synthesis was truly one which started from inorganic materials. The experiments of these early synthetic chemists gradually removed the boundary between the inorganic and the organic world.

The basis of our approach to the problem is an evolutionary philosophy. The process may be traced forward from the primeval cloud of hydrogen gas or backward from the primordial germ which Charles Darwin placed at the beginning of life. The Darwinian theory of evolution has postulated the unity of the Earth's entire biosphere. According to Darwin, the higher forms of life evolved from the lower over a very extended period in the life of this planet. Fossil analysis has shown that the oldest known forms of living systems may be about 2000 million years old. Life, indeed, had a beginning on this planet. The consideration of biological evolution thus leads logically to another form of evolution, namely chemical evolution.

The evidence available from practically every field of science suggests that nature is a unity which has been divided into categories for human convenience. The division of matter into living and non-living is, perhaps, an artificial one which is convenient for distinguishing such extreme cases as a man and a rock, but would be quite inappropriate when describing a virus particle. Indeed, the crystallization of a virus by Wendell Stanley almost 30 years ago precipitated the need for revising our definition of the terms "life" and "living." These sentiments were powerfully expressed by N. W. Pirie in an essay entitled "The Meaninglessness of the Terms 'Life' and 'Living'." He compared the use of the terms living and non-living to the words acid and base as used in chemistry. While sodium hydroxide is distinctly alkaline, sulphuric acid is a powerful acid. However, in between there is a whole variation in strength. The chemist has overcome the confusion arising from the use of these two terms by inventing the nomenclature of hydrogen ion concentration. He is thus able to describe all the observed phenomena in terms of one quantity; thus a fluid may have a pH of 4 or a pH of 8. According to Pirie, we may have to invent a similar quantity in order to avoid any vagueness that might arise in applying the term life to borderline cases such as the virus.

One of the first to speculate on the conditions necessary for the origin of life was Erasmus Darwin, the grandfather of Charles Darwin. In his "Temple of Nature" he had written: "All vegetables and animals now existing were originally derived from the smallest microscopic ones formed by spontaneous vitality." Perhaps this idea had influenced Charles Darwin in his own thinking. Several years later he wrote to a friend about "Some warm little pond with all sorts of ammonia and phosphoric salts, light, heat, electricity, etc., present" in which he postulated that a protein compound was chemically formed ready to undergo still more complex changes.

About the same time, the physicist John Tyndall argued that every portion of a living organism can be reduced to inorganic matter. In his essay on vitality, published in 1866, he suggested that one could conceive of the reverse change from the inorganic to the organic, and that the special arrangement of elements in living bodies led to the phenomenon of life. In 1868 Thomas Huxley delivered a lecture in Edinburgh in which he pointed out that protoplasm was substantially the same over the whole range of living things. To him, the existence of life depended on certain molecules such as carbonic acid, water and nitrogenous compounds. These compounds were lifeless but, when brought together, gave rise to protoplasm.

To the Russian biochemist A. I. Oparin, more than to anyone else today, do we owe our present ideas on the scientific approach to the question of the origin of life. In clear and scientifically defensible terms, he pointed out in 1924 that there was no fundamental difference between a living organism and brute matter. The complex combination of manifestation and properties so characteristic of life must have arisen in the process of the evolution of matter. The first English edition of his book "The Origin of Life" was published in 1938. A fourth edition of the book has recently appeared under the title of "The Chemical Origin of Life."

In 1928, the British biologist, J. B. S. Haldane, expressed his own ideas on the origin of life. He attributed the synthesis of organic compounds to the action of ultraviolet light on the Earth's primitive atmosphere. He suggested that the organic compounds accumulated till the primitive oceans had the consistency of a primordial "soup." Twenty years after the appearance of Haldane's paper in *The Rationalist Annual,* Bernal theorized before the British Physical Society in a lecture entitled *The Physical Basis of Life.*

Condensations and dehydrogenations are bound to lead to increasingly unsaturated substances, and ultimately to simple and possibly even to condensed ring structures almost certainly containing nitrogen, such as the pyrimidines and purines. The appearance of such molecules makes possible still further synthesis. The primary difficulty, however, of imagining processes going thus far is the extreme dilution of the system if it is supposed to take place in the free ocean. The concentration of products is an absolute necessity for any further evolution.

The growth of biochemical and geochemical knowledge in the 20th century has stimulated a fresh interest in this age-old problem. The possibility of discovering extra-terrestrial life has given a further impetus to its experimental study. The first international symposium on the origin of life was held in Moscow in 1957. Ideas presented were grouped under headings which described five stages in the evolution of life from non-life: primary formation of primitive organic compounds on the Earth; the transformation of primary organic compounds on the Earth; the origin of proteins, nucleoproteins and enzymes; the origin of structure and metabolism; and the evolution of metabolism. So much experimental work has since been done in laboratories all over the world that a second international symposium was convened in Wakulla Springs, Florida, in the autumn of 1963. The highlight of this meeting was the presence of both Oparin and Haldane, pioneer thinkers in the field.

Almost half a century ago, Jacques Loeb had studied the effect of electric discharges on mixtures of hydrocarbons and had suggested that a large number of organic compounds could be formed. However, the first experiment designed with the set purpose of testing some of the hypotheses on the origin of life was that of Melvin Calvin and his associates who, in 1951, treated water and carbon dioxide in the Berkeley cyclotron and obtained significant yields of formaldehyde and formic acid. In 1953, Stanley Miller, then a graduate student in Harold Urey's laboratory, assembled a sample of the assumed primeval terrestrial atmosphere consisting of methane, ammonia, water vapour and hydrogen, and exposed it to an electric discharge simulating lightning. Amino acids and other organic compounds found in living systems were formed.

Since this classic experiment, several investigators have entered the field. Notable among them are Sydney Fox of Florida State University and John Oro of the University of Houston. The majority of publications have dealt with the formation of amino acids and components of nucleic acid from a wide variety of conditions which may be considered prebiological. Fox's work centered on the origin of proteins. A plausible answer seems to have begun to take shape. Proteinoids have been obtained by the thermal polymerization of 18 amino acids. These proteinoids have a distinct tendency to form microspheres having diameters in a bacterial range. Starting with ammonium cyanide, Oro has synthesized adenine and a number of biochemical intermediates of purines.

A starting point for any such experimental work must take into account cosmic abundances. Astronomical spectroscopy reveals that the most abundant elements in our galaxy are, in the order of rank: hydrogen, helium, oxygen, nitrogen and carbon. With the exception of helium these are, indeed, the basic elementary constituents of all living organisms. We know from chemical equilibria that—in the presence of hydrogen—carbon, nitrogen and oxygen must exist in their reduced forms as methane, ammonia and water. The equilibrium constants for these reactions at 25° C are all of considerable magnitude. It is this atmosphere of methane, ammonia, water vapour and small amounts of hydrogen which we shall consider as the primitive atmosphere of the Earth.

The energies available for the synthesis of organic compounds under primitive Earth conditions were ultraviolet light from the Sun, electric discharges, ionizing radiation and heat. While it is evident that sunlight is the principal source of energy, only a small fraction of this is in the wavelength below 2000Å which could have been absorbed by the methane, ammonia and water (one Ångstrom is 10^{-8} cm). However, the photodissociation products of these molecules could absorb energy of higher wavelengths. Next in importance as a source of energy are electric discharges, such as lightning and corona discharges from pointed objects. They occur close to the Earth's surface and, hence, would transfer the reaction products to the primitive oceans more efficiently. A certain amount of energy was also available from the disintegration of uranium, thorium, and potassium-40. While some of this energy may have been expended on the solid material, such as rocks, a certain proportion of it was available in the oceans and the atmosphere. Heat from volcanoes was another form of energy that may have been effective but, in comparison to the energy from the Sun, this was only a small portion and perhaps not widely distributed.

In our experiments with ionizing radiation, we have found that the electron beam from the linear accelerator at the Lawrence Radiation Laboratory of the University of California, Berkeley, provided us with a convenient source of electrons simulating potassium-40 on the primitive Earth. When a mixture of methane, ammonia and water was irradiated with electrons for about one hour, resulting in a total dose of approximately 10^{11} ergs, the largest single non-volatile compound formed was adenine. The production of adenine in this experiment was significant in the light of the multiple role played by this chemical in biological systems. Not only is it a constituent of both deoxyribonucleic acid (DNA) and ribonucleic acid (RNA), but it is also a unit of many important cofactors in living organisms.

In our experiments with electric discharges, tesla coils and luminous tube-transformers were used to simulate lightning on the primitive Earth. In a typical experiment, lasting 48 hours, most of the methane was converted into more complex organic compounds. In this experiment some of the constituents of the nucleic acid molecule have been identified.

The action of heat on the Earth's primitive atmosphere was duplicated by passing a mixture of methane and ammonia, in the presence of water vapour, through a heated Vycor tube at about 1000°C. The effluent gases were absorbed in water. Analysis of the water-soluble material revealed the presence of several amino acids. This result has recently been reported by Fox, who identified 14 of the amino acids commonly present in protein. Analysis of the gas fraction has shown that a great portion of the methane was converted into higher hydrocarbons, including ring compounds such as benzene, toluene and anthracene.

Chemosynthesis by meteorite impact on planetary atmospheres has been suggested as a possible pathway for primordial organic synthesis. The reaction is probably a result of the intense heat generated momentarily in the wake of the shock wave following the impact. In a very preliminary experiment simulating these conditions, by firing a ballistic missile into a mixture of methane, ammonia and water vapour, we have been able to identify some amino acids and a few ultraviolet absorbing compounds which may be of biological significance.

In all the experiments just described, whether using ionizing radiation, electric discharges or heat, one of the primary products appears to be hydrogen cyanide. The second product is formaldehyde. S. L. Miller and Urey identified both these compounds in their early work. C. Palm and Calvin recorded similar results. Our own experiments point to the same conclusion. In subsequent experiments we have, therefore, used hydrogen cyanide and formaldehyde as our starting materials.

When a dilute aqueous solution of hydrogen cyanide is exposed to ultraviolet light, a wide variety of organic compounds can be formed. Among these have been identified adenine, guanine and urea. Adenine and guanine are the two purines in the nucleic acids. Urea is an important biochemical intermediate. The reaction with hydrogen cyanide appears to proceed even without an external source of energy. When a solution of hydrogen cyanide is left standing at $-10°C$, it is spontaneously converted into more complex organic compounds. In experiments with very dilute solutions of formaldehyde as starting material, the two sugars, ribose and deoxyribose, have been identified.

The same forms of energy that have been instrumental in the production of the sugars and of the purines have now been demonstrated to be responsible for the synthesis of nucleosides, nucleotides and peptides. When a solution of adenine and deoxyribose, in the presence of the cyanide ion, is exposed to heat or ultraviolet light, the nucleoside deoxyadenosine is rapidly formed. This result confers a unique role on hydrogen cyanide. Not only is it a pathway for the purines but also, in the synthesis of nucleosides, it performs the function of a catalyst.

Since the Earth's primitive atmosphere was reducing in nature, some ultraviolet light in the region between 2400Å and 2900Å must have reached the surface of the early oceans. The activation of dissolved purines, pyrimidines and their nucleosides which absorb ultraviolet light in this range may have been a step in the synthesis of nucleoside phosphates.

To test this hypothesis, several experiments were performed. The conversion of adenine to adenosine, adenosine to adenosine monophosphate, adenosine monophosphate to adenosine diphosphate, and the diphosphate to the triphosphate has been experimentally established. In these experiments, ethyl metaphosphate was used as a source of phosphorus. It can be expected that this was not the most abundant source of phosphorus on the primitive Earth but it is likely that other, more abundant, phosphate salts can substitute for ethyl metaphosphate.

The synthesis of peptides under abiological aqueous conditions has been considered to be a matter of great difficulty. In our laboratory, however, we have recently found that when an aqueous solution of glycine and leucine was exposed to ultraviolet light in the presence of cyanamide, the dipeptides glycyl-glycine, glycyl-leucine, leucyl-glycine, leucyl-leucine were formed. The action of cyanamide may be analogous to that of di-cyclohexylcarbodiimide which has been extensively used by H. G. Khorana and his co-workers for the synthesis of nucleotides.

These results show that, under simulated primitive Earth conditions, molecules of biological significance can be synthesized. They lend support to the hypothesis of chemical evolution because the starting materials are the simple constituents of the primordial atmosphere; the sources of energy used are those that are most likely to have existed under primitive Earth conditions; the concentrations of materials used are very small; and the conditions are aqueous.

Recent studies in quantum biochemistry by B. Pullman and A. Pullman of Paris have thrown new light on some very significant aspects of chemical evolution. It is a striking fact that many of the molecules which are essential to living systems are conjugated systems exhibiting the phenomenon of electronic delocalization. In the nucleic acids, for example, the purines and pyrimidines are conjugated systems. Although the proteins do not, at first sight, appear to enjoy this property, a closer look shows that the matrix of hydrogen bonding which exists in a protein molecule provides a certain measure of electronic delocalization. In the high energy phosphates, there is interaction between the mobile electrons of one phosphoryl group with those of another. The porphyrins, such as chlorophyll and haem, which are of paramount importance in living systems, are highly conjugated molecules. This leads to the following conclusions:

(a) Evolutionary selection used the most stable compounds.

(b) On account of electron delocalization these compounds were best adapted for biological purposes.

(c) The possibility of life as we know it was made more probable by the appearance of the compounds.

There is no reason to doubt that we shall rediscover, one by one, the physical and chemical conditions which once determined and directed the course of chemical evolution. We may even reproduce the intermediate steps in the laboratory. Looking back upon the biochemical understanding gained during the span of one human generation, we have the right to be quite optimistic. In contrast to unconscious nature which had to spend billions of years for the creation of life, conscious nature has a purpose and knows the outcome. Thus the time needed to solve our problem may not be long.

49

Chemical Evolution

Melvin Calvin

How did life come to be on the surface of the Earth? Darwin himself recognized that his basic idea of evolution by variation and natural selection must be a continuous process extending backward in time through that period in which the first living things arose and into the period of "chemical evolution" which preceded it. We are approaching the examination of these events by two routes.

One is to seek for evidence in the ancient rocks of the Earth which were laid down before the time in which organisms capable of leaving their skeletons in the rocks to be fossilized were in existence. This period is somewhat more than *ca*. 600 My* ago. The Earth is believed to have taken its present form approximately 4700 My ago. We have found in rocks whose age is about 1000 My certain organic molecules which are closely related to the green pigments of plants, chlorophyll. This seems to establish that green plants were already flourishing before that time.

We have now found in rocks of still greater age, namely, 2500 My, the same kinds of molecules mentioned above which can be attributed to the presence of living organisms. If these molecules are as old as the rocks, we have thus shortened the time available for the generation of the complex biosynthetic sequences which give rise to these specific hydrocarbons (polyisoprenoids) to less than 2000 My.

The second approach is to attempt to reproduce in the laboratory those chemical processes induced by energy of various kinds—radiation from the sun, from radioactivity, from electrical storm, etc.—which could give rise to simple organic molecules and polymeric combinations of them, ultimately leading to systems which could be called alive. This attempt has also succeeded along a variety of lines, and many of the present-day

Melvin Calvin, "Chemical Evolution," *Proceedings Royal Society*, A., Vol. 288 (1965), pp. 441-466. Reprinted by permission. Only the official abstract is used here. Serious students are referred to the complete text.

*My (megayear) is equal to one million years. (Ed.)

biologically important molecules have been constructed abiogenically from the primeval atmosphere, thus providing laboratory evidence for the hypothetical processes. The latest step in this approach has been to demonstrate the formation of polypeptides in dilute aqueous solutions through the agency of molecules formed in the primitive atmosphere of the Earth.

Finally we must seek evidence for the same processes in material found elsewhere than on the Earth, such as other parts of our solar system, e.g. the Moon and Mars. We can expect to know whether such materials exist at all in the rocks of the Moon within this decade. We may even know something more definite about the botany of Mars during this same period.

50

Life Begins

Samuel Moffat
Elie A. Shneour

The planet earth was solitary and desolate four billion years ago. Oceans tossed breakers against lifeless shores. Often dark clouds blotted out the searing sunlight, and lightning stabbed from thunder clouds. Volcanoes erupted, pouring lava over the barren land and along the ocean bottom. You could not have breathed the atmosphere that surrounded the globe then. The air was made up of ammonia, methane, hydrogen, and water vapor.

Yet somehow, out of this seemingly inhospitable environment, life emerged. There are a number of explanations of how it might have happened. One of the most widely accepted assumes that the vast amounts of energy available acted on the simple gases in the atmosphere to produce the substances that led to life. Most of the energy came as ultraviolet radiation from the sun, but there was also energy in the form of heat from

Samuel Moffat and Elie A. Shneour, "Life Begins," *Life Beyond the Earth*, Vistas in Science No. 2 (Washington, D.C.: National Science Teachers Association, 1965). Reprinted by permission.

volcanoes and radioactive elements in the earth, and electricity from lightning. Once the right substances were produced, it was likely that life would emerge.

The substances that could have been produced included amino acids, sugars, proteins, and organic acids such as acetic acid (vinegar) or the lactic acid found in milk and muscles. These compounds rained down and collected in the oceans until they made a "hot thin soup," to use the phrase of the British biologist J. B. S. Haldane (1892-1964), who had many pioneering ideas about the origin of life. From this soup more complicated materials developed.

It may seem as though we are indulging in science fiction here. But the basis for this sort of thinking was worked out in great detail by the Russian biochemist A. I. Oparin (1894-   ) in his book *On the Origin of Life*. Oparin suggested several steps along the path to life that scientists have been able to confirm by laboratory experiments.

A KEY EXPERIMENT

One of the most important of these experiments was conducted in 1953 by Stanley L. Miller, then a graduate student working in the laboratory of Harold C. Urey at the University of Chicago. Into a glass apparatus Miller put a mixture of the gases that probably made up earth's early atmosphere. For a week this mixture was subjected to continuous electrical discharge from a spark coil. When the products of the experiment were analyzed, Miller found several new materials, particularly amino acids. Since this pioneering investigation, other scientists have confirmed and extended Miller's experiments.

For instance, John Oró of the University of Houston in Texas heated a concentrated solution of hydrogen cyanide ($H-C\equiv N$), and ammonia in water for several days at temperatures up to the boiling point of water. He used hydrogen cyanide as a starting material because it is formed in large amounts in Miller's procedure, and because it has been detected in the tails of comets. When Oró analyzed the mixture that had been heated, he found adenine in his solution. And adenine, as we know, is one of the two purines of DNA.

Cyril Ponnamperuma of the National Aeronautics and Space Administration's Ames Research Center in California demonstrated that adenine could be produced by another process. His technique involved exposing ammonia, methane, and water to high-energy electrons from a device known as a linear electron accelerator.

The first experiments of this sort were carried out by Melvin Calvin of the University of California. Further ingenious experiments were performed by Philip Abelson of the Carnegie Institution of Washington and others. These are only a few of the investigators in this field, and the number of researchers is increasing.

The important point about the research that has been completed is this: It is clear that an atmosphere rich in hydrogen and hydrogen compounds is essential for the synthesis of the substances that support life. So far no one has succeeded in making compounds of biological importance using gases or solutions to be found as part of an oxygen-rich atmosphere such as the earth has today.

THE EFFECTS OF ULTRAVIOLET RADIATION

And so some of the pieces in the history of life are beginning to fall in place. We have not explained one important part of the story, however. How did the hydrogen-rich atmosphere of those early ages change to the atmosphere we breathe today?

The ultraviolet radiation that long ago penetrated to the earth's surface affected the water vapor in the atmosphere. It broke the bonds holding the atoms together so that hydrogen gas and oxygen gas were produced. Gradually the very light hydrogen escaped into space and the heavier oxygen stayed behind, making up a greater percentage of the atmosphere. Other reactions led to the breakup of ammonia and methane, too, and the escape of more hydrogen.

This mechanism did not provide all the oxygen in the air today, since much is produced by plants from carbon dioxide. But it was an important step in the earth's development. We not only breathe oxygen—it also protects us from the burning effects of ultraviolet radiation. This radiation breaks the bonds of oxygen molecules, O_2, to produce a much more active form of the gas, called ozone, which is written O_3. There is a layer of ozone 14 to 15 miles up in the sky. This layer, known as the *ozonosphere*, might be thought of as a coating of suntan lotion for the earth, screening out the ultraviolet but allowing other radiation from the sun to pass through. Today enough ultraviolet still penetrates to the surface to make a sunburn painful or even deadly on occasion.

CHEMICALS THAT HELP THEMSELVES

Even after producing the building blocks of life's chemicals, we are a long way from producing those substances that actually support life. How could proteins and nucleic acids have come into being?

One series of experiments has demonstrated that artificial proteins can be made by heating amino acids under the proper laboratory conditions. These experiments were carried out by Sidney W. Fox of Florida State University. Dr. Fox has been able to make microscopic spherules (sphere-shaped bodies) that appear to behave in water very much like the natural proteins of a living cell. This is not to say that natural proteins were first formed by such processes. But the studies do show that it is possible to synthesize these complicated substances outside the intricate chemical-manufacturing plant of the cell.

There are many ways life's chemicals may have been put together originally, and only a few of these processes have been satisfactorily duplicated in the laboratory. As you read in the next few paragraphs about one of the ways that has been suggested, you should bear in mind that all of these ideas are subject to revision as more information is acquired in the coming years. Furthermore, the steps described represent only one line of thinking; many other approaches are being explored by biologists in many parts of the world.

One step in the development of the molecular structure of proteins and nucleic acids has been suggested by Dr. Calvin. It would depend on substances known as *catalysts*, materials that can speed up or slow down the rate of a chemical reaction. There are catalysts that speed up the rate of their *own* formation. These are known as *autocatalysts*. When an autocatalyst is produced, it tends to cause the formation of more molecules like itself. An autocatalyst would have had a great natural advantage over other substances, for it would have become more plentiful than substances that lacked this characteristic. This would have permitted a kind of chemical evolution.

Oparin has pointed out that certain proteins tend to attract each other when they are in a water solution. This attraction occurs because the proteins are electrically charged. These clumps of proteins are then encased by water molecules which form a sort of skin. The clumps with their water "skins" look very much like amoebas—the single-celled organisms that are among the simplest animals known. Oparin discovered that certain chemical reactions that occur in living cells will take place in such clumps. So it is conceivable that living cells might have been formed by a clumping of molecules.

Another characteristic of large molecules is their tendency to settle out of solution in a flattened form, like stacks of molecular waffles.

HOW DID CELLS DEVELOP?

Given molecules with more than one of the characteristics we have discussed, one can imagine what might happen. For instance, the key links in DNA are large, flat molecules that might have tended to settle in layers. If a very elementary nucleic acid were to be assembled this way, it does not seem unreasonable to speculate that eventually some duplication of the molecule might occur. This seems particularly likely in view of the fact that a synthetic DNA that is autocatalytic has been manufactured in the laboratory. This DNA has only two bases instead of four—adenine and thymine without guanine and cytosine. When placed in a suitable mixture, this DNA stimulates production of more DNA.

Thus it might have been possible for substances manufactured from the raw materials in the earth's early atmosphere to have gathered in the oceans. They could have interacted and, by well-established natural processes, produced primitive cells having some of the characteristics we associate with life. Whether this hypothetical pathway can be substantiated by experiment remains to be seen. Many of our ideas about the beginnings of life may have to be revised. Many scientists are confident, though, that they will be able to demonstrate how life's progression from nonliving forms might have occurred.

It must be clearly understood, however, that there is a huge gap in our knowledge about the way building-block compounds came together to form living organisms capable of reproduction, mutation, and response to their surroundings. Although the ideas we have discussed here were put forward by highly qualified scientists, there is as yet no real evidence to help us fill the gap. All is speculation, and we will have to hope that as yet unperformed experiments will provide us with the clues we need to begin piecing together this part of the picture.

LIFE WAS MORE THAN ACCIDENTAL

Nevertheless, the evidence about the formation of the building blocks has led scientists to become more and more convinced that life on earth did not come about by mere accident. Given the chemical conditions after the earth had coalesced, and given the inherent characteristics of these chemicals, it seems very likely that life should have come into existence. That it took perhaps two or three billion years is no surprise. In the universe, time is not measured in the brief lifespan of man, but in eons. Sometime, somewhere, when all the conditions were right, life began. We probably will never be able to say "Life started then," and name a specific time. It may have started when the first molecule of some DNA-like substance was formed. Even though it would have been a small occurrence it would have been a profound one.

You might well ask at this point whether life is originating today, right here on earth. If it is so probable an occurrence, why can't we see it coming into existence now, under our very noses? This is a fair question, and there seems to be a good answer for it. In the distant past, the collections of molecules leading to life were able to accumulate in the first seas because there were no organisms about to "eat" them or use them up. There were no complicated chemical life forms taking in simple foodstuffs and converting them to sugars and starches, proteins and nucleic acids. Today the chemicals leading to life are consumed before they can generate their own new forms. This is evolution in action again. The organisms already in existence are far better able to compete for food and vital materials than the simpler chemicals that once spawned these organisms.

Although we seem to have made a good guess as to which path life took in its meanderings through time, we still have many puzzles to solve. What we would like to know most of all is how specific proteins and nucleic acids first appeared. If we knew this, we would be better prepared to understand the further development of life. It is here that space exploration could help us complete our chart. We might find on other planets, or in the dust that swirls between them, some signs of life.

We have shown you something about the nature of life as a chemical process and from the standpoint of evolution. You have seen how living things might have developed, and you can follow future events in this area, events that are sure to make headlines for years to come. . . .

51

On the Origin and Evolution of Living Machines

Harold F. Blum

If we wish to contrast the living and the non-living we may compare a living cell with a mixture of chemicals in a test tube. If we wish to find similarities we may do better to compare the living cell with a man-made machine, say an automobile, which may also be contrasted with the contents of the test tube. Clearly we would not try to describe an automobile by grinding up its various parts and subjecting them to chemical analysis, and we would not expect to learn all about the living machine by follow-

This article originally appeared in *American Scientist*, Vol. 49 (1961), pp. 474-501. Reprinted by permission. The advanced student is urged to read the entire article.

ing, exclusively, a similar attack. It seems hardly necessary to say this and yet we seem at times to go astray in just this direction, whether we are trying to study the nature of viruses, the growth of cancers, the mechanism of genetic inheritance, or, as in the present case, the origin and evolution of life.

A certain parallel may be drawn between the non-living machine and the living machine in that both have evolutionary histories even though these are of different kinds. In tracing the evolution of the non-living machine we might begin a few hundred thousands of years ago when the first usable tool was chipped out of a piece of stone by an ancestor of modern Man. Then trace the story through innumerable steps including the first smelting of metal in Neolithic times, and the development of the effective steam engine less than two centuries ago, to the modern automobile and other complex machines. Viewed in this way it is seen that the evolution of the non-living man-made machine pre-supposes the evolution of Man himself; and this takes us into the history of living machines, as one of which Man has evolved.

With the story of the non-living machine so entangled with that of the living machine, the definition of a point of origin for the former must be vague or quite arbitrary. And if we try to imagine the various functional components of a living machine emerging from a mixture of chemical compounds—which we think happened sometime within, say, the last four thousand million years—we meet similar difficulty in defining the moment of emergence; perhaps we do better to think of the origin of life as spread over a considerable interval of time, blurred to our view with regard to both the kind and order of the steps that occurred. How the chemical compounds from which the living machine could be constructed, themselves came into being may be regarded as another problem. But again, separation of this problem from that of the origin of the living machine itself may be quite arbitrary. The analogy between living and non-living machines probably should not be pressed much farther than to point out that neither could be expected to arise spontaneously from a mixture of their component molecules; that is, without some special conditions or events extraneous to the simple chemical mixture itself. It should hardly be necessary to point out that I do not mean by this statement that extraphysical factors or vitalistic concepts need be invoked—the present argument is surely a mechanistic one.

We could find many properties of living machines that do not have their counterparts in non-living ones; but perhaps that which is most striking and most important from the standpoint of origin and evolution is the property of self-replication. Up to now such a property has not been built into any non-living machine. Self-replication of parts, and of the machine as a whole, is of particular importance in the present discussion; for if we are to assume that evolution of living systems has taken place by a mechanism of variation and natural selection, using these terms in the sense of modern Darwinism, this property becomes of paramount importance. The existence of a distinguishable biological species depends upon the accurate replication of a pattern which determines the characteristics of that species. And yet if this pattern were always copied exactly there could be no evolution by natural selection: for this, errors in copying must occur and be replicated in subsequent generations. If by such a copied error—or mutation— a characteristic is conferred that better fits the species to the environment in which it has to exist, the chances of survival of that species are increased, whereas species with disadvantageous mutations tend to be eliminated. This is the process of evolution by natural selection described in oversimplified fashion.

Our knowledge of some aspects of the process of replication is increasing rapidly at the moment—so rapidly that we may at times forget, in our enthusiasm, that the origin of a replicating machine is something different from the copying of such a machine once it exists. The point was emphasized by the late John Von Neumann who, while conceiving a machine that could replicate itself, admitted his inability to imagine a machine that could create itself. The difference between replication and origin was pointed out by Sir William Hardy a good many years earlier in an essay entitled, "To Remind" (which seems to have reminded few), basing his argument on the difficulties of the origin of a machine that could manufacture one only of two possible optical isomers, as living organisms do.

But to be more specific, let us consider the process of self-replication as we see it in modern living machines. And for the sake of argument let us try to reduce this process to a minimum of functional components that have to do with replication, leaving aside many other intriguing properties of living systems. If we are to give any physical solidity to our ideas of replication it seems necessary to assume some sort of spatial pattern, which we may think of as a template composed of large molecules having specific configurations that provide necessary genetic information for the construction of the individual organism making up the species. We have to think that not only are materials replicated by building against this template but that in some way the template itself is replicated in the course of self-duplication of the machine as a whole, so that the pattern can be passed along from generation to generation. Such replication entails the expenditure of free energy, since assembling the material against the template and taking the replica off cannot both be spontaneous acts; so there must be an energetic, or thermodynamic, component of the machine. And, as we shall see later, the mobilization of free energy in the living cell also entails a kinetic component. Thus it is necessary to think of the replicating machine in terms of no less than three functional components;* let

---

*In an earlier paper (1957) I described the minimum requirement of these three functional components, which I there called "functional properties." It should be pointed out, perhaps, that every reacting system involves, in an analytical sense, spatial (or structural), energetic and kinetic components; and that when the terms are used here with reference to living systems they refer to specific components of the latter systems.

us refer to them as spatial, energetic, and kinetic. So in thinking about the origin and evolution of such a machine we must take into account the origin of all three of these components rather than of any one of them alone. It is difficult to conceive how a machine that embodied all three could have come into being as a sudden act; and it would seem more likely that the different components were introduced separately. At any rate, until the complete self-replicating machine had emerged, evolution by natural selection, in the sense in which this word may properly be used, was not possible; and here an error may creep into our thinking about the origin of living systems. For natural selection is sometimes wrongly invoked, directly or tacitly, to explain the origin of things which had to be present before evolution by natural selection could take place, that is, to explain events leading up to the appearance of the self-replicating machine in terms of things that could have happened only after such a machine was already in existence. This incorrect application of the concept of natural selection may lead into the realm of teleology and finalism.

Undoubtedly there was going on before living machines were perfected to the point where natural selection was possible, a process which I like to call "chemical evolution"; and from this evolution resulted many types of compounds that are indispensable components of living machines today. An outstanding example is the amino acids, which, combined in proteins, are found playing basic roles in all living species. . . .

SOME IMPLICATIONS

What are the implications of the argument that has just been presented? First, let us review the similarities and differences between choice of mutants by natural selection and choice of reaction pathways in non-living systems. Perhaps the differences and the similarities one sees depend somewhat on where one stands. I think most biologists recognize intuitively a difference between the two processes, whereas chemists may stress the similarities. Applying the same framework of physicochemical mechanism, as I have attempted here, may emphasize similarities, tending to subordinate the differences in evolutionary result. But the functional differences remain nevertheless real.

In chemical evolution in a non-living world the direction of the pathway taken is a function of thermodynamics and kinetics, even when the expected direction of reaction is upset by radiant energy or other physical factors. In such a system, the reaction pathway may respond immediately and directly to a change in the environment, say the introduction of a catalyst which speeds up a given reaction step. The catalyst may be a product of the reaction itself, which then is an autocatalytic reaction; but this does not alter the picture very much because it is difficult to distinguish between such a reaction system and its environment. In the living, replicating system, on the other hand, this distinction is more clear-cut, there being little direct influence—and virtually no specific influence—of the external environment on replication of pattern. In chemical reaction, a given molecule which has reached a high enough energy level to react is for the moment different from its fellows to that extent; but, the reaction once achieved, that particular molecule is not distinguishable from other product molecules. The molecule does not maintain its individuality with respect to its energy content beyond a fraction of a second—the product state represents a new average condition, so in the long run it is the average and not the individual that counts. The same argument applies to formation of free radicals or intermediates in chemical reactions, which are transitory steps in the reaction that do not replicate and so perpetuate their kind.

Presumably, mutation too involves a temporary increase in energy at some place in the molecule in order to get over a barrier, but this is a fleeting change. In the case of a "successful" mutation the resultant alteration in pattern is maintained by replication. The individuality of the mutant pattern may thus be preserved for a very long time, being duplicated over and over again and so persisting through many generations, long after the particular molecule that was originally altered has ceased to exist as such. There is a sort of "memory" in this process that does not enter into strictly chemical evolution. Natural selection of a new pattern is a slow process in which many generations may be involved in accomplishing a single step; it amounts to picking out altered replicating patterns, that is, mutated genes. This is not accomplished directly, but by the overt changes the mutation produces in a larger system, the cell or multicellular organism, that contains the new pattern. Thus the gene is isolated from direct impingement of the environment upon it; and if we wish to consider natural selection as a feed-back mechanism we must include the environment in our system, and the impingement of the organism and environment may be difficult to analyze.

We see from all this that living machines may, in a sense, arrest the ordinary time course of events to an extent not paralleled in any simple, cyclic, physical, or chemical system, at least any that I am able to picture. And this offers correspondingly greater opportunity for the development of complexity in the living world as compared to the non-living.

Does the picture I have presented modify in any way our ideas about evolution by natural selection? Basically I think it strengthens the concept by giving it a more intimate and plausible physical basis. It is a great tribute to Charles Darwin that we are still seeking today in the light of a century of scientific progress to explain with greater exactitude the principle he laid down, and which we still accept. But, on the other hand, consideration of the more intimate mechanism may tend to weaken our anticipation of perfection in the results of evolution by natural selection. It emphasizes to us that while mutations may be regarded as accidental events there are great limitations as to the kinds of accidents that can occur. Fundamentally these limitations are set by properties of the molecules that make up the cell; but how much these properties have influenced the course of evolution by natural selection would be difficult to express in rigorous form. It is also difficult to know to just what extent one must attribute the direction taken by biological evolution to the direction taken by the chemical evolution that preceded it. We find reason to think that some substances are common to all living systems because they were present at the beginning as the result of previous chemical evolution. The amino acids, for example, seem already to be reasonably accounted for in this way, and no doubt other essential components of living material will be. There are certain dominant themes in the biochemical tapestry, but there are many details that seem to have been woven with considerable vagary suggesting both the guiding hand of natural selection and incidental "accidents" of mutation, some of which may have little or no survival value. We are constrained to view the role of natural selection in terms of the fossil record since the beginning of the Cambrian, 500 million years ago; and one of the things this record tells us, when we combine the evidence with that of comparative biochemistry, is that the major molecular patterns of inheritance must have been pretty well-established before that time. What has happened since would seem to have involved relatively small changes, considering the degree of biological organization already established then. But living systems had existed and evolution has been going on for a long time before the beginning of the Cambrian—possibly for two or three thousand million years. The major themes of organic evolution were established in the course of this earlier period, and it seems likely that strictly physico-chemical factors played a more prominent role in setting limits upon the direction natural selection could take then than they did later.

But however the limits were set they must have continued to restrict the possible directions evolution might take. The first replicable and mutable cell would seem to have had before it the possibility of vastly more mutations than has any modern cell of any existent species. Of course, I do not mean by this that the primordial living system contained in a physical sense all these possible patterns, for surely more became possible by recombinations in the course of the many millions of years of evolution than were present in the first living machine. What I mean to say is that the limitations on the direction of evolution are much greater for any existing species than they were for the primordial system from which it ultimately stems. The limitations imposed by physico-chemical factors upon the possible directions of mutation must constitute restrictions on the degree of perfection of adapation to environment. I think this is sometimes lost sight of. There seems to be widespread tendency to disregard such limitations and to assume complete randomness of mutation, which may encourage overemphasis of the perfection of adaptation of the organism to the environment, and encourage a kind of teleology that may be misleading—we may risk turning Darwinism into a cult. This may also encourage false social analogies.

As regards the idea of randomness in mutation, we must remember that this is something we use as a tool and should not let it confuse us in thinking about evolution in an over-all or global sense. What we mean by randomness of mutation is that at a given instant, given a particular set of conditions, there is an array of possibilities for mutation; and for purposes of analysis, we may proceed to treat this array as though it were a fixed thing. But thinking evolutionarily we see that the possibilities for mutation are continually changing, and the environment as well, and that used in this way the term, randomness, only applies to a given instant we have chosen to study.

The question whether life exists on other worlds and how it originated there has occupied thinkers for a long time but there has been recent increase in interest, particularly since Sputnik and the development of the so-called Space Age. With recognition of the vast extent of the universe, which seems only to grow larger as we extend our observations, there has been a tendency to people this universe with living organisms. It may be estimated that there is a very large number of planets in our galaxy that are sufficiently like our earth to support life as we know it. But to assume on this basis that such life exists there, tacitly admits that, given the same kind of a chemical environment as once existed on our earth, living organisms will come into being as a matter of course. If the conditions for origin of life are more exacting, the probabilities become less, however, and such estimates need to be revised downward. From what has just been said it seems that one should assume more specific conditions than just an appropriate mixture of molecular species in order for a living, replicating machine to arise. Just how detailed the specifications were to permit the origin of life on this planet, and just how many rarely probable events were involved, it would be very difficult to estimate. When we think of the broad array of living species which exists, we realize that their evolution by natural selection has also involved a great many rare events. For each mutation represents a rare event and there must have been many mutations involved in the evolution of each species. As we look back, it appears that had things happened in slightly different ways our present array of species might be quite different. The farther back we go the more critical the picture becomes, that is, a mutation happening sometime early in pre-Cambrian time might have had much more effect on the direction of evolution of species than a mutation that occurred, say only a few million years ago. If we include in our thinking Man's cultural evolution, which has entailed many rare events of a still different kind, we see that the chances of finding beings very much like ourselves elsewhere in the galaxy may be small indeed, even though there may be many planets that could have accommodated them, had the hazards of history followed the same course. That there may somewhere be replicating machines constituted from the same molecular species as our own seems somewhat more likely, but the conditions and sequence of events that were required to establish them may make this, too, a tenuous possibility. Such thinking should, perhaps, not dampen enthusiasm for the exploration of the possibility of life on other planets, but it might temper our expectations of what we may find, and affect planning as regards what to look for.

A great deal of what I have said in this paper has, of course, been in the nature of speculation, but I hope that I have paid reasonable respect to established observation and theory in the various fields of science it has been necessary to touch upon. No doubt I have stretched both the chemical and the biological picture but I hope I have not distorted them unduly in trying to get them into the same frame. It seems to me it is time to take that risk; for have we not been trying for too long to approach many problems of life from opposite ends, with only a vague hope that we may somehow come together in the middle.

52

Spontaneous Generation

Irving W. Knobloch

INTRODUCTION

From antiquity up to the end of the nineteenth century, there existed a theory called "spontaneous generation." This entailed a belief in the origin of living forms, both plant and animal, from nonliving substances.

Swallows and frogs, for example, were thought to spring from mud in the spring. Likewise, flies were generated from pieces of meat.

Today, belief in spontaneous generation has largely disappeared from the minds of educated people. The theory opposed to this is called "biogenesis" and it can be described as favoring the genesis of plants and animals from other living things; in other words, all life comes from life.

So many modern concepts and practices depend upon the fallacy of the theory of spontaneous generation that life would be considerably changed were it true.

The belief that biogenesis is true enables biologists to control nature for the good of mankind and to predict what is likely to happen in nature in the light of our present knowledge. In the field of entomology, for example, we can predict that the eggs of a certain kind of insect came from the female of that same species and that the eggs will eventually develop into an insect like one of its parents. By destroying the eggs or larvae of this insect we can control its numbers on the earth, an especially desirable situation if the insect in question is carrying malaria or yellow fever organisms.

The practice of sterilization in the laboratory, the hospital, and elsewhere is grounded in the firm conviction that organisms do not arise without parents. The housewife heats her fruits and vegetables for a certain length of time at a certain temperature, seals the cans or jars, puts them away, and feels certain that, barring a failure in sealing, the cans or jars will remain unspoiled and wholesome. This means that the organisms in them have been killed and that others cannot arise from the contents by spontaneous generation. In the laboratory, culture media are subjected to heat and pressure for predetermined times and will remain sterile indefinitely. Surgical instruments are likewise sterilized in the hospitals and remain in that condition until needed. Pasteurization, named after the great Louis Pasteur, is also an adaptation of our knowledge about biogenesis. In the pasteurization of milk, wine, or beer, for example, the harmful organisms are killed and others of the same kind can not arise as long as the mixture is kept unopened.

The germ theory of disease also rests upon the foundation of biogenesis. For example, one of the troublesome problems of surgery was to prevent infection during an operation. Hospitals, as late as the middle of the last century, were in a very deplorable state. To decide upon an operation was tantamount to a death sentence because almost all surgery was accompanied by infection and death. The medical profession was very conservative and refused, for a long time, to realize the presence and importance of bacteria. Antisepsis, which is said to have started with the great physician Dr. Joseph Lister, Professor of Surgery at the University of Edinburgh, means the control of disease-causing organisms; in this case, on the operating table. If these organisms can be killed off completely, an infection will not occur and the patient has a much better chance of recovery. Dr. Lister's work, with phenol as the antiseptic agent, stems directly from the work of Louis Pasteur. Amputations which were almost universally fatal were made safer. Dr. Lister, for example, had only six fatalities out of a group of forty such cases, a remarkable achievement in those days.

It took several centuries to disprove the theory of the spontaneous generation of life. The following history of the struggle leading to the death of the theory illustrates many of the problems of scientific investigations.

EARLY IDEAS

Science has been one of the most successful fields leading to the improvement of man's lot upon the earth because, while working in the present, it leans very heavily upon all verified data of the past. Let us take a look backward into history to learn what we can of the early trends of thought on the subject of the continuity of life.

It can be said that early man had no doubts as to his own immediate ancestry; the fact of human birth was self-evident. He also knew the origin of many of the common animals. He probably realized, too, that the way to obtain a desired plant for agricultural purposes was to gather seeds of that plant and sow them in the ground. The well-known Greek, Aristotle, (384-322 B.C.), had some fairly modern ideas about reproduction. He said:

The nightingale produces her young at the beginning of summer. She produces five or six eggs—insects copulate and produce their young during the winter —wild animals produce their young once a year, unless, like the hare, they breed while they are nursing their young—fish also generally breed once a year—the scorpius breeds twice—the crustaceans incubate upon their ova, which are placed beneath them.°

In various places in Aristotle's *History of Animals* we find mention of such things as ova, copulation, semen, uterus, and so forth. Naturally, there were comparatively few investigators in those days and large segments of knowledge remained undiscovered. Aristotle had a tremendous wealth of information but there were many things that he could not know. For example, he could not completely understand the developmental cycle of certain insects. He said:

Whatever are produced spontaneously in living creatures, in the earth, or in plants, or in any part of them, have a distinction in the sexes, and by a union of

°Aristotle, *History of Animals*, Richard Cresswell, trans. (London: George Bell Sons, 1878).

the sexes something is produced, not the same in any respect, but an imperfect animal, as nits are produced from lice and from flies and butterflies are produced egg-like worms, from which neither similar creatures are produced, not any other creature, but such things only."°

Knowledge almost always proceeds from the obvious to the less obvious. Aristotle knew of sex and the union of sexes—he knew the facts of generation when the offspring resembled the parent, but he was somewhat at a loss to follow an insect egg through a caterpillar stage to a resting stage and back to the adult again.

From such cases and others dealing with less easily observable species, Aristotle and those who worked with him and after him sponsored the doctrine of spontaneous generation. When a life history was not clear, this doctrine was invoked. Some of his ideas on this follow:

> Some (plants) are produced from the seed of other plants, and others are of spontaneous growth; some animals are produced from animals of a similar form, the origin of others is spontaneous and not from similar forms—those which spring from putrid matter, this is the case with many insects; others originate in the animals themselves, and from the excrementitious matter in their parts—(the productions of others) is spontaneous, for some of them (insects) spring from the dew which falls upon plants. Some originate in rotten mud and dung.†

Eels, which are fish, have always been somewhat mysterious creatures. Their life cycle was a puzzle for centuries and even at the present time many facts about them are not yet known. We cannot understand how adult eels find their way to the breeding grounds in the region of the Sargasso Sea. We do not know how it is possible for the young eels, hatched there, to find their way over many miles of ocean back to their parent's home. It is not surprising that, several hundred years before Christ, Aristotle had this to say about eels—

> Eels are not produced from sexual intercourse, nor are they oviparous nor have they ever been detected with semen or ova—the originate in what are called the entrails of the earth, which are found spontaneously in mud and moist earth.‡

It is very interesting to remember the Bible teaching about the creation of life as recorded in Genesis. Those scientists who favored biogenesis and those who advocated spontaneous generation, at least for certain organisms, quoted the Bible as favoring their side of the question. The biogenesists said that God made man and all other organisms at one time and "set up the rules" of reproduction and lineal descent. Presumably there could be nothing new on the earth. The other school

°*Ibid.*
†*Ibid.*
‡*Ibid.*

pointed to the statement by the author of Genesis that God made man out of the dust of the ground. He made organic things (man and other creatures) out of lifeless material, dust.

In the Bible there is also an interesting account of bees arising from the body of a lion. This is found in the book of Judges and reads as follows:

Then went Samson down—and, behold, a young lion roared against him. And the Spirit of the Lord came mightily upon him and he rent him as he would have rent a kid. . . . And after a time—he turned aside to see the carcass of the lion; and, behold, there was a swarm of bees and honey in the carcass of the lion.

We should hasten to add here that the above passage does not prove that the biblical writers believed in spontaneous generation.

SEVENTEENTH-CENTURY INVESTIGATIONS

Van Helmont, physician and plant physiologist from Brussels, said in 1652,

All that is required is to cork up a pot containing corn with a dirty shirt; after about twenty-one days a ferment coming from the dirty shirt combines with the effluvium from the wheat, the grains of which are turned into rats, not minute and puny, but vigorous and full of activity.[*]

Alexander Ross, in the same century, is reported to have said—

So may he doubt whether in cheese and timber, worms are generated; or if beetles and wasps in cow dung; or if butterflies, locusts, grasshoppers, shell-fish, snails, eels, and such like, be procreated of putrefied matters, which is apt to receive the form of that creature to which it is by formative power disposed. To question this is to question reason, sense, and experience. If he doubts of this let him go to Egypt, and there he will find the fields swarming with mice begot of the mud of Nylus, to the great calamity of the inhabitants.[†]

It seems almost incredible that the life cycle of mice and rats should not be fully known. It would have been a simple matter to put a male and female together and note that the young come from the union of the sexes and not from rags or mud. That would entail making an experiment and men at this stage in history still preferred speculation to experiment. In fact, they probably had only the haziest idea of experimentation.

[*]F. M. van Helmont, *Ortus medicinae, id est initia physicae inaudita* (Amsterdam, 1652).

[†]Alexander Ross, *Arcana microcosmi* (London, 1652).

That is why the simple experiments of Redi, to be recounted next, caused such surprise. People were so accustomed to saying "it is written" or "so says Aristotle" that they were startled when Redi, disregarding authority, proved that certain insects came from eggs and were not spontaneously generated in meat.

Francesco Redi, poet and physician to the Grand Dukes of Tuscany, became interested in the relationship between flies and meat. He was possessed of great curiosity and, apparently, a unique originality. His great hypothesis of 1668 is described below in his own words.

I shall express my belief that the Earth, after having brought forth the first plants and animals at the beginning by order of the Supreme and Omnipotent Creator, has never since produced any kinds of plants or animals, either perfect or imperfect; and everything which we know in past or present times that she has produced, came solely from the true seeds of the plants and animals themselves, which thus, through means of their own, preserve their species. And, although it be a matter of daily observation that infinite numbers of worms are produced in dead bodies and decayed plants, I feel, I say, inclined to believe that these worms are all generated by insemination and that the putrefied matter in which they are found has no other office than that of serving as a place, or suitable nest, where animals deposit their eggs at the breeding season, and in which they also find nourishment; otherwise, I assert that nothing is ever generated therein.*

Redi made a number of experiments to validate his belief. His most classical ones are recorded as follows:

I continued similar experiments with the raw and cooked flesh of the ox, the deer, the buffalo, the lion, the tiger, the dog, the lamb, the kid, the rabbit; and sometimes with the flesh of ducks, geese, hens, swallows, etc., and finally I experimented with different kinds of fish, such as sword-fish, tuna, eel, sole, etc. In every case, one or other of the above-mentioned kinds of flies were hatched, and sometimes all were found in a single animal. Besides these, there were to be seen many broods of small black flies, some of which were so minute as to be scarcely visible, and almost always I saw that the decaying flesh and the fissures in the boxes where it lay were covered not alone with worms, but with the eggs from which, as I have said, the worms were hatched. These eggs made me think of those deposits dropped by flies on meats, that eventually became worms, a fact noted by the compilers of the dictionary of our Academy, and also well known to hunters and to butchers, who protect their meats in Summer from filth by covering them with white cloths. Hence great Homer, in the nineteenth book of the Illiad, has good reason to say that Achilles feared lest the flies would breed worms in the wounds of dead Patrocles, whilst he was preparing to take vengeance on Hector.

*Francesco Redi, *Experiments on the Generation of Insects*, translated from the Italian edition of 1688 by Mab. Bigelow (Chicago: Open Court Publishing Company, 1909).

Having considered these things, I began to believe that all worms found in meat were derived directly from the droppings of flies, and not from the putrefaction of the meat, and I was still more confirmed in this belief by having observed that, before the meat grew wormy, flies had hovered over it, of the same kind as those that later bred in it. Belief would be vain without the confirmation of experiment, hence in the middle of July I put a snake, some fish, some eels of the Arno, and a slice of milk-fed veal in four large, wide-mouthed flasks; having well closed and sealed them, I filled the same number of flasks in the same way, only leaving these open. It was not long before the meat and fish, in these second vessels, became wormy and flies were seen entering and leaving at will; but in the closed flasks I did not see a worm, though many days had passed since the dead flesh had been put in them. Outside on the paper cover there was now and then a deposit, or a maggot that eagerly sought some crevice by which to enter and obtain nourishment. Meanwhile the different things placed in the flasks had become putrid and stinking; the fish, their bones excepted, had all been dissolved into a thick, turbid fluid, which on settling became clear, with a drop or so of liquid grease floating on the surface; but the snake kept its form intact, with the same color, as if it had been put in but yesterday; the eels, on the contrary, produced little liquid, though they had become very much swollen, and losing all shape, looked like a viscous mass of glue; the veal, after many weeks, became hard and dry.

Not content with these experiments, I tried many others in different vessels. In order to leave nothing undone, I even had pieces of meat put under ground, but though remaining buried for weeks, they never bred worms, as was always the case when flies had been allowed to light on the meat. One day a large number of worms, which had bred in some buffalo-meat, were killed by my order; having placed part in a closed dish, but in the second worms had hatched, which changing as usual into egg-shape balls (pupae), finally became flies of the common kind. In the same experiment tried with dead flies, I never saw anything breed in the closed vessel. [*]

Redi's classical experiment is not only unusual in that it was an experiment but that he prepared two sets of vessels. One he covered and the other he left open. Both sets contained the same kinds of meat and fish. Therefore, the results obtained could only be attributable to the covering, because this was the only part of the experiment that he varied. This type of experiment is called a controlled experiment and is the best kind from which to draw conclusions. It is well to emphasize this point because the layman and many pseudo-scientists are continually trying out this or that idea with the desire to "prove something." Uncountable thousands of people assemble some facts, make up their minds and come to a conclusion, but their conclusions will have little or no value unless they run a "controlled" experiment and are careful to vary only one factor at a time. In the case of Redi, the only thing he varied was the use of gauze over one set of vessels.

[*] *Ibid.*

It should be mentioned that Redi was interested in proving that certain flies came from the eggs of the flies. This idea was not original with Redi because he had read in the nineteenth book of Homer's *Iliad*, as he mentions, that Achilles was afraid lest flies enter the wounds of the dead Patroclus and breed worms therein.

Redi noted that in both sets of jars the meat became putrid, but knowing nothing of the cause of decay or putrefaction, he knew nothing of the role of bacteria in these processes. The discovery of bacteria did not come until 1676, and the linking up of decay and bacteria had to wait until the discovery of Schwann in 1837, almost one hundred fifty years later. It is interesting to note that Redi still believed that gall-flies were spontaneously generated in galls. This, of course, was disproved later by other scientists.

The great furor over spontaneous generation subsided somewhat as a result of Redi's experiments, but in 1676, an amateur Dutch scientist by the name of Antony van Leeuwenhoek unintentionally started the controversy all over again. Working with pepperjuice in an attempt to find the cause for its acridity, he saw minute organisms which subsequently became known as bacteria. He said, "by chance observing this water on the 24th of April, 1676, I saw therein, with great wonder, incredibly many very little animalcules, of divers sorts."*

The careful observations of Leeuwenhoek, communicated in a series of letters to the Royal Society in London, initiated the science of bacteriology and led to thousands upon thousands of research projects, the end of which is not yet in sight. Some of the important fruits of the work on bacteria are: the control of spoilage, water sanitation, Pasteurization, sterilization, lactic acid fermentations, vinegar formation, ensilage, crop rotation, and last but not least, the germ theory of disease.

The science of bacteriology might not have developed in the absence of suitable means for magnifying the organisms so that they could be seen. Leeuwenhoek, by tireless perseverence, succeeded in grinding lenses from tiny bits of glass so that he had finer hand-lenses than anyone else. They were not microscopes as we think of them today but they were at least sufficiently powerful to detect the tiny bacteria.

EIGHTEENTH-CENTURY INVESTIGATIONS

From the discovery of bacteria by Leeuwenhoek in 1676, to about the middle of the next century, investigators worked successfully on vari-

*Clifford Dobell, *Antony van Leeuwenhoek and His "Little Animals"* (New York: Harcourt, Brace & World, Inc., 1932).

ous aspects of bacteriology but were unable to prove or disprove the spontaneous generation of the microscopic bacteria. Their abundance, rapid rate of reproduction and the ability of some of them to withstand unfavorable conditions made the work difficult.

Joseph Needham, an English priest, published some of his researches in 1745. He put some mutton broth in flasks, boiled them a short time, put corks in their mouths, and set them aside. After a suitable waiting period, he examined them and found that each held a good growth of bacteria. Reasoning from his data, Needham spoke out for the spontaneous generation of bacteria in his cultures.

Abbe Lazaro Spallanzani of Italy is said to have been the first man to witness the division of bacterial cells under the lens, the first to isolate a single organism of very small dimensions, and the first to use glass flasks. Spallanzani is noted most of all, however, for his famous controversy with Needham and others who supported the theory of spontaneous generation.

Needham's experiments had three serious flaws. First, he boiled his infusions for too short a time, second, he stoppered them with corks, which are porous enough to admit bacteria, and third, he failed to record exact information on the temperature and time of boiling. The recording of data is very important in scientific work. Spallanzani sealed his flasks shut by melting the glass and heated them longer than had Needham. Upon examination, he was able to say, "Nineteen vessels, containing infused substances, were hermetically sealed and kept an hour in boiling water. Being opened at a proper time, not a single animacule was to be seen."*

Ordinarily this experiment would have settled the argument but Needham rejoined that the good priest had boiled his flasks so long that he had destroyed the "vegetative force" in the infusion and naturally the organisms could not grow. Let us see how Spallanzani met this challenge.

To this experiment of mine, it was objected that the long continuance of heat had perhaps entirely destroyed the vegetative power of the infused substances, or materially injured the elasticity of the air remaining included in the vessels; thus it was not surprising if animacula did not appear.

To estimate the weight of these objections, I conceived an experiment apparently decisive; which was, to make nineteen infusions, and boil some of them a short time, others longer, and the rest very long. If it was founded, the number of animacula would be less according to the boiling, if not, the number would be alike in all cases. . . . White kidney beans, vetches, buck-wheat, barley, maize, the seeds of mallows and beets were infused. . . . The yoke of an egg . . . was also infused.—A certain quantity of each infusion (was boiled) half an hour; another quantity, an hour, a third, an hour and a half; and a fourth, two hours. —Each of the four classes was marked with a different number, to avoid all

*Lazaro Spallanzani, *Tracts on the Natural History of Animals and Vegetables*, 2nd ed., John Graham Dalyell, trans. (Edinburgh, 1803).

hazard of confusion or error: and because an equal temperature was most essential, all were deposited in the same place. The vessels, containing the infusions, were not hermetically sealed, but loosely stopped with corks; the only object of this examination being to discover, whether long protracted ebullition would prejudice or destroy the property of infused substances in producing animacula; if it did, there would be no difference whether the vessels were open or closed. . . . On the 15th of September, I made—infusions; and on the 23rd examined them for the first time. Animacula were in all; but the number and species different in each—From this it may seem, that although long continued heat had not prevented the production of animacula, it had contributed to diminish the number, or alter the kind.°

Spallanzani thus clarified several important aspects of the problem. He proved that heating substances to kill whatever organisms they contained and then sealing them to prevent the entrance of any others, caused the infusions to remain clear and sterile. There was no spontaneous generation in his flasks. He also proved that long boiling did not destroy anything in the air that organisms required for their growth. Boiling did not alter the *mythical* "vegetative force" as charged by Needham.

Although Spallanzani's work seemed conclusive, there always was the lingering doubt that hermetically sealing the flasks deprived any organisms that might be present of the air they required. The work on oxygen by Antoine Lavosier and John Priestley in 1774 and 1775 had opened up a new field and showed the relationship between this gas and living organisms. Joseph Gay-Lussac then showed that oxygen was lacking in flasks boiled and sealed. The enemies of biogenesis took heart from the discovery of oxygen for was not this gas necessary for cellular respiration? Apparently more clever experiments would have to be devised, experiments which showed the relationships among air, oxygen, and the origin of living organisms.

NINETEENTH-CENTURY INVESTIGATIONS

Not until 1836 did anyone have a real contribution to make to the solution to the problem. An investigator by the name of Schultz made up infusions. He allowed the tubes to remain open to the air with this proviso—the entering air had to pass over sulphuric acid or potassium hydroxide. Although his flasks usually remained sterile, they sometimes spoiled. (Tyndall found later that germs can sometimes pass unharmed through the acid.) His fellow scientists, remembering Needham, protested that the acid deprived the air of the "vegetation force" in those cases where cultures remained sterile.

°*Ibid.*

The emphasis now seemed to be on the entering air. Much work was being done on fermentations. This work was closely allied with spontaneous generation. Meanwhile Cagniard de la Tour made a great contribution when he found that yeasts were organisms and ventured the opinion that they caused fermentation. Theodor Schwann, co-founder of the cell theory, heated infusions and passed air into them through red-hot tubes and of course he observed no growth in his flasks. He also said that putrefaction and fermentation were due to living organisms. The great chemists of the day, however, ridiculed de la Tour and Schwann because they felt certain that fermentation was purely a chemical process caused by a ferment (or enzyme as we now call it). Schwann's experiments could not always be duplicated, particularly with sugar infusions, and this was due, no doubt, to the fact that resistant bacteria entered the flasks at times. The chemists had sport, with Schwann in particular. As so often happens, both the chemist and the biologist were each partly right about fermentation but this knowledge came later. Both Oliver Wendell Holmes and Ignaz Semmelweis were of the opinion that puerperal or childbed fever was a disease caused by organisms and that it was spread from patient to patient by the unclean hands of the obstetrician. They were subjected to villanous attacks by colleagues but eventually proved that keeping the hands and operating rooms sterile with antiseptics controlled the disease.

In the middle of the nineteenth century, two men made another contribution to the solution of the mystery surrounding the genesis of bacteria. Their names were Schröder and von Dusch. They proceeded as had many other investigators but instead of sealing their flasks or passing the air through strong acid or through hot glass they simply plugged the flasks with ordinary cotton. After suitable boiling, the flasks remained sterile. This is our procedure today in bacteriological work but it was argued by some that cotton, being of vegetable origin, required air for its own metabolism and hence no air or oxygen got into the flask and naturally the organisms could not grow. Sometimes, too, media with milk or meat without water, spoiled. Their experiments were not conclusive and were not universally accepted.

In 1859, Félix Archimede Pouchet, Director of the Museum at Rouen, published a treatise on spontaneous generation in which he said: "when after meditating on the question it became clear to me that spontaneous generation was still one of the means employed by nature to reproduce living beings, I set about finding means by which the phenomenon could be demonstrated." He added, "what then will these opponents say if I succeed in introducing the generation of living organisms, while substituting artificial air for that of the atmosphere?"*

Pouchet performed the following experiment. He sealed a flask of boiling water, inverted it over a mercury bath and thrust the neck of the

*Félix Archimede Pouchet, *Hétérogénie ou traité de la génération spontanée, basé sur de nouvelles expériences* (Paris: Ballière, 1859).

bottle under the mercury. He broke the neck of the bottle under the mercury, and connected it with an apparatus which, when heated, produced oxygen. The gas bubbled in and displaced the water. When half full of gas and half full of water, he took a piece of hay which had been heated and, with sterilized forceps, pushed it underneath the mercury and into the mouth of the bottle. The hay floated in the water. After a few days, the infusion was found to be full of small organisms. Triumphantly Pouchet asked where this evidence of life could have come from—not from the hot water—not from the heated hay—not from the oxygen which had been produced artificially?

Pouchet's experiment was the trigger mechanism which "set off" Louis Pasteur, Scientific Director of the Ecole Normale, and almost led to the ultimate solution of the problem of spontaneous generation. Pasteur's name is known to almost every educated person because of his great contributions from 1860-1864 on the question we are considering. He is revered, however, because of the great number of his contributions to the safety and welfare of mankind. Some that are worth remembering are his work on crystals, the improvement of the French wine industry, the diseases of the silk worms, his work on anthrax, and his famous work on hydrophobia or rabies.

When Pasteur began his work on the problem, he had before him the results obtained by many investigators. He probably admired the cleverness of Spallanzani, Needham, Schultz, Schwann, Schröder, and von Dusch, as well as some others. His problem, however, was to make a foolproof experiment, one to which no one could object. First of all, he repeated the work of his predecessors by sealing flasks shut with a flame, by stoppering others with cotton and still others with asbestos, and by passing air through heat.

In 1843, Helmholtz had given him another lead. This investigator showed that the air contained contaminants and that this contaminant was a solid since it could not pass through a moist animal membrane. Pasteur pursued this line since he had a "hunch" that this was the proper avenue of approach. He sucked air through a tube fitted with a cotton plug. The plug caught the dust particles in the air and when he dissolved the plug and put the dust into sterile broth, the broth became filled with organisms. The relationship between dust and organisms was thus established. He was now ready to perform his most crucial experiment in the field of spontaneous generation.

Pasteur used a yeast broth in his flasks. He realized that he must not bring his air into the flasks over heat nor must he pass it through acid, nor must he stopper the flasks with corks or cotton. How then could he silence the critics who would be sure to arise? He simply drew out the necks of his heated flasks into the shape of a swan's neck, set the flasks aside and, after waiting until he could stand the strain no longer, he examined them and found that every one remained organism-free.

The air with its own oxygen entered the flask but the heavier dust particles (and the bacteria) settled in the low parts of the neck. Thus the flasks remained sterile. Bacteria did not appear if the dust was excluded. If he broke the neck of a flask and admitted air, the broth became alive with organisms or if he tilted an unbroken flask so that the medium picked up some of the dust in the neck, the same thing happened.

There remained, however, the successful and unexplained experiments of Pouchet. Before a large audience, Pasteur threw a powerful beam of light onto the mercury in Pouchet's apparatus and disclosed a film of dust on the mercury. It was easy to see that Pouchet had pushed some of the dust (and also bacteria) into his sterile flasks along with the hay. That was his error! However, even without this, Pouchet's flasks might have developed life. Pouchet had used an alkaline (basic) medium and hay. An alkaline medium is very favorable to bacterial growth and the hay, no doubt, contained spore-forming bacteria. This type is able to produce a very thick wall about itself and resist unfavorable conditions. The boiling to which they were subjected by Pouchet was not enough to kill them in the spore form, and after the flasks cooled, they germinated in the favorable alkaline medium. No wonder Pouchet thought he had a good case of spontaneous generation. Pasteur, on the other hand, used an acid medium and, luckily enough, there were no spore-formers in his flasks. (Spallanzani also had been lucky in regard to spore-formers.) No wonder Pasteur thought he had disproved spontaneous generation. Today we know that if we wish to inhibit spoilage in milk, an alkaline fluid favorable to bacterial growth, we have to heat it to 62 degrees centigrade for thirty minutes.

Thus we see that although Pasteur's discovery was both glorious and simple, it was built up from the knowledge gained by a great many other earnest workers, plus a certain amount of "luck."

We must now describe the decisive experiment on this subject, devised by the brilliant John Tyndall of England and reported upon in 1876, twelve years after Pasteur's researches. Pasteur's experiments had been good but were rather simple in nature; Tyndall's experiments were sophisticated and his results conclusive.

Tyndall decided to combine his knowledge of optically pure air with an experiment on spontaneous generation. His apparatus was in the form of a box. This box had four legs attached to it. The front of the box had a large glass window and each of the two sides had a small glass window. The back had an air-tight door. The bottom of the box had holes in it through which Tyndall inserted test tubes in such a manner as to exclude any air. On top of the box he inserted some coiled glass tubes through which air, but no dust, could enter. Another hole in the top held a thistle tube. Tyndall now applied a sticky material to the inside of the box to hold the dust particles securely once they had settled.

He then directed a beam of light through one of the small side windows, through the box, and out the other side. By looking through the front window, Tyndall noted the light beam in the box as long as there were dust particles present; when none were in the air, the beam became invisible.

At this point, Tyndall inserted the thistle tube in the top and filled the test tubes with various kinds of broth. Then the apparatus was moved so that the tubes could be boiled (by immersion in boiling oil). This procedure was to kill any organisms in the broth so that it would be "lifeless."

Tyndall found that the tubes of broth remained sterile. Some objected that the boiling had rendered the broth unfit to support life so Tyndall, taking a cue from the researches of Pasteur and others, opened the door in the back of the box for a short time. This exposure allowed some dust (with the adhering germs) to enter. The tubes spoiled in a few days. Boiling had not destroyed the "vegetable force" in the broth.

This clever experiment and the work of Pasteur, plus that of others, gave mankind a real understanding of the distribution and means of control of bacteria.

The long trail which led to Pasteur and Tyndall stopped only momentarily. It continued on to Robert Koch, the discoverer of the cause of tuberculosis; to Schaudinn, the discoverer of the syphilis organism, and to dozens of others. It will continue on for a long, long time. There is still much to be learned, there are still diseases to be understood and conquered.

In 1935, a chemist by the name of W. M. Stanley opened up an entirely new field of speculation about the nature of life and its origin by crystallizing substances formerly thought to be living. These substances are known as viruses. Stanley worked with a virus causing a disease of tobacco plants called tobacco mosaic.

Now, as is well-known, living organisms do not enter a crystal stage; this is a property of non-living matter. If the virus is really non-living, then this would be the first instance of a non-living particle causing an infectious disease like tobacco mosaic.

Stanley and his co-workers pursued the matter and eventually found another amazing aspect of viruses. The viruses were very large protein molecules and had the property of reproducing themselves. Here, then, we had a characteristic of living things. Were these viruses the "missing link" between the living and the dead? Were they generated spontaneously from inorganic matter? Was Pasteur's work all for naught?

Some scientists, impressed by the simplicity and ultramicroscopic nature of the viruses, cried out that here were the primeval forms of life. The boundary between the living and the non-living had been bridged. More cautious men pointed to the fact that the viruses were obligate parasites, depending upon living organisms for their perpetuation. This fact probably removes the viruses quite far from primitiveness.

Over thirty years have passed since Stanley's monumental work and we are not now sure as to the exact nature of viruses. We can not be sure that they are not spontaneously generated. Redi, Spallanzani, and Pasteur did not prove that the theory of spontaneous generation is false. They proved, however, that certain organisms did not arise from inorganic matter under the conditions of their experiments. To say that spontaneous generation never occurred or never will occur is a universal negative and cannot be proven. Real scientists have ever been cautious about being too dogmatic. They remember too well how countless popular theories, seemingly backed by irrefutable proof, have been overthrown during the long history of science. Two quotations might be brought to bear upon this point:

> Scientific research does not lead to a knowledge of nature which is free of error but it is an unending process in which the degree of truth is always increasing. We uncover errors in existing theories, we discover more and more things of significance, but the goal of absolute truth keeps on receding.*

> In no case does science tell us why natural phenomena occur in order—every scientific explanation rests upon something which is granted. The discovery that nature is orderly can throw no light on the origin of anything in nature.— Order is not an explanation of anything but something that itself calls for explanation.†

Those who couple the question of the origin of life with the theory of evolution have a feeling that because we have never witnessed an example of life arising from the inorganic world during several centuries of investigations, it has never occurred. However, they still feel that in the prehistoric past, when conditions upon the earth were different and more favorable for such an event, the first particle, endowed with at least some of the properties of life, arose.

Thus we have the extremely anomalous situation existing in which scientists believe in a physiochemical origin of life on the one hand and conduct experiments proving its unlikelihood on the other hand.

We have finished with our story of spontaneous generation and have noted the long, sometimes bitter, struggle that attended the "defeat" of the theory. We have seen that the pure speculation of Aristotle was replaced by the modern science of experimentation. This experimentation, carried on rather simply by Redi, culminated in the brilliant researches of Pasteur and Tyndall. It is to the credit of scientists that they tested one another's theories, that their experiments, if sometimes faulty, were honestly done, and that they constantly strove to discern the phantom light of ultimate truth.

*David Bohm, *Casuality and Chance in Modern Physics* (Princeton, N. J.: D. Van Nostrand Co., Inc., 1956).

†W. Keith Brooks, The Foundations of Zoology (New York: Lemcke, 1907).

X
Evolution

53

Man and Natural Selection

Theodosius Dobzhansky

MAN'S EVOLUTIONARY UNIQUENESS

By changing what man knows about the world, he changes the world he knows; and by changing the world in which he lives, he changes himself. Herein lies a danger and a hope; a danger because random changes of the biological nature are likely to produce deterioration rather than improvement; a hope because changes resulting from knowledge can also be directed by knowledge.

The human species, *Homo sapiens,* mankind, is the unique and most successful product of biological evolution, so far. This has sometimes been questioned, I suspect without too much conviction on the part of the doubters, perhaps only to mock man's pretensions or to challenge his values. But man *is* the most successful product of evolution, by any reasonable definition of biological success. Man began his career as a rare animal, living somewhere in the tropics or subtropics of the Old World, probably in Africa. From this obscure beginning, mankind multiplied to become one of the most numerous mammals, for there will soon be about three billion men living. Numbers may not be an unadulterated blessing, but they are one of the measures of biological success of a species.

Moreover, man has spread and occupied all the continents and most islands, except for the frozen wastes of Antarctica and of the interior of Greenland; he has learned to traverse seas and oceans and deserts; he is well on the way towards control or elimination of the predators and parasites which used to prey on him; he has subdued and domesticated many animal and plant species, made them serve his needs and his fancies, broadened enormously the range of utilizable food supplies, and learned to make use of a variety of energy sources. Modern man lives no longer

This article originally appeared in *American Scientist,* Vol. 49 (1961), pp. 285-299. Reprinted by permission.

at the mercy of wild beasts and vagaries of the climate; he has reached a status where his continuation as a species is in no danger, except perhaps as a result of man's own folly or of a cosmic accident.

The evolutionary uniqueness of man lies in that in mankind the biological evolution has transcended itself. With man commences a new, superorganic, mode of evolution, which is the evolution of culture. Culture is a tremendously potent instrument for adaptation to the environment. A very large part of the evolutionary progress, both biologically and culturally, has come from adversity. Life faces environments which are more often niggardly than bountiful, more frequently inimical than benign. For life to endure, it must develop defences and adaptations. Biological adaptation occurs through natural selection; new genes arise through mutation, sexual recombination creates new combinations of genes, and natural selection acts to multiply the successful genetic endowments and to reduce the frequencies of the unsuccessful ones. In man and in man alone, adaptation may occur also through alteration of culture. Many species of mammals have become adapted to cold climates by growing warm fur; man alone has achieved the same end by donning fur coats. Birds have mastered the air by becoming flying machines; man has conquered the air by building flying machines.

Biological and cultural evolutions of man are not independent; they are interdependent. The superorganic has an organic basis. Formation and maintenance of culture presuppose a human genotype. Even the most clever ape cannot learn human culture. Some writers have jumped to the conclusion that the genetic development of the human species was completed before culture appeared, and that the evolution of culture has replaced biological evolution. This is not true. The two evolutions go together, interacting and usually mutually reinforcing each other. There is feedback between genetics and culture. Culture is an adaptive mechanism supplemental to, but not incompatible with, biological adaptation. To be sure, adaptation by culture proved to be more efficacious, and, before all else, more rapid than adaptation by genes. This is why the emergence of the genetic basis of culture was the master stroke of the biological evolution of the human species. The genetic basis of culture should be improved or at least maintained. It should not be allowed to deteriorate.

NATURAL SELECTION, STRUGGLE, AND FITNESS

Man has not only evolved; for better or for worse, he is also evolving. Is he to become a superman or a demigod? Or will the fate in store for him be like that of so many successful species of the past, which eventually declined and became extinct? Long-term prophecies do not expose the prophets to the risk of being proved wrong too soon. I nevertheless do not wish to indulge here in prophecies or in designing utopias. I wish rather to investigate some of the evolutionary forces currently at work in the human species.

According to the theory set forth by Darwin and Wallace more than a century ago, adaptation occurs in biological evolution by way of the process of natural selection. Does natural selection operate in modern mankind? This has to be answered obviously in the negative, if by "natural" you mean a world uninhabited and uninfluenced by man. But it is here that we must proceed with the greatest caution. What, indeed, is selection, and when is a selection "natural" and when is it not? Darwin said that natural selection is the outcome of the survival of the fittest in the struggle for life. "Struggle" suggests strife, contention, competition. Darwin himself wrote that ". . . from the war of nature, from famine and death, the most exalted object we are capable of conceiving, the higher animal, directly follows."

However, natural selection does not ineluctably depend on any of these things. Birch has defined competition thus: "Competition occurs when a number of animals (of the same or different species) utilize common resources the supply of which is short; or if the resources are not in short supply, competition occurs when the animals seeking these resources nevertheless harm each other in the process." Natural selection may, however, take place when resources are not limiting, if the carriers of some genes possess greater reproductive potentials than others. Some cases have been observed in experiments with animals and plants when a genotype superior under competition is inferior in the absence of competition, or vice versa.

And who is the "fittest," whose survival results in natural selection? Does natural selection make us fit for life in the society of other men, or for wisdom, or for good will, or for unselfishness? It does not necessarily ordain any of these qualities. Darwinian fitness is a measure of the reproductive proficiency. Its guiding principle is "be fruitful, and multiply, and replenish the earth." It is quite indispensable to distinguish Darwinian fitness from excellence in human estimation. The two may go hand in hand, but sometimes they may be in opposition.

It is man and man alone who can probe, scrutinize, and question the wisdom of the evolutionary process which brought him into being. He may improve what nature hath wrought. When man chooses the individuals who are to become parents of the succeeding generation he practices artificial selection. According to Lerner, artificial selection is a process which has a goal that can be visualized. Any selection which is not artificial is natural selection.

MUTATION AND THE NORMALIZING
NATURAL SELECTION

There are several forms of natural selection operating in the human species, as well as in other organisms. Although the distinctions between these forms of selection are neither absolutely rigid nor always clear-cut, they are helpful for straight thinking about evolutionary problems. Stabilizing or normalizing natural selection is the simplest and most obvious. It is a conservative force; it counteracts the spread in populations of detrimental mutants, hereditary diseases, and weaknesses of various kinds. Failure, or at least relaxation, of the normalizing selection in human populations leads to fears that an insidious process of genetic decay is at work in the human species. Is there a basis for these fears?

Mutations continue to arise in man, even as they have been arising since the dawn of life. Some mutants cause grave and even fatal hereditary diseases, such as retinoblastoma, hemophilia, epiloia, etc. Others cause malformations, such as achondroplasia, arachnodactyly, or brachydactyly. Still others, and probably a majority of mutants, cause small and unspectacular changes in the appearance of physiology or behavior of their carriers. Small mutations are difficult to study quantitatively. Not enough is known about them, even in Drosophila and in other organisms more favorable for experimentation than man. Large mutations are certainly more often deleterious than useful, at least in the environments in which the species normally lives, and at least in homozygous condition. A useful major mutant is like a needle in a haystack; it may be there but it is notoriously hard to find among the many harmful ones. It is tempting to suppose that all or most small mutations will also be harmful, in various small and devious ways. This is what geneticists who are adherents of the "classical" hypothesis of the population structure believe to be the case. The evidence on which this belief rests is not fully convincing (see below).

A brief consideration of some examples of the operation of the normalizing selection in man will be useful at this point. Achondroplasia or chondrodystrophy are formidable names for a rather common type of dwarfism in man, caused by the presence of a single dominant mutant gene. Achondroplasts have bodies and heads of about normal size, but their limbs are very short. Some achondroplastic dwarfs are born in families in which at least one of the parents is a dwarf. Such dwarfs evidently inherit the genes for the abnormality from the affected parents. But some dwarfs are children of parents of normal stature; these dwarfs carry the dominant gene for dwarfism newly arisen by mutation. Mørch has recorded the birth of eight dwarf mutants among about 94 thousand children in Denmark; this indicates that about one sex-cell per 24,000 sex cells produced by normal parents transports a newly arisen gene for achondroplastic dwarfism, a mutation rate of the order of 4×10^{-5} per generation.

The genes for achondroplastic dwarfism newly arisen by mutation are introduced into the gene pool of human populations; this happens relentlessly in every generation. Does it follow that the dwarfism will grow more and more widespread in the course of time? Not necessarily. The spread of the genes for dwarfism is opposed by natural selection. Mørch found that the achondroplastic dwarfs in Denmark produce only about twenty per cent as many children as do their nondwarf brothers and sisters. This means that the adaptive value, or the Darwinian fitness, of the achondroplastic dwarfs is only 0.2 normal; it can also be said that the gene for the dwarfism is opposed by a normalizing natural selection of a magnitude of 0.8.

How does natural selection operate on this gene? Why do the dwarfs produce so few children? It turns out that this is chiefly because many of them remain unmarried. And their failure to find mates is not due to a weakened sexual drive but to their external appearance being not in accord with what is regarded in our society as handsomeness or attractiveness. Here, then, is an example of a natural selective process which operates not by causing early death of the carriers of certain genes, but acting instead via certain culturally conditioned forms of human behavior. A person who remains childless may be described as genetically "dead"; but childlessness is a form of "genetic death" which does not immediately produce a cadaver.

Some mutant genes are, to be sure, eliminated by a normalizing selection acting through "genetic death" which is also real death. Retinoblastoma is a form of cancer of the eye, which afflicts infants and children; unless the eyes are removed promptly by a surgical operation early death is inevitable. Neel and Falls found the mutation from the normal to the dominant mutant gene causing retinoblastoma to be about as frequent as that causing the achondroplastic dwarfism (see above). Before the invention of surgery which saves the lives of retinoblastomatic children, the normalizing selection was eliminating in every generation all the mutant genes for retinoblastoma which arose in that generation (i.e., in the sex-cells which gave rise to that generation). The surgery may be said to frustrate this normalizing selection; the retinoblastomatics, though blind, grow up and become capable of being parents of children one-half of whom will now inherit the gene for retinoblastoma. The retinoblastomatics, like the achondroplasts, are now of two kinds—those due to new mutations and those having inherited the gene from their parents.

Genes which reduce the Darwinian fitness of their carriers less dramatically than do the genes discussed above are nevertheless also opposed by normalizing selection. Predisposition to diabetes mellitus, or at least to some of its forms, seems to be inherited through a recessive gene. The same seems to be true of some forms of myopia (short-sightedness). We do not know either the mutation rates which produce these genes, nor the selection rates which oppose their spread. What is of interest for our purposes is that these selection rates doubtless vary greatly depending on the environment. Myopia is likely to be more incapacitating to people engaged in some occupations (i.e., hunters or automobile drivers) than in others (i.e., handicraftsmen or clerks), and besides myopia can be "cured" by wearing glasses. The onset of diabetes mellitus may be early or late in life; it may thus strike after the close of the reproductive age, and thus fail to reduce the number of the children produced and hence to reduce the Darwinian fitness. And some forms of diabetes may be "cured" by insulin therapy.

Now, to "cure" a hereditary disease obviously does not mean to change the genes which have caused it. Health and disease refer however to the states of well-being or infirmity of a person; a person consulting his doctor does not ask the latter to alter his genes, but only to advise how to change the environment in a way such that the genes with which the person has been born will react by producing a reasonable state of well-being. A myopic wearing glasses, or a diabetic having received his insulin injections, is no longer incapacitated, or at least less so than both were before the "cure." The relief of the incapacitation may however increase their Darwinian fitness, and mitigate the severity of the normalizing natural selection.

THE "NORMAL" MAN

The removal of a mutant from a population is called a genetic death or, less dramatically, genetic elimination. The death of a child with retinoblastoma eliminates from the population one mutant retinoblastomatic gene. When an achondroplastic dwarf fails to marry, or raises a family with fewer children than he would have if he were not a dwarf, a mutant gene for achondroplasia is eliminated. The classical hypothesis of population structure assumes that there exists for every biological species, or may appear or be produced in the future, one normal, or best, optimal genetic endowment. This genetic endowment would give the ideal, the normal, the archetypical man, or the ideal Drosophila fly, or the ideal corn plant—the man, the Drosophila, the corn as they ought to be. The way to produce this normal man is to let the normalizing natural selection remove, eliminate, purge from the population all the mutant genes. What then would remain would be the ideal constellation of genes.

This hypothesis has the advantages of simplicity, though not necessarily of accuracy. It is a product of typological thinking, which has, to be sure venerable antecedents. It goes back to Plato's eternal ideal types. Many scientists find the appeal of the typological mode of thought irresistible. Indeed, if the classical hypothesis were justified, the problem of the guidance of the biological evolution of the human species would be theoretically simple, however difficult it might still remain in practice. We would have to arrange for the normalizing natural selection to protect the ideal normal human genes from contamination by mutations. Or, to put it in positive rather than negative terms, we might strive to obtain a mankind in which everybody would be a carrier of the normal genetic endowment. The three billion humans, or whatever numbers this "normal" mankind might contain, would then be as similar genetically as identical twins. But they would presumably be strong and healthy and happy identical multitudes!

DIVERSIFYING NATURAL SELECTION

Fortunately or unfortunately, depending upon one's point of view, the classical hypothesis of population structure is perhaps only a half-truth. That it is true to some extent is clear enough. Harmful mutants do arise, and some of them seem to be unconditionally harmful. It is hard to imagine an environment in which retinoblastoma could possibly be harmless, not to speak of usefulness. Accumulation of such mutants in human populations can only augment human misery. To counteract this accumulation, one could, conceivably, reduce the mutation frequencies, or else eliminate the mutants as painlessly as possible. Unfortunately, for the time being, man has learned how to increase the mutability by exposure to high-energy radiations and by other means, but not how to decrease the mutation rates.

The concept of a single genetic endowment, ideal or optimal for each living species, is however a typological fiction. No living individual, and certainly no population and no species, exist in absolutely uniform environments. Environments vary in time and in space. How does life solve the problem of adaptation to a multiplicity of environments? There are two possible solutions, and, with its habitual opportunism, evolution has used them both. The first is the genetically-conditioned physiological and developmental plasticity. The organism reacts to changes in the environment by adaptive modifications. For example, the human body has physiological mechanisms which enable it to conserve an almost constant internal temperature despite external temperature variations. In man, the most important kind of plasticity is his educability. Most humans can be trained for, and can acquire skills to perform passably in, any one of the many employments which most human societies have to offer.

Secondly, a population facing a diversity of environments may become genetically diversified. Natural selection favors different genetic endowments in different environments. This is the diversifying (also called disruptive) form of natural selection. Instead of one perfect genotype, diversifying selection favors many genotypes; it favors genetic polymorphism. A population which abounds in genetic variety has a better grip on a complex environment than a genetically uniform population; polymorphism is one way of exploiting the environment more fully.

DIVERSITY AND EQUALITY

Adaptations by way of plasticity and by way of genetic diversity are not mutually exclusive. They are complementary. Culture is by far the most potent adaptive mechanism which has emerged in the evolution of life. Its potency is due to its being transmitted by teaching and learning, instead of by genes. The ability to be trained, and to become competent in whatever occupation a person meets his opportunity, increases the social and usually also the biological fitness. Genetic specialization for one vocation may confer very high fitness for that particular vocation. But educability permits a choice of vocations, and thus confers fitness in complex and changeable environments. In an evolving culture new occupations constantly arise. Who needed aircraft pilots a century ago, but how many blacksmiths are now needed in technologically advanced countries?

Culture is, however, an adaptive contrivance to make people diversified, not to make them alike. If uniformity were advantageous, genetic fixity would most likely have emerged in evolution. Genetic diversity or polymorphism joins force with developmental plasticity. I could have probably learned many kinds of jobs other than that I actually fixed upon. But no amount of effort and training could make me a first-rate wrestler or sprinter or painter or concertmaster. I just do not possess the genetic wherewithal for these occupations. Other people do, and this genetic diversity enriches the store of man's capabilities. It is the leaven of cultural progress.

The facts of biology are compatible with the lofty vision of human equality. All men have been born equal; they certainly are not all alike. It is nonsense to think that only identical twins can be equals. Human equality is not predicated on identity, or even on identity of ability. It presupposes, however, something approaching an equality of opportunity to develop whatever socially useful gifts and aptitudes a person's genes have provided him with, and which he may choose to develop.

Culture fosters a multitude of employments and functions to be filled and served; equality of opportunity stimulates division of labor rather than sets it aside; it enables every person to choose among occupations for which he is qualified by his abilities. It is wrong to think that equality of opportunity makes genetic variation unimportant. It does precisely the opposite. It makes the difference between people reflect meaningfully their genetic differences. Inequality of opportunity acts, on the contrary, to hide, to distort, and to stultify the genetic diversity.

BALANCING NATURAL SELECTION

Far from being an unfortunate deviation from the ideal state, genetic diversity is an adaptive response of life to its environment. A gene useful in one environment may cause a genetic disease in another; a mutant harmful in combination with some genes may be useful in other combinations. Some adaptively ambivalent genes increase the fitness of their carriers when in single dose, in heterozygous state, but are harmful, or even lethal in homozygotes.

The sickle-cell anemia and the Mediterranean anemia, or thalassemia, are the best known human examples. These almost invariably fatal diseases are due to homozygosis for genes which in heterozygous condition seem to confer a relative immunity to certain kinds of malarial fevers. Heterozygous carriers consequently enjoy a superior fitness, hybrid vigor, or heterosis, in countries where these particular forms of malaria are prevalent. The genes for sickle-cells and for thalassemia are common in tropical and subtropical parts of the Old World, and they have been introduced in the New World as well.

Natural selection holds the "normal" and the sickle-cell and thalassemia genes in balanced polymorphism in populations of malarial countries. This is the balancing form of natural selection. How important is balancing selection in the human species is an open issue. It may well be that many of the genes responsible for the individual differences which we observe among so-called "normal" persons, differences in facial features, body build, health, intelligence, longevity, etc., are kept in balanced polymorphism. Morton and Chung have presented evidence that the genes for the M and N blood types are maintained by balancing selection. The heterozygotes MN have a Darwinian fitness superior to MM and NN homozygotes. Just what is the advantage of the heterozygous state is unknown, nor is the nature of the drawback in homozygotes. The homozygotes are certainly viable; I am one of them. A very slight superiority in fitness in heterozygotes is, however, sufficient to maintain a balanced polymorphism.

There are grounds to suspect that the O-A-B blood types in man are also held in balanced polymorphism. The evidence for this is at present inconclusive, but recent works of Levene, Rosenfield, Morton, Crow, and others show that the genes involved are subject to a still different kind of selective pressure. This is a relative incompatability between the mother and the fetus when they differ in genetic constitution in certain ways. Such incompatibility has been known to arise because of the genes for a still different system of blood types, the Rhesus, or Rh system. An Rh positive fetus in an Rh negative mother may suffer injury or even be aborted.

DIRECTIONAL NATURAL SELECTION

The form of natural selection most important in the long run is directional selection. It was pivotal in Darwin's theory of evolution. Living species may respond to challenges of their environments by genetic changes. Genes once useful become inferior to others and are gradually eliminated, replaced by superior gene variants. The whole genetic system of the species is eventually rebuilt.

There is a fairly general agreement among biologists that the emergence of the human species was due in the main to directional selection. It has, however, been questioned whether directional selection, or indeed any form of natural selection, has continued to operate after the genetic basis of culture has taken shape. Now, let us admit that the success of mankind as a biological species was due precisely to man's culture being able to change ever so much faster than his genes can. Man adapts his environments to his genes more often than he adapts his genes to his environments. But, as pointed out, the two methods of adaptation are complementary and not alternative. Far from making human environments stable and uniform, culture increases the tempo of change. Given an environmental flux, the necessary and sufficient condition for genetic change is availability in the populations of genetic variants, some of which are better and others less well adapted to shifting environments. Natural selection will multiply the favorable and depress or eliminate the unfavorable variants.

We do not know exactly how much genetic change has taken place in mankind at different stages of its history. Modern man might or might not be able to survive, even if properly trained, in the environments of his ancestors of 100,000, or even 10,000 years ago. Or, if he survived, he might not be as efficient or as happy in those environments as his ancestors were. We do not know for sure. Neanderthal man may or may not have been capable of becoming a reasonably well adjusted citizen if raised in New York or in New Orleans. Perhaps some Neanderthals might have been fit to become Ph.D.'s and to be elected members of the Society of Sigma Xi. But, on the other hand, they may have been unfit for any now existing education. Modern women are alleged to experience greater difficulties in childbirth than did their great-grandmothers. All this is conjectural and not rigorously proved. It is, however, a fallacy to assert that what is unproved did not occur. In point of fact, some of the above changes probably did occur.

ARE CULTURE AND NATURAL SELECTION COMPATIBLE?

We have seen that several forms of natural selection operate in modern mankind. But they certainly do not operate as they did during the Stone Age, or even as they did a century ago. Neither does natural selection operate always in the same way in wild and "natural" species, quite "unspoiled" by culture. This is inevitable. Natural selection depends on environments, and environments change. Human environments have changed a great deal in a century, not to speak of millennia.

The real problem is not whether natural selection in man is going on, but whether it is going on towards what we, humans, regard as betterment or deterioration. Natural selection tends to enhance the reproductive proficiency of the population in which it operates. Such proficiency is however not the only estimable quality with which we wish to see people endowed. And besides, a high reproductive fitness in one environment does not even insure the survival of the population or the species when the environment changes.

Normalizing selection is, as we have seen, not the only form of natural selection. The relaxation of some of its functions is, however, a cause of apprehension. Medicine, hygiene, civilized living save many lives which would otherwise be extinguished. This situation is here to stay; we would not want it to be otherwise, even if we could. Some of the lives thus saved will, however, engender lives that will stand in need of being saved in the generations to come. Can it be that we help the ailing, the lame, and the deformed only to make our descendants more ailing, more lame, and more deformed?

Suppose that we have learned how to save the lives of persons afflicted with a hereditary disease, such as retinoblastoma, which previously was incurably fatal. In genetic terms, this means that the Darwinian fitness of the victims of the disease has increased, and that the normalizing selection against this disease is relaxed. What will be the consequence? The incidence of the disease in the population will increase from generation to generation. The increase is likely to be slow, generally no more than by one mutation rate per generation. It may take centuries or millennia to notice the difference for any one disease or malformation. However, the average health and welfare of the population are liable to show adverse effects of relaxed selection much sooner.

The process of mutation injects in every generation a certain number of harmful genes in the gene pool of the population; the process of normalizing selection eliminates a certain number of these genes. With environment reasonably stable, the situation tends to reach a state of equilibrium. At equilibrium, the mutation and the elimination are equal. If mutation becomes more frequent (as it does in man because of exposure to high-energy radiations and perhaps to some chemicals), or if the elimination is lagging because of relaxation of normalizing selection, the incidence of harmful mutant genes in the population is bound to increase. And take note of this: If the classical theory of population structure were correct, all harmful mutations would be in a sense equivalent. For at equilibrium there is one elimination for every mutation, regardless of whether the mutation causes a lethal hereditary disease like retinoblastoma, or a malformation like achondroplasia, or a relatively mild defect such as myopia.

The problem is, however, more complex than this theory would suggest. It calls for research in what Wright describes neatly as "unfortunately the unpopular and scientifically somewhat unrewarding borderline fields of genetics and the social sciences." Although at equilibrium there may be one genetic elimination for every mutation, it is unrealistic to equate the human and social consequences of different mutations. The elimination of a lethal mutant which causes death of an embryo before implantation in the uterus is scarcely noticed by the mother or by anyone else. Suffering accompanies the elimination of a mutant, such as retinoblastoma, which kills an infant apparently normal at birth. Many mutants, such as hemophilia or Huntington's chorea, kill children, adolescents, or adults, cause misery to their victims, and disruption of the lives of their families. There is no way to measure precisely the amount of human anguish; yet one may surmise that the painful and slow death of the victims of so many hereditary diseases is torment greater than that involved in the elimination of a gene for anchondroplasia owing to the failure of an achondroplastic dwarf to beget children.

Looked at from the angle of the costs to the society, the nonequivalence of different mutants is no less evident. Myopia may be inherited as a recessive trait. Increases of the frequencies in populations of the gene for myopia are undesirable. Yet, it may become more and more common in future generations. However, only a fanatic might advocate sterilization of the myopics or other radical measures to prevent the spread of this gene. One may hope that civilized societies can tolerate some more myopics; many of them are very useful citizens, and their defect can rather easily be corrected by a relatively inexpensive environmental change—wearing glasses. The effort needed to eradicate or to reduce the frequency of myopia genetically would exceed that requisite to rectify their defect environmentally, by manufacturing more pairs of glasses.

Diabetes mellitus is, given the present level of medicine, more difficult and expensive to correct than is myopia. Some diabetics may nevertheless be treated successfully by insulin therapy, helped to live to old age, and enabled to raise families as large as nondiabetics. The incidence of diabetes may therefore creep up slowly in the generations to come. Now, most people would probably agree that it is better to be free of diabetes than to have it under control, no matter how successfully, by insulin therapy or other means. The prospect is not a pleasant one to contemplate. Insulin injections may perhaps be almost as common in some remote future as taking aspirin tablets is at present.

TOWARDS GUIDANCE OF HUMAN EVOLUTION

Are we, then, faced with a dilemma—if we enable the weak and the deformed to live and to propagate their kinds, we face the prospect of a genetic twilight; but if we let them die or suffer when we can save them we face the certainty of a moral twilight. How to escape this dilemma?

I can well understand the impatience which some of my readers may feel if I refuse to provide an unambiguous answer to so pressing a problem: Let me however plead with you that infatuation with over-simple answers to very complex and difficult problems is one of the earmarks of intellectual mediocrity. I am afraid that the problem of guidance of human evolution has no simple solution. At least I have not found one, nor has anybody else in my opinion. Each genetic condition will have to be considered on its own merits, and the solution which may be adopted for different conditions will probably be different. Suppose that everybody agrees that the genes causing myopia, achondroplasia, diabetes and retinoblastoma are undesirable. We shall nevertheless be forced to treat them differently. Some genetic defects will have to be put up with and managed environmentally; others will have to be treated genetically, by artificial selection, and the eugenic measures that may be needed can be effected without accepting any kind of biological Brave New World.

Let us face this fact: Our lives depend on civilization and technology, and the lives of our descendants will be even more dependent on civilized environments. I can imagine a wise old ape-man who deplored the softness of his contemporaries using stone knives to carve their meat instead of doing this with their teeth; or a solid conservative Peking man viewing with alarm the new fangled habit of using fire to make oneself warm. I have yet to hear anyone seriously proposing that we give up the use of knives and of fire now. Nor does anyone in his right mind urge that we let people die of smallpox or tuberculosis, in order that genetic resistance to these diseases be maintained. The remedy for our genetic dependence on technology and medicine is more, not less, technology and medicine. You may, if you wish, feel nostalgic for the good old days of our cave-dwelling ancestors; the point of no return was passed in the evolution of our species many millenia before anyone could know what was happening.

Of course, not all genetic defects can be corrected by tools or remedies or medicines. Even though new and better tools and medicines will, one may hope, be invented in the future, this will not make all genetic equipments equally desirable. It is a relatively simple matter to correct for lack of genetic resistance to smallpox by vaccination, or for myopia by suitable glasses. It is not so simple with many other genetic defects. Surgical removal of the eyes is called for in cases of retinoblastoma; this saves the lives of the victims, but leaves them blind. No remedies are known for countless other genetic defects. Human life is sacred; yet the social costs of some genetic variants are so great, and their social contributions are so small, that avoidance of their birth is ethically the most acceptable as well as the wisest solution. This does not necessarily call for enactment of Draconian eugenic laws; it is perhaps not over-optimistic to hope that spreading biological education and understanding may be a real help. Make persons whose progeny is likely to inherit a serious genetic defect aware of this fact; they may draw the conclusions themselves.

The strides accomplished by biochemical genetics in recent years have led some biologists to hope that methods will soon be discovered to induce specific changes in human genes of our choice. This would, indeed, be a radical solution of the problem of management of the evolution of our species, and of other species as well. We would simply change the genes which we do not like, in ways conforming to our desires. Now, if the history of science has any lesson to teach us, it is the unwisdom of declaring certain goals to be unattainable. The cavalier way in which the progress of science often treats such predictions should instill due humility even in the most doctrinaire prophets. The best that can be said about the possibility of changing specific genes in man in accordance with our desires is that, although such an invention would be a great boon, it is not within reach yet. And it cannot be assumed to be achievable.

Let us also not exaggerate the urgency of the problem of the genetic management of the evolution of our species. Another problem, that of the runaway overpopulation of our planet, is far more immediate and critical. If mankind will prove unable to save itself from being choked by crowding it hardly needs to worry about its genetic quality. Although the problems of numbers and of quality are not one and the same, yet they may be closely connected in practice. As steps towards regulation of the population size will begin to be taken, and this surely cannot be postponed for much longer, the genetic problem will inexorably obtrude itself before people's attention. The questions "how many people" and "what kind of people" will be solved together, if they will be solved at all.

Some people believe that all would be well with mankind, if only natural selection were permitted to operate without obstruction by medicine and technology. Let us not forget, however, that countless biological species of the past have become extinct, despite their evolution having been directed by natural selection unadulterated by culture. What we want is not simply natural selection, but selection, natural and artificial, directed towards humanly desirable goals. What are these goals? This is the central problem of human ethics and of human evolution. Darwinian fitness is no guide here. If, in some human society, genetically duller people produce more progeny than the brighter ones, this simply means that, in the environment of that particular society, being a bit thick-headed increases the Darwinian fitness, and being too intelligent decreases it. Natural selection will act accordingly, and will not be any less "natural" on that account.

Human cultural evolution has resulted in the formation of a system of values, of *human* values. These are the values to which we wish human evolution to conform. These values are products of cultural evolution, conditioned of course by the biological evolution, yet not deducible from the latter. Where do we find a criterion by which these values are to be judged? I know of no better one than that proposed by the ancient Chinese sage: "Every system of moral laws must be based upon man's own consciousness, verified by the common experience of mankind, tested by due sanction of historical experience and found without error, applied to the operations and processes of nature in the physical universe and found to be without contradiction, laid before the gods without question or fear, and able to wait a hundred generations and have it confirmed without a doubt by a Sage of posterity."

54

The Two-Million-Year-Old Man

Discovery in East Africa of an entirely new species of primitive human being believed to be the direct ancestor of modern man was announced by Dr. Louis S. B. Leakey.

The British anthropologist and two other scientists who have studied the fossil remains have given the name *Homo habilis* to the new species within man's genus. The name means "able" or "having ability."

Homo habilis was smaller than a present-day pygmy, though manlike in most of his known characteristics. He first appeared nearly two million years ago in what is now Olduvai Gorge, Tanganyika.

Dr. Leakey and his wife Mary have found fossil parts of five individuals, including a young woman and child. The species was not alone. Existing at the same time in prehistoric East Africa were much more primitive types of Hominidae, the family of mammals to which man and his ancestors belong.

FIRST PUBLIC ANNOUNCEMENTS

The dramatic discoveries were announced publicly for the first time here by Dr. Leakey at a press conference at the National Geographic Society, which supports his work.

Simultaneously, formal announcement was made in London in a scientific paper published in the April 4 issue of the British journal Nature. The authors were Dr. Leakey; Professor Phillip V. Tobias, of the Medical School of the University of Witswatersrand, Johannesburg; and Dr. John R. Napier, of London University's Royal Free Hospital Medical School.

Fossil bones of the five *Homo habilis* specimens were found over a period of four years in different deposits at Olduvai representing a geological time span estimated to cover more than a million years. Announce-

From "Dr. Leakey Announces Discovery of New Species of Human Being Almost Two Million Years Old," *National Geographic Society* Press Release (April 3, 1964). Reprinted by permission.

ment was withheld pending evaluation by the Leakeys and scrutiny of the actual material by other scientists.

Professor Tobias went to East Africa to study the fossils with Dr. Leakey in his laboratory at Nairobi, Kenya. Dr. Napier made a study of skeletal material in London.

American anthropologists to whom Dr. Leakey has shown casts of specimens include Dr. T. Dale Stewart, Smithsonian Institution; Dr. William Straus, Jr., of Johns Hopkins University; Dr. W. W. Howells, Harvard University; and Dr. Clark Howell, Chicago University.

JAVA MAN FOUND IN 1891

The discovery of *Homo habilis* may profoundly change present concepts of physical anthropology, the science that took a long leap forward in 1891 when Dubois found the skullcap of *Pithecanthropus erectus* (erect ape-man) in a Java stream bed.

In time, so-called Java Man (*c.* 500,000 years ago) and his close relative, Peking Man (*c.* 400,000 years ago), came to be regarded as very important landmarks in the search for early man—and not as primitive as originally thought. Lately they have been referred to as *Homo erectus*.

"It now seems likely that the species of present-day man, *Homo sapiens*, is more likely to have evolved in Africa from *Homo habilis* than from some of the other hominids of the Pithecanthropine type in the Far East," Dr. Leakey says.

This theory would take man's story very deeply into the prehistoric past. *Homo habilis* was living in Olduvai Gorge before, alongside, and after another type of hominid, *Zinjanthropus*, whose fossil bones were found by the Leakeys in 1959 sealed in by volcanic ash dated by the potassium-argon method as 1,750,000 years old.

Both *Homo habilis* and *Zinjanthropus* were tool makers. But *Zinjanthropus* dropped out of the picture, as did contemporary South African near-men (Australopithecines) to which he seems closely related. It would appear that nature experimented with these manlike creatures, found them wanting, and rejected them.

Zinjanthropus's skull shows that he was low-browed and long-faced, with a relatively small brain. He certainly did not know the use of fire, though he probably shared the obvious ability of *Homo habilis* to plan and make tools.

Homo habilis had a greater brain volume than *Zinjanthropus*. The former's brain was about three-fourths the size of that of a small modern man, according to Dr. Leakey. *Homo habilis* could use his hand with a precision grip, thus was well equipped to look after himself in the Early Pleistocene age of Africa.

CHILD WAS FIRST EXAMPLE

The story of *Homo habilis* is closely interwined with that of *Zinjanthropus*. Evidence of *Zinjanthropus* came to light first at Olduvai in 1959 in the form of a shattered skull whose 400 fragments had to be put together like a three-dimension jigsaw puzzle.

During excavations in 1960 and 1961, Dr. and Mrs. Leakey found the lower jaw of a child and parts of its skull and hand, as well as the foot attributed to an elderly woman. These were in a deposit lower, thus older, than that of *Zinjanthropus*.

The new discoveries had the effect of a thunderbolt on the Leakeys. The pre-Zinj child, though older than *Zinjanthropus*, was much more advanced. Strikingly different were the characteristics of the teeth.

At the time, Dr. and Mrs. Leakey were unwilling to give a scientific name to the new hominid, though they expressed the belief that it was related to present-day man. It was neither an Australopithecine like *Zinjanthropus* nor an aberrant of *Zinjanthropus*.

"During the closing months of 1963," Dr. Leakey said today, "Olduvai Gorge yielded very important new fossil hominid remains which fully establish that a species of the genus Homo—which is new to science—was living in East Africa side by side with *Zinjanthropus* in Lower Pleistocene times."

The main new material comes from an excavation site the Leakeys call M.N.K. in Bed II, a more recent geological stratum than Bed I in which *Zinjanthropus*, the pre-Zinj child, and the elderly woman were discovered.

Dr. Leakey says the best of the new material consists of skull parts, a nearly complete lower jaw, and portions of the upper jaw of a young woman, 20 or 21 years old, whom he nicknamed "Cinderella."

Additional fossil parts of at least two other individuals were there—consisting of teeth and skull fragments.

MATERIAL CONFORMS

"The new 1963 material conforms exactly, in morphological character, to the earlier 1960-61 material," Dr. Leakey says.

For scientific purposes, the fossils from Bed I have been made the basic type of the new species *Homo habilis*. The best of the material from Bed II becomes the first paratype.

Dr. Leakey says, "The skull wall is very thin and has a rather small brain capacity, but in its morphological character it resembles a small skull of *Homo sapiens* more than anything else.

"Possibly the most important single feature of the brain case is to be seen in the occipital bone at the back of the skull," he adds. "This, in its morphological features, closely resembles *Homo sapiens* and is wholly unlike the form to be seen either in the Australopithecines or in *Homo erectus.*"

The jaw and upper and lower teeth of the new species recall primitive *Homo sapiens* and are not like those of the near-man. Explains Dr. Leakey:

"In all of the Australopithecines, or near-men, the premolars are wide from side to side, and always wider than they are long from back to front. In the new species of *Homo* the opposite is the case."

"In *Homo habilis*, the canine teeth are large relative to the premolars. In the Australopithecines, including *Zinjanthropus*, the canine teeth are very small relative to the size of their premolars and the size of their large jaws."

The manner in which *Homo habilis'* teeth were worn is significant. He apparently had a softer diet which probably included the flesh of small game. The massive teeth of his contemporary *Zinjanthropus* were ground down by a coarse plant diet that probably included gritty roots.

OVER-ALL PICTURE

"The over-all picture represented by the new species is one which has a number of resemblances to present-day man, rather than to the Pithecanthropines," Dr. Leakey said.

However: "In spite of a number of resemblances with *Homo sapiens*, both in the teeth and the skull of the new species, there are also a number of primitive pecularities to be seen. In particular there is the small size of the brain and the primitive characteristics of the hand. It is these things which made it necessary to set up a new species."

Recent excavations at Olduvai have been concentrated on Bed II. Prior to coming to the United States in February, Mrs. Leakey worked there continuously for 13 months with scarcely a break.

Excavations at Fort Ternan, Kenya, another important fossil site being developed by the Leakeys, have slackened off due to unusually heavy rains last year and the new finds at Olduvai.

Another important fossil discovery was made in Tanganyika in early

1964 by Richard Leakey, the Leakeys' 19-year-old son. The site was at Lake Natron, about 50 air miles from Olduvai.

The youth made a reconnaissance in a light plane over the rugged area, then led a small overland expedition by Land Rover and truck from Nairobi, Kenya. Members of the expedition crossed the lake on a pontoon boat and set up a base camp near steep escarpments where layers of volcanic ash and clay are exposed by erosion. Earlier, in 1959, Mrs. Leakey had spotted the inaccessible gorges from the south and thought them promising for excavation.

JAWBONE DISCOVERED

The small party led by Richard Leakey and joined by Dr. Leakey's assistant, Glynn Isaac, made a systematic search of a part of the badlands. An African employee named Kamoya spied bleach-white bone gleaming from a wall of a gorge. The extraction of it began, and the specimen turned out to be the perfectly preserved lower jaw of a *Zinjanthropus* type of hominid.

To the Leakeys' surprise, the new jawbone fits almost precisely onto the *Zinjanthropus* skull found more than four years earlier at Olduvai. (The original *Zinjanthropus* skull still lacks a lower jaw.) Geologically, the Natron deposits are more recent than the lower beds at Olduvai.

Says Dr. Leakey: "The jawbone shows us that this type of Australopithecine continued to evolve practically unaltered for a very long period. It did not—as we once believed—gradually evolve in the direction of *Homo sapiens.*

"It also confirms the view that the *Zinjanthropus* type of hominid probably lived on a rough vegetarian diet. Both in the original *Zinjanthropus* palate and in the new mandible, the crowns of the premolars and the first and second molars show a considerable amount of wear to the enamel, in spite of the fact that the third molars, or wisdom teeth, were just coming into wear when the owner died.

"In contrast to this, the premolars and molars of the paratype of the new species *Homo habilis*, whose age at death was comparable to the two Zinjanthropus specimens, are very much less worn."

55

Continuity and Change

Samuel Moffat
Elie A. Shneour

If life comes from life, then we should be able to trace a chain of life back through the ages. And we can. It is possible to take an animal such as a horse and identify the early relatives of today's husky specimens. This can be done by carefully examining the buried remains of horselike animals found in many parts of the world.

As the record of millions and millions of years is studied, it becomes clear that life forms are not static. Several of the ancestors of today's horses were equipped with three toes on each front foot instead of a single hoof. A still earlier ancestor had four toes. There have been many other changes since the time, 55 million years ago, when that four-toed animal roamed the earth. That ancestor of the horse was no bigger than a terrier dog and was accustomed to eating soft foliage, not the harsh grasses that horses eat today. Only when they developed a harder tooth surface could horses begin to live off the grasses that were covering the earth between 13 and 25 million years ago. Only then were their teeth suitable for grinding the new food.

It is important to note, however, that there were horses in the past other than those in the main line of development, other than those that were direct ancestors of modern horses. Scientists who have studied fossils —ancient bones and other traces of life—have found that there were many more members of the family outside the main line than within it. These types have since become extinct and they have no present-day descendants.

In part, the concept of evolution explains the change and progression

Samuel Moffat and Elie A. Shneour, "Continuity and Change," *Life Beyond the Earth*, Vistas in Science No. 2 (Washington, D.C.: National Science Teachers Association, 1965). Reprinted by permission.

of living things over millions of years. The idea of such a pattern is actually very old. Some of the ancient Greek philosophers speculated about the nature of life and arrived at conclusions that occasionally come quite close to the theories we hold today. Empedocles of Agrigentum (495-435 B.C.) has been called the father of the idea of evolution. He believed that plants developed first and that animals came later, following a long series of trial efforts. Some scholars have seen in his thinking a hint of one of Darwin's theories: that the fittest organisms survive by chance instead of design. Empedocles argued that some forms of life were gradually replaced by others better suited to live in their surroundings.

Among the Greeks, Aristotle (384-322 B.C.) came closest in his thinking to our modern concept of evolution. He saw a single chain of life, an orderly progression from certain water animals to human beings. His ideas anticipated current theories in many ways. although he was entirely wrong in many of his beliefs. Since Aristotle's time, men have continued to puzzle over the pattern of evolution.

EVOLUTION IN ACTION

Convincing evidence about whether evolution actually occurred, however, was not gathered together until the 19th century. The gatherer was Charles Darwin, who was then a young man in his twenties and much more a sportsman than a scientist. He had signed on aboard the H.M.S. *Beagle* as naturalist during a round-the-world surveying voyage. His first clues to evolution came in South America. There he observed the remains of large, extinct animals that were clearly related to smaller ones still living on the continent. He found a huge fossil animal with armor resembling that of the existing armadillo. He also noted signs of gradual changes in animal forms as the ship progressed southward. Many forms seemed related, but had obvious differences too. How had this come about?

Darwin received an answer when he reached the rocky Galápagos Islands off the west coast of South America. There he observed some finches, a common breed of bird. He found 14 species of finches, none of which was known elsewhere in the world. True, they resembled a species found on the mainland, but three species that ate seeds depended on seeds different from those the mainland finches ate. The others fed not on seeds at all but on cactus plants or insects. One species even grasped a cactus spine in its beak to pry bugs from the bark of trees!

Eventually young Darwin reasoned that the birds must have originated from some mainland finches that had found their way to the islands.

Over many, many years they must have developed widely varying feeding habits and in this way had evolved into separate species.

We now know that food supply is only one of many forces at work in shaping the nature of the world's populations. Predators or other natural enemies may bring about a change in living habits. During thousands or millions of years, the climate may change so that one living form may prove more successful than another, and thus multiply at the expense of a competitor.

THE FOSSIL RECORD

Working with Darwin's concept, scientists have since filled in many parts of the story of evolution. One of the most productive lines of investigation has been the study of fossils. Fossils are traces of life long past. Such a trace may be a bone, an impression of a skeleton, seashell, or leaf in the hardened mud of ancient seas, or a whole animal, such as an ant preserved in jewel-like amber. The fossil record has been studied all over the world by hundreds of researchers investigating everything from the microscopic remains of protozoans to the bones of gigantic dinosaurs. Such fossils offer overwhelming evidence that evolution must have occurred.

A startling fact uncovered by these researchers into time is that all the basic types of animal structure are visible among fossils more than 350 million years old. This does not mean that the higher animals were developed then, but only that the pattern of bodily organization had been established. There were single-celled protozoans. Their forms, preserved in stone, are visible because of the tiny skeletal structures some of them had developed. There were sponges, coral, worms, clamlike brachiopods, starfish and their relatives, mollusks of all sorts. There were arthropods equipped with horny skeletons outside the body, and chordates with skeletons of living bone inside the body. The various vertebrates (backboned animals) evolved from the early chordates, and include today's fishes, amphibians, reptiles, birds, and mammals. Invertebrates, animals without backbones, were more abundant than vertebrates. In fact, they still are.

WHEN THE ANIMALS CAME ASHORE

Both vertebrates and invertebrates came ashore from the ancient seas in several forms. The ancestors of today's insects were primitive jointed arthropods related to the remote ancestors of crabs. But the most dramatic change in the earth's life forms began when backboned animals came ashore.

If you look at a goldfish or a trout, it is difficult to imagine how a fish could have evolved into an amphibian such as a frog or a toad, which seems to be perfectly at home on land. But there are fish alive today that show us the connection is not impossible. One species has both gills and lungs. There are others that breathe air through their stomachs or through accessory lungs, called air bladders. There is a mudskipper that chases insects, eats worms like a bird, and can use its fins to get up trees.

Certain primitive fish that roam the deeps of the Indian Ocean have fins very different from those of modern ones. These fins project from the body and can be turned about like the arm or leg of a land animal. The ancestors of amphibians might have had such fins and used them as flippers to squirm from pool to pool at the shoreline. And they had to have some way of gulping air when they were out of water. At first they must have changed so that land became as much a home as water. Then some of them became more at home on land than in water.

The step from amphibian to reptile represented a further adjustment to living ashore. Amphibians have a moist skin and lay eggs in water or moist places; their young usually begin life looking like fish and living in the water. Reptiles, on the other hand, are dry-skinned, usually lay eggs on dry land or give birth to their young, and the offspring can immediately begin breathing in the air. Reptiles in their various forms dominated animal life on land for some 150 million years. One form even led to today's many types of birds.

FROM MAMMALS TO MEN

Most of the reptile types failed to stand the test of time. It was an offshoot from the varied reptile stock that produced the next dominant group, the mammals. Mammals are characterized by hair or fur, and by suckling of their young. Only two of the transitional forms survive today, the duckbill platypus and the spiny anteater. These two animals have hair and somewhat better temperature control in their bodies than reptiles. The females produce milk, but they also lay eggs, like their reptile ancestors.

The mammals in their early evolution must have been small creatures, hardly worth the attention of the mighty reptiles. But within about 10 million years the majority of the large reptiles became extinct and the mammals came into their own. Their built-in temperature control made it possible for them to exploit all sorts of environments, from steaming jungles to chill mountain ranges. Because of this internal temperature control, mammals are called warm-blooded. Reptiles are said to be cold-blooded; they cannot maintain warmth in cold weather. Birds also developed a warm-blooded system.

Over the ages the mammals expanded tremendously in type and number. They grew large, as the reptiles had done, but today's species are often smaller than their earlier counterparts. They also produced the ancestral line that led to man.

Of course, the evolution of animals could not have taken place without plant life abounding on the earth. Green plants supply food in the form of compounds that animals can turn into energy and tissues. Plants also remove carbon dioxide from the atmosphere and replenish the oxygen supply needed by animals. Plants too have adapted to life on land, with its fluctuations and changes in environment. More than a million and a half species survive today.

The results of evolution appear even more spectacular when you stop to think that a world now teeming with living things was once devoid of life.

ANCIENT CHEMISTRY ALIVE TODAY

Perhaps the most important thing we learn from studying the concept of evolution is that all living things are related. Despite all the changes that have occurred, there is continuity—continuity more fundamental than the similarities between parent and child. An interesting bit of chemical evidence in the fossil record bears this out. Proteins are substances involved in the vital processes of every living thing. They are made of simpler materials called amino acids. Recent studies of some fossils 300 million years old showed that the amino acids found in these ancient samples are the same proteins that serve life's purposes today.

This brings us back to the possibility of finding a way to detect life in space. Is there a chemistry common to living things on earth, a series of characteristics that we might look for to determine if life has evolved elsewhere? If so, our task may be greatly simplified. We should be able to send an automatic laboratory to a planet to identify a known substance. This would be easier than having to explore a planet's surface for all the possible forms of life.

56

The Role of Paleontology
in the Formulation of Evolutionary Thought

Everett C. Olson

Each of the disciplines of the biological sciences has played a dual role in the formulation of evolutionary theory: contributing data that have led to modern theory and providing a reservoir of fact and theory against which various facets of the evolutionary concept can be tested. A few of the disciplines have contributed directly to the development of the general idea of organic evolution, to the proposition that the history of life has been one of change with continuity through the agency of reproductive processes. Others, being recent in origin or in maturity, have been effective in contributing inductively only to the nuances of sophisticated modern versions of evolutionary theory.

Each of the biological disciplines is in some degree made more meaningful in itself and brought into logical relationship to others under the broad cover of the theory. Paleontology, a discipline separated from others by the temporal scope of its materials and by its methods, has to some extent fulfilled the two roles, as an agent of induction and a target of deduction, especially in the form of a tangible life history, and certainly takes on meaning when viewed in light of current evolutionary theory. In this essay an effort is made to assess these various roles of paleontology.

The theory of natural selection, which in one form or another is the most widely accepted today, and the broader and simpler idea that life has altered in an evolutionary way through time are quite different with respect to their relationships to origins in terms of paleontological data. We will deal with them separately and in their historical sequence.

The threads of the intellectual activities of the 16th and 17th centuries, and traces that go back even farther into the 15th, appear to have

Everett C. Olson, "The Role of Paleontology in the Formulation of Evolutionary Thought," *BioScience*, Vol. 16(1) (1966), pp. 37-40. Reprinted by permission.

made emergence of a full-fledged concept of organic evolution virtually inevitable. Perhaps the most impelling base lay in the concept of evolutionary development of social history, formulated in particular by the philosopher Hegel. But the astronomy of Galileo and Copernicus, the cosmology of Kant and Laplace, Descartes, Newtonian mechanics and the rise of materialism, recognition of uniformity and evolution in the physical history of the earth, travel and the expanding knowledge of zoogeography, and elucidations of the basic data of anatomy and embryology all begged for interpretation couched in a materialistic concept of the continuous change of life with time. First causes were removed, at least to a point beyond the scope of the immediate phenomena.

Speculations about an orderly change of life were certain, then, to emerge during these centuries, as indeed they did, just as they had appeared many times before when a philosophy of flux as a basic reality had arisen, contrasting to the concept of fundamental changelessness. There is no very clearly demonstrable relationship between the very early ideas of evolution, formulated for the most part in the pre-Christian eras, and our own, which finds its roots largely in events from the 15th century on. Thus in this discussion the evolutionary ideas of the earlier times, interesting as they may be, will be dismissed as only tangentially relevant.

It appears highly probable that some concept of organic evolution could and would have developed in the absence of any fossil record. Just what form it might have taken and how current theory might have been altered cannot, of course, be determined. It would have arisen, but it might have found the road to general acceptance much more difficult in the absence of the tangible evidence of life's history given to the layman by geology and the fossils in the rocks. The actual course of development of evolutionary theory, in any event, shows that the fossil record was very important in the thinking of those students who were the most influential in promulgating the idea of organic evolution. *Vestiges of the Natural History of Creation* by Robert Chambers, published in 1844, while ridiculed for many reasons, presented the concept of evolution based on the factual evidence of the fossil record. The first one-third of the book is devoted in large part to the presentation of this evidence. The first edition was published during the time that Charles Darwin was developing his ideas and created considerable stir and interest in evolution and aided in establishing a climate in which the evolutionary philosophy of Herbert Spencer could flourish. Long before, Erasmus Darwin, the grandfather of Charles, in his *The Temple of Nature* drew heavily if obscurely in poetic presentation upon the past history of life. His *Zoonomia* and other works also carried a transformationist doctrine. Buffon, struggling with the problem of origin and demise of species, similarly was stimulated by the existence in the rather recent past of animals now extinct. Lamarck, of course, was a knowledgeable paleontologist and was strongly influenced in his acceptance of the mutability of species by his understanding of the fossil record of life. This list could be enlarged, but these are some of the persons who are justifiably well known for their part in the origin of the theory of evolution. Some evolutionists, on the other hand, seemed to pay little heed to the fossil record, or, perhaps, to be little aware of it. They were less influential. For the most part, those who gave evidence from the fossil record were the ones who stirred the interest that led to discussions and either recognition or rejection of the theory. They touched upon ground common to many and thus comprehensible as material for debate. The more erudite and subtle presentations, such as those of Tennyson in his "In Memoriam" and, to some extent those of Erasmus Darwin, being literary or poetic in form, seem to have stirred less controversy, being read more for their poetic and literary than scientific content.

Today there are few serious students of biology who do not adhere to a broad concept of evolution of life in one form or another. By far the greatest number of these students subscribe to evolutionary theory that incorporates natural selection as a basic factor. In contrast to the importance of paleontology in the origin of the general concept of organic evolution is the very minor part that it appears to have played in the development of the theory of natural selection. This is evident in the works of Charles Darwin, of Alfred Russel Wallace, and in studies and comments of those who had the germ of the concept in earlier times, for example, David Hume in his *Dialogues on Natural Religion*, published in 1739, or in the works of Charles Bonnet and Denis Diderot who first used the term evolution. Darwin, in referring to the evidence of natural selection in the fossil record in Chapter IX of the *Origin of Species*, succinctly stated that, "Geology assuredly does not reveal any such finely graded organic chain; and this, perhaps, is the most obvious and general objection that can be urged against my theory." In a broad sense, he pointed out, the record is in accord with the theory, and then proceeded to an excellent analysis of the reasons that there is no detailed correspondence. In no specific sense, however, can it be said that the idea of natural selection arose from the facts of the record of life.

It is notable in this regard, as well as with reference to the general idea of organic evolution, that many paleontologists were among the strongest critics of evolutionary theory. Cuvier and Owen are well known examples. Then as now, unless the record is viewed under the unifying evolutionary concept, its negative aspects are so pervasive that tremendous latitude in interpretation is possible. This has often been seized upon by critics of evolutionary theory as a point of departure. Upon publication of a paper entitled "Morphology, Paleontology, and Evolution," in which some of the problems of interpretation of the fossil record were outlined, I received a great many papers and letters that presented "alternative hypotheses," some seriously conceived and some quite otherwise. Most took their beginnings in inferences based on the incompleteness of the record of life, relying heavily upon its negative aspects.

In summary of what has been said to this point, I will reiterate that paleontology appears to have played a very important role in the origin of the general concept of organic evolution, but it had only an insignificant and largely negative role in the development of the theory of natural selection.

We may now turn to the post-Darwinian phases of the development of theory, to examine what paleontology has contributed during the last century. The crux of the problem of natural selection after Darwin lay in the question of the origin of variations. This, along with the problems of preservation and dispersal, formed the special world of Mendel, de Vries, Weismann, Morgan, Fisher, Wright, Muller, Waddington, Dobzhansky, among many others, and more recently Beadle, Crick, Watson, and their colleagues. Other biologists, operating in many fields (for example, Huxley, Mayr, Stebbins, and Schmaulhausen), were among the synthesizers of current evolutionary theory. Among paleontologists Simpson stands out as the one who more than any other successfully applied concepts of neobiology such as population genetics to the fossil record. He emerged as a master of the synthetic approach and greatly enhanced the understanding of the fossil record and the integration of its data with those of other disciplines of biology. This era of synthesis, from about 1930 to 1955, probably marks the peak of both substantive and theoretical contributions of paleontology to evolutionary theory, at least up until now. Its history to the late 1940's has been written clearly and concisely by Simpson.

An important fact emerges from a study of what went on during this time. As significant as any substantive role that paleontology has played is another and subtler one, its effects upon the ways of thinking of those who have become thoroughly acquainted with the history of life. The synthesis brought this history to the attention of many who were not paleontologists proper and, in reciprocal fashion, enriched its impact upon paleontologists as they became more acutely aware of biology beyond the narrow limits of their own field. Even some of the most sophisticated approaches to evolutionary theory today, in fields applying molecular biology or multivariate mathematics, show this impact as their new conclusions are often tested against the backdrop of phylogenies from the fossil record. The faith in these phylogenies is sometimes rather startling to the paleontologists who were instrumental in their formulations. The all-over effect of this infiltration of the sense of history through neobiology, which is far from 100% effective, is hard to evaluate, but it surely has considerable significance.

If evolutionary theory is considered in its broadest sense as a complex of theories, as argued by Beckner, then paleontology as a discipline with its special data must be thought of as one of the bulwarks of modern theory. It is tempting to launch into a discussion of the specifics, into considerations of matters of rates of change, of directional evolution, of chronofaunal evolution, community concepts, and other well-known areas with which paleontology has been intimately concerned. These illustrate the roles that interpretation of the history of life can play in enriching, clarifying, and ramifying the concepts that contribute to the complex we call evolutionary theory. Such a diversion is not possible in the space available and not essential to the main purposes of this essay.

That the fossil record plays a fundamental role in furnishing a history is self-evident. But it assumes this role only under the aegis of one or another governing concept to which it can itself contribute directly in only a minor way. To attempt to visualize the importance of this point, it is amusing to speculate upon the conclusions that might be reached by some hypothetical observer totally unaware of life as we now know it, who saw only the evidence of the fossil record with its remnants of organisms arranged in rough temporal sequences. I will leave this speculation, the ground rules, and the conclusions to the readers to whom such "scientific fantasy" appeals.

As in the early days of evolutionary theory, (in the 18th and first part of the 19th century) there were many paleontologists who rejected the general theory of evolution, so later, after natural selection was proposed as a dominant aspect of the theory, many, accepting evolution, rejected natural selection as a critical element in it. So, of course, have many others who were not paleontologists or even scientists—Henri Bergson, for example. But among the biological scientists it was predominantly some of the paleontologists who failed to follow along the lines being revealed by developments of genetic theory.

There are good reasons for this. There was some degree of isolation between the various disciplines. More important, however, are the data revealed by the fossil record. There are great spatial and temporal gaps, sudden appearances of new major groups, equally sudden disappearances of old, including very rapid extinctions of groups that had flourished for long periods of time. There were mass extinctions marked by essentially simultaneous death of several apparently little associated groups of organisms. At the time the record first is seen with any real clarity, the differentiation of phyla is virtually complete. As far as major groups are concerned, we see little clear evidence of time succession in differentiation with the simpler first and the more complex later.

Over shorter periods of time, but still far beyond man's capacity to observe directly, directional change with little fluctuation or diversion is a striking feature. "Bizarre" organisms seem to argue against a concept of nice adjustment through selection of the adapted. "Bizarreness" seems to be a prelude to extinction, often without tangible evidence of change of conditions of existence. The seemingly most superbly adjusted organisms sometimes were lost, while their awkward neighbors kept on. Catastrophism, saltations in origins, innate directional forces, directional change in direct response to environmental stimulus, various finalistic, vitalistic, and teleological interpretations were the outcome. Cope, as a neo-Larmarckian, Osborn with his concept of aristogenesis, Schindewolf and catastrophism or neocatastrophism, and Tielhard de Chardin with the Omega point will serve for illustration.

While it is true that all of the problems posed by the record can be rationalized under selection theory, the studies of students who followed "unorthodox" lines have made significant contributions to the knowledge and understanding of the history of life and, in one way or another, positively or negatively as may be the case, to evolutionary theory. Much has come from efforts toward refuting what their work inspired, from the interest in evolution that it aroused (because often the conclusions were more palatable to laymen than the alternatives), and from insights into processes that were integrated into the broader theory of evolution developed later. Modern theory, however, depends very little upon any concepts developed *de novo* by these students. Most of their basic tenets, both those later accepted and those rejected, had been in existence, sometimes in less mature form, well before the exposition of the theory of natural selection by Darwin.

The metaphysical aspects of theories held by some paleontologists and by other evolutionists, while interesting, are beyond the scope of scientific treatment and will not concern us. But such things as catastrophism, parts of Lamarckian and neo-Lamarckian doctrines, or directional evolution at the level usually seen in the fossil record logically are proper subjects for scientific treatment. The concept of inheritance of environmentally induced characters has, of course, been tested many times and, at least at the gross level recognized by neo-Lamarckians, support has been consistently wanting.

Such phenomena as those covered by catastrophism and conceived as involving causality remain proper matters for study. We see no evidence of major catastrophic alteration of the direction of evolution of life in observations of modern organisms. Catastrophies do occur on various scales and a sub-species or species or even some ecological complex may sometimes be markedly affected. But this has not been clearly related to the sorts of things that seem to appear in the fossil record, with its instances of many kinds of events that may be widely spaced in time or are not *per se* repetetive and may occur only once. The lack of documentation over a short period of time cannot be taken as an indication that such events have not been important.

This, so it seems to me, points to a dilemma of the evolution-minded paleontologist and to a weakness of the fossil record as an agent of innovation as far as the fundamental, central core of evolutionary theory is concerned. First of all, the paleontologist cannot demonstrate that natural selection has or has not been a fundamental caustive factor in evolutionary events that he observes. The record can serve as a basis for testing and evaluating hypotheses based on modern materials and subsumed under the synthetic theory, or any other theory that may be considered acceptable on the basis of modern materials. Similarly viewed, it can supply data and hypotheses that can suggest pertinent studies by experimentation with living organisms.

In the realm of evolutionary events that emerge to view only with observations encompassing long periods of geologic time, an experimental interplay with living organisms is impossible. There are, however, many apparently long term processes and widely spaced nonrecurrent events that are not yet fully understood and that eventually may lead to new and important perspectives in evolutionary theory. It is in this area of research that the paleontologist can make unique contributions. He will have to rely primarily on induction, not because he is denied deduction but because he may have to make deductions that can be satisfied only by observation rather than by experiment, and he may not discover the fossil finds necessary to test his deductions.

This possibility of disappointment should not stifle a search for theoretical meaning. Two positive solutions are always possible. First, a theoretical breakthrough in an unrelated field may furnish the clue necessary to tie together the tag ends of the puzzle. Second, paleontologists themselves might sometime, somewhere, find fossil evidence giving their deductions a remarkably high degree of probability.

57

Flowers, Insects, and Evolution

Herman F. Becker

Any endeavor to unravel the evolutionary history of our fascinating flower-insect relationships reveals divergent interpretations among scien-

Herman F. Becker, "Flowers, Insects, and Evolution," *Natural History*, Vol. 74 (1965), pp. 38-45. Reprinted from *Natural History*.

tists. For such an undertaking a comprehensive knowledge of the natural sciences is required, especially of geology, botany, entomology, and above all, of paleobotany, paleoentomology, and evolution. Many people realize the existence of interdependence between some plants and insects, but few are aware of the aeons of time involved during which this process reached its present state of development. Evolution has no definite end result and never a deliberate, predestined direction. In the case in point, it is expressed by a high degree of specialization and an intricate relationship that developed into such widely divergent biological entities as the flowering plants and the insects.

First, of course, we must consider the interdependency between plants and insects that exists in nature today; then we must apply the dictum, "The present is a key to the past." The geological record presents a chronicle of 400 million years of fossil life that can be traced through each subsequent younger formation. The evolution of each living plant and insect has been a continuous chain of events, which, if broken, would have resulted in extinction. In turn, a complex and harmonious interdependency—or mutualism—exists between many plant and insect species. If that interdependency should be severely disrupted, mutual annihilation could result.

Early organization of flower structures appears to have been a slow, gradual process of adaptation and specialization without functional stimulus by insects. When the first insectlike animals appeared during Devonian time, the evolution of highly specialized reproductive structures among such plant groups as the seed ferns, the treelike club mosses (*Lepidodendron, Sigillaria*), and the giant horsetails or scouring rushes (*Calamites*) was already well on its way. Early "insects," according to fossil evidence, were doubtless primitive, wingless, and unspecialized. Their food requirements were not restricted, but may have comprised a varied diet of decaying debris.

The reasons for the sudden rise and expansion of the angiosperms—the higher plants, which have seeds enclosed in an ovary—are still shrouded in mystery, but a phylogenetic plasticity coupled with favorable ecological opportunities surely played a major role in their rise. Their explosive diversification and dispersal in the late Cretaceous and early Tertiary nearly parallels an equally momentous rise and diversification, or speciation, among insects. An intimate interdependence between these two groups, therefore, must be considered a relatively recent geological phenomenon—one initiated about 70 million years ago. Most earlier relationships probably were essentially haphazard, and at first contributed little to the eventual physiognomy and requirements of either plant or insect.

Nothing in nature is constant but change. In a nutshell, organic evolution, expressed in terms of phylogenies, is "descent with modification" as a function of perpetual genetic variation, mutation, and natural selection. Those traits that do not contribute to species survival are gradually discarded. In rare cases, according to fossil evidence, species remain in a state of what might be called "evolutionary suspension," or *status quo*. That is, they have changed relatively little either because their environment has not changed, or because they are adapted to a wide range of environments. Cases in point are such examples as the "living fossils" of the Dawn Redwood (*Metasequoia*), the Katsura tree (*Cercidiphyllum*), Ginkgo, and, to some extent, the roses. Among the insects, the dragonflies, roaches, and silverfish fit into the living fossil category.

Essentially, then, over a long period of time, each gradual and minute change in both flower and insect morphology was triggered by subtle genetic and environmental changes. In some cases, our interpretation of an early phylogeny is only as valid as the fossils on which it is based, and additional fossil material that comes to light frequently causes us to reconsider and modify previous conclusions. This procedure permits a flexibility to amend previously established plant–insect relationships according to new evidence.

Some of the early insects of the Carboniferous and Permian periods were doubtless carnivorous or omnivorous, while herbivorous forms were destructive to plant life. It has been suggested—as a hypothetical beginning to plant–insect interdependencies—that there gradually appeared cells that secreted nectar. These surrounded the reproductive (flower-like) regions, and the feeding activities of insects began to be channeled toward such central lures. This, then, may have resulted in the preservation of vegetative structures and, concurrently, promoted the transfer of microspores and insured pollination. From such convergent developments arose a mutualism that was beneficial—in some cases a survival factor—for plants and insects alike.

It is sometimes assumed that flower types were determined by their exploiters, the pollinators. To the uninitiated, the examples are superficially plausible when we say that "bumblebee flowers," such as clover, arose in response to specific structures of the bumblebees; that "bird flowers," such as cardinal-flower or trumpet-vine, arose in response to parrots and hummingbirds; and that "bat flowers"—*Kigelia* (the tropical sausage tree) or certain cacti—developed in response to bats. Such reasoning assumes an independent "leading" development of the fauna with a resulting adaptation of flowers to their visitors. It can hardly be argued that the insects are the sole exploiters of flowers for food as long as the flowers equally "exploit" insects for pollination—an exchange that results in harmonious relationships to each other's advantage.

Many instances of insect behavior toward plants may be traced to a functional structure, color, or fragrance in plants, and one might be tempted to say that insects "behave" in a particular fashion *because* of these attributes. Whether the insects directed or caused the evolution of flowers to conform to their own entomological specializations is certainly not decipherable from the geological record. But if they did so, it would follow that flowers must always have lagged behind insects in their optimum adaptation. It is more realistic to assume that reciprocal adaptation among primitive and advanced flowers and insects was achieved contemporaneously or in a limited, seesaw fashion.

Secretion of nectar, for instance, is physiologically linked with flower maturity, the opening of stamens, and the discharge of pollen. Nectar glands, or nectaries, of the earliest flower types attracted primitive arthropods of the class Insecta. Floral parts provide a region where sugars, starch, albumen, fats, and vitamins accumulate to be incorporated into developing fruits and seeds. Nectar and pollen thus furnished, then as now, a concentrated and palatable food for the arthropod visitors who "learned" to utilize these sources for their daily needs.

Today, insects are divided into two great subclasses, the wingless Apterygota and the winged Pterygota. Wingless insects entered the geological stage during early Devonian time and have remained relatively unchanged and primitive to this day. They contain the present orders of Thysanura, with bristle tails or caudal filaments and chewing mouthparts (silverfish), and the Collembola, minute—or even microscopic—vegetarian springtails. Only one in a thousand of all insect species is wingless today. Pterygota appeared somewhat later, but the exact time of derivation from the wingless forms is problematical, and the morphological changes that resulted in wing development are still not clearly understood. The attainment of winged flight precedes that for reptiles and birds by nearly 100 million years. This mode of locomotion obviously unlocked new vistas and evolutionary potentialities for the whole group. Nearly 200 million years elapsed before the greatest number of insect species took to the air, which coincided with the early Tertiary ascendancy and diversification of the flowering plants.

Among the Pterygota, the Palaeoptera, or ancient-winged, had outstretched, non-flexible wings that could not be folded flat over their bodies. Dragonflies and mayflies are examples. They were mainly predaceous, and evolved into the largest insects that ever lived. Fossil dragonflies with a wingspread of 30 inches are not uncommon. Toward the end of the Carboniferous the Palaeoptera gave rise to the new-winged insects, the Neoptera, which could fold their wings. Today, 90 per cent of all existing orders of Pterygota, comprising 97 per cent of all species, belong to this group.

For the first 100 million years following the origin of the winged insects, the air was shared with no other organism. They reigned supreme until the Jurassic and the advent of the birds, which soon turned the insects into a source of food. Neopterous insects of the Upper Carboniferous, related to our cockroaches and stoneflies, had an incomplete, or hemimetabolous, metamorphosis, in which each stage was larger than the previous until adult size was reached. Insects with a complete, or holometabolous, metamorphosis—that is, those that go through grub and pupal stages—appeared in Lower Permian times and comprised about 5 per cent of all insects. Today, 88 per cent of all insects are in this group; their larvae and caterpillars differ from adults in structure and in food and ecological requirements.

One of the keys to the successful evolution of pollinating relationships is the faculty of insects to distinguish diagnostic forms of basic flower types that consist of a definite number of sepals and petals. Such structures are termed "numeral" patterns and were first recognized in "flowers," or fructifications, in the cycad-like plants of the early Mesozoic. Gradually, through various evolutionary lines, they attained their present angiospermous complexity of ovary-enclosed seeds. Perhaps one evolutionary system of flower "type classes" may be equated with a complementary sensory evolution of pollinating insects. During the progress of natural selection, each previous sign of "recognition" on the part of the insects was augmented by a new, more adaptive, and more successful sign. Primitive, spirally arranged, beetle-pollinated magnolias of the Cretaceous, for example, gave rise to some modern species (*Magnolia denudata, M. coco*) with a radial symmetry and a more efficient pollination by Hymenoptera.

The following botanical terms in their evolutionary sequence telescope these trends:

Amorphic, or "structureless," extinct flower types usually possessed dense whorls of leaves or bracts, often without definite form, and growing beneath the floral reproductive structures. Some of the Triassic ancestral cycads with amorphic "flowers" (*Wielandiella*) attracted certain primitive beetles and roaches, and possibly some wingless insects that learned to associate the pollen and secretory food supply with the density of whorls of bracts or basal leaves of the flowers.

Haplomorphic, or "simple," flowers, in their often "spiral" arrangements of variously colored petals and sepals (the perianth), trace their ancestry to the middle and late Mesozoic Era. Magnolias, the tulip tree, and waterliles belong in this group, which is considered to be one of the most primitive among the angiosperms.

Actinomorphic, or "regular," flowers have emerging "radial" and two-dimensional symmetries. Roses and peonies, which have all floral parts and nectaries on one level, are examples. Here are associated composite, radial forms of from three- to six-perianth segments that probably are perceived by the insect as a unit. Together with color and fragrance, these flower types represent a food attractant for certain flies or bees and a few other well-adapted pollinators, including beetles, that need no specific ability to gather the abundant pollen offered. No flowers of the truly radially symmetrical types have been reported from the Cretaceous Period.

Pleomorphic flower types (the root word means "more than one"), with a four- or five-part recognition pattern, were found in Cretaceous beds, but they became abundant only in Tertiary floras. Some lily-like compressions of the Tertiary suggest bee pollination, as in modern, colorful monocotyledonous flowers with a three- or six-part perianth. Flowers of the mustard and dogwood families were first recognized in the Oligocene Ruby shale deposits of southwestern Montana, of some 35 million years ago. Bees (including bumblebees) and flies (including flower flies) were abundant by then, and may often have chosen specific flowers on which to feed.

Stereomorphic, or three-dimensional, often tubular, flowers with a symmetrical three-, five-, or six-parted perianth, are a late Tertiary derivative from pleomorphic ancestry. They include gentian, bellflowers, columbines, primroses, phlox, and daffodils. Their corollas protrude considerably above the deep-set and often concealed nectaries. Butterflies and hawk moths, some of which have refined adaptations of mouthparts (a long, curled tongue, for instance), or certain bees (which, with long tongues or very small bodies, are able to force entry into the tubes) feed on and pollinate stereomorphic flowers.

Zygomorphic, or bilaterally symmetrical, floral development represents the highest and most intricate evolution of morphological structures in response to, or contemporaneous with, a very limited number of pollinators whose sensory organization is attuned to a highly specialized perianth. These perianths offer complicated recognition patterns together with nectar and fragrance that must be grasped in their entirety, as was experimentally shown, no matter how ornamented their symmetry may be. Zygomorphism crosses the boundaries of many families (orchids, milkweeds, legumes) and demonstrates what may be the ultimate in floral specialization. Orchids and their pollinators pose the greatest morphogenic and taxonomic problems to an investigator. They do not always conform to botanical criteria that are considered valid for other families. For instance, they possess unique pollen structures, the pollinia, which adhere as units to the visiting insect (often flies and moths), and are thus assured of delivery to a receptive stigma of the same species. This is made easier because the highly adapted pollinators regularly visit the same kind of flower.

Throughout evolutionary time each flower type, from the amorphic to the zygomorphic, has corresponded to a concurrent level of sensory adjustment in those pollinating insects that had the greatest reaction to a particular plant. Such adjustments continue to evolve, if imperceptibly, without the sacrifice of previously existing, advantageous flower–insect relationships. The story of the present adaptation of insects to their flower hosts, and the intricate endowment of flowers to lure, attract, trap, deceive, and feed pollinators to their own ends is a source of wonder. Even birds and bats entered the competition when specialized structures and functions, serving the pollination of the host, arose with equally efficient features for food requirements of their vertebrate visitors. This resulted in an advantageous, mutual dependence.

After these more or less theoretical considerations, let us now look at some specific aspects based on relatively recent discoveries of plant and insect compressions in our own western backyard. During the summer of 1947, I found the first Tertiary plant compressions in the upper Ruby River basin of southwestern Montana. I could not foresee, however, the significance of that find until I showed a shoe box full of fossil leaves and assorted insects to Dr. C. A. Arnold of the University of Michigan. He immediately recognized the scientific potential of the flora and encouraged me to expand the collection. That suggestion resulted in seven additional field trips during the next fifteen years, and an accumulation of about 12,000 specimens, including some 200 species of plants and a great number of insect remains.

Among paleoentomological regions, the Oligocene Florissant sites of central Colorado had been the most lucrative and best-known in the United States, and this fauna was exhaustively described seventy-five years ago by S. H. Scudder. The Ruby plant sites rank second only to those of Florissant in richness of insect species and may surpass them in detail of preservation.

The Ruby River valley is 70 miles from Yellowstone National Park in a basin of the Rocky Mountains formed by geological faulting. It is flanked by the Ruby and Gravelly ranges. During most of Tertiary time, the entire valley was occupied by a lake in which a sequence of sediments was deposited. A vegetation much denser and more varied than that of today supplied leaves and other plant debris that were carried into the lake by numerous streams and buried in the mud. A high mineral content of the water and a possible absence of decay organisms provided favorable conditions for the preservation of organic remains, including insects that had been washed or blown into the lake.

Fossil sites exposed along the walls of dry washes consist of laminated, light-colored shale that separates along some of its bedding planes. Where such rock is exposed to annual sub-zero temperatures and to baking during the summer, it splits into progressively thinner slabs. These are the "books" of shale with their "pages," or layers, so thin that the slightest breeze will waft them into the air. It is this "paper shale" that contains the fossil compressions of most plants and insects at the Ruby sites.

We rightfully assume that the large, varied Ruby River basin insect fauna was attuned to the equally varied angiospermous flora of trees, shrubs, and herbaceous plants, and that a dependent relationship existed between these two groups. This image is recreated from fossils nearly fifty times as old as mankind itself—from plants and insects that left nothing but films of carbon, which are sharp, clear replicas of their former selves.

The Ruby fossil plant assemblage provides an eloquent basis for local divisions of vertical life or climatic zones, each with its adapted entomological fauna. In most cases, diagnostic criteria for fossil insect identification are sufficient to place them in their proper orders, families, subfamilies, tribes, and even genera. Their taxonomic status is therefore accurate except on the species level. The entomological sample of the Ruby shales probably represents but a small fraction of the genera and species that actually existed. Recognizable fossil insects thus indicate a reliable, if not a specific, correspondence with then-existing plant relationships and with plant–insect interdependence.

In light of applied evolutionary principles, the botanical and entomological participants of the Ruby flora give us a glimpse into antiquity that allows us a sharp focus on present phenomena. Our limited picture can only dimly suggest the meanderings of the evolutionary path, the immensity of geologic time involved, and the astronomical numbers of species and individuals that fell by the wayside as links between past and present.

58

Crop Plant Evolution

Sir Joseph Hutchinson

In considering crop plant evolution it is appropriate to begin with the time scale. In the Old World the beginnings of agriculture, which include the beginnings of the culture of the major Old World cereals, the wheats and barleys, can now be identified with some confidence in northern Iraq and neighbouring regions in Iran, Turkey and Jordan. They have been

From *Essays in Crop Plant Evolution*, Sir Joseph Hutchinson, ed. (New York: Cambridge University Press, 1965). Reprinted by permission.

dated at between 7000 and 6000 B.C. Godwin has assembled the evidence for the belief that the practice of agriculture reached north-western Europe about 3000 B.C. Thus the period during which the evolution of our oldest crop plants has gone on, is about 9000 years. In the early part of the period various plants went through the early stage of domestication and were then abandoned—*Chenopodium, Polygonum, Camelina*—and some late comers were adopted and successfully established—rye and oats. These, having been more recently domesticated, have reached their present state in a shorter time. For the New World the most recent evidence indicates that the beginnings of agriculture probably date from about 5000 to 3000 B.C., giving for the New World a maximum evolutionary span of about 7000 years.

Of the crops discussed in these lectures, wheat and barley date from the beginnings of agriculture, and oats and rye from a later period. Doggett has suggested that the domestication of *Sorghum* may have been undertaken by people who brought primitive wheats with them when they migrated into regions where wild *Sorghums* occur, and *Sorghum* must therefore be grouped with the secondary crops. Maize and potatoes are New World crops, and considerable evidence is now available on the beginnings of maize cultivation, giving the earliest date as about 5000 B.C. in Central America. There is no evidence as yet on the antiquity of potato cultivation, but from what is known of the date of the beginnings of agriculture in South America, it seems likely that potatoes have been cropped since 3000 B.C.

It appears, therefore, that the whole vast complex of cultivated plants has evolved in about 9000 years, and some of our advanced and successful crop plants have been developed from their wild ancestors in half that time. The rate of change involved must be greater than in any other group of organisms, and it is not too much to say that for the student of evolution, the crop plants provide the most rewarding material to be found in all biology. There are not only the ancient crops with 9000 years of history, but also the recently adopted crop plants, such as the forage plants where the wild progenitors and the cultivars are still to be found side by side, and even such an evolutionary phenomenon as *Hevea* rubber, of which some individuals of the original domestication are said to be still alive.

Godwin has commented on the wide range of plants that contributed to the diet of early agricultural man, and it is interesting to speculate on the factors that governed the choice of plants for domestication, and determined their success in more advanced agricultural systems. The food needs of mankind may be classified under three heads, carbohydrates, oils and fats, and proteins. For his carbohydrate supplies the wide range of plants with which he has experimented has been narrowed down to two main groups, with only a very few plants that do not fall within them. The most important group comprises the grain-producing species of the Gramineae. Second in importance to these is the very diverse group of dicotyledonous roots and tubers. Among the grains, such dicotyledons as *Chenopodium* in the Old World and *Amaranthus* and *Chenopodium* (Quinoa) in the New have given place to the cereals. And such exceptional carbohydrate suppliers as the banana are giving place to roots and tubers, such as yams and sweet potatoes. One might hazard a guess that among grain producers, the highest ratio of grain to vegetative matter is achieved in the monocotyledonous Gramineae and that an equally favourable ratio of edible to inedible material is only achieved among the dicotyledons among those that produce roots and tubers.

Vegetable oil production comes from monocotyledons and dicotyledons alike, from coconut and oil palm on the one hand, and groundnut, sunflower and the *Brassicas* on the other.

In the provision of the other great human need, protein, the Leguminosae occupy the position held by the Gramineae in the supply of energy. They have a subordinate position in agriculture, partly because the cereals also provide substantial amounts of protein, and partly because they are not as productive as the cereals. Here again, as seed bearers the dicotyledons are not as productive as the monocotyledons.

The choice of wild plants for domestication depended upon their immediate attractiveness. We can see the process going on in the collection and study of grasses and legumes for pasture improvement in Australia, in many developing tropical countries, and even in western Europe and North America. Of those initially selected, only a few are successful and spread, and these only persist so long as they maintain their place in competition with other crop plants. Thus even so long established a forage crop as Sainfoin has almost disappeared, since it did not respond as well as alternative fodder crops to the changing circumstances of British agriculture.

A striking feature of the accounts of crop plant evolution here recorded is the great importance of the continuing genetic contact between the crop plant and its wild relatives. Dodds has described the association between cultivated and wild forms of the potato in South America. Mangelsdorf has drawn attention to the importance of teosinte in the evolution of modern maize. Bell has reported on the persistence of wild relatives of wheat as weeds in wheat fields, and on the opportunities for hybridization and polyploidy that have followed. Doggett has described the situation in the *Sorghum* crop, where weed forms persist in the crop throughout its African range.

In *Sorghum* in particular, the existence and significance of hybridization between the crop plant and its wild relative is apparent to the careful observer, and the effectiveness of gene exchange is evident from the similarity between weed and cultivar throughout the African range of the crop. The maintenance of the distinction between them is an excellent illustration of the strength and effectiveness of 'disruptive' selective forces in a field crop. *Sorghum* appears to have reached India uncontaminated with its weedy relative, and it would be an interesting comparative study to enquire whether the rate of change and the extent of adjustment to agricultural circumstances have been any greater in India without the weed than in Africa in its presence. That change and differentiation are not dependent upon the differentiated gene pool established under disruptive selection is shown by the cottons, in which the crop has evolved in isolation from its wild relatives, and disruptive selection situations are very rare.

One of the major consequences of domestication is an enormous increase in the area of distribution of the species. This is most striking in the spread of crop plants formerly confined to one hemisphere. The spread of wheat and barley to the New World, to South Africa and the high altitude tropical latitudes, and to Australia, and of maize throughout the tropics, subtropics and warm temperate regions of the Old World has all taken place in the last four hundred years. Similar vast extensions in distribution have taken place with most of the important crop plants of the world, and indeed in many cases the chief areas of production are beyond what was the range of the species until quite recent times. Cacao production is concentrated in West Africa, rubber in South-east Asia, bananas in the New World, and cotton in regions of North America well beyond the limits of the species at the time of Columbus.

These vast increases in range of the major crop plants could only have been possible in very plastic organisms. Limits can be discerned beyond which a crop plant cannot be established. Well known examples of such limits to distribution are those to which continental tropical or sub-tropical crops such as maize and soy beans are subject. All attempts to establish them in the agricultural system of the mild, damp, cloudy British Isles have failed, whereas in the drier and hotter summers of continental Europe the selection of well adapted strains has not been difficult. Though limits can be recognized, it is not the limits but the range and variety of the climates in which adaptation is successful that is remarkable. Probably the most remarkable of all is the example of the annual cottons. Six hundred years ago all cottons were perennial shrubs, and since they are all frost susceptible, the crop was entirely confined to frost-free tropical countries. In each of the four cultivated species, however, the range of variability in morphology was such as to permit of the selection of forms that fruited early enough to give a worth-while crop in the first season. These early fruiting cottons were grown in countries with hot summers but cold winters, and the annual habit was imposed on them by frost in the winter. Selection for high productivity completed the process, and now obligate annuals make up almost the whole of the world's crop, and are grown not only in areas with cold winters but also in countries with hot dry seasons which likewise limit the success of the more primitive perennials. Thus in no more than 600 generations, the whole habit of the plant has been changed in response to the limitations of a climate to which the early cultivated forms were quite unsuited.

A similar, though less extreme, change in habit has been established in a much shorter period following the introduction of *Sorghum* into the agriculture of the United States. The common African forms, 8 ft. to 12 ft. tall, were quite unsuited to mechanized agriculture, and since the produce is a coarse grain used for stock feed, low cost was essential for successful production. Short forms were known, but these also were too tall for convenient mechanical harvesting. In quite a short period, however, *Sorghums* were bred that were short enough for full mechanization, and on them the whole of the present American crop is based. Their genetic structure is well understood, the commercial types carrying a small number of major dwarfing genes, together with a polygene complex that magnifies the major gene effects. It is instructive to note that whereas the major gene effects can be studied conveniently within the American *Sorghum* population, crosses between American dwarfs and Indian agricultural types underwent such complex segregation that the effects of the major genes were lost.

These enormous increases in the distribution of our crop plants have been followed by extremely rapid differentiation of geographical races. The nature and consequences of the differentiation have varied with the circumstances of the particular crops. The nature of the sample of the population from which the original supply of seed was taken has almost always left its mark on the race developed in the new area. Ellis has recently shown that the maize of Nyasaland can be sorted into a group of races that matches fairly closely the races that have been described from north-eastern South America, and the evidence is consistent with the view that the crop is descended from Portuguese introductions from Brazil. Among the cottons of American Upland descent established in the Old World, those of India were derived from the medium staple New Orleans types of the 1860's, and their modern derivatives are shorter in staple than current American types. Those of Africa, on the other hand, came from introductions of a small range of long staple American varieties of the first decade of the present century, and they are still longer in staple than the bulk of the American crop.

The sample that was originally introduced was the raw material of the new race. The race was then fashioned by the selective forces of the new environment, and these have had the most striking effects, in a surprisingly short time. The selection of hairy leaved types in American cottons both in India and in Africa has given rise to a highly distinct phenotype, resistant to the jassid pest that is ubiquitous in the Old World tropics. In cotton, these changes can be fairly accurately timed, and it appears that the development of jassid resistance by natural selection in the fields of the Indian cultivator took no more than about fifty generations. Under selection by plant breeders in southern Africa, the establishment and spread of jassid resistant types was accomplished in a much shorter time. Similar racial differentiation is evident in the potatoes. The European and North American forms have become widely distinct from the types still to be found in the home of the potatoes in South America, even though the number of sexual generations involved must be quite small. Moreover, improvement in South American potatoes now depends heavily on the return to their original home of the modern advanced cultivars developed in the new areas of cultivation.

This complex pattern of spread and differentiation depends upon the existence of a pool of genetic diversity out of which new genotypes emerge under the selection of the diverse environments to which man subjects his crop. In considering the differentiation of the cottons one cannot fail to be impressed by the contrast between the genetic uniformity of the wild species and the enormous genetic diversity of the cultivated species. It seemed necessary to postulate some process by which diversity could arise within a species in the course of domestication and development as a crop plant. Fisher's demonstration that an expanding population would become more variable through the survival of a larger proportion of the naturally occurring mutants provides a statistical basis for increasing variability, and there is good reason to suppose that in other crop plants as well as cotton, the gene pool has been augmented in this way. Nevertheless, it appears that in other crop plants there is not the same disparity between the variability of wild and cultivated species as there is in cotton. Bell has remarked on the variability of the weedy relatives of wheat. Doggett's wild *Sorghums* match the cultivated forms in diversity, though some at least of this may be ascribed to gene exchange. Most important of all, Cooper's forage plants at the very beginning of domestication have within their current limits all the variability that one is accustomed to find in a wide ranging crop plant. Moreover, recent work with *Drosophila* makes it clear that superficial uniformity may conceal an extensive gene pool in a wild species—if indeed *Drosophila* can be regarded as a wild species. Consideration of the time scale discussed above suggests that many stocks of *Drosophila* must have been bred in captivity for as many generations as some of our crop plants, and we ought perhaps to class *Drosophila* with the honey bee in a small category of domestic insects.

The structure of the crop population and the distribution of the variability within it, depends upon the breeding system and the impact of selective forces. Breeding systems in crop plants range from free gene exchange throughout large populations through wind pollination, as in maize, to virtually complete genetic isolation through sterility, with clonal propagation, as in bananas. The wide range of gene exchange through wind pollination is associated with high individual heterozygosity, and the twin phenomena of inbreeding depression and hybrid vigour. A more limited degree of gene exchange occurs in crop plants that are partly self-pollinated and partly cross-pollinated often by insects. Cotton falls in this category, and while the extent of heterozygosity as indicated by segregation on inbreeding, is less than in maize, gene exchange is adequate to ensure the occurrence of the recombination on which progress under selection depends. It serves as a warning against overconfidence in plant breeding techniques to note that the gene exchange from which the modern bacterial blight-resistant Upland cottons of West Africa arose, would not have taken place if the early agricultural botanists had taken the precautions against cross-contamination that we now regard as part of the plant breeder's routine.

Many crop plants, including wheat, barley and oats, are self-pollinated in those parts of their range where the greater part of their crops are produced. They have become virtually mixtures of pure lines, the genetic diversity being partitioned between individuals, and hardly assorted within the genotype of the individuals at all. In the most extreme case, where sexual reproduction has been replaced by clonal propagation, genetic change may be restricted to that which arises by mutation within the clones, and re-assortment of the gene material has then ceased altogether.

In all crop plants the flower structure is such that cross-pollination must have occurred in the past. The Old World cereals have flowers suited to wind pollination. The legumes have the flower pattern characteristic of insect-pollinated plants. Moreover, it is now apparent that at least some of the self-fertilizing crop plants are normally cross-pollinated in their original areas of distribution. The Howards showed that cross-pollination occurs in wheat in India. Rick reported cross-pollination in tomatoes in South America and demonstrated the relationship between spread beyond the range of the pollen vectors and the development of a flower type that facilitated self-pollination. Moreover it now appears that the classical Vavilov type of distribution of variability in a crop plant, with a progressive decline in diversity from centre of origin to periphery, is associated with the development of self-pollination. Crops such as wheat and barley lose in variability with every move to a new area since any pure line not represented in the mother stock for the new crop is lost forever. Cross-pollinated plants such as maize and cotton do not exhibit the Vavilov effect, but on the contrary develop new centres of diversity wherever the crop is established. Indeed it may be that it was this versatility of a cross-pollinating crop that led Anderson to read the Maize story backwards, from Asia to America.

The loss of sexual reproduction must bring evolution in a crop plant as in anything else, almost to a halt. Some increase in clonal diversity will come about by mutation, as is to be seen in the bananas. But with the end of segregation and recombination, there is an end also to the spectacular evolutionary progress characteristic of the crop plants. Only in the banana has the degeneration of the sexual cycle gone to the point where seed production has completely ceased and even in this crop, breeding progress is still possible. The banana breeders have developed an ingenious technique, first proposed by Dodds (1943), whereby they breed superior genomes in seeded, inedible bananas, and then by hybridization add an improved genome as a complete unit to the genome of a sterile, parthenocarpic edible banana. A splendid example of doing good by stealth!

Root and tuber-producing crop plants do not necessarily become seed sterile, and though seed production may be reduced even to vanishing point in commercial crops, it can generally be stimulated sufficiently to make progress by plant-breeding methods possible. There is thus a range in the potential for adaptive response, depending on the breeding system. Outbreeding crop plants may be expected to change in response to changing environments by natural processes alone. Inbreeders will be much less responsive, and adaptation and improvement is only likely through the deliberate intervention of the plant breeder. For those crop plants that are no longer propagated by seed, improvement depends upon the intervention of the plant breeder to re-establish the sexual cycle, though such plants differ from inbreeding seed producers in that the clonal material is generally highly heterozygous, and a seedling progeny consequently segregates widely. We are well aware of the fact that long continued selection to meet the needs of man results in the loss of characters that are essential for survival in the wild. What is perhaps not generally recognized is the further consequence that the breeding system may be so altered—by the development of obligate self-fertilization or by the loss of sexual reproduction—that any further evolutionary changes may also be dependent on the active intervention of man.

The nature of the genetic changes that have gone on during the development of the advanced crop plants is of great importance for an assessment of future prospects. These can be classified under three heads, changes in ploidy, major gene changes, and changes in polygene complexes. Polyploidy is very common among crop plants, but it is evident that increases in chromosome number are by no means necessarily related to crop plant improvement. The most important species of cultivated wheat and oats are polyploid, and polyploidy is common among vegetatively propagated crop plants. Sugar cane, bananas and potatoes are outstanding examples. But development in polyploid wheats has been no greater or more successful than in diploid barley, maize or rice. The tetraploid New World cottons are larger, more vigorous, more productive, and yield produce of higher quality than the diploid species of the Old World. But among the cultivated species of *Phaseolus* the New World species excel those of the Old World in ways that are almost exactly parallel, and the species of both hemispheres are diploid.

It seems probable that the occurrence of polyploidy depends more on the breeding structure of the crop plant than on the selective forces of domestication. In genera of the Gramineae where crosses are possible over a wide range of related species, polyploidy is very common. Moreover, it is common in wild species and in species such as forage grasses that are in the early stages of domestication, as well as in advanced crop plant species such as *Triticum* and *Avena*. In the Leguminosae, on the other hand, crossing between species is difficult, and often impossible, even between those that appear to be closely related, and polyploidy is rare.

The incidence of polyploidy depends not only on the chances of occurrence but also on the prospects of the polyploid after it has arisen. Riley's demonstration of the genetic nature of the stabilization of meiosis in polyploid wheats is of the greatest importance in elucidating the steps that must occur in the establishment of a successful polyploid. Kimber's analysis of the data on meiosis in polyploid cottons is sufficient indication that the system of genetic stabilization demonstrated in polyploid wheat may occur in other genera also.

Where vegetative propagation is possible, a polyploid may be successfully established, though its meiotic cycle may be unstable or even very irregular. Thus what has come to be known as 'nobilization' in sugar cane breeding involves exploiting the occurrence of unreduced gametes to increase chromosome number by the addition of a whole set through crossing. The resulting seedling is then propagated solely by cuttings. In such material, progress through plant breeding depends on exploiting the genetic variability in the simpler, sexually normal members of the species or genus, and producing commercially valuable clones by crossing with their complex polyploid relatives. It is then important for the breeder to maintain a clear distinction between his breeding stocks and these commercially acceptable clonal products, the latter being 'dead end' stocks of no further use for breeding.

In considering the importance of major genes in crop plant evolution, it is necessary first to make it clear that all the evidence indicates that genes do not fall into two categories, large and small, but cover the whole range in magnitude of effect. A 'major' gene is no more than a gene having an effect that is large in comparison with the variation due to environmental causes, and hence one that can be identified and studied individually. In this respect, Knight's analysis of the genetics of blackarm resistance in cotton is important, since in the arid climate with irrigated agriculture in which he worked it was possible to identify a number of genes with effects of different but measurable magnitudes, and to demonstrate the existence of yet others that had too small an effect to be studied individually. Moreover, in the variable climates of the rain-fed regions of Africa, even Knight's major genes became 'minor' genes, in the sense that they could not be individually identified.

There is, nevertheless, a real sense in which changes in major genes have been an instrument of evolutionary change. It is difficult to conceive of the persistence of an unstable polyploid long enough for meiotic stability of the kind demonstrated by Riley to be built up by the selection of a constellation of genes of small individual effect. The major changes which made possible the development of modern maize involved two loci. The origin of spinnable lint from the seed hairs of the wild relatives of the cottons can be accounted for by a change in a single gene. And the difference between brittle and tough rachis in cereals is in general simply inherited. Turning to recent breeding improvement, the short stemmed *Sorghums* bred for combine harvesting in the United States depend basically on a few major dwarfing genes.

It is easy to see that the occurrence of a large mutation would provide an effective stimulus for human selection, whereas the existence of a range of variation in the same character due to minor genes might not. In this way, the establishment of disease resistance, awnlessness in cereals, some forms of pest resistance, besides such quality characters as grain colour and texture, has been brought about in large measure by selection of major genes.

A major change in any important character, however, is rarely adequate in itself. That the American dwarf *Sorghums* have acquired minor genes as well as major dwarfing genes is indicated by the complexity of segregation for height in crosses with tall Indian strains. Major genes for disease resistance seem to be particularly liable to a major responsive change in the parasite, and plant breeders are turning increasingly to minor gene controlled 'field resistance' as more likely to give consistent resistance. In fact the greater part of the genotype of any organism, and of the genes controlling any character, consists of genes of small individual effect. In crosses between related types there may be clear segregation of a single gene, but if the relationship is not close, or if for other reasons there is wide diversity in the segregating populations, the effect of the same major gene may be obscured by the segregation of many other genes having minor effects on the character. To take an example from animal breeding, the transfer of the hornless character from a polled to a normally horned British cattle breed is a simple Mendelian exercise. The establishment of the polled character in a heterogenous African race of cattle is a much more complex operation, involving minor genes for horn size, differences between the sexes in expression of the character, and changes in dominance relations, all indicative of the segregation of genes with widely different effects. It follows that whatever major changes may arise from simple gene differences, the establishment of a new and superior stock is unlikely to occur unless the minor gene constitution of the material is also subjected to selection, but given the initial improvement conferred by the major gene, further progress of great significance may well follow from selection in the polygenic variation. The efficient manipulation of polygenic variation is only now becoming possible, and in breeding programmes with all kinds of crops, statistical analyses of heritability are likely to lead to much greater exploitation of genes of small individual effect.

XI

Population and Birth Control

59

How Many People
Have Ever Lived on Earth?

Annabelle Desmond

How many people have ever been born since the beginning of the human race?

What percentage does the present world population of three billion represent of the total number of people who have ever lived?

These questions are frequently asked by the Population Reference Bureau's Information Service. Because of the perennial interest and because of the credence sometimes given to what would seem to be unrealistic appraisals, this issue presents an estimate prepared by Fletcher Wellemeyer, Manpower, Education and Personnel Consultant, Washington, D.C., with Frank Lorimer of American University, Washington, D.C., acting as advisor. This estimate based on certain statistical, historic and demographic assumptions, should be regarded as no more than a reasonable guess. It assumes that man first appeared about 600,000 years ago, a date which has been proposed for the dawn of the prehistoric era. However, this date obviously is a compromise, anthropologically speaking, between varying extremes.*

Since then, it is estimated that about 77 billion babies have been born. Thus, today's population of approximately three billion is about 4.0 percent of that number. . . .

Since man first appeared on earth, human arithmetic has moved from a relatively simple exercise in addition to a complicated one of geometric

Annabelle Desmond, "How Many People Have Ever Lived on Earth?," *Population Bulletin* (February, 1962). Published by Population Reference Bureau, Inc., Washington, D.C. Used by permission.

*Man (*Homo habilis*) is now thought to have appeared about two million years ago. (Ed.)

progression. It took all of the vast reaches of time to build today's population of slightly over three billion. But it will take only 40 more years for
the population to reach six billion, if the present growth rates remain unchanged.

Rapid population growth cannot be maintained indefinitely in any
part of the world. If birth rates do not decline in overcrowded lands,
death rates eventually will rise to check growth.

The gulf which exists today between the peoples of the world has
widened: life is better than ever before for those who live in the Western
industrial countries. But the majority of the world's people still live close
to the subsistence level, in poverty and squalor reminiscent of the Middle
Ages. If the demographic transition to a balance between low birth and
death rates could be hastened in the less developed countries, this gulf
might yet be bridged in time to avert a Malthusian disaster.

60

The World's No. 1 Problem

Earl L. Butz

At the rate the population is growing, how can the world feed all its
people? Consider these facts; in the next 35 years, the world's population
will almost double; the biggest increases, more than 100%, will come in
the less developed nations of Asia, Africa and most of Latin America,
where diets already are inadequate, and where the ratio of food production to people already is declining.

Just to maintain the world's inadequate level of diet will require a
doubling of the world's output of food by the year 2000, though nearly
all the virgin lands of the world have already been brought into production.

From Earl L. Butz, *The World's No. 1 Problem*, an address given at the International Industrial Conference, San Francisco (September, 1965). Reprinted by permission.

Only a generation ago, Asia, Africa and Latin America were regions with food surpluses which exported grain to the more advanced countries, especially to Europe. Now Latin America as a whole and most of Africa are compelled to import food to feed their own peoples. Red China is forced to buy grain in large quantities. The millions of India are heavily dependent on food supplies from the United States.

If great famine is to be avoided, two things must be done. They are: (1) increase food production greatly, (2) reduce the world's birth rate. In the long run, birth control is the only solution.

61

The Population Explosion

Leroy Augenstein

THE DIMENSIONS OF THE PROBLEM

The average increase in population throughout the world is 2% per year. Putting this number into the formula for compound interest allows us to calculate the number of people there will be at any given time, assuming that this rate is neither increased nor decreased. At this rate, population will double in 35 years: we will go from the present 3 billion people to 6 billion by the year 2000. In 500-600 years there will be 1 square yard per person over the whole face of the earth: if we stacked people in 1 per square yard, we could get more than one-third of the three billion people now alive in the entire world into Detroit and its immediate suburbs. If it were possible to continue this same rate of increase indefinitely, in 1700 years the mass of people would exceed the mass of the earth and in 6000 years the mass of people would actually exceed the mass of the known universe.

From Leroy Augenstein, *The Population Explosion*, an address delivered at the regional conference of the Michigan Education Association, Cobo Hall, Detroit (1965). Reprinted by permission.

It is of great concern that the increase in population is not uniform throughout the world. Although the average increase is 2%, it is less than that in the western world and Japan, whereas in the areas containing ⅔ of the world's population—most of Asia, all of Africa, and most of Latin America—the increase is almost 3% at the present time. This means that the above numbers becomes 25 years, 350 years, 1200 years and 3500 years.

THE CONSEQUENCES

Two-thirds of the world's population go to bed hungry even now. Agricultural experts state that if we made a maximum effort for 25 years, we could increase the productivity of land already under cultivation and bring enough new land into cultivation to give all of the present world population a minimally adequate diet. Unfortunately, in that length of time, the population in the underdeveloped areas will have doubled at their present rate of increase. To cite a specific example: the building of the Aswan Dam is one of the most remarkable engineering feats in all history. Irrigation made possible by this tremendous accomplishment will increase the food production potential by 20%—yet in the time required to build this dam, the population of Egypt will increase by 30%.

To industrialize just one country such as India would be a stupendous undertaking. For example, 50% of her population are engaged in agriculture compared to only about 5% in this country. A truly industrialized country has no more than 25% of the people on farms. Thus, to industrialize India will require 150 million new jobs. Although it costs $50,000 to create a new job in this country, the average might be held as low as $3,000 in India. If so, industrialization would require $450 billion dollars: thus, to create enough jobs just to industrialize for their present population, would require reinvesting 100% of India's GNP (Hitler and Stalin could never reinvest more than 25-28%), for approximately 20 years. Unfortunately, during this interval, the Indian population will increase by more than 200 million at their present rate.

Although the above two problems, as well as water resources, appear to be very critical matters for consideration, most of us feel that the most crucial factor will be simply "living room." Experiments with a variety of animals show that with only mild crowding, animals very quickly become extremely neurotic and dangerous in their behavior. Very probably, the crowded living conditions in Harlem and also in the Watts Subdivision of Los Angeles were a major contributing cause of the bloody riots in the past few years.

THE CAUSES

Man's attempts to apply the discoveries of science and technology in a humane way have created the present inhumane population danger. In ancient times, it appears that there were 40 births per thousand of population per year and essentially the same number of deaths. Better housing, better nutrition, and above all, better medical knowledge and application has reduced the number of deaths to about 12 to 16 per thousand per year. Except in a few countries like the United States, there has not been a similar decrease in the birth rate. Subtracting these two numbers gives the average increase of about 2% a year.

THE CURES

In the past, three factors have controlled the size of animal populations: starvation, disease and pestilence, and predation (man is his own predator by means of war). If we had a moratorium on population increase, science could beat starvation and the advent of antibiotics has wiped out large scale plagues. Even a large scale nuclear war would not permanently stop the population increase: if one-half of the population of the entire world were destroyed at any given time, a growth rate of 2% would return us to our pre-war population within 35 years. Thus, all thoughtful men agree that a fourth method must be instituted—some form of rational control.

Some argue futilely that the solution to the problem is not control, but exporting people to other planets. If, as the experts feel is essential, we are to hold population constant at 10 billion people, then in 50 years we would have to export 200 million people per year if our rate of increase is still 2% a year. Such large numbers would quickly overpopulate any seemingly habitable planets in this solar system, and so we would have to send them to other neighboring solar systems hoping they have habitable planets. A spaceship travelling at 1 million miles per hour (the Mars probe achieved a speed of approximately 10,000 miles per hour) would require 2500 years to go to the nearest star, Alpha Centauri, 4.3 light years away. Those who would refuse to practice strict population control on earth would be unlikely to in a spaceship; and so two people, continuing to procreate at 2% per year would produce 8000 people during a 2500-year trip. Thus, it would be necessary to send off 100 million spaceships a year, each carrying two people initially, but capable of holding 8000. This would mean launching 3 spaceships per second. Surely this must not be Man's ultimate destiny.

Some countries such as Czechoslovakia and Japan use legalized abortion to control population. According to my code of ethics this is increasing the death rate.

The most favorable method seems to be some form of reducing the birth rate. A number of methods are now available, and we have fairly good evaluation of their efficiency. For example, if 1000 normally fertile married women carry out normal intercourse with their husbands, 900 will become pregnant within a given year if they practice no birth control; 400 will become pregnant using the so-called rhythm method; 100 or less if either the man or the woman uses contraceptives in the prescribed way; 10 or less if the ovulation control pills are used properly; and of the 900 or so women who can retain the interuterean spirals, none will become pregnant; with sterilization, of course, essentially zero would become pregnant.

Unfortunately, as detailed below, simply having these methods available does not resolve the problem. To do this on a world-wide basis means that there must be careful consideration given to the ethical and moral attitudes towards these various methods. Equally important is getting the information in time.

THE PROGRAM NEEDED

Within 50 years, we must have a *world-wide* control of population. This probably means treaties, which are policed as carefully as the nuclear testing treaties, involving all countries—we all know what would happen if the rest of the world controlled population and Red China, for example, did not. This means that we have not more than 25 years to disperse the necessary information throughout the world. Certainly, if the information is not disseminated, then we will have either a catastrophic war or some form of dictatorial control or both. No thinking or humane man would choose either alternative.

The problem facing educational people throughout the world is how to get the needed information to the underdeveloped parts of the world where it is not sufficient simply to hand out printed material because most of the people cannot read. The requirements of a global educational program literally stagger the imagination. *If* people in underdeveloped countries can learn from teaching machines, *if* they can be taught to read a common language in a matter of six months to a year, *and if* we can design a common curriculum for the world, then it should be possible to teach the needed 300 million people each year at a cost of about $11 billion.

The above considerations bring into sharp focus the desperately short timetable facing us, since in the Western world major decisions invariably require 25 years to get the public alerted and another 25 years to get the problems resolved—and here we have high levels of education and instant communication. Can we possibly meet this timetable in the portions of the world where the population increase is the largest and has the most tragic consequences?

We must begin to provide information and help on methods of population control to those countries already requesting it, such as India and Pakistan, via foreign aid. Unless we help them with their attempts to control population, it is futile to provide them with economic aid and in particular with medical help which by reducing the death rate further complicates the population explosion problem.

THE MORAL DILEMMA

This need for immediate action makes it imperative that we resolve almost immediatly the moral differences concerning the methods to be used. As a practicing Protestant, I rule out abortion since I consider this murder, but approve of interuterean spirals, the pills, contraceptives if they are used in a proper way, and even the rhythm method although it has a very low efficiency. My Catholic friends would not agree on some of these methods. Yet probably this is placing the emphasis on the wrong argument. The real problem is "Which child shall not be conceived so that another child can have a fruitful life?" This is where the critical moral decisions lie; and to secure any answer in this area requires that we carefully consider, "What is Man and what is his purpose here?" Very likely, if we could resolve the question of what criteria should be used in determining which child shall not be conceived, then it would be possible to determine much more easily which methods should or should not be utilized. However, if our main arguments are concerned with the negative questions, "Which methods *shall not* be used?" and "Which children *shall not* be conceived?," the discussion is unlikely to be completely successful. Probably, we will only begin to secure the most profitable decisions when we realize that the real question we must resolve is, "Under what conditions should any human life be started?" If the population problem forces us to face this issue squarely, we will receive a real bonus. Unfortunately, this all-encompassing question must be surmounted within the next 5-10 years if our children are to have any hope of resolving the population problem in time. However, only if we address ourselves to this extremely crucial question in a positive sense can Man truly achieve his divine purpose.

62

How Good is the Rhythm Method?

Garrett Hardin

How good is the rhythm method? Is it capable of being perfected? To begin with, we must admit that it can hardly be the method of choice among illiterate or undisciplined people, which the impoverished of the world generally are. The user of the method must at least be able to count and keep track of days if she is to make it work. And we should not be very optimistic about persuading the impoverished to use it unless we offer them other amusements to replace the one we propose so much to deprive them of. These other amusements—radios, televisions, automobiles, what have you—cost money, so it is hardly conceivable that the rhythm method will be the most economical method to export to what we euphemistically call the "underdeveloped nations." If all costs are considered, the rhythm method is probably the most expensive of the lot.

Given ideal conditions, does the rhythm method work? Fortunately we have a statistically sound study that answers this question. The statistic utilized is the "number of conceptions per 100 woman-years exposure"—that is, exposure to copulation. By way of background: if no birth control methods at all are used (not even the rhythm method), the number is 90 or a bit higher. It is less than 100 because some couples are naturally sterile; the percentage varies from one population to another, but in the United States sterility affects about 10 per cent of all married couples.

As of the mid-twentieth century, the medical profession regarded the diaphragm and contraceptive jelly as the best method of contraception. This method decreases the conception rate to about 6.5 per 100 woman-years exposure. This sounds good, though one cannot but ask: Why is the figure not zero? No definitive answer is available in the literature, but there is *no* reason to distrust the spermicidal quality of the jelly or the impermeability of the rubber. Taboos against the discussion of sexual matters are still not wholly at an end in the medical profession. The reported failure rate of 6.5 is undoubtedly due to undiscussed psychological matters; and we will just have to accept this rather high figure as the control rate against which we must compare the efficacy of other methods.

In evaluating the rhythm method, Tietze, Poliakoff, and Rock first sorted out their women patients into those with and those without regular rhythms. *The latter, approximately one-sixth of the population, were eliminated from the study.* The rhythmic women were so identified only after the completion of three regular cycles during which they (and their husbands) voluntarily abstained from coitus. (Is this a random sample?) These rhythmic women were then carefully indoctrinated in the method. Their records were supervised throughout the study. It was assumed that "the fertile period extends from and includes the nineteenth day before the *earliest* likely menstruation up to and including the ninth day before the latest likely menstruation." Stated more simply, and approximately: in terms of a presumptive standard 28-day menstrual cycle this means no intercourse from day 9 to day 19. If we add to these days of continence the (approximately) 6 days of menstrual flow, we find that this "natural" method of birth control requires continence during 57 percent of the days of cohabitation.

Among the 387 women cooperating in the subject 57 "accidental" pregnancies were reported. When the time involved was reckoned in, this indicated a conception rate of about 9.4 per 100 woman-years. This is only about 50% higher than the diaphragm-jelly rate, which seems not bad. Had the authors been as unscientific as many of their predecessors they no doubt would have reported this figure, and stopped. But they noticed that a number of their subjects had dropped out of the study. Drop-outs always occur in any voluntary study, of course; but one should never assume that they are a random sample of the total population. When the authors flushed the dropouts from hiding they found that there had been a total of 87 accidental pregnancies, yielding a final conception rate of 14.4 ± 1.5 per 100 woman-years exposure, using the rhythm method. Why were the drop-outs a nonrandom sample? Were they ashamed at having "let the doctor down?" Were they disillusioned with science? Interesting questions, these; but clearly minor.

What does the inferiority of the rhythm method mean in the emotional life of a couple practicing it? A chemist, A. J. de Bethune, has pointed out the human implications of the principles of probability as applied to the rhythm method. If p is the probability of failure (that is, conception) during any one month, then $(1 - p)$ is the probability of success. Success for a given number of months necessarily requires success during each and every month of the period. The product rule of probability tells us that the probability of success during m months is $(1 - p)^m$.

A numerical example should make the point clear. Let us suppose that the probability of success during any one month is 0.9. Most people would regard a 90 percent probability figure as high; but notice what happens as we lengthen the period of exposure to the risk of conception. The probability of success during two successive months is $(0.9)^2$, or 81 percent; during three successive months it is $(0.9)^3$, or 72.9 percent. The probability of success for an entire year (13 cycles) is only 25 percent. Plainly, a hypothetical monthly probability of success of only 90 percent is none too high for comfort.

What is the actual monthly probability of success when the rhythm method is used? Obviously, a number of factors determine it, among the more important of which are the length of the fertile period (that is, the time during which the egg is fertilizable), and the number of copulations per menstrual cycle. The calculations are somewhat complicated, but it takes little imagination to understand the emotional meaning of de Bethune's conclusions: "Even if the fertile period is as brief as 12 hours . . . a couple who desire a 2-year spacing [of children] are limited, statistically, to two acts of coitus per cycle. Couples who desire a 4-year spacing are limited to a maximum of one act of coitus per cycle. It is not surprising that the rhythm method has become a source of mental torture to many couples."

63

Interstellar Migration
and the Population Problem

Garrett Hardin

Anyone who discusses population problems with lay audiences is, sooner or later, confronted with questions of this sort: "But why worry about overpopulation? Won't we soon be able to send our surplus popula-

"Interstellar Migration and the Population Problem," by Garrett Hardin is reprinted by permission from the *Journal of Heredity* (50: 68-70. 1959). Copyright 1959 by the American Genetic Association. Reprinted by permission of the author.

tion to other planets?" It is not only the audience that adopts this point of view; sometimes the lecturer does, as appears from an Associated Press dispatch of 6 June 1958. Monsignor Irving A. DeBlanc, director of the National Catholic Welfare Conference's Family Life Bureau is reported as favoring such mass migration, "deploring an often expressed idea that birth control is the only answer to problems created by a fast-growing world population."

Neither physicist nor professional demographers have, so far as I know, recommended extra-terrestrial migration as a solution to the population problem, but the idea appears to be gaining ground among the laity even without scientific support. The psychological reasons for embracing this idea are two. On the one hand, some Roman Catholics welcome it because it appears to offer an escape from the dilemma created by the Church's stand against "artificial" methods of birth control. On the other hand, citizens of all churches worship the new religion called Progress, of which Jules Verne is the prophet. In this religion all things are possible (except acceptance of the impossible). Who is to set limits to Science (with a Capital S)? Yesterday, the telephone and the radio: today, television and ICBM's; and tomorrow— Space!— which will solve all our earthly problems, of course.

This is heady stuff. Strictly speaking, since it springs from an essentially religious feeling and is non-rational it cannot be answered by a rational argument. Nevertheless, for the sake of those bystanders whose minds are still open to a rational analysis it is worthwhile reviewing the facts and principles involved in the proposal to solve the population problem by interplanetary travel.

THE COST OF SPACE TRAVEL

It now seems possible that, before the century is out, manned landings may be made on Venus or Mars, with the establishment of temporary quarters thereon. But all evidence points to the unsuitability of these, or any other planets of our sun, as abodes for *Homo sapiens*. We must, therefore, look beyond the solar system, to other stars for possible planets for colonization.

The nearest star is Alpha Centauri which is 4.3 light-years away. How long would it take us to get there? The rockets that we are now planning to send to the moon will have a maximum velocity in the neighborhood of 10 kilometers per second, or about 19,000 miles per hour. This may sound fast. But a body traveling at such a speed towards Alpha Centauri (which is 4.07×10^{13} kilometer distant) would require 129,000 years to reach its destination. Surely no one believes that a fleet of space ships with so long a transit time would solve our explosive population problem. The question is, then, what is the probability of improvements in space travel that would significantly cut down the time required to make such an interstellar journey? In trying to answer this question I have relied on an analysis by L. R. Shepherd. . . .

Shepherd presumes a technology in the release and utilization of nuclear energy that may take several centuries to achieve. To give the worshippers of Progress the maximum advantage we will assume that such an advanced technology is available *now*, and see how long it would take to travel to the nearest star. Using fantastically optimistic assumptions, Shepherd calculates that it might be possible to make the transit in a mere 350 years. The average speed of the trip would be about 7,000,000 m.p.h., though the maximum speed would be somewhat more, since 50 years would be required for acceleration at the beginning of the trip and another 50 years for deceleration at the end. (In passing, it should be noted that acceleration is more of a limiting factor than is velocity.

To evaluate interstellar migration as a population control measure we must examine its economics. Here the unknowns are obviously great, but from data assembled by A. V. Cleaver it appears that the forseeable cost of a rocket ship could hardly be as little as $50 a pound, assuming economies of mass production and allowing nothing for research and development costs. How many pounds of ship would be required per man? Since we have no data on such a spaceship, let us borrow from our knowledge of atomic submarines, which are perhaps not too dissimilar. A spaceship designed to be self-maintaining for 350 years could hardly be less complicated or less bulky than an underwater craft capable of operating away from its depots for only a month or two. According to a news release the submarine *Seawolf* weighs 3,000 tons and carries 100 men, a burden of 60,000 lbs. per man. A spaceship of a similar design, at $50 a pound, would cost $3,000,000 per man travelling in it. Would this be a reasonable cost for solving the population problem? Those who propose such a solution presume, or even recommend, that we do not alter our present reproductive habits. What would it cost to keep the population of the United States fixed at its present level by shipping off the surplus in spaceships?

According to a recent estimate of the U. S. Bureau of the Census our population is increasing by about 3,000,000 people per year. To ship this increase off to other planets would, on the above conservative assumptions, cost about 9,000 billion dollars per year. The Gross National Product is now nearly 450 billion dollars per year. In other words, to solve our national population problem by this means we would, then, have to spend 20 times as much as our entire income on this purpose alone, allowing nothing for any other use, not even for food. It would surely be unrealistic to suppose that we shall do this in the near future.

Another aspect of the population problem is worth commenting on.

Many philanthropically minded citizens feel that it is an obligation of the United States to solve the population problems of the entire world, believing that we should use the riches produced by our technology to make up for the deficiencies in luck or foresight of other peoples. Let's examine the economics of so doing. According to a recent estimate the population of the world is increasing at a rate of 123,000 per day. To remove one day's increment by the postulated spaceship would cost about 369 billion dollars. In other words, we Americans, by cutting our standard of living down to 18 percent of its present level, could in *one year's time* set aside enough capital to finance the exportation of *one day's increase* in the population of the entire world. Such a philanthropic desire to share the wealth may be judged noble in intent, but hardly in effect.

In passing, it should be noted that we have so far made no mention of certain assumptions that are of critical importance in the whole picture. We have assumed that our nearest star has planets; that at least one of these planets is suitable for human habitation; that this suitable planet is uninhabited—or, if inhabited, that the humanoids thereon will gracefully commit suicide when they find we need their planet for our *Lebensraum*. (The tender feelings that would make impossible the control of reproduction on earth would presumably not interfere with the destruction of life on other planets.) Should Alpha Centauri have no planet available for migratory earthlings, our expedition would presumably set out for an even more distant star, perhaps eventually becoming a latterday interstellar Flying Dutchman.

PARADOXES OF SPACE EMIGRATION

Cogent as the economic analysis of the problem is, it does not touch on issues that are of even greater importance. Consider the human situation on board this astronautical Mayflower. For 350 years the population would have to live under conditions of complete sociological stasis, the like of which has never been known before. No births would be permitted, except to replace the dead (whose substance would, of course, have to be returned to the common stores). Marriages would certainly have to be controlled, as would all other social interactions, and with an iron hand. In the spaceship, Progress would be unendurable. The social organization would have to persist unchanged for 10 generations' time, otherwise there would be the risk that some of the descendants of the original crew might wish to change the plans. It would be as though the spaceship had to set sail, so to speak, under Captain John Smith and arrive at its goal under President Eisenhower, without the slightest change in ideas or ideals. Can we who have so recently seen how fragile and mutable a flower Education is suppose that we could set up so stable a system of indoctrination? Paradoxically, only a people who worship Progress would propose to launch such a craft, but such worshippers would be the worst possible passengers for it.

Those who seriously propose interstellar migration as a solution to overpopulation do so because they are unwilling to accept the necessity of consciously controlling population numbers by means already at hand. They are unwilling to live, or to admit living, in a closed universe. Yet—and here is the second paradox—that is precisely the sort of universe the interstellar migrants would be confined to, for some 10 generations. Since the present annual rate of growth of the world's population is about 1.7 percent, by the time the first ship arrived at its destination, the whole fleet of spaceships enroute would enclose a total population six times as large as that still present on the earth. This is, in attempting to escape the necessities of living in a closed universe, we would confine to the closed universes of spaceships a population six times as great as that of the earth.

Moreover, there would be a differential element in the emigration from the mother planet. The proposal to emigrate is made by those who, for religious or other reasons, are unwilling to curb the reproductive proclivities of mankind. But not for such as these is the kingdom of a spaceship. They must stay behind while the ship is manned by those whose temperament creates no need for emigration. The reproductively prudent would be exiled from a world made unbearably crowded by the imprudent—who would stay home to perpetuate the problem into the next generation. Whether the difference between the two groups is basically biological, or merely sociological, would not matter. In either case, natural selection would enter in. The end result of this selective emigration would be to create an earth peopled only by men and women unwilling to control their breeding, and unwilling, therefore, to make use of the very means they propose to escape the consequences.

The proposal to eliminate overpopulation by resort to interstellar migration is thus seen to yield not a rational solution at all. The proposal is favored only by men who have more faith in gadgetry than they do in rationality. Should men of this temper prevail, and should the gadgetry prove equal to the quantitative demands put upon it, the result would nevertheless be the ultimate production of a world in which the only remaining controls of population would be the "misery and vice" foreseen by Malthus 169 years ago.

XII
Philosophy and Science

64

A Biologist's Reflections on History

Max Hamburgh

It is the thesis of this paper that if the models and concepts derived from organic life-sciences in general and the theory of evolution in particular have proved of value to historical thought, then some of the more recent concepts developed by the science of genetics may be even more to the point and thus deserving of some attention by the historian.

PART I

In bare outline, the mechanism of evolution as seen by the geneticist runs as follows: Mutations, or changes in the gene material, arise in every animal species with a certain finite frequency and thus supply the raw material for evolution. Most mutations, being accidents of nature, are more likely to be deleterious than beneficial at the time they occur. They may cause a change in the structure of one of the organs, or they may simply change the rate of a physiological process, rendering the affected organism more susceptible to disease or metabolic failure. Some mutations may affect the coloration of all or some external parts of the body (skin, eye color, hair color), others may affect the size, shape or structure of body-parts (cleft palate, hydrocephalus), while still others may just affect purely physiological reactions, like irritability, rate of metabolism or glandular secretion (hemophilia, Parkinsonism, pituitary dwarism). But while most mutations, because of their deleterious effects, would be expected to be lost by simply impairing the afflicted animals in their competition with healthier members of the species, they have a way of being maintained and perpetuated in the population. This is probably due to the

From Max Hamburgh, "A Biologist's Reflections on History," *AIBS Bulletin*, Vol. 10 (1960), pp. 15-20. Reprinted by permission.

circumstance that newly mutated genes are usually not permitted to express themselves in the presence of the homologous older normal gene on the other chromosome of the pair. This relationship is referred to among geneticists as "recessivity," a term denoting the fact that genes are present in each cell in *pairs,* and if one of the pair changes (i.e. mutates) the other unchanged member of the pair as a rule still exerts the dominant influence. The majority of the so-called "visible mutants" resulting from the random union of two mutated genes, can at best give us an inkling of the far higher frequency of the number of such mutated genes present, though hidden, in the population by virtue of their recessivity.

Ultimately however the success or failure of a gene to maintain itself in a population depends upon the "selective" action of the environment to which all biological variations are exposed. The more "fit" genes survive in greater numbers than the less "fit." It is important to realize however that fitness is defined in terms of the environment. There is no such thing as fitness per se. In the regions of Africa where it lives, the giraffe with long legs and a long neck is more fit than a stubbier giraffe. If the giraffe were transported to the arctic tundra, where all food grows within a few inches of the ground, its great height would no longer make it more fit, but rather less so. Fitness then of a gene or its mutated allele is a property conveyed upon it by the environment. It is a value as changeable as the environment itself.

The essentials of the relationship between environment and biological variants was first proposed in scientifically acceptable form by Charles Darwin in 1859 in his *Origin of Species by Natural Selection.* His theory of selection can be reduced to the simple logical proposition "that those variants which are better adapted to their environment will reproduce in greater numbers" than their less favored contemporaries. Darwin's theory of natural selection is really no theory at all. It is merely a statement of the observation that some organisms survive and others do not. The theory gives us no information as to how some organisms persist and others fail to do so.

It fell to the science of genetics to provide the explanation of the mechanism through which evolution operates. This new theory which supplements Darwin's is called by T. Huxley: "Evolution, the modern synthesis" and it was formulated mainly by the insights and in the language of modern genetics

Evolution, then, may be conceived of as a resultant between two fundamental biological phenomena.

a) The raw material of evolution is provided by a discrete number of accidents (mutations) which presumably occur during gene reduplication. Each results in ever so slight changes in the germ plasm, which in their totality give rise to the whole store of biological variations.

b) The direction of evolution is determined by the environmental situation within which the organism has to accommodate itself. In biology we have come to personalize this "tete a tete" between a biological population and its environment by referring to it as "Natural Selection." Natural Selection however is not an all or none proposition. Unlike "artificial selection" as practiced by a breeder, natural selection is merely a difference of survival of competing genotypes, and often this difference is exceedingly slight.

But the "bad" genes of today may become the most desirable genes in the changed environment of tomorrow. It would be nice if organisms were able to respond to the changes of its environment by producing only the proper genetic alterations when needed. Nature however has hit upon a different solution. Instead of discarding the accidents which happen during the difficult process of gene duplication (i.e. mutations), it preserves them, shielded by the protective cover of recessivity, for future use. The greater the genetic variability producd in this manner within species, the greater the choice of switches into which a species can be directed in response to changing environments.

The risks are obvious. By allowing possibly deleterious mutations to "hide behind" the dominant "normal" allele, and thus protecting them from total extinction, a species population may accumulate an ever-growing number of deleterious genes.

It is a gamble, but a gamble which apparently must be taken.

A few examples taken from observations of microbiology, paleontology and anthropology may illustrate the point.

If a population of bacteria like *Escherichia coli* (the ordinary symbiont type inhabiting the colon of men) is cultured in the presence of the mold *Penicillium* or *Streptomyces*, multiplication of the cells in the culture will soon cease, and all the members of the bacterial population will die. Occasionally a bacterial cell survives despite the presence of such actinomycetes. From such a survivor a new strain of bacteria may develop which may be completely resistant to the bactericidal substance produced by the mold. These observations may be interpreted in one of two ways. One might account for the change by assuming that the presence of *Penicillium* itself induced the mutation to resistance or at least accelerated it.

The alternate hypothesis explains the change by assuming that mutations conveying resistance to Penicillium have occurred in bacteria from time to time regardless of whether the strain was exposed to the mold or not. In the absence of the mold the resistant mutants have held no advantage over the ancestral susceptible form. They may even have a slight disadvantage, because the same gene responsible for resistance may have other yet unknown side effects.

When exposed to penicillin the obvious happens: All the susceptible cells succumb, leaving only the few of the randomly arisen resistant mutants to survive and reproduce, thus transforming the original susceptible strain into a resistant one.

The genetic reinterpretation of Darwinism has thus given an explanation of evolution so that it can now actually be "repeated in the test tube," as the example from microbiology illustrates. The new genetic synthesis of evolution has provided also the key by which the transformations of species and their descent from one another as recorded in the paleontological past, can rationally be fitted together.

Although the paleontological record presents us with remains in which only abrupt and discontinuous changes are observable, most students of the fossil record agree that these changes must have been preceded by a slow and gradual accumulation of morphological variants, which though invisible to the paleontologist, were nevertheless real.

The construction of the fleshy lobed fin, which enable certain crossopterygian fishes to seek terrestrial surroundings, must have been preceded by an accumulation of a fantastic number of mutated genes at a time when any deviation from a primarily fin ray type could only have been disadvantageous.

The simultaneous accumulation in those fishes of a large block of mutated genes, which in their additive effect resulted in a saclike outpocketing from the gut, the lung, which could serve for exchange of gases from the air, rather than of gases dissolved in water, as is the customary situation in gills, gave the crossopterygian fishes their unique advantage during the severe droughts of the Devonian period.

A final example from anthropology. Like other plants or animal species *Homo sapiens* has diverged genetically in the several environments in which different human groups have come to settle. However, unlike other animal species, the isolation between these groups was never complete enough to prohibit interbreeding and therefore free gene flow. As a result, the accumulation of genetic differences was never of a sufficient magnitude to allow species separation in "*Homo sapiens.*" But the different environments selected different genes giving rise to at least five distinct racial types, distinguished by the frequency with which certain genes are present in their population.

We do not know why it might be better to have frizzy hair if one lives in Africa. But we know at least something about the value of one of the most obvious and dramatic racial characteristics in man, the presence and quantitative distribution of pigment cells. It is evident that in an environment where sunshine is intense and prolonged the presence of cells in the skin endowed with an enzyme system capable of synthesizing pigment granules in response to exposure to the rays of the ultraviolet spectrum is of considerable advantage. It is reasonable to assume then that in the native population of Africa the frequency of all those genes directing the differentiation of a large number of pigment cells would be far greater than in the nordic population of Scandinavia.

In Africa, therefore, a block of genes assuring heavy pigment production in the skin at all times has been selected for, while in more temperate climates characterized by seasonal variation, a more plastic pigment setup is established where the pigment forming reaction is started upon exposure to the sun's spectrum and lost in its absence.

The fundamental difference between this and the Lamarckian scheme (according to which organisms invent new structures and modes of functioning in direct, adaptive responses to change) often escapes those unfamiliar with contemporary genetics. The genetic interpretation has indeed made short shrift of the teleological argument popularized by Lamarck. Life, or living organisms, do not deliberately and purposefully respond to external stimuli by modifying themselves into structures more capable of meeting new situations, in the way that a corporation may attempt to meet the pressure of rising competition by reshuffling its table of organization. Actually, if some changes occur in nature in this way they can be shown only to be transitory. Thus, to quote one classic experiment, Weissmann cut off a great many mouse tails without ever succeeding to produce a race of tail-less mice.

If one insists on looking for "purpose in life," one might as well be satisfied with the realization that "life" appears to anticipate a whole set of possible conditions which may or may not arise and that "it" gets ready for them by making the necessary provisions by way of genetic "freaks" which, if not of much use at one time, may touch off the most useful genetic re-groupings at dramatic periods of large-scale environmental change. To put the matter paradoxically, it is only the freak who has a future and the blessings of the fully "adjusted" organism cannot last longer than the context within which they are studied.

PART II

Such being the genetic side of the modern story of evolution, can biology in its most advanced version offer as suggestive a model for interpreting historical processes as it did in its earlier Lamarckian version? In the present paper, we will not concern ourselves with Spengler who proposed that civilizations or cultures be conceived as organisms undergoing youth, maturity and unavoidable decline and death. Suggestive as many of the conclusions which Spengler has drawn from this thesis may be, a growing number of historians have found it even more difficult to overlook the rather far-reaching difference between organism and society upon which Spengler's thesis is erected. Instead we shall turn to a more recent "Study of History," namely Toynbee's conception of a "society-civilization."

Toynbee's conception of history resembles Spengler's with civilizations going through the same cycles. He differs from Spengler in denying that this process is predetermined.

But the essential outlines of the process, namely the birth of a civiliza-

tion, its growth and differentiation and its subsequent failure to adjust to
a new challenge, leading to its subsequent breakdown, have been repeated
according to Toynbee 21 times throughout recorded history. Only five of
these civilizations are listed as surviving, in the sense that they have not
yet reached the stage of inner breakdown, though a number of them seem
to be approaching their own destruction rather rapidly. These survivors
include: the Western, the Hindu, the Islamic, the Far Eastern and the
Orthodox Byzantine civilizations. The list of the less fortunate victims includes: the Egyptiac, the Andean, the Sinic, the Minoan, the Sumeric, the
Mayan, the Yucatec, the Mexic, the Hittite, the Syriac, the Babylonic and
the Hellenic.

The genesis of each of these civilizations is conceived by Toynbee as
the outcome of a unique, rather heroic group response of a community to
the challenge of fairly difficult, unpleasant and unusual situations. Often
the adverse stimulus is provided by the terrain, such as the barrenness of
the land which started Minoan and Hellenic cultures.

A more recent example of terrain directing the birth of a nation may
be the experience and efforts of a group of Puritan refugees who settled
along the coast of New England 300 years ago.

Other effective challengers which can organize a herd of people into
a community able to master its surroundings and assure its collective survival are: pressures from outside enemies, such as was experienced by the
Iberian Christians from their neighbors the Moors; penalization such as
was applied to the Jews of the Diaspora. Even slavery has provided adequate challenges with creative consequences.

Once established, a new community will have to add something to its
bag of tricks in addition to whatever new inventions were responsible for
it emerging successfully in the first place. The conquest over its adver-
saries, whether in the form of an outside oppressor, enemy or just rough
terrain, must be followed by less dramatic accomplishments of building a
state, a society or a way of group living. A community must make arrangements to assure its continued existence by organizing itself, making laws,
writing constitutions, setting up governments and establishing rules of
conduct and norms of action. This phase of the life cycle of a civilization
is designated by Toynbee as its "Growth and Differentiation."

Growth and differentiation is dependent on the emergence of what
Toynbee calls the "creative minorities," who must come up with the ideas
by which to shape governments, strategies, social contracts, codes of laws
and ethics.

The emergence of a multiplicity of voices in the form of creative minorities should endow the community with a polymorphism of its own
which would guarantee that new solutions can be found to meet new challenges if and when they present themselves.

Unfortunately, on that score the record of history Toynbee recites is
not too reassuring. The leaders who successfully responded to one chal-

lenges are rarely the successful respondents to the next. Those who have succeeded once are apt on the next occasion to be found resting on their oars.

While this brief paragraph certainly does not adequately state Toynbee's thesis, it may suffice to convey the similarity of his conception of a "society-civilization" with the biological "species population."

However, the biological parallel is to Lamarck, not Darwin, and not to the evolutionary synthesis as formulated by the science of genetics.

PART III

In what follows I should like to suggest in the roughest outline how historians might bring their biological model-thinking up to date. The first thing that would become apparent is that questions of absolute origin, or of first "causes" of ancestral civilizations would continue to elude our methods. As of now, biology cannot satisfactorily answer the question of how life ever got started, but it can both describe and explain how subsequent life-forms connect up with previous ones. Analogously, we may be able to explain how successor-civilizations succeeded where their predecessors failed. What we cannot explain is why man, at one particular time, should have become a culture-building animal. Not that there is any scarcity of speculation on such matters which have intrigued and continue to intrigue man's imagination through his available knowledge is not yet equipped to satisfy his curiosity on this point respectably.

In biology we have learned to live with this limitation ever since Pasteur's experiment proved rather conclusively that there is no such thing as "spontaneous generation" and that all living things come from previous living things.

With the issue of the "first" origin of cultural organizations shelved, how can we account for their survival or adaptation to an ever-changing environment? If culture-change is not clarified in the direct teleological Lamarckian fashion, perhaps on the social level there takes place some sort of "cultural selection" of social mutants? Just as a biological species prepares itself against a variety of unpleasant and possibly lethal external changes by permitting in its population a pool of randomly mutated genes (fit to meet such emergencies), so perhaps each society must harbor in its midst its own contingent of "mutants" or "irregulars," called respectively freaks, misfits, deviants, radicals or non-conformists.

Now, the existence of such non-conforming minorities within the framework of any existing (and past) society is surely not a new discovery. Their role in all sorts of historical processes has intrigued the biographically-inclined historian as much as it has aroused those of the "historical materialist" school of thought. The former contend that all of history is but the product of the non-conformist hero or "great personality" who imposed his or her visions upon the human multitude. According to the historical determinists, on the other hand, the "great men" function merely as the mouthpieces of social forces, at best riding the crest of a wave which they delude themselves to thinking they have personally created. The historical materialists are quite content to surmise that if Isaac Newton had never lived to see that legendary apple fall off the tree, some other British gentleman would have sooner or later observed some other fruit's descent from some other tree or arrived at similar conclusions by some analogous observations.

To evaluate properly the nature of the relationship between the individual and the non-conforming minorities on the one hand, and the social forces which interact with them in producing changed patterns of group living, on the other, we must not be misled by focusing too sharply upon such minorities as proved to be of major historical significance.

"Many are called but few are chosen." The ones who are "chosen," however, as carriers of new life-patterns, be they organic or social, turn out to be those who appear as "deviants" in the old patterns of (natural or social) environmental adjustment. In biological terminology, the non-adjusted individuals might be called "social mutants."

Having established the existence of a fair sized potential stock of "social mutants" we must turn our attention to two questions: 1) What manner of circumstances is involved in creating such social mutants and 2) What forces determine their eventual success or failure in shaping historical events to their liking? The answer to both of these questions is, "We do not know." The question as to why some members of a social order are always prevented from finding their peculiar needs gratified within the arrangements permissible at given times and places is as fascinating and unanswerable as the question about the nature of the processes leading to gene mutations. All we know of the later is that they happen continuously and spontaneously and that under certain conditions, such as radiation, e.g., they will occur with sharply increased frequency. In other words, mutations are accidents and accidents happen. Analogously, we have not yet hit upon a satisfactory theory which would explain the chain of events by which an individual is alienated from his group within which he was nourished. In the absence of confirmable theory, there is, of course, speculation. Thus we are told that a sudden and miraculous enlightenment on the road to Damascus changed Paul of Tarsus from a leading member of the Jewish upper-upper class to a converted and converting hermit in the Arabian desert. The sacking of Kapilavastu presumably so impressed the young aristocrat Siddharta Gautama that he renounced a world which appeared to become inhospitable to aristocrats and he thus was motivated to attempt withdrawal as a new better form of life. Eloquent and powerful as are the figures of Paulus and Buddha, of Moses, Jesus, Mohammed, St. Augustine, Luther, Cromwell, Herzl, Lenin, Marx

and Gandhi, of ultimately even greater significance is perhaps the less eloquent band of apostles, disciples, fighters and martyrs which make up the
nucleus of the "great man's" effectiveness. If the great and lonely figures
which lead into the future are the "macro-mutations," then the small minority, forming their initial followers, could be called the micro-mutable
material. They form that strange collection of misfits, cranks, visionaries,
impractical idealists and dreamers to whom perhaps Christ addressed himself when he said: "Thou art the salt of the earth and the leaven that
makes the dough."

As regards the second question, we must profess an equal measure
of ignorance.

The analogy to biology here is to the formula established for selection.
Just as there are selective forces operating in biological speciation, "quasi-
selective forces" might be at work in history.

In more articulate language, "selection" in an historical sense implies
that under a different set of conditions, i.e., under a slightly different constellation of outside factors to which culture patterns are required to respond, the influence of a great personality or the outcome of a given historical adventure or movement might have either failed, or succeeded or
taken on an entirely different direction from the one it actually did take.

PART IV

To many historians the ultimate decline of practically all known
civilizations points up better than any other factor the resemblance to
organic life. No matter how triumphant a people's history and civilization,
the ultimate fate of extinction and defeat is shared by all. So, at least,
says Toynbee.

The similarity to biological laws is obvious—does not the story of
paleontology reflect the coming and going of one species after another,
much like history records the rise and defeat of different civilizations?

But is extinction really in the cards for each and every civilization? Is
Western civilization, in particular, approaching its "decline" or final
agony, or its passage into a technologically monolithic power-structure as
foreshadowed by new departures from Western norms in both the USSR
and China? This question, if not answered, is raised again and again by
serious-minded historians, taking their cue either from Spengler's earlier
and gloomy prognosis for the "occident" or from Toynbee's detached re-
counting of all history as a series of unsuccessful civilizational attempts to
respond adequately to the ever-changing challenges of natural and social
circumstances. Civilization's ball game with destiny scores a measly 21 to
5, according to Toynbee. Statistically this is indeed somewhat less than a
good omen for the present.

Fortunately the biologists can provide a more cheerful outlook. Few biologists will quarrel with the belief that all living organisms have limited life-spans, *but no biologist is in possession of evidence which can be used for a proof that what holds for the individual organism must hold for the species.* Many species, to be sure, have come and gone, but others have been around for a long time and their careers, if limited in the cosmological end, may have futures of as many millions of years as their past. By contrast, the human species, whether ultimately limited or not, has hardly *started,* instead of *declining* towards its "inevitable death." Thus, while death is a fact of life, there is nothing in evolutionary theory to indicate that extinction is the final end to which all evolution is mysteriously directed by some unfathomable power. Quite to the contrary, there appears on the time scale of biological evolution a large number of "Methuselahs" who seem to be strangely immune to extinction. Among the invertebrates particularly we have in the sea-shell "Lingula" an organization which is still amazingly like what it was 400 million years ago. The silica-secreting radiolaria are claimed to have existed since the Cambrian. An oyster of 200,000,000 years or more in the past would look quite familiar if served in a restaurant today. Among the vertebrate immortals, the reptilian Sphenodon deserves a place of honor, just as the opossum which has survived unchanged since the Cretaceous. The way to achieve or approach immortality, it seems, is to be fortunate in having made an early adaptation to an environment which does not ever change, or to be ready with new adaptations where environmental changes cease to favor earlier conditions.

The one fatal fallacy which some of the otherwise most successful species have committed was to make too perfect an adaptation. By sacrificing versatility for perfection they failed to adapt to new environments. To make too complete an adjustment—putting all one's eggs in one basket —appears to be as lethal a course to take, as to make no adjustment at all.

The sabertoothed tiger, appearing in the early Oligocene became extinct only yesterday, i.e., in the Pleistocene, some 20 or 30 million years ago. According to Simpson, the ever-lengthening saber-tooth of this beast started out as a perfectly effective biting mechanism until eventually it became an impeding and destructive occlusion. The antlers of the Irish elks, which originally were highly adaptive weapons for offense and defense in time became so cumbersome a burden that their owners were ultimately doomed before they had a chance to use them: "Study of History" is a storehouse of historical parallels of sabertoothed tigers and Irish elks.

The analogous fate of the knights in shining armour comes to mind. In the late Middle Ages they had perfected such all-protective "panzers" for themselves that, while shielded against blows and thrusts, they were also effectively imprisoned and immobilized and thus easy victims for more movable yeomen, fighting according to changing rules of combat.

The fate of the once-mighty Armada at the hands of the British pirate vessels is another case in point.

As the gist of all this, two lessons are respectfully offered to the historian: 1) The final agony of all dying civilizations is marked by the desperate attempt to meet a crisis by too rigid a code. For society, just as for biological species, the inability to change beyond already successful changes, is the most general cause to which all more specific causes of downfall can be reduced. Rigidity, conformity, inflexibility spell extinction for societies as well as for organisms. The liberal mind may take some comfort from the historical lesson that demands of absolute obedience and conformity repeatedly made by society upon its members in time of trouble and crisis have rarely, if ever, succeeded in overcoming the difficulties for the sake of which they were invoked. Imperial absolutism, the Inquisition, the police-state or fascist dictatorship, they all have a way of succumbing in the end. 2) Only the readiness to change offers promise of survival. Democracy as a form of government most likely to maximize change through multiple representation, may be defined as being itself one of the most potent, if not indispensable, social tools for providing optimal conditions for permitting and maximizing human diversity, filling the reservoir of social mutants whose presence and freqency co-varies with the success or failure of social organisms to meet unanticipated environmental changes from within or without. It is probably safe to say that given the correct momentum and frequency of change which instead of happening to man can now be produced by him in both deliberate and unforeseeable ways, there will be no society that can hope to survive without holding in readiness some of the "openness-to-change" which Western people attribute to democracy alone.

65

Front Seats for Biologists

Wallace O. Fenn

We are all convinced that Biology is the Queen of the Sciences, although it is often regarded as only a handmaiden, the weakest of the sciences and the least well supported. I want to discuss some of the reasons for this situation as well as the reasons why it is not true. Biology needs no

From Wallace O. Fenn, "Front Seats for Biologists," *AIBS Bulletin*, Vol. 10 (1960), pp. 13-18. Reprinted by permission.

apologies. Finally I want to express my conviction that mankind needs a well-defined reason for living. For what purpose if any are we, intelligent, thinking, reasoning persons, placed in this thin film of air which clings to the surface of this whirling planet? Obviously it is our business to discover the answer if we can—by the ardent pursuit of knowledge and particularly biological knowledge. Therefore from a very long range point of view biological research becomes the highest objective that can be thought of for human life. In this respect the biologists deserve front seats in the halls of learning.

FRACTIONATION OF BIOLOGY

One of the main reasons why biologists appear to occupy only the back seats rather than the front seats is the fractionation of biology. One group of scientists after another has seceded from biology, and what remains under the strict designation of biology in the public mind is nothing more than some superficial natural science. Agriculture and medicine are both applied biology but neither group admits to belonging to biology and biology gets little or no credit for all their great advances. Anything chemical belongs to the biochemists and anything physical to the biophysicists and neither group admits to being biologists—anyhow they do not belong to AIBS and biology gets no credit. It is indeed hard to beat the biophysicists in this respect. Recently a prominent biophysicist defined for me the limits of his subject. "Anything which has rational explanation," he said, "belongs to biophysics and biology can have all the rest of it." Even so, a lot remains. . . .

No longer does biology cover all the sciences concerned with living organisms and clear evidence of this is the repeated use of the term "life science" in place of biology, especially in military documents. The plain and sad fact is that the term biology inevitably has a very special and limited connotation to the public mind and even to most scientists so that it does not mean the same thing as the expression "the life science." Perhaps AIBS would thrive better under the term AILS—American Institute of Life Sciences. This spells however "ails" and indicates again the sick man of science. Further AIBS means *all in back seats,* and I think it should mean *all in the best seats.*

I do not seriously complain about the fractionation of biology. It is too broad a subject to be covered by any one mind and these specialties are of course a sign of progress. But fractionation makes unification increasingly difficult and it is important that all the biological sciences should belong to AIBS as a sign of their common interest. Without the concerted action of all biologists many economies and accomplishments are beyond our reach. . . .

ACHIEVEMENTS OF OTHER SCIENCES

Perhaps the recent brilliant accomplishments of other sciences have also contributed to the relatively backward position now occupied by biology in the public mind. Astronomers can show us marvelous photos of millions of galaxies, thousands and millions of light years away—each galaxy as big as our own, and each containing I suppose millions of stars and solar systems like our own. So man and his troubles and his life processes fade away into insignificance and we are left gazing in awe and wonder at our universe. . . .

It is no wonder then that biology has been thrust aside while the world contemplates all these new marvels of the physical sciences. But the wonders of biology are far greater than all these wonders of physics and chemistry. The trouble is perhaps that the phenomena of biology are too familiar to us and familarity breeds contempt. We have all seen great oaks grow out of acorns, birds hatched out of eggs, and babies born after matrimony. Such is life, they say. Don't expect to understand it—just enjoy it. Living things have their ways. You can describe them in as much detail as you like and that is biology—a descriptive science but not a basic science. Don't ever expect to get to the bottom of the problem. Life was created by God. Possibly man evolved from simpler forms as the fossil records appear to indicate. But the nature of life itself is God's secret and must forever remain beyond our reach. So runs the common argument—and it is perhaps another reason for the back seat status of biologists. For the real fundamentals of biology seem to be the responsibility of the theologians and the philosophers and do not belong in the realm of the experimental sciences. Therefore we might even ask the question whether biology is really a science at all—since we are denied access to the fundamentals of the subject.

SOME REASONS FOR FRONT SEATS

Well, this of course is nonsense and the advances in biology have been as great as in any other science. True it is however that the truly basic aspects of biology seem quite beyond our reach at present—the nature of consciousness for example. What a phenomenon that is compared to the physical world! The eye of the astronomer receives light from a galaxy million of light years ago—an incredible thought. But even more wonderful is the fact that the astronomer is *aware* that he is seeing a distant galaxy. He *knows* where that light came from. The first records of man on earth are only 500,000 years old. Therefore since that ray of light started on its journey there has developed on the earth a conglomeration or organization of atoms and molecules which functions as a whole and is somehow *aware* of its surroundings, and it can think and reason and knows, or believes that it knows, when and where that ray of light set out on its long journey. Even more important, he knows that he knows, and tries to understand the real meaning and mechanism of knowing. He wants to know how he knows and how his brain works.

This problem of consciousness is one which biology has never cracked. No one has the slightest clue or knows how to begin the study. Some believe that only man is conscious because God endowed him with a soul. Others believe that all living things have some sort of consciousness in a primitive form. Still others would argue that the essence of consciousness or the mechanism of consciousness must reside somehow in the molecules of which we are composed. When we know enough about the molecules and the certainties and uncertainties of their arrangements, we will understand consciousness and all the secrets of life. Thus even the stones might be considered to have the elements of a certain sort of inherent molecular consciousness. . . .

Biology is still making rapid progress, and it is even now experiencing a revolution which may turn out to be as dramatic as the revolution in physics. The advances in nucleic acid chemistry have greatly illuminated the structure of genes and chromosomes to such a degree that growth and development and inheritance of parental characteristics become almost understandable. Viruses can almost be synthesized in the laboratory. Several reasonable explanations for the origin of life have been offered. The modern biology department is not complete without someone who knows biochemistry and biophysics and mathematics and is exploring fundamental problems of cell function. Modern biology is a dynamic analytical science and not merely descriptive. Much of this modern spirit is being introduced into the teaching of biology in schools and colleges and AIBS with its teaching film series and Curriculum Study is playing a most important role in the process.

In the advance of civilization biology has a great role to play, in medicine and agriculture, in the ocean and out in space. From the ocean may come food for man and out in space, we know not what, but anyway food for thought. The solution of the photosynthesis problem would revolutionize human life as much as the development of a practical device for using the energy of nuclear fusion for peaceful purposes. A big crash photosynthesis program comparable to the cancer program might well pay big dividends in 10–20 years and, incidentally, if successful it would not only contribute to human nutrition but would solve the problem of pilot maintenance during space travel. As biologists we have a right to be proud of our science, and we want AIBS to tell the world about it, and we see no reason for being content with back seats.

There are other reasons for front seats, and in this connection I have the temerity to speak about biology in its relation to religion for they are in a sense contiguous subjects, religion being defined as an interpretation, perhaps an emotional interpretation, of those problems of life to which biological science has not yet been able to provide any reasonable answers.

As a college student I almost followed my father into the liberal ministry before I began my scientific career in physiology. I have therefore a great respect for religion which supplies some meaning and purpose to life for many people. Even so, as biologists, most of us would be happy to have more facts and less imagination for our religious guidance. Now certainly it may be that there *is no* meaning to life and man may be just a chemical accident of the environment under the impact of radiant energy from the sun. Even so, here we are, and we had better find some meaning or invent one for ourselves so that we have some definite mission to lend dignity to our life. If there is a meaning, it obviously lies somewhere in the vast areas of biology which are still unknown to us, and we should have faith that it is at least worth looking for by the usual rational experimental approach. In such a search all the sciences contribute, but it is the biologist who applies the new developments in science to the problem and who is therefore the spearhead of the attack. We do not yet know where we came from, where we are going to, or why we were here or what life is all about. We are however blessed with truly remarkable brains, and it behooves us to use them to the limits of their capacity to find out all we can about whatever there is that might be defined as God's purpose. This effort *per se* seems to me to satisfy man's yearning for a purpose or mission in life. This is a sort of religion which places the emphasis on striving rather than arriving. It might be described as pantheism or just agnosticism coupled with a determination to find out—or perhaps "biologism." Unlike the physical sciences biology can be almost a religion in itself.

66
The Road Traversed and the Road Ahead

Theodosius Dobzhansky

People used to talk about the march of history. Marching, i.e., walking, was a suitable metaphor. Nowadays history bestrides a motor vehicle

Reprinted by permission of Yale University Press from MANKIND EVOLVING, by Theodosius Dobzhansky. Copyright 1962 by Yale University Press.

or maybe an airplane (thank goodness, not yet a rocket). Anybody in mid-life or older has witnessed great changes. Has not the "unchanging East" changed greatly? Where are the ancient European monarchies and their loyal subjects? Even in "primitive" societies people no longer live as they used to. A few years ago I heard a young Papuan, grandson of a cannibal, whistle the Toreador song from *Carmen* in the Owen Stanley Mountains of New Guinea!

Most of these changes evidently occurred not because human populations were altered genetically, but because they were altered culturally. The human species is biologically an extraordinary success, precisely because its culture can change ever so much faster than its gene pool. This is the reason cultural evolution has become adaptively the most potent extension of biological evolution. For at least 10,000 and perhaps for 1,000,000 years man has been adapting his environments to his genes more often than his genes to his environments. And the supremacy of culture in adaptation doubtless will continue in the foreseeable future. In this sense, but in this sense only, it may be said that man has escaped from the clutches of his biological past and has become to some extent the master, rather than a slave, of his genes.

The craving of the human mind for either-or categories is, however, a powerful one (perhaps genetically so?). Hence the widespread belief that the evolution of culture has suspended and superseded biological evolution. Since we live in the world of culture, it is, allegedly, a derogation of human dignity to say that we live in the biological world as well. But the biological world is not such a bad place in which to keep a toehold; it contains many joys for which no fit substitutes have yet been devised. Not only do we live in both worlds, but the world of culture can endure only so long as most of mankind possesses genetic equipments which are favorable for culture. Conversely, most of these genetic equipments are now such that their carriers probably could now survive without the benefit of culture. So, interdependence should be the watchword.

IS THE BIOLOGICAL EVOLUTION OF MAN COMPLETED?

Far-reaching cultural transformations have manifestly taken and are taking place. Do genetic changes accompany the cultural ones? White believes that "in the man—culture equation over a period of a million years, we may assume some absolute increase in magnitude of the biological factor. But during the last hundred or even the last fifty thousand years, we have no evidence of an appreciable increase in mental ability." The assumption of the psychic unit, or uniformity, of mankind is probably pivotal in the working philosophy of a majority of anthropologists, psychologists, sociologists, and of not a few biologists. They maintain that biological evolution has achieved the genetic basis of culture and run its course; it is now a matter of the past. The genetic basis of culture is uniform everywhere; cultural evolution has long since taken over.

Up to a point the above view is justified. All healthy individuals of *Homo sapiens* have a capacity to learn a language, any language, and to acquire a culture, any of the cultures any group of people have anywhere. This capacity is one of the biological universals of our species, like walking erect, the approximately nine-month pregnancy term, or the non-opposable big toe. There are no genes for the French or Chinese or Hottentot language or culture. Our genotype confers on us a remarkable plasticity of cultural development. It cannot be too strongly emphasized that this plasticity is itself a species trait, formed by natural selection in biological evolution.

It is, however, a fallacy to think that specific or ordinal traits do not vary or are not subject to genetic modification. Phenotypic plasticity does not preclude genetic variety. There may be variations in the degree of plasticity; or some of the functions or roles which exist within a culture may be more congenial, and hence more easily learned, than others.

White is on firm ground when he denies that an "appreciable" change in the "biological factor" of human mental ability during the last fifty thousand years can be rigorously proven. If anything, he is overgenerous when he concedes that such change is proven for the last million years. There is no way to make the experiments necessary to secure such a proof. We cannot plant some identical twins to be reared by Peking man or by the Neanderthalians and leave cotwins to grow up in a modern society. We cannot give IQ tests to a sample of Cro-Magnons or, for that matter, to contemporaries of Plato or Charlemagne. The "proof" has to be based on inference. It cannot be otherwise, since what is at issue is whether certain historical events have or have not occurred. Anti-evolutionists have said again and again that evolution is not "proven." We cannot reproduce in the laboratory the changes which transformed the three-toed horse into the one-toed one or those which led from *Australopithecus* to *Homo*. It is an inference (and at that, one questioned by some competent authorities) that the bones of our ancestors were once upon a time not very different from those of *Australopithecus*. Darwin did not claim to have observed evolution, except that under domestication. He claimed that evolution can be inferred from what he did observe.

Emergence and development of culture makes adaptation to changing environments by means of genetic changes less binding than it was in precultural times. Man did not need to grow warm fur to cope with cold climates, because he donned warm fur garments. But there is really no way for culture to ward off genetic change altogether. Culture does not make human environments stable and uniform; far from it. The tempos of environmental changes have grown and are growing. Given environmental flux, the necessary and sufficient condition for genetic change is availability in populations of genetic variants, some of which are better and others less well adapted to shifting environments. Natural selection will do the rest—it will multiply the favored variants and depress or eliminate the unfavorable ones. The crux of the problem is, thus, how much genetic variance is available in human populations. This can be established by observation and experiment.

The diversity of human beings is seemingly endless. Granted that our senses are better trained to perceive differences between humans than between sheep, sparrows, or Drosophila flies, the human species must be regarded an extraordinarily variable one. What parts of the variance are genetic and what environmental is inadequately known. Human genetics has much to learn. This much is, however, certain: whenever the matter has been studied, both genetic and environmental components of the variability have usually come to light. And this is what one might have expected on theoretical grounds.

THE FEEDBACK BETWEEN GENES AND CULTURES

 . . . No modern geneticist thinks that there existed in our ancestors or that there appeared by mutation some special genes "for culture." The transformation of the pre-human ancestral species into the "political animal" involved mutational changes in most or perhaps in all gene-loci. It is the whole genetic system which makes us human. However, many, or most, genes are represented in human populations by two or by several alleles. Has this genetic variability any relevance to culture? I believe that it has. Discussions of this matter are often plagued by a sheer misunderstanding. Some people are looking for a one-to-one correspondence between genetic and cultural traits. They find no such correspondence: there are no genes to make you a painter or statesman, or gangster; the Negro race is not homozygous for a nonexisting gene for jazz music, nor are the Balinese genetically dancers or the Jews merchants. The matter is considerably more subtle.

Genes create the setting for cultural traits, but they do not compel the development of any particular ones. An imaginary, extreme but, I hope, instructive illustration has been given in Chapter 1—if mankind consisted of individuals of one sex only, countless cultural changes would follow. The suggestion of Brues was referred to—the way of life of settled agriculturists favored and was favored by different bodily constitutions than the cultures based on hunting and pursuing game. It was also shown that rigid caste structure has genetic consequences different from and less desirable than those of social systems which accord to their members a rough equality of opportunity. Indeed, any major social or political change is bound to be reflected in an alteration of the gene pool of the population subjected to such change. This is a consequence of the fact that the magnitude as well as the direction of natural selective pressures depends on the environment, and the environment that exerts a decisive influence on the human species is the social environment.

The changes taking place in our modern world need rethinking in the light of genetics as well as that of sociology and politics. From the beginning of human history until recently, countless multitudes endured scarcity, hunger, disease, exposure to the elements, and misery of all kinds. Privations were believed to be the order of nature. Industrial and scientific revolutions have taught people otherwise. People learned that misery is unnecessary, that the world has the means for providing a decent living to all. There will be no return to the old beliefs, not even if the "population explosion" would result in a real shortage of the wherewithal for decent living. In one way or another, people will check the uncontrolled population growth and will secure what they now regard as their just right.

Certain consequences seem probable, not to say inevitable. Instead of most of the world producing raw materials and a few countries arrogating to themselves the roles of industrial and cultural centers, industrialization on a global scale is assured. Technical and scientific training will be widespread if not universal. Urbanization, more and more people living in urban communities, will continue. Now, city life favors a different kind of relation between people than does rural existence. Rural folk were traditionally members of communties in which everybody knew everybody else and everybody felt morally obligated to give and entitled to receive help in case of need from other members of their community. Urban life favors replacement of the desire for neighborliness by the desire for privacy: many an inhabitant of New York City neither knows nor cares to know who is living on the other side of a partitioned wall. It is chiefly, if not exclusively, from members of one's nuclear family that one hopes to receive assistance and succor when in need.

A Russian adage had it that "God is too high, the Czar is too far." But nothing is too far with modern means of communication. While expecting little from their immediate neighbors, people expect more and more from their states, nations, and governments. Democratic or totalitarian, governments will assume greater and greater responsibilities for the welfare of their citizens. Demands for a closer approach to an equality of opportunity for all citizens of a state, and eventually for all citizens of the world, will be irresistible. The advice of a high church authority to the poor, "to take delight in the prosperity of elevated persons and to expect confidently their assistance," is unlikely to be accepted, least of all by members of a society atomized to a multitude of nuclear families. With relationships between members of a community becoming more and more impersonal, people expect and indeed demand assistance from the state. And everybody feels equally entitled to such assistance.

Now, equality of opportunity has genetic consequences different from those of hierarchical, stratified, and caste societies. Equality decreases the wastage of the genetic potential of the human species. It favors manifestation of talents which remain hidden in societies that let high culture and refinement flourish while a great majority of people live in misery and ignorance. We need not raise here the difficult question of the role of the individual in history. It will be generally conceded that persons like Leonardo, Newton, Beethoven, Darwin, Dostoevsky, or Einstein have made priceless contributions to the treasury of culture of our species. And although this cannot be proven rigorously, it is extremely probable that these individuals carried rare and precious constellations of genes. Now, if these gene constellations had appeared among Indian untouchables or Negro slaves or even in the slums of our cities, their carriers might not have accomplished much. Humanity would be the loser.

Equality of oportunity is an ideal not uniformly appealing to everyone. Continuation of hereditary priveleged classes has found an outspoken and highly articulate defender in the poet T. S. Eliot. To Eliot, equality of opportunity endangers the refinements of civilization. In his view, a culture must be an "organic" whole, while equality of opportunity presupposes "an atomic view of society"; only an entrenched aristocracy can guarantee continuity of culture from generation to generation. Hardin fears that as class competition decreases, competition between individuals increases in intensity and vindictiveness. "The complete elimination of classes would mean the installation of a dog-eat-dog society." He insists that mankind's biological as well as cultural welfare demands competition of many separate class or race populations; some of these will become extinct, while others will survive and repopulate places "left vacant by those that have succumbed."

The basic error of these views lies, it seems to me, in the implied assumption that equality of opportunity and mitigation or elimination of inter-group competition is tantamount to uniformization, leveling, disappearance of genetic and cultural variety. But this is not necessarily the case at all. Genetically, the gene exchange between Mendelian populations leads to their fusion in a single population, but there will be much greater inter-personal variability, and, I suppose, a greater number of nervous breakdowns, in that single population than there was in the previously isolated, separate populations. The variety of human genotypes, and hence of inclinations and abilities, is increased, not decreased, by hybridization. I suppose the same is true on the cultural level also. A large and complex society should be better able to provide for specialized talent and to tolerate unconformity than a small homogeneous group. I, for one, do not lament the passing of social organizations that used the many as a manured soil in which to grow a few graceful flowers of refined culture.

OF RATS AND MEN

The failure of some nations and races to evolve high cultures is often taken as evidence of their genetic incapacity. Unfavorable environment is at least as likely to be responsible. Cultural advancement is hamstrung in populations where most people are infected with malaria, hookworm, or other infectious or parasitic diseases. The state of public health inevitably has repercussions in the cultural sphere. Populations in which the life expectancy is twenty-five years offer different cultural settings from those with a life expectancy of seventy years. Hereditarians as well as environmentalists will be well advised to remember that health is conditioned by environmental as well as genetic variables. However, as medicine and hygiene reduce or eliminate environmental hazards, the importance of genetic variables will loom larger and larger.

The National Health Education Committee estimates that about 17 million people in the United States suffer from some form of mental disease, about 4.8 million are mentally retarded, about 70 million have eye defects, 345 thousand are blind, etc. It is at present futile to try to estimate what proportion of these afflictions are genetic and what environmental. As pointed out repeatedly, these are not discrete categories. One may hope that, at least in the long run, only a fraction, perhaps a small fraction, of this human misery will remain incurable. Myopia is an eye defect which often has a genetic basis, yet it is corrected environmentally —by wearing glasses. The magnitude of the genetic load may, nevertheless, be influenced by culture and may influence culture at least by speeding up or applying a brake to its progress.

Richter is one of the writers who foresees the biological twilight of human evolution brought about by the influences of culture. His argumentation may be taken as representative of a school of thought having many adherents. Our ancestors lived the wholesome lives of wild animals. They struggled and fought for survival; natural selection held full sway; the strongest and cleverest survived; the rest succumbed. This has resulted in the development of man's finest qualities. In technologically advanced societies natural selection has come to a halt: birth and death rates being low, necessities of life assured to everybody, environmental hazards and epidemics controlled—the unfit survive and reproduce their kind. According to Richter, the process that has transformed the wild rat into the domesticated laboratory rat is also working in human evolution.

Norway rats (*Rattus norvegicus*) have been kept in laboratories since sometime between 1840 and 1850. The modern laboratory rat belongs to a well-defined variety that differs from its wild progenitor in many ways. The laboratory rat is entirely dependent on "the protected state of the laboratory where food, water, mates, and shelter are provided, and the struggle for survival no longer exists." Among other differences, laboratory rats have smaller adrenal glands and less resistance to stress, fatigue, and disease than wild rats. Thyroid glands have also become less active in laboratory rats, while, on the contrary, sex glands develop earlier and permit a greater fertility. They have smaller brains and are tamer and more tractable than the active and aggressive wild rats.

The genetic changes which occurred in the laboratory rat would, undeniably, make them unable to compete successfully with wild rats in the environments in which the latter normally live. But it does not follow that laboratory rats are decadent and unfit; nor does it follow that the "welfare state" is making man decadent and unfit—to live in a welfare state! What Richter has overlooked is the obvious fact that the laboratory rat is manifestly fit to live in its environment—which is the laboratory cage. Indeed, laboratories maintain stocks of laboratory rats, not of wild rats. The laboratory rat is not a decadent product of the absence of natural selection, it is a product of rigid natural selection in laboratory environments. Being tame, tractable, unaggressive, and fecund confers upon it a high fitness. And inasmuch as these qualities depend upon the lessened activity of the adrenal and thyroid glands, having these glands less active than in the wild rat is also a part of the high fitness. The contention that civilization or the "welfare state" set aside natural selection in man is not necessarily true either.

MULLER'S BRAVEST NEW WORLD

Utopias are seldom used as blueprints for action, even when their authors intend them for this purpose. Utopias may, however, fire the popular imagination and goad people to action, or they may indicate the intellectual climate at the time when they are composed. The genetic utopia painted by Muller will have an interest of at least this latter kind.

Muller is the leading advocate of the view that the genetic loads which human populations carry are unconditionally deleterious, that civilization increases the mutation and decreases the selection rates, and that the genetic load of mankind threatens to swell until it becomes too heavy to carry. One can hardly contemplate a prospect of doom without looking for an escape. Muller has attempted to find one. He recognizes that the measures which he advocates run counter to the mores of all human societies. The decision to have or not to have children (and when and how many) is a prerogative of the individual; attempts, even benevolent ones, to dictate or sermonize on these matters evoke resentment. He thinks, however, that people will have to "recognize a duty on the part of individuals to exercise their reproductive function with due regard to the benefit or injury thereby done to society." This would make possible the introduction of the measures which Muller discusses under the headings of "Presently available genetic techniques," "Technical advances in the offing," and "More distant prospects."

Although frowned upon by some legal and ecclesiastic authorities, artificial insemination of human females is practiced on a small scale in the United States at present. It is applied mostly to women whose husbands produce no functional spermatozoa; the sperm donors are not, however, chosen with genetic or eugenic considerations. Therefore, "here is an excellent opportunity for the entering wedge of positive selection, since the couples concerned are nearly always, under such circumstances, open to the suggestion that they turn their exigency to their credit by having as well-endowed children as possible," and this can be done by "choosing as donors individuals of the most outstanding native mental ability." Muller endorses also a plan credited to Dr. R. Meir, which, in his opinion, "does not involve as radical a departure from present day customs and attitudes as does artificial insemination." This is for "couples of high native endowment" to "be willing to bear more children than they could bring up and give them out for adoption." Since this would presumably mean that the highly endowed parents would have a part of their progeny brought up by less highly endowed ones, the former must be very eugenical-minded indeed.

Animal semen (at least bull semen) can be frozen and kept for a long time at low temperatures, presumably without deterioration. Muller visualizes preserving the semen of outstanding men for future use in artificial insemination. Then when they will have long been dead a mature and dispassionate judgment of their real value could be reached. In the first version of his utopia Muller believed that no woman would refuse to bear a child of Lenin, but in the more recent one he nominates Einstein, Pasteur, Descartes, Leonardo, and Lincoln. Furthermore, with the passage of years the real value of the progenies begotten by these men in their lifetime by the more old-fashioned methods would also become clear. This is the technique of "progeny testing" which is known and widely employed in animal breeding.

If using the semen of select fathers with the egg cells of unselected mothers will lead to racial improvement, utilizing selected eggs as well as selected sperm should be even more successful. The number of children produced by a human female is limited not so much by the number of the egg cells she matures as by the total length of the pregnancies. It is estimated that the ovaries of a normal woman can shed several hundred egg cells. Techniques could be developed to flush these at present wasted egg cells from the reproductive tracts of outstanding women and to fertilize the eggs by spermatozoa of well-endowed men. The fertilized eggs thus obtained could then be implanted into the uteri of eugenically less desirable females, develop there, be born in the old-fashioned manner, and be brought up by the foster parents as though they were the biological parents.

When people will be enlightened enough to accept the foregoing, still better techniques could be evolved. Would not humanity profit enormously if instead of one Leonardo, one Einstein, or one Pasteur numerous individuals could be manufactured having genetic endowments *precisely* similar to those of the above great men? Not even having available for use the germ cells of the actual parents of these persons would make it possible to obtain replicas of their genotypes. For gene recombination takes place when the germ cells are formed, and it is, alas, well known that some of the progeny of outstanding parents fall short of the parental standards. It is, however, perfectly imaginable that techniques may be invented to dispense with sexual reproduction altogether, by implanting nuclei of body (somatic) cells into enucleated eggs and making them develop without fertilization (parthenogenetically).

Suppose then that we have available body cells of truly great men and women, preserved in special cultures or in deep-frozen condition, and that a technique is available to make these cells develop into whole organisms. One could at any time bring into the world any number of persons who would resemble the respective donors of the cells as much as if these donors had identical twin brothers or sisters. The limit would be to select the ideal man, or the ideal woman, and to have the entire population of the world, the whole of mankind, carry this ideal genotype. All men (or all women—one could, if desired, have individuals of one sex only) would then be born not only equal but indeed genetically alike. If this would seem too monotonous, the (perhaps unreasonable?) craving for diversity could be gratified by engineering environmental differences. The resulting people would be as different as identical twins apart.

Nor are still greater advances in human evolution excluded. "The biological distance from apes to men is a relatively slight one, yet how potent! Our imaginations are woefully limited if we cannot see that, genetically as well as culturally, we have by our recent turning of an evolutionary corner set our feet on a road that stretches far out before us into the hazy distance."

It might be argued that the only fair way to criticize a utopia is to compose a substitute. I am not prepared to do so. Muller's sweep of imagination is so great that his utopia has a certain romantic appeal.

To point out difficulties, such as the possibility that detrimental mutations might arise in the germ cells or the somatic cells of the outstanding persons during their storage, would seem almost picayune. Such difficulties probably could be overcome; if only a fraction of the money and effort now being wasted on bombs and missiles were to be invested in biological research, new and remarkable techniques would certainly result. However, are we "hastily made-over apes," ready to agree what the ideal man ought to be like? Granted that mankind would profit immeasurably from the birth of more persons with the mental stamina of Einstein, Pasteur, and even Lenin, do we really want to live in a world with millions of Einsteins, Pasteurs, and Lenins? Muller's implied assumption that there is, or can be, *the* ideal human genotype which it would be desirable to bestow upon everybody is not only unappealing but almost certainly wrong—it is human diversity that acted as leaven of creative effort in the past and will so act in the future.

SOCIAL COSTS OF VARIANT GENES

Among the biological problems which mankind has to face, that of the management and direction of the biological evolution of our species is second in urgency only to the awesome problem of overpopulation. This problem, in turn, has two fairly distinct aspects: the alleged failure, or weakening, or normalizing natural selection and the improvement of the present genetic endowment of humanity by directional selection.

Muller's utopia envisages a radical solution for the management of our evolution. The trouble with this solution is not only that it gives short shrift to the deepest of human emotions. It may be doubted that we know enough genetics to plan so ambitious a program. The situation cries out for more research in what Wright so aptly describes as "the unpopular and scientifically somewhat unrewarding borderline field of genetics and social sciences."

It is plain that normalizing selection does not act at present as it did in the Stone Age. The carriers of some genotypes who would have had no chance to survive then do survive and reproduce now. It is often forgotten that the reverse is also true—with respect to some genotypes selection has increased in severity. Natural selection is conditiond by the environment; its direction and intensity cannot remain constant when people adopt new ways of life. The selection is now as "natural" as it was a hundred thousand years ago, but it cannot be relied upon to do what is best in our—human—estimation: selection tends to increase Darwinian fitness; Darwinian fitness is reproductive fitness, not necessarily fitness for social progress.

It is uncertain how much genetic change there has been in mankind owing to the shifting direction of normalizing selection. Modern man might or might not be able to survive, even if properly trained, in the environments of his ancestors of one hundred thousand years ago. Or if he survived, he might not be as efficient or as happy in those environments as his ancestors were. We do not know for sure. It is often alleged that modern women experience greater difficulties in childbirth than did their great grandmothers, that more people suffer from weak teeth, etc. This is unproven. But it is a fallacy to conclude that what is unproven did not occur. In point of fact, it probably did.

Medicine, hygiene, social agencies, technology, and civilization save many lives which would otherwise be extinguished. This situation is here to stay; we would not want to alter it even if we could. Now, some of the lives thus saved carry genes which will engender other lives that will need to be saved in the generation to come. What are the consequences? No one has stated the principles on which the assessment of this problem must be based more clearly than Wright.

Wright rejects the basic assumption of the classical theory of population structure that there is, or can be, a single best, optimal, normal, or typical homozygous human genotype, all deviations from which would be detrimental and would be selected against. We have seen that the corollary of this assumption is that for each mutation there must be on the average one elimination (genetic death), and that a population must suffer, at equilibrium, a number of eliminations equal to that of mutations which arise. Equating the effects of all mutations is unrealistic. The elimination of a lethal mutant which causes the death of an embryo before implantation in the uterus is scarcely noticed by the mother or by anyone else. But grief and suffering accompany the elimination of a mutant, such as retinoblastoma, which kills an infant apparently normal at birth. Mutants such as hemophilia, sickle-cell anemia, and Huntington's chorea cripple, maim, and kill children, adolescents, or adults, cause misery to their victims, and disrupt the lives of their families. There is no way to measure precisely the different amounts of human anguish and woe, yet one may surmise that the painful and slow death of the victims of so many hereditary diseases is a torment greater than that involved in the elimination of a gene for achondroplasia owing to the failure of an achondroplastic dwarf to marry and beget children.

Looked at from the angle of the costs to the society, the nonequivalence of different mutants is no less evident. Myopia, or rather a predisposition to myopia, is believed to be inherited as a recessive trait. Being myopic is advantageous perhaps only under some exceptional circumstances; increases of the frequencies in populations of the gene for myopia are undesirable. Yet only a fanatic would advocate sterilization of the myopics or other radical measures to prevent the spread of this gene. Society can tolerate some more myopics: many of them are very useful citizens, and their defect can rather easily be corrected by a relatively inexpensive environmental change—wearing glasses. The effort that would be needed to eradicate or reduce the frequency of myopia would exceed that requisite to rectify the defect environmentally.

Diabetes mellitus, a rather widespread defect also believed to be inherited as a recessive, is, given the present level of medicine and technology, more difficult and expensive to correct than myopia. The incidence of diabetics may creep up slowly in the generations to come. How long it would take to be doubled, for example, we do not know—probably centuries or millennia. This prospect is not pleasant to contemplate, but insulin injections may, conceivably, have to be as common in some remote future as taking aspirin tablets is at present. Let us face this fact: our lives depend on civilization and technology, and the lives of our descendants will be even more dependent on civilized environments. The remedy for our genetic dependence on technology is more, not less, technology. You may, if you want, feel nostalgic for the good old days of our cave-dwelling ancestors, but the point of no return was, in the evolution of our species, passed many millennia before anyone could know what was happening.

It does not, however, follow that we may sit idly by, hoping that our posterity will learn how to correct any and all genetic defects. Timely surgery may save the lives of the carriers of retinoblastoma genes, but it leaves them blind. Should not these people be warned that if they reproduce, approximately half their children will inherit the defect? If all the retinoblastomatics were saved and had the same number of children as do other people, the frequency of retinoblastoma would after n generations be approximately $2nu$, where u is the mutation rate (and half the present frequency) of retinoblastoma.

Retinoblastoma is one of the many genetic defects which, unfortunately, are serious enough to make their correction too costly and incomplete, if possible at all. We cannot sacrifice our fundamental ethic, which commands that lives, no matter how wretched, be saved if at all possible, even though this frustrates normalizing natural selection. The only solution open is replacement of natural with artificial selection. Persons known to carry serious hereditary defects ought to be educated to realize the significance of this fact, if they are likely to be persuaded to refrain from reproducing their kind. Or, if they are not mentally competent to reach a decision, their segregation or sterilization is justified. We need not accept a Brave New World to introduce this much of eugenics.

Mention must be made of the distant possibility of a radically different solution. A method may some day be discovered to induce directed mutations, i.e., to change specific genes in desired ways. This would enable one to alter certain genes in the sex cells or in the body cells, and thus "cure" hereditary diseases by removing their causes. Now, if the history of science has taught us anything, it is the unwisdom of declaring that certain things will never be discovered. I must nevertheless concur with Muller's opinion: the problem of the management of human evolution should not be postponed until the conjectural time when directed mutation in man will have been discovered.

SOCIAL CONTRIBUTION AND SOCIAL COST

The social fitness of human phenotypes and genotypes is even more difficult to evaluate than their Darwinian fitness. Wright suggests that the problem may be treated in terms of the balance between the contributions to the society and the social costs of the different genotypes. He distinguishes, very tentatively of course, the following categories:

1. A rough balance between contribution and cost, both at relatively modest levels. This category includes the bulk of the population, the much-maligned "mass man": the ordinary, orderly workingman or bourgeois—the humble or the not-so-humble citizen.

2. A balance between contribution and cost, but at relatively high levels. This includes professional men and women, technicians, experts, and specialists of average competence, but with an education and a standard of living above the average of the whole population.

3 and 4. This is the intellectual and technological elite: top artists or experts, creative and seminal minds, persons of genius who make extraordinary contributions, either at a low cost (3) or at a high cost (4) to the society.

5. Persons whose capacities are those of class 1 or 2 (rarely 3 or 4) but who repay the society much less than the costs of their maintenance. Possessors of unearned wealth, nobles, aristocrats, and personages whose social contribution consists chiefly of high life and conspicuous consumption.

6. Criminal and antisocial persons of otherwise normal mental capacity.

The above categories, at least 1–5, correspond to the adaptive norm of the human species. Even at a risk of belaboring the obvious, it must be stressed that these categories embrace a great multitude of genotypes. Moreover, many or most of these genotypes are not fated to produce persons of any one of these categories. People whom we meet are what they are because of their genotypes and their environments. Surely, some (but probably not all) of these distressing fellows we see choosing the vulgar, the inane, and the banal instead of the beautiful, the rational, and the original could have been egg-heads and members of the avant-garde had they had the chance to learn the difference. And equally certainly, some of the snobs who are contemptuous of the plebeians are better endowed financially than genetically. Genetic equipments of classes 3 and

4 may arise among the children of the parents whose phenotypes place them in other categories.

The remaining categories, in which the social costs outweigh the returns, may be regarded as manifestations of the genetic load, provided, of course, that the phenotypic traits observed are genetically conditioned.

7. Subnormal physical constitution and health.

8. Low intelligence, but sufficient to take care of self under the existing social conditions.

9 and 10. Normal to maturity, but early physical or mental breakdown. Here belong many of the hereditary diseases, mentioned in Chapter 5 and elsewhere in this book, in which the ages of onset and incapacitation fall in youth or adulthood, thus interfering with self-realization and productive life. Many mental diseases, such as schizophrenia, belong to this category (except, of course, childhood schizophrenia).

11. Physical or mental incapacitation throughout a life of more or less normal duration.

12. Death before maturity, too early for any appreciable contribution to society.

13. Death at or before birth.

Categories 11–13 include some of the hereditary diseases, as well as many lethal mutants which cause early or late abortions, miscarriages, or neonatal deaths. Although mutant genes which cause early fetal deaths involve, in general, graver disturbances than those which kill later, the attendant distress is probably smaller the earlier the death. With categories 5–13, the social costs outweigh the social contributions. These categories may be said to constitute the social load. Wherever the genetic variables are more or less strongly implicated, the genetic and social loads coincide.

BIOLOGICAL FLAWS IN MAN'S NATURE

In 1691 John Ray saw "the Wisdom of God Manifested in the Works of Creation," in that living beings show "the admirable contrivance of all and each of them, the adapting all the parts of animals to their several uses." For a century and a half this idea dominated biology. In 1858 Darwin and Wallace advanced a different idea, better attuned to the spirit of their time, and of ours. The adaptedness is a product of natural selection.

Natural selection is, however, neither a stern master nor a benevolent guide. Selection does often bring about ostensibly purposeful results— genetic changes that increase the probability of survival and reproduction.

Yet natural selection is automatic, mechanical, planless, and opportunistic. The adaptedness of organic structures and functions, though a source of wonder and fascination, obviously falls short of perfection.

A flagrant example of imperfection is the genetic load. Adaptation involves genetic elimination of countless ill-adapted variants. The welfare of the species is paid for by the misery of many individuals. Another example is the debility and infirmity of old age. Natural selection may promote the welfare of the postreproductive age groups only if by so doing it benefits the reproductive ages. Indeed, Darwinian fitness of a genotype is measured by the contribution its carriers make to the gene pool of succeeding generations. To be sure, animals and humans may go on living for some time after their youngest children have been born. A homely analogy with cheap watches, which are "guaranteed" to function properly for a year or some other specific period, may be helpful here. Most of these watches work longer than the period of the guarantee. A watch that would stop running immediately after the expiration of the guaranteed period would have to be a high-precision mechanism, difficult and expensive to make. Spry and healthy oldsters are like the watches that go on ticking beyond their appointed time. Yet "the thousand natural shocks that flesh is heir to" in old age are, indeed, "natural" biological shortcomings. Painless death willingly accepted in the fullness of age would be preferable, if death can be accepted at all.

It may seem paradoxical that adaptively useless and harmful traits are not uncommonly established in evolution as specific and group characteristics. The principle of the utilitarianism of natural selection is not thereby negated. Natural selection perpetuates or eliminates genes and genotypes, not traits; what survives and reproduces, or dies or remains sterile, is an organism, not a characteristic. Useless and harmful traits are often byproducts of the same genetic constitutions which also yield useful traits. Evolutionary transformations of living bodies succeed or fail as wholes, not as aggregates of traits in isolation from each other. Evolutionary success may, therefore, be due to the excellence of the organism in only one or in a few important respects. Similarly, evolutionary failure, extinction, may be caused by a breakdown of some one important function.

The more general and radical a transformation, the more likely it is to contain weaknesses in particulars. Now, "man is an entirely new kind of animal in ways altogether fundamental for understanding of his nature" (Simpson). As a product of evolution, man is only roughhewn: he lacks the biological polish that comes from a long and slow adaptive improvement through natural selection. Among the pioneers of evolutionism, Mechnikov devoted most attention to the "disharmonies" in man's biological organization. The difficulty of childbirth in the human female is perhaps the most striking example of such disharmony.

Darwinian fitness is reproductive fitness; birth is a biological function obviously of prime importance. One would expect the performance of this function to become as safe, if not individually as pleasurable, as the similarly important function of copulation. And yet, "in sorrow thou shalt bring forth children." In the human female, and apparently in her alone among mammalian females, parturition is attended by intense pain and suffering. And as though this were not enough, the process of childbirth exposes both the mother and infant to risks of accidents and infections. From two to twenty per cent of the mothers were dying of puerperal infections in some hospitals during the seventeenth, eighteenth, and early part of the nineteenth centuries. What a strange miscarriage of natural selection!

Consider, however, that man is a mammal walking erect. Erect posture has necessitated considerable alterations in the body structures. As Coon puts it, "in many respects man's shift to erect walking is comparable to the development of organs of flight in birds." Man's spinal column has an S-shaped curvature instead of being arched, the pelvis has become massive enough to support the whole weight of the upper part of the body, and the organs of the abdominal cavity have changed their positions with respect to the gravity pull. The difficult childbirth may be one of the components of this pattern of change. The pattern as a whole is highly adaptive. Freeing the hands from walking duties has facilitated tool-making and hence the process of "hominization." But the female of *Homo faber* has to bring forth children in "sorrow." This is one of the payments for the unrequited debt of being human. The human species is, however, able to afford this payment from the proceeds of its humaneness.

SELF-AWARENESS AND THE FALL OF MAN

Cogito ergo sum—I think hence I am. This was what Descartes (1596-1650) found he could not doubt when he resolved to doubt everything. This famous formula has withstood the efforts of most resolute doubters, even to Sartre with his "being-in-itself." Self-objectivation is a late product of evolution. When and at what stage of the evolutionary development it entered upon the scene is conjectural. Rensch finds its rudiments in some animals, but affirms emphatically that a fully developed self-awareness is diagnostic of humanity. Teilhard de Chardin writes: "The animal knows, of course. But certainly it does not know that it knows."

For a generation (about 1910–1940), many psychologists found it possible "to write psychology" without using such words as self-awareness, self-objectivation, consciousness, or ego. More recently these words were legitimized. No one has set forth the adaptive significance of self-awareness more clearly than Hallowell:

The attribute of self-awareness, which involves man's capacity to discrimi-

nate himself as an object in a world of objects other than himself, is as central to
our understanding of the prerequisites of man's social and cultural mode of
adjustment as it is for the psychodynamics of the individual. A human social order
implies a mode of existence that has meaning for the individual at the level of
self-awareness. A human social order, for example, is always a moral order. . . .
It is man's capacity for and development of self-awareness that makes such unconscious psychological mechanisms as repression, rationalization, and so on of
adaptive importance for the individual. . . . Man, unlike his animal kin, acts in a
universe that he has discovered and made intelligible to himself as an organism
not only capable of consciousness but also of self-consciousness and reflective
thought. . . . An organized social life in man, since it transcends purely biological
and geographical determinants, cannot function apart from communally recognized meanings and values, or apart from the psychologocial structuralization of
individuals who make these their own.

The meaning of the acquisition of self-awareness in human evolution
is expressed beautifully in the biblical symbol of the Fall of Man. Self-
awareness is a blessing and a curse. Through self-awareness man attained
the status of a person in the existential sense: he became conscious of
himself and of his environment. He is able to form mental images of
things and situations which do not yet exist but which may be found,
brought about, or constructed by his efforts. Man can create in his imagination worlds different from the actual one and can visualize himself
in these imaginary worlds. Before you build a house, construct a machine, write a book, or go on a vacation, you have already built, constructed, or written them, or gone vacationing in your mind. The adaptive
value of forethought or foresight is too evident to need demonstration. It
has raised man to the status of the lord of creation.

Self-awareness and foresight brought, however, the awesome gifts
of freedom and responsibility. Man feels free to execute some of his
plans and to leave others in abeyance. He feels the joy of being the
master, rather than a slave, of the world and of himself. But the joy is
tempered by a feeling of responsibility. Man knows that he is accountable
for his acts: he has acquired the knowledge of good and evil. This is a
dreadfully heavy load to carry. No other animal has to withstand anything
like it. There is a tragic discord in the soul of man. Among the flaws in
human nature, this one is far more serious than the pain of childbirth.

It would not do for a student of human evolution to ignore the tragic
human predicament, although scientists in general have prudently
avoided coming to grips with such problems. Here we arrive close to
that ill-defined line which is the boundary of science, at least of science
as at present understood and constituted. Let us simply acknowledge that
on the other side of the line there exist profound insights into human

nature, the nature we know to be an outcome of the evolutionary process. The psychoanalytic schools have attempted to describe this nature in quasi-scientific terms. Their conclusions are stamped with deep pessimism. The view of Freud is characteristic:

In all that follows I take up the standpoint that the tendency to aggression is an innate, independent, instinctual disposition of man, and I come back now to the statement that it constitutes the most powerful obstacle to culture. [But the evolution of culture is] the struggle between Eros and Death, between the instincts of life and the instincts of destruction, as it works itself out in the human species.

Plato and Plotinus, St. Augustine and Luther, Kierkegaard and Nietzsche, Shakespeare and Dostoevsky, and many others have explored the abyss of human nature. It is a dark abyss, but the greatest of the explorers discerned a bright light shining up from it.

Reason is only reason, and it satisfies only man's reasoning capacity, while the desire is a manifestation of the whole life, of human life in its entirety, including the reason as well as all the quirks. . . . I, for example, quite naturally want to live in order to satisfy my entire capacity to live and not in order to satisfy only my rationality, which may amount to only one-twentieth of my entire capacity to live.

But the same Dostoevsky who wrote the above wrote also that "beauty will save the world." It is a sad fact that man has always been able to depict hell more convincingly than paradise, and not even Beato Angelico and Dostoevsky were exceptions to this rule.

And yet, man has also risen, not only fallen. We are, in Muller's words, "hastily made-over apes." The evolutionary process has managed, the haste notwithstanding, to do more than equip the made-over ape for mere survival. It implanted in us extraordinary strivings for self-actualization and self-transcendence, for beauty, and for rectitude. *Homo sapiens* is not only the sole tool-making and the sole political animal, he is also the sole ethical animal.

EVOLUTION AND ETHICS

Almost two centuries ago, Kant pointed out that ethics are exclusively human possessions. Animals as well as man obtain, via their sense organs, information about the states of their bodies and their surroundings. But only man distinguishes what is from what ought to be. Man has normative as well as cognitive faculties. Darwin and Wallace agreed that evolutionary changes are brought about by natural selection. But they parted company when it came to the evolution of the human brain and its faculties. Wallace felt it necessary to invoke supernatural agencies, which Darwin considered uncalled for.

The origin of ethics had been happy hunting ground for speculation long before Darwin. Not even a brief review of these speculations can be given here. Supernatural sanctions for ethics have been looked for most frequently. However, Spinoza (1632–1677) attempted an *Ethica more geometrico demonstrata*—ethics proved like a series of theorems of geometry. Spencer (1820-1903) started working on his theory of evolutionary ethics even before Darwin published his great books and continued for many years thereafter. The influence of Spencer's philosophy on his contemporaries was enormous; Keith's anachronistic *New Theory of Human Evolution* is the most recent incarnation of this philosophy.

Essentially Spencer thought that life is good and death is bad, that general evolution and the evolution of man are progressive, that progress and evolution enhance life and are therefore good. Ethical conduct is that which helps to promote life and hence the evolutionary progress. All this sounds reasonable, but unfortunately difficulties develop. Evolutionary progress arises, so Spencer thought, from the struggle for existence and the survival of the fittest. In the human species, the struggle for existence gave rise to a "code of amity" which operates between members of the same family, clan, or nation, but it also produced a "code of enmity" between different groups. Although human progress is believed to make amity more widespread than enmity, Spencerian ethics are clearly tinged with Social Darwinism.

A devastating critique of evolutionary ethics was given by T. H. Huxley in his famous Romanes Lecture, in 1893. However much we may admire what evolution has produced, "there is a general consensus that the ape and tiger methods of the struggle for existence are not reconcilable with sound ethical principles." Huxley never faces the problem of where these sound ethical principles come from, but establishes the sad fact that "what we call goodness or virtue involves a course of conduct which, in all respects, is opposed to that which leads to success in the cosmic struggle for existence." Accordingly, "cosmic evolution may teach us how the good and evil tendencies of man have come about; but, in itself, it is incompetent to furnish any better reason why what we call good is preferable to what we call evil than we had before."

The force of these strictures has never been overcome, although Julian Huxley, Waddington, and Leake and Romanell have made valiant efforts to deduce evolutionary ethics from our modern conceptions of evolution. What T. H. Huxley called "the gladiatorial theory" of the struggle for existence is, indeed, no longer a part of our understanding of how natural selection operates in evolution. Social Darwinism really never had sound biological roots, even though it was, and in some places continues to be, an ideological prop of laissez-faire capitalism. Not only organisms which are the products of evolution but also the mechanisms of evolution itself evolve. The ways of the apes and tigers are not incumbent upon men because human evolution entered a new phase when it evolved culture; ethics are products of evolution which themselves evolve.

Julian Huxley believes:

> Ethics *must* be based on a combination of a few main principles: that it is right to realize ever *new* possibilities in evolution, notably those which are *valued for their own sake;* that it is right to respect human individuality and to encourage its fullest development; that it is right to construct a mechanism for further social evolution which shall satisfy these prior conditions as fully, efficiently, and as rapidly as possible [emphasis supplied].

And he also maintained that "anything which permits or promotes open development is right, anything which restricts or frustrates development is wrong. It is a morality of evolutionary direction."

Unfortunately, as Simpson and Raphael have convincingly shown, these ideas have no greater validity than those which T. H. Huxley criticized in 1893. It is, indeed, right to realize possibilities which are valued for their own sake, whether they be new or old; but what is there to show that new possibilities will be most valuable; and, anyhow, from where are the criteria of value to come? How do you prove from what we know of evolution that human individuality is more valuable than human society? Societies are biologically newer than individuals, and they presumably have more possibilities for "open development." And yet we do feel that individuals should not be sacrificed for attainment of social aims. As Simpson has observed: "All trend ethics demand the postulate that the trends of evolution, or some particular one among those, is ethically right and good. There is no evident reason why such a postulate should be accepted." Attempts to find evolutionary ethics have at best "produced partial answers which are indeed ethically good although not achieving a general and firmly based evolutionary ethics."

EVOLUTION, VALUES, AND WISDOM

It is certainly possible that natural selection may have favored in human evolution the establishment of certain patterns of behavior which we regard as "ethical" or "unethical." The disposition of the parents, and particularly of mothers, to protect and care for their offspring, even to the point of self-abnegation and self-sacrifice, seems to us admirable, whether it is found in man, a bird, or any other animal. We are apt to forget that in an animal this behavior is really "forced"; the animal cannot choose to behave otherwise, while man can and occasionally does. Just the same, the disposition is a built-in feature and is basically genetic.

Haldane showed long ago that genes for "altruistic behavior" may have spread when mankind was divided into many small endogamous groups, but are unlikely to do so in a large undivided species. Indeed, such a "gene" may depress the Darwinian fitness of its carriers, if the latter sacrifice themselves for the benefit of their fellows in ways which jeopardize their chances of leaving progeny. Nevertheless, a small tribe containing genes for altruism may gain an advantage through the sacrifice of some of its members and hence may multiply and spread. In large societies natural selection is likely to operate in the reverse direction and eliminate the genes for altruism. Conversely, a gene for selfish or criminal behavior, which benefits its carriers and their progenies, is likely to be eliminated if it appears in a small tribe, but may spread in a large society.

It is unlikely that many of the human values could have become established in human societies by means of selective processes similar to those envisaged for "altruistic" and "criminal" genes. It is true that certain value judgments and ideas may further, and others hamper, the success, including the biological success, of the society in which they appear and are entertained. Several authors saw here analogies with mutations and gene combinations perpetuated or eliminated by natural selection. Analogies are interesting, yet to think that a mutant gene may not only make a person an inventor or entertainer of ideas but also determine which ideas he will invent or entertain, seems hardly compatible with the present trends in human genetics, anthropology, and psychology. For the crucial adaptation in human evolution has been the ability to learn a great variety of ideas and to make a variety of inventions, not to learn fixed ideas and only a certain invention. It seems to me on the whole more likely that natural selection has established in man a drive toward what Maslow denotes as "self-actualization" and avoided fixation of the means whereby the self-actualization may be achieved.

Waddington steers clear of the pitfalls in which previous theories of evolutionary ethics were trapped. He recognizes that natural selection has provided man not with ethics and values but with a capacity to acquire ethics and values. Values are products of human culture, not of the human genotype. But in order to become an "ethicizing being" man must be an "authority acceptor," a receiver of socially transmitted information. Waddington makes good use of the findings of psychoanalysts who describe the processes whereby a new born child develops an "authority-bearing system." He finds, however, that these processes have adaptive as well as unadaptive aspects. The former concern the development of the of the "superego"; a successfully socialized infant grows to become an effective member of his society. The latter leads to the curious result of "producing ethical authorities which have the qualities of other-worldliness and absoluteness that we find in our ethical feelings, as well as guilt and anxiety which are another of their unexpected but obtrusive characteristics."

All this goes to explain how we develop our belief that certain things are good and others evil; it does not explain why we *ought* to regard them good and evil respectively. However, Waddington believes: "The framework within which one can carry on a rational discussion of different systems of ethics, and make comparisons of their various merits and demerits, is to be found in a consideration of animal and human evolution." The process of evolution has produced a human species capable of entertaining ethical beliefs: the biological function of ethics is to promote human evolution, ethics may consequently be judged by how well they fulfill this function. This Waddington calls the criterion of biological "wisdom." He compares the biological "wisdom" of ethics with the "wisdom" of eating. The function of eating is to promote healthy growth; if somebody would say that he prefers to grow in an unhealthy and abnormal manner, one can only tell him that he is "out of step with nature." Similarly, the "wisdom" of evolution cannot be doubted; evolution is "wise" by definition.

This solution is too easy. Do we always know what is and what is not in step with nature? Is, for example, Muller's utopia discussed above in step with nature? Some people think that all would be well with man if natural selection operated freely, but we have seen that this is at most a half-truth, since the kind of "natural" selection which operated in the Stone Age would be unnatural in modern man. "Wisdom of the body" and "wisdom of evolution" are good metaphors, but they are not synonymous with wisdom which is the source and validation of ethics. This has been stated splendidly by Simpson: "The means to gaining right ends involve both organic and human evolution, but human choice as to what *are* the right ends must be based on human evolution. . . . The old evolution was and is essentially amoral. The new evolution involves knowledge, including the knowledge of good and evil."

I do not think (and neither does Simpson) that understanding of evolution, biology, or science is irrelevant to wisdom. Wisdom is itself evolving, and it includes the insights derived from cumulative knowledge, which subsumes biology. As Bronowski put it: "Science is nothing else than the search to discover unity in the wild variety of nature—or more exactly, in the variety of our experience." But wisdom includes also other insights. St. Augustine said: *Surgunt indocti et rapiunt coelum*— ignorants come and grasp the heavens. This is not an apologia for ignorance or even for the irrational man. Waddington himself asks for something more than the wisdom of biology when he writes:

> I would not say that the scientific ideal alone is a wholly adequate foundation for the good life of the individual or the highest civilization of society. . . . It needs, in my view, to be supplemented by the ideal of the creative artist—an ideal which expresses itself in thought processes which move in a different dimension to those of logic and experiment.

We do not know whether it is a by-product of the aesthetic faculty or of the more fundamental faculty of self-awareness which confers upon some persons a quality of wisdom which seems curiously unrelated to their mastery of cumulative knowledge. In *War and Peace*, Tolstoi makes his aristocratic and cultured hero learn wisdom from an ignorant peasant turned soldier. And the highest wisdom of all was at one time entrusted to a group of unlettered Galilean fishermen.

Human values and wisdom are products of cultural evolution, conditioned of course by biological evolution, yet not deducible from the latter. In point of fact, man will not be dissuaded from the arrogant aspiration to query whether the biological and cosmic evolutions, which produced him among countless other things, do or do not conform to his wisdom and his values. I know no better criterion of wisdom and values than that proposed by the ancient Chinese sage:

> Every system of moral laws must be based upon the man's own consciousness, verified by the common experience of mankind, tested by due sanction of historical experience and found without error, applied to the operations and processes of nature in the physical universe and found to be without contradiction, laid before the gods without question or fear, and able to wait a hundred generations and have it confirmed without a doubt by a Sage of posterity.

MAN, THE CENTER OF THE UNIVERSE

Civilization has helped most of mankind to change from ignorance, undernourishment, and filth to education, at least relative abundance, and sanitation. That these changes are to the good is unquestionable. Yet in the process of change man has also lost and failed to recapture some things of inestimable value. Man no longer enjoys the certitude that he stands at the center of a universe created especially for his sake or the twin certitude that this universe is presided over by a Power which can be implored or propitiated and which cares for man, individually and collectively. Copernicus and Galileo suddenly broke the news that the world does not revolve around man but man, instead, revolves around the world.

And in this world, vast and merciless instead of snug and familiar, man is incidental and almost superfluous. The feeling of schism between man and nature was expressed with unsurpassed poignancy by Pascal (1623–1662):

When I consider the short duration of my life, swallowed up in the eternity before and after, the little space which I fill, and even can see, engulfed in the infinite immensity of spaces of which I am ignorant, and which know me not, I am frightened, and am astonished at being here rather than there; for there is no reason why here rather than there, why now rather than then. . . . The eternal silence of these infinite spaces frightens me.

Attempts have been made to relieve man's alienation from the world he inhabits. Descartes thought that while animals were machines man possessed an immortal soul; Locke pointed out, however, that there is nothing in man's mind that did not enter there via the sense organs. Romantics revolted against the tyranny of mechanistic science, trusting the poet's inspiration more than the scientist's plodding toil; but it was physics, not poetry, that led to the industrial revolution, to the abundance of material goods, and eventually to the frightening power of atomic energy. Nothing succeeds like success, and the man in the street became convinced that material power is to be admired above intellectual power. To many Darwin seemed to have delivered the heaviest blow, making the schism in man's soul irreparable: far from the world having been made for man, man himself proved to be merely one of some two million biological species, a result of material processes of a rather unedifying sort, called struggle for existence and survival of the fittest, and a relative of creatures as disreputable as monkeys and apes. With Freud the depreciation of the human condition reached the lowest level. Freud mocked man's pretensions to spirituality, by denying him not only spirituality but rationality as well.

The most important point in Darwin's teachings was, strangely enough, overlooked. Man has not only evolved, he is evolving. This is a source of hope in the abyss of despair. In a way Darwin has healed the wound inflicted by Copernicus and Galileo. Man is not the center of the universe physically, but he may be the spiritual center. Man and man alone knows that the world evolves and that he evolves with it. By changing what he knows about the world man changes the world that he knows; and by changing the world in which he lives man changes himself. Changes may be deteriorations or improvements; the hope lies in the possibility that changes resulting from knowledge may also be directed by knowledge. Evolution need no longer be a destiny imposed from without; it may conceivably be controlled by man, in accordance with his wisdom and his values.

An inspiring attempt to sketch an optimistic philosophy of the cosmic, biological, and human evolutions has been made by Teilhard de Chardin. I must, however, gainsay the admonition which the author makes in the opening sentence of the Preface to his remarkable book: "If this book is to be properly understood, it must be read not as a work on metaphysics, still less as a sort of theological essay, but purely and simply as a scientific treatise." The book must be read as science, and as metaphysics and theology, and, furthermore, as something its author does not mention at all, namely poetry (though this last named component has been sadly mauled in the English translation).

Is evolution a theory, a system, or a hypothesis? It is much more—it is a general postulate to which all theories, all hypotheses, all systems must henceforward bow and which they must satisfy in order to be thinkable and true. Evolution is a light which illuminates all facts, a trajectory which all lines of thought must follow—this is what evolution is.

Teilhard de Chardin saw that the evolution of matter, the evolution of life, and the evolution of man are integral parts of a single process of cosmic development, of a single and coherent history of the whole universe. Furthermore, he saw in this history a clear direction or trend. Regrettably, he described this trend as "ortho-genesis," but if I understand him aright, he did not mean to imply that evolution is an uncreative unfolding of preformed events; unfortunately he lacked familiarity with modern biology.

He chose to designate the direction in which evolution is going as "The Point Omega." This is

a harmonized collectivity of consciousness, equivalent to a kind of superconsciousness. The Earth is covering itself not merely by myriads of thinking units, but by a single continuum of thought, and finally forming a functionally single Unit of Thought of planetary dimensions. The plurality of individual thoughts combine and mutually reinforce each other in a single act of unanimous Thought. . . . In the dimension of Thought, like in the dimension of Time and Space, can the Universe reach consummation in anything but the Measureless?

Such grand conceptions are patently undemonstrable by scientifically established facts. They transcend cumulative knowledge; it is sufficient that this one is not contradicted by this knowledge. To modern man, so forlorn and spiritually embattled in this vast and ostensibly meaningless universe, Teilhard de Chardin's evolutionary idea comes as a ray of hope. It fits the requirements of our time. For

Man is not the centre of the universe as was naively believed in the past, but something much more beautiful—Man the ascending arrow of the great biological synthesis. Man is the last-born, the keenest, the most complex, the most subtle of the successive layers of life. This is nothing less than a fundamental vision. And I shall leave it at that.

67

Earthlings in the Space Age

Ritchie Calder

Sixteen times a day, a man-made satellite can circumnavigate the Earth. By his own ingenuity, *Homo sapiens,* the Earthling, has shrunk his work to the dimensions of a very small planet. In the arrogance of our conceit, which puts Man and his brain at the very centre of the universe, we have never been quite convinced by the astronomers when they have tried to tell us how insignificant the world is in the immensities of Space. But now the Space Engineers, and the Astronauts, beating the bounds of our global parish, have reminded us how relatively small it is.

In the spirit of new adventure, one may regard the world as a departure platform for fugitives to the moon or a launching pad for escapades to other planets, or even beyond our solar system, into other universes. But the Earthlings who cannot so escape must recognise that, on its relatively limited surface, 3000 million people today, 4000 million in 1980, and 6000 million or 7000 million thirty years from now, will have to contrive to live and work together. Or by the neglect of wisdom or the abuse of human ingenuity, to die together. . . .

OUR FELLOW LODGERS

A lump of soil no bigger than a football contains a micro-organic population greater than the human population of the world. That micro-organic population includes the germs and fungi which evocatively suggest disease or danger but which, in other forms are indispensable to our existence. In the same way, we think of insects as deserving insecticide and other creatures as deserving pesticide but in the process we can kill

Reproduced by permission of the Editor from *The Advancement of Science*, Vol. 19 (1962), pp. 11-20.

those which are essential to our ultimate needs. For example, in order to get margarine, we cleared big areas in Tanganyika of brush and tsetse flies which it harboured, but in the process we got rid of the bees which were needed to pollinate alternative crops.

Similarly, for our short-term, and short-sighted needs, we have destroyed the vegetation cover. We have cut down forests—the Sunday edition of one American newspaper consumes in a single year the yield of a forest area half as big again as that of my native county of Angus. We have damaged the vegetation cover in other ways, preventing the absorption of water by the natural sponge through which it seeps into the underground springs. As a result, the scouring rains sluice the soil off the hills, cause floods and eventual erosion. In the lifetime of the United States, over two hundred and eighty million acres of arable, crop and rangeland have been destroyed—more than ten times the productive acreage of the United Kingdom.

In the 1930's, there was the apocalyptic warning when the mid-day sun of New York was blotted out by the dust of the Dakotas over a thousand miles away. But only five years ago, the airliner on which I was flying to Winnipeg could not land because at noon we had flown into night. When we finally broke through it was to find the city and everything in it covered with yellow mud, spread by the rain which had enabled us to land. The "night," the pall which had blotted out the sun, was dust. Samples had been taken by the weatherman. At 8000 feet the dust had been that of Texas, 1500 miles away. At various levels, the samples were from Oklahoma, Nebraska and the Dakotas. The heavy particles nearer the ground were those of Manitoba itself. We had been caught in the climax of a dust storm which had whipped topsoil from the middle of a continent.

Only slowly—and recently—have we come to recognise that wild animals are not something with which mankind is at war but a part of the balance of life, which is delicately adjusted. A few weeks ago, I was at the Arusha Conference, in East Africa, called by the International Union for the Conservation of Nature, under the sponsorship of Unesco and the Food and Agriculture Organisation. It was an emergency meeting because so many new states are becoming independent and the naturalists of Europe and America were afraid that the Africans might decimate the game animals by slaughter and destroy their habitat by immature husbandry and indiscriminate cattle raising.

It was gratifying, and at the same time humbling, to find that the Africans themselves were traditionally more aware of the role of wildlife in their own ecology than the white man has hitherto shown in his intervention in that continent. The Africans recognised that in the precarious nature of the savannah lands, big game—and even the tsetse fly—were a decisive factor. Nearly four million square miles of the African continent are held in fief by the tsetse fly. Because of the fatal diseases which its bite produces in man and his domesticated animals but does not produce in the wild animals the tsetse has preserved great tracts which might have been destroyed by shifting cultivation and by over-grazing. It was suggested at Arusha that a monument ought to be raised to the tsetse fly as "The Saviour of Africa" and it was the Africans who insisted that before modern methods to remove the tsetse were employed their people must be trained to husband well this legacy of land.

MAN'S POWER OF VETO

For the first time in history, man has the power of veto over the evolution of his species. We share the biosphere. Into that we have injected, in the past sixteen years, man-made radioactivity. Elements which did not exist in nature have been indiscriminately scattered over the face of the earth, to combine in all living things. Today there is not a child in the world which does not have, in some degree, radiostrontium in its bones. The amounts may be insignificant and the possible effects may be emotionally exaggerated and medically in dispute. Much is unproven, much is unknown. But that only emphasises that men, on defective evidence or in positive ignorance, are recklessly tampering with the biosphere on which the present and future of their race depends.

We have had plenty of reminders of the dangers of neglecting Claude Bernard's warning to his fellow-scientists a century ago—"true science teaches us to doubt and in ignorance to refrain." Radiostrontium was overlooked in the calculations of the possible effects of H-bomb testing, because the mechanism by which radioactive krypton decays into strontium-90 had not been taken into account and because the mechanism of stratospheric storage and the reappearance of radioactive particles in the atmosphere had not been realised. Nature, with grim irony, brings the radioactive chickens home to roost. Nuclear tests may be made in remote places—the Marshall Islands, Christmas Island, the Sahara, behind the Urals or in the Arctic, but the radioactivity will reappear in the countries which originated such tests—as well, of course, as countries which were not party to them. Whether exploded near the Equator or beyond the Arctic Circle, the radioactive garbage of those bombs will be swept into the jet streams of the Radioactive Forties, the latitudes which include the United States, Britain, France and the Soviet Union.

This, with all the emotional and political overtones which it produces in international relations, is another reminder that we all share one biosphere and the global risks of tampering with it. . . .

THE MECHANICS OF DIPLOMACY

Science and technology have revolutionised the mechanics as well as the contents of diplomacy.

Some years ago, I wrote what was supposed to be a lighthearted article called "Waiting for my Psyche." It described how I had had late dinner in New York, had caught my Trans-Atlantic 'plane and had been lunching in my garden in Surrey the following noon. I just was not there with my family. My heavy baggage was coming by sea and it was obvious that I had packed my psyche and it had not caught up with me. The psychiatrist Jung sent me a stern message from Zurich saying that this was no laughing matter. The speed of travel was such that people could not psychologically get adjusted. They would step out of one environment suddenly into another without waiting for their psyche to catch up with them. And he warned that this was causing great stresses in international affairs because statesmen and politicians, rushing from one crisis conference to the next, never had time to make the necessary psychological adjustments.

Today, jet aircraft have diminished time and distance even more. (One morning last week I was talking with President Nkrumah in Ghana about what would happen if Khrushchev let off a super bomb and, nine and a half hours and 3600 miles later, I arrived in London to find that he had.) Statesmen engage increasingly in direct negotiations—Summits and the like—and depend less and less on their Ambassadors who are at least locally acclimatised, and less on the diplomatic pouch or even on the coded cable. In fact, it probably takes longer to decipher a top-secret cable than it takes the Prime Minister to fly the Atlantic. Everything has a crisis urgency which does not give men of affairs time to think about the fundamen nature of the crisis. So the *petit mal* of minor political epilepsy is liable to build up into the *grand mal* of a major convulsion. . . .

THE CONTENT OF DIPLOMACY

Science has helped to change the mechanics of diplomacy but it has even more drastically changed the world with which diplomacy has to deal.

The winds of change are etheric. The instruments of mass-communication—radio, television, films and the printing press—have completely changed the approach to people and to problems. When we disapprove of what they have to say we call it "propaganda"; when it suits us, we call it "projecting a better way of life." But even when facts are selective, they have a habit of sticking like burrs, and like burrs, of being carried into unlikely places to produce surprising growths. Even in apparently remote places, the new nations owe their birth to the radio. Ideas penetrate; the demand for freedom spreads like an infection and it becomes epidemic. Sometimes it goes off, like a political time-bomb when it is least expected. Sometimes, as in the physical propagation of radio-waves themselves, there is a curious skip.

Nine years ago, I was in the hills of Central Java. I was there for the United Nations and its specialised agencies to see how science was applied in a beneficial way. With the advent of penicillin, it is possible to cure that horrible disease yaws—once not unknown in Scotland—which afflicted and crippled tens of millions of people of all ages in the tropical countries. With one shot of penicillin you can cure yaws. And this had been done effectively, and on the scale of a military campaign, by the World Health Organisation and UNICEF, and this whole region in Central Java had been cleared. In one of the hill villages I asked the beneficiaries, the illiterate Javanese peasants, whether they had ever heard of the United Nations. You will know that it was the intervention of the Good Offices Commission of the United Nations which confirmed the Indonesians in their freedom and, if you like, involved the Dutch in the loss of an empire. They had never heard of the United Nations but in the conversation, which I was conducting through an interpreter, two phrases came through in English. One was "Atlantic Charter" the other was "Atom Bomb." To them it was the Atlantic Charter, not the UN, which had given them their freedom—a delayed action perhaps of our war-time propaganda on the Four Freedoms. The second, the release of atomic energy and the greatest material advance Man has made since the mastery of fire, was to those illiterate peasant "The bomb which the White Man dropped on the Yellow and would never have dropped on the White." Here is a matter of the most profound importance in international relations, something you cannot negotiate through diplomacy. . . .

STOPPING THE MISERY-GO-ROUND

It can be done. We do not need to await food artificially produced by photosynthesis. The scientific know-how for better yields already exists. The knowledge we have got, applied with wisdom, can increase the yields from existing acreages. By plant breeding we can extend the food-growing acreages into what have seemed inhospitable regions. The Unesco Arid Zone Committee has done a remarkable work in showing how deserts might be developed. I have no doubt, having been in the Arctic seeing whether it might become part of our habitable world, that production, if need be, can be extended there. As far as those oceans which cover seven-tenths of our globe are concerned, we are at the cave-man stage. We hunt our food and do not husband it. Sea-farming and sea-ranching are perfectly feasible. The great international survey of the Indian Ocean, sponsored by Unesco, in which twenty-five survey ships of fifteen nations are taking part, will not only tell us a great deal about that birthplace of the monsoons but also about its biological possibilities and its food prospects.

The World Health Organisation and the United Nations Childrens Fund have done a great humanitarian work in conquering disease and relieving suffering. It is not too much to claim that, with their very considerable help, modern medicine, with scientific drugs, such as penicillin, has saved more lives in the last ten years than have been lost in all the wars in human history. They are the instruments of death control and, as such, have part responsibility for the rising tide of population. (The World Health Organisation is not allowed to promote researches in the biology of reproduction, much less into the methods of its control.)

But, reverting to our Misery-Go-Round, I would remind you that ill people cannot produce, or earn, food. People who are well can. In rice-growing regions, the critical, and very manual, functions of transplanting and harvesting rice coincide with the malarial seasons. Three out of five may be sick of the fever. Relieved of malaria, there will be five pairs of hands and the yields will be increased. Malaria control extends acreages by recovering land from the mosquito, and clearing malarial jungle for cultivation.

Yet even this work is in hazard. Malarial control, through modern insecticides, has freed hundreds of millions from the fever. But the mosquitoes are developing insecticide resistance and are multiplying and what was endemic malaria may become epidemic malaria. It is a race between Man and the Mosquito. It means malaria eradication, not just control. If, by modern drugs which are available, the parasite of malaria can be removed from the blood of humans before the resurgence of the mosquitoes there will be no disease for the mosquito to transmit. It is perfectly feasible. What is needed is the will and the financial support of governments for the World Health Organisation's Campaign. . . .

And now to all you Earthlings here gathered, I should like to say this:

For the first time in history, Man, the Earthling, has the power of veto over continuing evolution. He can exercise that veto by the nuclear destruction of the race, or he can, by default in handling the problems of starvation, prove that Malthus was right. He can ambitiously reach out to the farther planets but his species as such must survive on the surface of the earth, subsist from the nine inches of top-soil which feeds, clothes and shelters him or from the seas from which he emerged hundreds of millions of years ago.

All the majesty of his mind can be dethroned by his stomach. Man can feast like Belshazzar and ignore the writing on the wall. He can spend £40,000 million a year on the defence of peace and ignore the real content of the peace he is supposed to be defending. He can say "My group— my way of life—at least, shall survive" and like the locust-men of Attila, Genghis Khan and Tamerlane and Hitler, try to wrest *lebensraum* at other people's expenses. He can split the atom and release the power of matter and use this, his greatest discovery, to poison the goodness of his earth and destroy his species. He can outboast the Ancients, who in the arrogance of their material success built pyramids as the gravestones of their civilisations but Modern Man can throw his pyramids into Space and they may orbit eternally round a planet which died of his neglect. Or he may choose to use his science and his wisdom to cooperate with all his kind in the peaceful enrichment of his Earth and of the people who live on it.

68

The Logical Basis of Biological Investigation

Herbert H. Ross

Biological science constitutes the field of human investigation that seeks an understanding of the living world. Such an understanding involves knowing the *what* of life and its myriad parts, the *why* and *how* of their functioning, the *when, where,* and *why* of their origins and peregrinations, and *predictions* of their future. The "what" is the basic inventory; the "why, how, when, and where" express various relationships between the units of the inventory and between these units and their environment. These relationships are not immediately apparent, but must be adduced

Herbert H. Ross, "The Logical Basis of Biological Investigation," *BioScience*, Vol. 16 (1966), pp. 15-17. Reprinted by permission.

or deduced by subjecting sensed data to various kinds of reasoning. So multitudinous is living diversity, so varied and intricate the apparatus used in its study, and so endless the intricate life processes beckoning to be studied, that these details may engross the investigator to the point that he neglects an appreciation of those mental processes that alone can bring cohesiveness to his conclusions.

These mental processes are concerned intimately with the science of logic, which may be called the *modus operandi* of reasoning in the scientific method. But the logic of the scientist is, in simpler fashion, also the method used by the average person in assorting and generalizing his objective experiences. The method is based on our belief that all sensed phenomena are somehow related. This belief is bolstered by innumerable orderly examples that keep our faith in an orderly world. To give some very ordinary ones: we associate *chair* with *sitting, leaves* with *plants, barking* with *dogs,* and *song* with *birds.* If the world were otherwise, if fishes and dogs occasionally sang like birds, if leaves sporadically grew out of lamp posts and teacups, we could not associate different phenomena because there would be no orderly association between them. Throughout our lives we are aware that there is an orderly association or relationship between phenomena we see, feel, hear, or smell, and, as we grow up, we become aware of and store in our minds more and more examples of relatedness.

As a result, all of our observations, thinking processes, analyses, and conclusions are the attempts of the peculiar structure called the human mind, stimulated by its arsenal of sensing devices, to make sense out of the relationships of the individual with the surrounding world. The primary basis of this reasoning comes down to the proposition that we relate sensed phenomena either between ourselves and specific items of the external world, or between different items of the external world. Relationships that prove orderly are expressed as basic concepts, premises, or hypotheses, and these, in turn, are used as a basis of prediction or deductions.

These thoughts may seem to imply that the scientific method is simply a construct of logic and reason, but this is not the case. The scientific method is actually a philosophy or faith espoused by certain persons having a particular aim, outlook, and practice.

The *aim* of the group is an understanding of the universe and all its workings, an aim shared by other than scientists.

Concerning *outlook,* Randall and Buchler have pointed out that there are three common types of faith: (1) believing what you want to believe, (2) believing what you are taught to believe, and (3) believing only what is based on objective evidence, ultimately grounded in sensed data. This latter is the outlook or belief of the scientific group. Introducing evidence as a basis for belief opens the door to accommodating all good evidence in arriving at conclusions. Where the evidence is inconclusive or contradictory, this belief requires a search for new evidence or new ways of interpreting old evidence. The minute we realize that evidence may be contradictory, we cannot escape the conclusion that new evidence may contradict previous evidence and undermine or require modification of previous conclusions. As a consequence, the greater the amount of evidence supporting any one problem the greater the probability that the conclusion is correct. Thus, although he cannot prove the ultimate truth, the scientist can approach it with varying degrees of confidence. This empirical outlook, in which degree of probability replaces the concept of absolute truth, seems first to have been realized by Huygens about 1670.

The *practice* of the group called scientists consists in a rigid adherence to the type of reasoning and formal logic that has been shown over the centuries to be most likely to avoid fallacious results.

The logic is essentially the syllogistic logic of Aristotle, with its various rules to insure that the thinking is kept straight. For example, one may observe many robins nesting, always laying blue eggs. Upon seeing a robin starting a nest, one can say with a high degree of probability that it will lay blue eggs. But if one finds a nest having blue eggs, it is not logically safe to say that these eggs were laid by a robin. This could be said only if one had ascertained the color of eggs laid by all other birds inhabiting the area and finding that none of them ever laid blue eggs. In point of fact, catbirds, cuckoos, and many other birds occurring with robins do lay blue eggs. This case is only one simple example of the many permissible and nonpermissible permutations allowed by formal logic in expressing the relationship between generalized and specific categories. In logic, "formal" does not mean white tie and tails, but rather the *form* or arrangement of items or ideas in a statement, a concept perhaps better understood as the root of the word *formula*, with its connotation of exactitude in the arrangement of its parts. Some claim that syllogistic logic is not used in present day biological science but, as Bechner has indicated, most scientific propositions and tests represent a compounding of many simple logical units, most of which are left unsaid but are contained in the taken-for-granted context of the specialty involved.

The form of reasoning used by scientists is the tried and true inductive-deductive method. Although inductive reasoning is often described as a type separate from deductive reasoning, in our actual use of them the two form a peculiarly spiral type of mental activity. In the inductive part, individual data or concepts are assembled, and from a consideration of them we reach a general proposition, model, or hypothesis that explains them. For the deductive part, we deduce from our hypothesis that certain results or conditions would follow, and from this in turn other results or conditions would follow. This chain of reasoning is continued until we reach a result or condition that is subject to test, and we make this test. If the test is not as predicted, but the steps in our deductions were correct, then our hypothesis is false. If the result of the test is as predicted, this supports the original hypothesis. It is important that a positive result *supports* but does not *prove* the hypothesis, because some other hypothesis or emendation may later be found that is a much more plausible explanation of the result. For example, in the early tests for residues of chlorinated hydrocarbons, the basic hypothesis was that in samples treated with certain chemicals and subjected to certain tests only chlorinated hydrocarbons would be measured. Suddenly, indications of unusually high chlorinated hydrocarbon residues appeared in routine samples of horseradish grown in fields that had been treated only sparingly with such compounds. Subsequent investigation showed that the compound producing the bitter taste of horseradishes gave the same reaction in the prescribed test as did the chlorinated hydrocarbons. The original hypothesis needed to be changed to "If samples are treated with certain chemicals and subjected to certain tests, then chlorinated hydrocarbons, horseradish extract, and *perhaps some other as yet untested substances* will give a certain, similar result."

The spiral character of the inductive-deductive method lies in the fact that data and concepts do not automatically organize themselves in our minds. We mentioned the array of specific instances that started the inductive part of the reasoning process. Someone had to get the bright idea that organizing certain specific instances might lead to a useful hypothesis. What leads to such an organizing effort? It usually stems from a question arising from a previous explanation that has proved untenable, from curiosity about what something does, how something works, or why something happens, or from a discrepancy in a series of expected results. The results of this questioning or curiosity are really deductions based on previous hypotheses or on alternative hypotheses proposed for tenuous hypotheses. These deductions always include an element of induction in the form of our own past relevant experiences, which have the habit of flashing back and forth through our minds in times of doubt (our mind really recalls the experiences from our memory, *which may be faulty*). Thus when faced with a new question, we actually go from deduction to the organization of additional specific instances, from these through induction, and back to deduction.

In organizing our attack on a new question, we choose between the operational methods—analysis and synthesis. If we decide that separating a larger system into its component parts will give us clues to our dilemma, we have chosen the avenue of analysis; if we decide that we will get the desired information by adding together various building blocks and combining them into a more highly organized structure, we have chosen synthesis. In a general way analysis corresponds to deduction; synthesis, to induction. In actual practice both analysis and synthesis involve long programs of many steps, and each step is accomplished by the spiral of inductive-deductive reasoning.

The cornerstone of our thinking is in our basic concepts or premises. Biological science differs from many aspects of the mathematical, physical, or chemical sciences in that its basic concepts or premises may not form as secure a platform on which to build a framework of logical deductions as those in the more exact sciences. The mathematician can rely on basic concepts that cannot be proved, only demonstrated, yet which seem obviously true; for example, that the sum of the parts is equal to the whole, that things equal to the same thing are equal to one another, or that two straight lines cannot enclose a space. In biology the basic premise is often a type that does not lend itself to neat mathematical consequences; for example, the premise that all living units have an ontogeny and a phylogeny or that genetic difference produces physiological difference (but not that physiological difference is always due to genetic difference). The laws of genetic inheritance are more precise but not infallible. The biologist is also acutely aware that he is dealing with a world of change; not only do all living things change from moment to moment and generation to generation, but the environment on which life depends for its existence, and which in part fashions life's form, also changes. This means that the exact conditions under which an experiment is performed or an observation is made never occurred before and will never occur after the time of the experiment or observation. This leads to a realization that the *happenings* or *course* of life can be expressed only as modal functions; only the *underlying causes* of biological happenings have any chance of being expressed as rigid values. The modality of so many living phenomena and the immense number of variables in life and its environment have necessitated a greater and greater reliance on complex models and statistics as a basis of achieving a greater understanding of life.

Now that we have brought the *complex model* into the picture, we must add an extra word of caution. A complex model is simply a compounding of simple models or hypotheses. As pointed out above, if we insist on admission of new evidence, there is always a chance of demonstrating that any of our premises are either faulty or incomplete. For this reason, all of our conclusions can at the most be hypotheses. This means that, although we seldom say it, we should always realize that the word "if" precedes all of our assertions. Returning to the robin, we should say "If robins always lay blue eggs, this robin will lay a blue egg." This "iffy" nature of our basic premises has a serious consequence for our biological reasoning. On these basic premises biologists constantly build complex models that are superstructures of operational hypotheses, such as those revolving around the Hardy-Weinberg formula, the construction of phylogenetic trees, and explanations of physiological processes, and use these models as a means of extending questioning further or devising tests for the basic premises upon which our theoretical structures rest. Because our basic premises must be preceded by "if," all subsequent premises resting on them carry this "if" with them. Because of this, Popper insists that no hypothesis is truly scientific unless it is stated in such a way that it can be proved wrong. Although not all logicians agree with such a rigorous view, few would deny that a hypothesis should be so stated as to invite tests that will demonstrate possible falsity.

Complex models of all kinds, including phylogenetic trees, charts of internal chemical processes, and the behavioristic and population models of physiology and ecology, are structures each containing a remarkable number of individual premises strung together to form one diagram or one formula. It is especially important that experiments be so devised or observations so ordered that each component hypothesis of a complex model can be tested individually.

Criticism is frequently leveled at biological scientists of all types that they are extending their hypotheses far beyond the point permitted by their data. If one wished to compile the largest book in biology, it could well be a collection of these accusations, each asserting that such-and-such an author is indulging in "speculation" or "guesswork." Probing into the dark, however, is one of the most important features of the scientific method. It can be dignified by the terms *abductive reasoning* or *inference*, but in plain language it is simply *stretching the mind.* Francis Bacon may have been the first to point out the importance of this activity; certainly he asserted it vigorously. Inference can take almost any form, from realizing inductively the general pattern contained in a set of data or deducing unrealized consequences of a hypothesis. At its best it is the flash of realization whereby we suddenly see a possible answer to a question that has been nagging at our minds. These engendered possibilities are then subject to test as would be a hypothesis and those that survive testing become our body of theory.

One of the most stultifying influences in biology (as in any science) is the suppression of differences of opinion within a field of investigation. There are both logical and philosophical reasons for such differences. If we bring together *all* evidence concerning a problem, we must admit that some of it may be *contradictory* evidence; to explain this may require two or more alternative hypotheses each with a relatively low probability. This is a logical basis for differences of opinion. The philosophical reason is equally simple. All scientists are humans, and no two have exactly the same backgrounds of personal experience against which to compare alternative hypotheses. It is to be expected that each person may consider different pieces of evidence as being more significant concerning any one problem, resulting in honest differences of opinion. But certainly the expression of these differences, *if clearly explained,* is one of the most powerful tools in stimulating greater search for new evidence or more careful examination of hypotheses and deductions.

In this connection, a special word should be said for airing differences of opinion in person-to-person discussion. Nothing brings out a flow of information or a cross-current of ideas like a well-informed group going hammer-and-tongs at a controversial point. Perhaps no new ideas come from such a gathering immediately, but the mental turmoil engendered seems often to jar old cerebral connections and churn up new ones that later result in the first glimmerings of a new scientific advance.

The scientific method, then, is the philosophy of questioning, of evidence, of curiosity, and of eternally stretching the mind. It uses logic as its servant. As is the case in other fields of science, the problems of biological science are extremely varied, and different types demand different applications of logic in their solution.

69

Science and People

Warren Weaver

Because I feel so deeply and so strongly concerning what I have to say on the subject of science and people, I shall run the risk of being dully pedagogical and state my plan at once. First, I am going to ask what successes man has had in his various endeavors and inquire why science seems to bulk so large among these successes. I am going to recount some foolish ideas concerning science that have arisen partly because of its successes. I am going to contrast these with a series of statements that seem to me more accurately to describe science and its relation to life. The main conclusion will be that science belongs to all the people.

MAN'S MAJOR SUCCESSES

Think of the various major tasks to which men have, over the ages, addressed themselves. They have sought food, warmth, shelter, and other guards against the physical assaults of nature. Each individual or group has also sought protection against attack from the rest of mankind.

Men have tried to understand the physical universe. They have striv-

Warren Weaver, "Science and People," *Science*, Vol. 122 (December, 1955), pp. 1255-1259. Reprinted by permission.

en to apply this body of understanding to attain control of and to exploit this power over physical nature.

Men have tried to understand organic nature—how it evolved, and how individual organisms reproduce, grow, and function. They have sought health of body. They have tried to understand the nature of mind, of consciousness, of memory, of the learning process. They have endeavored to manage personal relationships within family groups, the village, the tribe, the state, the nation, and the world at large. They have attempted social and eventually political organization at all levels of inclusiveness and complexity, and they have tried to understand human behavior as it affects all these interrelationships.

Men have created methods for ownership of property and have elaborated systems of customs and laws in an attempt to protect individuals and serve society. They have recorded history and have attempted to understand it. They have, at great cost and with high dedication, tried to strike a balance between regulation and liberty.

Men have sought to enrich life through development of the pictorial arts, literature, music, drama, and the dance. They have created systems of logic and metaphysics and have tried to analyze the nature of knowledge and reality. They have formulated codes of esthetics and morals and have contemplated the purpose and meaning of life.

In this vast and interrelated range of concerns and activities, where do the successes lie? What things have men really done well?

Each man is entitled to his own answer, but my own reply would go as follows. Probably the most conspicuous, the most universally recognized, and the most widely applied success lies in the understanding and control of the forces of physical nature. Coupled with this, I would place the progress that has been made—even though it is but a start—in the understanding of organic nature.

But along with these two I would want to bracket, without attempting to suggest an order of importance, two other major successes. The first of this second pair of successes is to be found in the grandeur and practicality of the principles of personal conduct that have been enunciated by the great religious leaders. I would suggest, for example, that the Ten Commandments, the Golden Rule, and the rest of Sermon on the Mount have the generality within their realms that Newton's laws of motion have in theirs, plus the fact that no religious Einstein has found it necessary to insert correction terms of higher order.

The second further success that seems of major proportion is to be found in the degree to which life can be and has been enriched by the arts. Thus it is my own conviction that the poet has done a job that science must thoroughly respect, and perhaps should envy.

In listing only these four major successes, some real unfairness may have been done to our social advances. Granting all the confusions and troubles that greet us with each issue of the newspapers, it remains true that man has made great progress in sorting out his human relationships. The cry "Who goes home?" which still adjourns the House of Commons, reminds us that not too long ago members required armed escort to protect them from the brigands who lurked between Westminster and the City. The constitutional experience of the American republic is impressive evidence that society does not always blunder. His Majesty's loyal opposition—the difference between political opposition and treason—is the basic treaty of political life in widening areas of the world. If science has made great contributions to man's well-being, the institution of contract has, in an unobtrusive way, made it possible. And it is deeply satisfying to recall that the daily lives of most people are saved from Hobbes' jungle by the presumption of good faith that infuses our relationships with one another.

To return to the four major successes, it seems interesting to note certain features that show how disparate they are. The first success—that of the physical sciences—is in a field where logic and quantitative measurement are dominant. The second—the dawning light of understanding of animate nature—is far less advanced, and it involves factors that are certainly nonquantitative and may well prove alogical. The third—the perfection of the codes of personal conduct—is curiously and unhappily more a matter of theory than of practice. I believe it was Chesterton who remarked that no one knows whether Christianity will work because no one has ever tried it. As an ex-mathematician, I would point out that one single clear exception proves that a presumptive general rule is incorrect, and I would therefore say that Chesterton's remark is characteristically vivid and interesting, but that it is false. The fourth success—man's enrichment of his life through the arts—presents features that are baffling to a scientist. Indeed, I am not sure that the word *success* really applies here, for success connotes a bad start and good progress. But the arts seem to constitute an almost completely nonaccumulative part of experience. Rutherford had a great natural advantage over Faraday, and he over Gilbert; with respect to electric phenomena, both theory and the techniques of experimentation kept advancing, and each step was built on top of the preceding one. But Emily Dickinson had no advantage over Sappho. Each simply had words, the challenge of beauty, and the ineffable genius to condense, purify, and universalize experience.

SUCCESS OF PHYSICAL SCIENCE

Of these four major successes, I believe it is rather clear that the most tangible and obvious is the success of physical science. And this is an instance in which success and danger are close companions, as they often are. I do not refer here to the danger—ominous as it is—that science has unleashed forces that can physically destroy us. I refer to the more subtle danger that this success may mislead us concerning the real nature of science and its relationship to the rest of life and thus destroy something that is in the long run more important than a factory or a city, namely, our sense of value.

What made possible the great success that the physical sciences have experienced, particularly during the last century and a half? The explanation appears actually to be rather simple. *Physical* nature, first of all, seems to be on the whole very *loosely coupled*. That is to say, excellently workable approximations result from studying physical nature bit by bit, two or three variables at a time, and treating these bits as isolated. Furthermore, a large number of the broadly applicable laws are, to useful approximation, *linear*, if not directly in the relevant variables, then in nothing worse than their second time derivatives. And finally, a large fraction of physical phenomena (meteorology is sometimes an important exception) exhibit *stability*: perturbations tend to fade out, and great consequences do not result from very small causes.

These three extremely convenient characteristics of physical nature bring it about that vast ranges of phenomena can be satisfactorily handled by linear algebraic or differential equations, often involving only one or two dependent variables; they also make the handling *safe* in the sense that small errors are unlikely to propagate, go wild, and prove disastrous. Animate nature, on the other hand, presents highly complex and highly coupled systems—these are, in fact, dominant characteristics of what we call organisms. It takes a lot of variables to describe a man, or for that matter a virus; and you cannot often usefully study these variables two at a time. Animate nature also exhibits very confusing instabilities, as students of history, the stock market, or genetics are well aware.

If the successes of physical theory had remained limited to those highly useful but none the less essentially simple situations covered by two variable equations such as Ohm's law in electricity, or Hook's law for elastic deformation, or Boyle's law for volume and pressure of gases, or even to the vastly greater range of dynamic phenomena that are so superbly summarized in Newton's second law of motion, then it seems likely that mankind would have preserved a reasonable, take-it-or-leave-it attitude toward science. But two further things occurred.

Physical science pushed on to much more subtle and more complicated realms of phenomena, particularly in astrophysics and in atomic and then nuclear physics. And it kept on having successes. Second, physical science (and remember that nowadays it is not really useful to discriminate between physics and chemistry) began to be applied more and more to certain limited sorts of problems of animate nature. Biochemistry, to take a very conspicuous example, began to deal successfully with phase after phase of the happenings within the individual cells of living creatures.

At the same time, of course, scientific theories kept getting more and more complicated and technical. Not only were they generally formidable to the public at large—scientific experts themselves had increasing difficulty in understanding anything outside their own specialties.

SUPERSTITIONS

All this has tended to create a set of superstitions about science. These seem to be rather widely adopted by the public, and some of them even have adherents among scientists! These superstitions go something like this:

Science is all-powerful. It can just do anything. If you doubt this, just look around and see what it has done. A procedure known as "the scientific method" would in fact, if we only used it, solve all the problems of economics, sociology, political science, esthetics, philosophy, and religion. And the reason why science has been so successful, and the basis of confidence that it can go on to do anything whatsoever, is that science has somehow got the real low-down on nature and life. It has found out how to capture absolute truth, exact fact, incontrovertible evidence. Its statements are just "mathematically true," and in the face of that, you had better be confident and respectful, even if you are confused.

But science (to continue the superstitions) cannot be understood by ordinary folk. It is too technical, too abstruse, too special, and too different from ordinary thinking and ordinary experience. There is a special small priesthood of scientific practitioners; they know the secrets and they hold the power.

The scientific priests themselves are wonderful but strange creatures. They admittedly possess mysterious mental abilities; they are motivated by a strange and powerful code known as "the spirit of science," one feature of which seems to be that scientists consider that they deserve very special treatment by society.

Now these are dangerous misconceptions about science. If they were wholly untrue, if they were total and complete nonsense, then one could confidently await the general recognition of their fraudulent nature. But there is just enough apparent and illusive evidence in favor of these statements to give them an unfortunate vitality.

ALTERNATIVE STATEMENTS

Let me list as briefly as I can a set of alternative statements which I believe to be more reasonable and accurate.

1. Science has impressively proved itself to be a powerful way of dealing with certain aspects of our experience. These are, in general, the logical and quantitative aspects, and the method works superbly for linear and stable physical problems in two or three variables. The physical universe seems to be put together in such a way that this scientific approach is exceedingly successful in producing a good, workable, initial description. And with that kind of solid start, physical science can then safely proceed to elaborate more sophisticated theories.

2. We simply do not yet know how far these methods, which have worked so well with physical nature, will be successful in the world of living things. The successes to date are very impressive. One feature after another that previously seemed to fall in a special "vital" category has usefully yielded to biochemical or biophysical attack. But it is also the case that we have as yet made only a beginning. How far the logical-quantitative method will succeed here, one would be rash to forecast, although the prospects do indeed seem extremely promising.

3. We have made small beginnings at extending the scientific method into the social sciences. Insofar as these fields can be dealt with in terms of measurable quantities, they seem to present closely intercoupled situations that can very seldom usefully be handled with two or three variables and that often require a whole hatful—for example, W. Leontief's input-output analysis of the U.S. economy deals with some 50 variables and regrets that it does not handle more. Science has, as yet, no really good way of coping with these multivariable but nonstatistical problems, although it is possible that ultrahigh-speed computers will inspire new sorts of mathematical procedures that will be successful in cases where the effects are too numerous to handle easily but not numerous enough or of suitable character to permit statistical treatment. If we try to avoid the many-variable aspect of the social sciences by using highly simplified models of few variables, then these models are often too artificial and oversimplified to be useful. The statistical approach, on the other hand, has recently exhibited—for example, in the stochastic models for learning—new potentialities in the field of human behavior.

4. It is, incidentally, not at all necessary that the particular analytic techniques of the physical sciences be forced upon biological or social problems with the arrogant assumption that they can and should make unnecessary other types of insight and experience. During the recent war, an extremely useful collaboration was developed, known often as operations analysis, in which reasoning of a mathematical type was applied to certain aspects of very complicated situations, but with no expectation that judgment, experience, intuition, or a vague sort of general wisdom would be displaced or superseded—rather only that these would be aided by whatever partial light could be furnished by quantitative analysis.

5. An important characteristic of science, which we must note in

passing, is its incapacity to be impractical. The most far-reaching discoveries and the most widespread useful applications flow regularly out of ideas that initially seem abstract and even esoteric. These ideas arise out of the unguided and free activity of men who are motivated by curiosity or who, even more generally, are thinking about scientific problems simply because they like to. The way in which apparently aimless curiosity stubbornly refuses to be foolish and leads to important goals doubtless seems strange or even incredible to some persons. The eventual usefulness of the initially impractical is widely held to be a very special feature of science, but I am not so sure of this. I think that apparent impracticality is more generally important than we are inclined to suppose.

6. Science presents the kind of challenge that attracts to it young men and women who tend to have a rather high degree of a certain kind of intelligence. Since this particular kind of intelligence is relatively easy to recognize and measure, and since many other types are subtle and illusive, even though perhaps more important, we tend to adopt this one type as the norm. In addition, this particular type of intelligence leads rather promptly to tangible results. These circumstances lead to the conclusion, which is then something of a tautology, that scientists are more intelligent than other people. This may or may not be true; more important, however, it may be neither true nor untrue in the sense that the attempted comparison is meaningless.

7. However, despite their appearing to be so bright, scientists are not special creatures: they are people. Like lots of other people, they are good at their own tasks. Off their jobs they seem, as Shylock remarked in another connection, "to be fed with the same food, hurt with the same weapons, subject to the same diseases, healed by the same means, warmed and cooled by the same winter and summer" as other men are. When you prick them, they do indeed bleed.

A. V. Hill, while he was president of the British Association for the Advancement of Science, stated: "Most scientists are quite ordinary folk, with ordinary human virtues, weaknesses, and emotions. A few of the most eminent ones indeed are people of superlative general ability, who could have done many things well; a few are freaks, with a freakish capacity and intuition in their special fields, but an extreme naïveté in general affairs. . . . The great majority of scientists are between these groups, with much the same distribution of moral and intellectual characteristics as other educated people."

8. One rather accidental fact has led many to think that scientists are strange and special, and this is the fact that scientists often use a strange and special language. Science does find it desirable to use very many technical words, and it has indeed developed, as a matter of saving time, a sort of language of its own. This gives to science an external appearance of incomprehensibility that is very unfortunate. The public

need not think intself stupid for failing intuitively to grasp all this technicality. Indeed, what has developed is not so much a language as a series of very specialized dialects, each really understood only by its inventors. "On faithful rings" is not a sociological discussion of marriage but an article in modern algebra. The "Two-body problem for triton" is not mythology but physics: a "folded tree" is not a botanical accident but a term in telephone switching theory.

9. If scientists are human, so also is science itself. For example, science does not deserve the reputation it has so widely gained of being based on absolute fact (whatever that is supposed to mean) of being wholly objective, of being infinitely precise, of being unchangeably permanent, of being philosophically inescapable and unchallengeable. There seem still to be persons who think that science deals with certainty; whereas it is the case, of course, that it deals with probabilities. There seem still to be persons who think that science is the one activity that deals with truth, whereas it is the case, of course, that—to take a very simple example—"the true length of a rod" is so clearly not obtainable by any scientific procedure that, insofar as science is concerned, this "true length" remains a pleasant fiction.

I could document this particular point at length, but will restrict myself to three quotations from the relatively mature fields of physics, astronomy, and mathematics.

Edmund Whittaker said of theoretical physics: ". . . it is built around conceptions; and the progress of the subject consists very largely in replacing these conceptions by other conceptions, which transcend or even contradict them."

Herbert Dingle, in his retiring address as president of the Royal Astronomical Society, said: "The universe . . . is a hypothetical entity of which what we observe is an almost negligible part. . . . In cosmology we are again, like the philosophers of the Middle Ages, facing a world almost entirely unknown."

Alfred North Whitehead has stated: "While mathematics is a convenience in relating certain types of order to our comprehension, it does not . . . give us any account of their activity. . . . When I was a young man, . . . I was taught science and mathematics by brilliant men; . . . since the turn of the century I have lived to see every one of the basic assumptions of both set aside."

10. These quotations indicate that the ablest scientists themselves realize the postulational and provisional character of science. Perhaps not so widely recognized or accepted is the extent to which the development of Western science, rather than constituting a uniquely inevitable pattern, has been influenced by the general nature of Greco-Judaic culture, including especially the standards, arising within that tradition, of what is interesting and important.

Confronted by the totality of experience, men select the features that seem interesting and important—and the criteria for interest and importance arise not just or even primarily within scientific thought, but rather within the entire cultural complex. One then seeks to find a way of ordering this selected experience so that the end result is acclaimed as satisfying and useful—again as judged within the total culture. This process has different possible beginnings and different possible procedures; so, of course, it has different possible end results. Clyde Kluckhohn has remarked, "What people perceive, and how they conceptualize their perceptions is overwhelmingly influenced by culture." H. M. Tomlinson said, "We see things not as they are, but as we are."

If, for example, a culture almost wholly disregards physical suffering, considers the present life an unimportant episode, and places a very high premium on prolonged mystic contemplation, then this viewpoint regarding values does more than, for example, underemphasize modern scientific medicine (using all these words in the Western sense). It produces something that is different *in kind;* I know of no criteria that justify calling one kind good and intelligent, and the other poor and ignorant.

Chang Tung-San, a Chinese philosopher, has said: Take Aristotelian logic, for example, which is evidently based on Greek grammar. The differences between Latin, French, English, and German grammatical form do not result in any difference between Aristotelian logic and their respective rules of reasoning, because they belong to the same Indo-European linguistic family. Should this logic be applied to Chinese thought, however, it will prove inappropriate. This fact shows that Aristotelian logic is based on the Western system of language. Therefore we should not follow Western logicians in taking for granted that their logic is the universal rule of human reasoning."

If this general line of thought seems to you either interesting or improbable, I urge you to read some of the fascinating papers of Benjamin Lee Whorf and of Dorothy D. Lee on the value systems and the conceptual implications of the languages of various American Indian tribes. Whorf, for example, points out that the Hopi Indian language "is seen to contain no words, grammatical forms, constructions or expressions that refer directly to what we call *time,* or to past, present, or future, or to enduring or lasting, or to motion as kinematic rather than dynamic. . . . At the same time the Hopi language is capable of accounting for and describing correctly, in a pragmatic or operational sense, all observable phenomena of the universe."

11. The ten preceding numbered comments concerning certain general characteristics of science all contribute, I believe, to a major conclusion—that science is a very human enterprise, colored by our general ideas, changeable as any human activity must be, various in its possible forms, and a common part of the lives of all men.

Indeed, even the impressive methods that science has developed—methods which sometimes seem so formidable—are in no sense superhuman. They involve only improvement—great, to be sure—of procedures of observation and analysis that the human race has always used. In the appeal to evidence, science has taught us a great deal about objectivity and relevance, but, again, this is refinement of procedure, not invention of wholly new procedure.

In short, every man is to some degree a scientist. It is misleading that a tiny fraction of the population is composed of individuals who possess a high degree of scientific skill, while most of the rest are indifferent or poor scientists. This creates the false impression that there is a difference in kind, when it is actually only one of degree.

If, when a window sticks, you pound it unreasonably, or jerk so hard that you hurt your back, or just give up in ignorant disgust, then you are being a poor scientist. If you look the situation over carefully to see what is really the matter—paint on the outside that needs cutting through, or a crooked position in the frame—then you are being a good scientist.

Even primitive men were scientists, and in certain aspects of accurate and subtle observation and deduction it would probably be hard to beat the ancient skilled hunter.

Indeed, one important contrast between the savage and the professor is simply that modern scientific methods make it possible to crystallize our experience rapidly and reliably, whereas primitive science does this clumsily, slowly, and with much attendant error. But it is, after all, well to remember that ephedrine is the active principle in an herb, Ma Huang, that has been empirically employed by native Chinese physicians for some 5000 years. Certain African savages when they moved their villages did take with them to the new location some dirt from the floor of the old hut. Moreover, it is true that they said that they did this to avoid the anger of their gods who might not wish them to move, fooling them by continuing to live on some of the same ground. But the fact remains that by this process they brought to the new location the soil microorganisms that continued to give some degree of protection from certain ailments. We quite properly honor Fleming and Florey, but Johannes de Sancto Paulo, a medical writer of the 12th century, did prescribe moldy bread for an inflamed abscess. "We are all scientists," Thomas Huxley said, because "the method of scientific investigation is nothing but the expression of the necessary mode of working of the human mind."

SCIENCE AS A HUMAN ACTIVITY

Let us now back away from the trees and look at the forest. Where have we arrived in this discussion?

I have just listed 11 points that, in my judgment at least, fairly characterize science as a universal human activity. These comments do not support the concept of science as some sort of super creed, magical and mysterious as it is all-powerful, arrogant from its successes, and avid to invade and conquer, one after another, all the fields of human activity and thought. This viewpoint does not justify the notion that science is so special as to be unique, as well as so curious as to be incomprehensible. This does not depict scientists as strange creatures who are in one sense so objective, judicial, and precise as to be incredible, and in another sense so apart from life as to be selfish and sinister. This does not set up quantitative analytic Western science as the only valid way in which man may approach and interpret experience.

On the contrary, these descriptive comments picture science as the servant of man, not his master; and as a friendly companion of art and of moral philosophy. This is a science that is the way it is because man wants it to be that way. It is a natural expression of both his curiosity and his faith.

If the public could be brought to understand and appreciate this position concerning science and scientists, I do not think that so many persons would harm this great enterprise of ours with a combination of mistrust, fear, and overestimation. I do not think that so many would treat scientists one-third of the time as amusing but beneficial eccentrics, one-third of the time as sorcerers, and one-third of the time as irresponsible rascals. I do not think that so many would view scientists as careless dabblers with danger, or as a selfish minority that, to quote a nationally syndicated columnist, "hold they are an extra special group not tied down by the obligations and rules under which the rest of us work. Hundreds of them are now bellyaching about the Oppenheimer verdict and saying it ruins their morale and makes them hard to get. What goes with those birds?" Or consider another newspaper writer who opened one of his columns with the sentence, "We Americans have been confronted with an arrogant proposition that persons presuming to call themselves intellectuals, and particularly those who claim the title of scientist, are a superior cult entitled to deference or even homage from the common man." One of our greatest universities takes a sound and courageous stand, and a newspaper writer complains, "Harvard has a peculiar fondness nowadays for putting security and the safety of the nation second to their fancy ideas of importance." If some speak out against the climate of fear resulting from the stupidities and iniquities of what is misnamed as the security system—doubly misnamed since it is not a system and does not achieve security—then their protest is labeled, as it was by Eugene Lyons in the *Saturday Evening Post*, as the "mock-heroic posture of this close-knit band of Cassandras"; he insultingly adds that these protesters do not themselves seem to have suffered, for "not one of them has as yet been muzzled, lynched, or denied his due royalties."

Anti-intellectual views such as these are widely expressed in those newspapers that combine a wide circulation with a narrow intellectual viewpoint, in some very popular national magazines, and even, one reports with shame, by highly placed persons in Washington.

It is hardly necessary to argue, these days, that science is essential to the public. It is becoming equally true, as the support of science moves more and more to state and national sources, that the public is essential to science. The lack of general comprehension of science is thus dangerous both to science and to the public, these being interlocked aspects of the common danger that scientists will not be given the freedom, the understanding, and the support that are necessary for vigorous and imaginative development. It is, moreover, of equally grave importance that science understand itself.

There are persons who are pessimistic concerning the prospects of materially improving the public understanding of science, and even the understanding that one branch of science has of the other branches. If one subscribes to the falsities and exaggerations that I stated in the first part of this article, then he could properly be pessimistic. If, on the other hand, he accepts the broader, more liberal, more human and humane view that I have advanced here, then—or at least so it seems to me—he can be very optimistic.

When David Brewster, a century and a quarter ago, was one of the prime movers in founding the British Association for the Advancement of Science, he said, "The principal objects of the Society would be to make the cultivators of science acquainted with each other, to stimulate one another to new exertions—to bring the objects of science more before the public eye and to take measures for advancing its interests and accelerating its progress."

This is a challenge which our own Association has always sought to meet. It is a challenge which, at this moment in history, requires renewed zeal and ever-renewed patience. Speaking of the present-day scientist, J. Bronowski has said, "Outside his laboratory, his task is to educate us in what goes on inside it, and to give it a meaning for us. In a world in which statesmen as much as voters are ignorant of the simplest implications in science, this is a formidable responsibility . . . [the scientist] has no other choice today but patiently to become a teacher, in a world in which distrust and prejudice are free. . . . There is no alternative to an informed public opinion: and that can exist only where scientists speak to voters and voters accept their responsibility, which is to listen, to weigh, and then to make their own choice."

If, as I believe, the sciences and the arts are lively and noncompetitive partners in the business of life, it is appropriate that we close, not with a scientist, but with a great artist. "Our privacy," Faulkner says, "has been slowly and steadily and increasingly invaded until now our very dream of civilization is in danger. Who will save us but the scientist and the humanitarian. Yes, the humanitarian in science, and the scientist in the humanity of man."